1979

MODERN TRIGONOMETRY

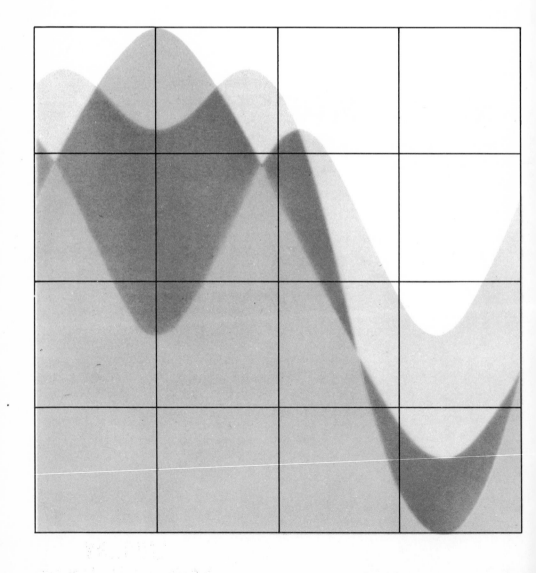

MODERN TRIGONOMETRY

EUGENE D. NICHOLS

E. HENRY GARLAND

HOLT, RINEHART AND WINSTON, INC.
New York, Chicago, San Francisco, Atlanta, Dallas,
Montreal, Toronto, London

ABOUT THE AUTHORS

Eugene D. Nichols, *Professor and Head,*
Department of Mathematics Education,
The Florida State University,
Tallahassee, Florida

E. Henry Garland, *Associate Professor,*
Department of Mathematics Education,
University School,
The Florida State University,
Tallahassee, Florida

PREFACE

The knowledge of trigonometry is essential as a prerequisite for the study of calculus. However, exclusive emphasis on computation is no longer valid, and a new emphasis on the study of properties of trigonometric functions is more appropriate in meeting today's mathematical expectations. Emphasis on the function concept is one of the characteristics of *Modern Trigonometry*.

A number of concepts must be understood by students before they undertake the study of trigonometry. They are: sets, equations and inequalities, segments, rays, lines, angles, circles and related sets of points, triangles, rectangular coordinate system, symmetry, relations, and functions. Since students who enroll in a trigonometry course have varied mathematical background, the first chapter of this text provides brief, but substantial, review of each of these concepts. The instructor may choose to cover all, some, or none of these topics, depending on the composition of his class. The review exercises or the chapter test at the end of Chapter 1 may be used as a placement test for assessing the extent of students' competence in these areas.

Trigonometry is important as a tool for the study of physical phenomena, as well as in further study of mathematics. In addition to that, it is uniquely suited for the study of circular functions, which have assumed increased importance in recent years. In this text, these functions are given diligent attention. Furthermore, the structural aspects of trigonometry are given due emphasis without sacrificing the training in the use of trigonometric concepts in physical applications.

There are several features of this text which deserve an explicit mention.

1. It begins with the development of the *wrapping function* and presents sine, cosine, and tangent as functions of real numbers. The conventional topics of analytical trigonometry are considered from this viewpoint first.

2. After the study of the wrapping function, the concept of a *generated angle* and its measure is developed (Chapters 6 and 7). Then six trigonometric functions are studied as functions of angle measures. The conventional topics of analytical trigonometry are then considered from this viewpoint.

3. As a result of the above two features, the concept of the generated angle in Chapters 6 and 7 is presented as a familiar concept but from a somewhat different point of view.

4. Thorough attention is given to periodic functions, periodic phenomena, harmonic motion, symmetry, vectors and their applications, and to applications of trigonometric functions in the sciences.

5. All of the conventional topics of a plane trigonometry course are presented and plentiful practice in the use of all concepts is provided.

6. The text is written for the student. The style is concise and clear. The student should be expected to read the textbook.

7. Since techniques of proving theorems is one of the most essential requirements of a mathematics student, proof is given most thorough attention.

8. To provide three important skills necessary in the study of trigonometry, appendices covering the following topics are provided:

Appendix A.   *Accuracy*
Appendix B.   *Interpolation*
Appendix C.   *Computation with logarithms*

9. Cumulative reviews are placed at the end of Chapters 4, 7, and 10. Other review items to facilitate reviews of chapters are provided. Answers to selected problems are also supplied.

In summary, *Modern Trigonometry* is an up-to-date treatment of the subject with a balanced presentation of the structural and applied aspects of trigonometry.

E. D. N.

E. H. G.

CONTENTS

CHAPTER 1

PRELIMINARY CONCEPTS

PRELIMINARY CONCEPTS

In this chapter we shall review some of the mathematical topics which are important to the study of trigonometry. Some topics will be very familiar to you; these topics you can review rather rapidly. Others will not be so familiar; these you should study more thoroughly.

Any mathematical topic which you study is usually dependent upon concepts that you learned earlier. This is true of trigonometry and we encourage you to ensure the mastery of each topic in this introductory chapter.

SETS

We shall often discuss *sets*, that is, collections of objects. These objects, the *members* of the sets, will usually be numbers, ordered pairs of numbers, or points. Two sets of numbers with which you are already familiar are

$$N = \{1, 2, 3, \ldots\} = \{\text{natural numbers}\}$$
$$I = \{\ldots, -3, -2, -1, 0, 1, 2, 3, \ldots\} = \{\text{integers}\}$$

Another set of numbers is

$$R = \{\text{real numbers}\}$$

When referring to a particular set, we need to be concerned that it is well defined. We should be able to tell whether or not a given number belongs to a particular set. For example, to know about the membership of the last set, you should understand that the set of *real numbers* R consists of two kinds of numbers. They are the rational and irrational numbers.

1

THE RATIONAL NUMBERS   These numbers are of the form $\frac{a}{b}$, a and b integers, $b \neq 0$; their decimal numerals are either *terminating* or *repeating*.

Examples of rational numbers are

$$\frac{3}{16} = .1875 \qquad 5\frac{2}{3} = 5.6\overline{6} \qquad -\frac{4}{33} = -.12\overline{12}$$

We use a bar over a digit or a group of digits to indicate that the digit or the group of digits repeats on and on forever.

THE IRRATIONAL NUMBERS   These numbers are not rational and their decimal numerals are *non-terminating* and *non-repeating*.

Examples of irrational numbers are

$$7.626226222622226 \ldots \qquad \sqrt{2} = 1.4142135 \ldots$$
$$\pi = 3.14159\ 26535\ 89793\ 23846 \ldots$$

We use the three dots to indicate that the decimal never ends.

In this text, if no set is mentioned, you can assume that we are working with the set of real numbers. Several ways can be used to indicate the membership of a set. Two methods which we shall use are:

THE ROSTER METHOD

Examples $\{7, 8, 9, 10, 11, 12\}$ is the set of all natural numbers between 6 and 13

$\{2, 4, 6, \ldots\}$ is the set of all positive even integers

Note that in using the roster method we list either all the members or enough members to establish a pattern. The three dots are used to indicate that the pattern continues on and on.

THE RULE METHOD

Examples $\{x \mid x^2 = 7\}$. This is read as "the set of all real numbers x such that $x^2 = 7$." This set contains two members, $\sqrt{7}$ and $-\sqrt{7}$.

$\{x \mid x > 0\}$ is the set of all real numbers x such that x is greater than zero. This set is *infinite* and contains every positive real number.

$\left\{x \mid \frac{5}{0} = x\right\}$ is the set of all real numbers x such that $5 \div 0 = x$. The set in this example has no members; that is, it is the *empty set*, which is symbolized by ϕ.

In the last example, we were considering if there were any real numbers such that $5 \div 0 = x$. If there were such a number x, then $x \cdot 0 = 5$. But we know that the product of any real number x and 0 is 0; therefore there is no real number x such that $x \cdot 0 = 5$. In like manner, we can conclude that for any real number y, $\dfrac{y}{0}$ is *undefined*.

Observe that in *the rule method*, a rule is given whereby the members (and only the members) of the set are selected. When using the rule method, we agree to assume that the replacement set of the variables is {real numbers} unless otherwise stated. Would the membership of $\{x \mid (x - 1)(3x - 2) = 0\}$ change if the replacement set of x were {integers}?

Consider the set of all *integer multiples* of 3, that is, $\{\ldots, -6, -3, 0, 3, 6, \ldots\}$. Another way to indicate this set is by $\{3k \mid k \text{ is an integer}\}$ or, more simply, $\{3k\}$ where k by agreement assumes all integer values. Another similar example using k is $\{3 + 4k\} = \{\ldots, -5, -1, 3, 7, 11, \ldots\}$.

So far we have considered examples of sets whose members are numbers. It is possible for sets to contain *ordered pairs* of numbers. To understand the idea of *order* in a pair of numbers, examine the ordered pair (2, 5). Its first component is 2, and its second component is 5. The ordered pairs (2, 5) and (5, 2) are different since they have different first components (as well as different second components). Study these two examples of sets of ordered pairs.

Examples $A = \{(2, 1), (4, 2), (6, 3), (8, 4)\}$
$B = \{(x, y) \mid x = 2y\}$

Set B is a set of ordered pairs of real numbers x and y such that $x = 2y$. Notice that each member of A is a member of B, but not every member of B is a member of A. Does B contain (7, 14)? $(-6, -3)$? (9, 4.5)? $(4\sqrt{2}, 2\sqrt{2})$? $(-6\pi, -3\pi)$?

It is also possible to have sets whose members are points. An example of a set of points is a segment. This set includes the segment's two endpoints and all points between them. Sets of points will be discussed later in greater detail.

EQUATIONS AND INEQUALITIES

Whenever we want to say that two symbols name the same object, we use the symbol "$=$". For example, $\dfrac{1}{2} = \dfrac{2}{4}$ means that $\dfrac{1}{2}$ and $\dfrac{2}{4}$ name the same number. The following are examples of *equations*.

$$5 = 3 + 2 \qquad\qquad 3x^2 + 5x - 3 = 0$$
$$2x = x + 5 \qquad\qquad 7x - 6 + y = x^2$$
$$1 = 2 \text{ (an equation, which is a false statement)}$$

The symbols for inequality "$<$" and "$>$" may be used to specify relations between real numbers. We use such symbols in the following ways.

$a < b$	means	a is less than b
$a > b$	means	a is greater than b
$a < b < c$	means	a is less than b and b is less than c

Frequently we combine "$=$" with "$<$" or "$>$" to obtain other symbols. Here are some examples.

$a \le b$	means	a is less than or equal to b
$a \ge b$	means	a is greater than or equal to b
$a \le b < c$	means	a is less than or equal to b *and*
		b is less than c

In the following examples, graphs on the *real number line* suggest the membership of the sets described by inequalities. Observe how the inclusion or exclusion of endpoints is indicated in each graph.

Examples

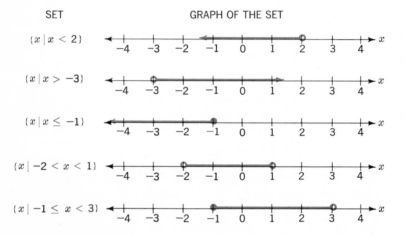

SET	GRAPH OF THE SET
$\{x \mid x < 2\}$	
$\{x \mid x > -3\}$	
$\{x \mid x \le -1\}$	
$\{x \mid -2 < x < 1\}$	
$\{x \mid -1 \le x < 3\}$	

Determining the members of a set will often require the use of some mathematics learned earlier. For example, to determine $\{x \mid 3x^2 + 5x - 3 = 0\}$ we would need to recall the quadratic formula and how to use it.

QUADRATIC FORMULA   For any equation $ax^2 + bx + c = 0$ where a, b, and c are real numbers ($a \ne 0$), the real number solution set of the equation is

$$\left\{ \frac{-b + \sqrt{b^2 - 4ac}}{2a}, \ \frac{-b - \sqrt{b^2 - 4ac}}{2a} \right\}, \text{ provided } (b^2 - 4ac) \ge 0$$

The real number solution set of $3x^2 + 5x - 3 = 0$ would be determined by using $a = 3$, $b = 5$, and $c = -3$ to obtain $\left\{ \dfrac{-5 + \sqrt{61}}{6}, \ \dfrac{-5 - \sqrt{61}}{6} \right\}$. Notice that the members of the solution set are irrational numbers. Determine the solution set of $x^2 + x - 1 = 0$. What would be used for a, b, and c? Are the members of the solution set rational or irrational?

Determine the solution set of $10x^2 = x + 3$. Describe the members of the solution set.

EXERCISES

1. Use the roster method to identify the membership of each set.

  a. The set of integers between -5 and 5

  b. The set of integers each of which is less than 2

  c. The set of integer multiples of 4

  d. $\{x \mid x \text{ is an integer and } 2 \le x < 6\}$

  e. $\{(x, y) \mid x \text{ and } y \text{ are integers and } x^2 + y^2 \le 4\}$

  Hint: This set contains 13 ordered pairs.

  f. $\{(x, y) \mid x \text{ and } y \text{ are integers and } x^2 + y^2 = 25\}$

  g. $\{8k\}$, k an integer

  h. $\{2 + 5k\}$, k an integer

  i. $\{2k\pi\}$, k an integer

  j. $\{\pi + 2k\pi\}$, k an integer

  k. $\{x \mid x^2 = 16\}$

  l. $\{c \mid c^2 = 12\}$

  m. $\{m \mid m^2 = -4\}$

2. For each number, tell whether it is rational or irrational.

  a. $-5\dfrac{1}{3}$

  b. $\pi + 2$

  c. $5.12112111211112 \ldots$

  d. $2.74\overline{74}$

  e. 3π

  f. $-\sqrt{25}$

  g. $\sqrt{3}$

  h. 0

3. Graph each set on the real number line.

  a. $\{x \mid x < 3\}$

  b. $\{x \mid x \ge 2\}$

  c. $\{x \mid -2 < x < 4\}$

  d. $\{c \mid -3 < c \le 2\}$

  e. $\{t \mid 1 \le t \le 4\}$

  f. $\{d \mid d \ge 0\}$

  g. R

  h. $\{x \mid x < 0\}$

  i. $\{x \mid 0 \le x < 2\pi\}$

  j. $\left\{x \mid -\pi < x < -\dfrac{\pi}{2}\right\}$

  k. $\{x \mid x^2 < 0\}$

  l. $\{x \mid 5 - (x - 2) = 7 - x\}$

4. For each of the following sets, list three ordered pairs of real numbers in the set.

  a. $\{(x, y) \mid y = 2x - 3\}$

  b. $\{(x, y) \mid 2y + 3x = 6\}$

  c. $\{(x, y) \mid y = 2\}$

  d. $\{(x, y) \mid xy = 1\}$

5. For each of the following sets, list six ordered pairs of real numbers in the set.

  a. $\{(x, y) \mid y = x^2 + 1\}$

  b. $\{(x, y) \mid x^2 + y^2 = 25\}$

  c. $\{(x, y) \mid x^2 + y^2 = 1\}$

  d. $\{(x, y) \mid x^2 + y^2 = 2\}$

6. Use the roster method in giving the real number solution set of each equation.

  a. $(2x - 3)(4x + 5) = 0$

  b. $2x^2 + 9x + 3 = 0$

  c. $3x^2 - 5x - 1 = 0$

  d. $\dfrac{x}{3} = 0$

  e. $\dfrac{2}{0} = x$

  f. $2x^2 = 1$

  g. $x^2 = \dfrac{3}{4}$

  h. $2\pi x + \dfrac{\pi}{2} = \dfrac{9\pi}{2}$

  i. $-\pi + 2\pi x = 7\pi$

SEGMENTS, RAYS, LINES

Every geometric figure may be thought of as a set of points. The simplest geometric figure is a *point*; it is usually indicated by a dot and named by a capital
letter. See Figure 1–1. Given two points, say B and C, the set containing B, C,
and all points between B and C is a segment, $\overline{BC}$. The endpoints of $\overline{BC}$ are B and
C. The length of $\overline{BC}$ is a positive real number, BC. Note that $\overline{BC}$ with the bar
is notation for a *segment*, a set of points; BC is notation for the *measure* of $\overline{BC}$.
Thus, if $\overline{BC}$ is a segment which is 3 units in length, then $BC = 3$.

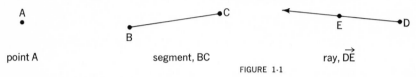

point A   segment, BC   ray, $\overrightarrow{DE}$

FIGURE 1-1

Given two points, say D and E, the set containing each point on $\overline{DE}$ and
each point P such that E is between P and D is a *ray*, $\overrightarrow{DE}$. See Figure 1–1. D is
the only endpoint of $\overrightarrow{DE}$; the arrow indicates that the set continues on and on in
one direction.

Examine the two rays, $\overrightarrow{FG}$ and $\overrightarrow{GF}$, of Figure 1–2. The geometric figure
containing each point on $\overrightarrow{FG}$ and each point on $\overrightarrow{GF}$ is the *line*, $\overleftrightarrow{FG}$. A line has no
endpoints and continues on and on in two opposite directions.

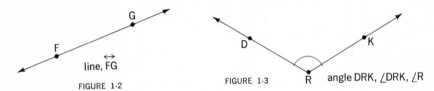

line, $\overleftrightarrow{FG}$

FIGURE 1-2

FIGURE 1-3   R   angle DRK, $\angle$DRK, $\angle$R

ANGLES

An *angle* is a set of points consisting of two distinct rays which have a common
endpoint and do not both lie on one straight line. See Figure 1–3. $\overrightarrow{RK}$ and $\overrightarrow{RD}$
form angle *DRK*, or $\angle DRK$. The common endpoint R is the *vertex* and the two
rays are the *sides* of the angle. This angle may be called $\angle R$ if it is clear which
two rays are the sides of the angle.

An angle may be assigned a real number *degree measure* between 0 and 180
by using a *protractor*. If the degree measure of an $\angle T$ is 32, we say that $\angle T$ is a
32° angle and write: $m \angle T = 32$, which is read "the degree measure of $\angle T$ is 32."

Angles may be classified into one of three groups. See Figure 1–4.

    1. $\angle A$ is *acute* if and only if $0 < m \angle A < 90$.
    2. $\angle A$ is *obtuse* if and only if $90 < m \angle A < 180$.
    3. $\angle A$ is *right* if and only if $m \angle A = 90$.

Furthermore, given a right angle A, the two lines which contain the sides of $\angle A$
are *perpendicular* to each other, as is shown in Figure 1–4.

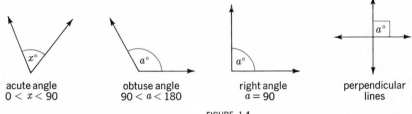

acute angle | obtuse angle | right angle | perpendicular
$0 < x < 90$ | $90 < a < 180$ | $a = 90$ | lines

FIGURE 1-4

Certain pairs of angles are given special names depending upon the sums of their degree measures. See Figure 1–5.

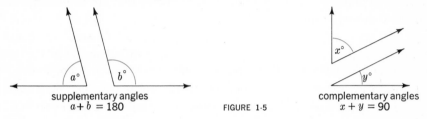

supplementary angles
$a + b = 180$

FIGURE 1-5

complementary angles
$x + y = 90$

1. $\angle A$ and $\angle B$ are *supplementary* if and only if $m \angle A + m \angle B = 180$. Each angle is the *supplement* of the other.
2. $\angle A$ and $\angle B$ are *complementary* if and only if $m \angle A + m \angle B = 90$. Each angle is the *complement* of the other.

An angle separates the plane into two sets. One set is the *interior* of the angle and the other set is the *exterior*. Figure 1–6 is a representation of the interior and exterior of an angle. The points of an angle are in neither its exterior nor its interior.

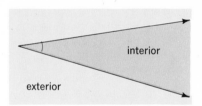

interior

exterior

FIGURE 1–6

CIRCLE AND ITS RELATED SETS OF POINTS

A set of points in a plane each at a distance r from a point A in that plane is a *circle* with *center* at A and *radius r*. See Figure 1–7. The linear measure of a circle is its *circumference*, a number C, given by the formula $C = 2\pi r$. We may use the center point, A in this case, to name the figure, circle A.

The points on a circle determine certain segments relative to the circle and its center. Suppose we are given circle A which contains distinct points $B, C, D, E, F, G,$ and H as indicated above on the right; any segment whose two endpoints belong to the circle is a *chord* of that circle.

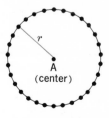

r

A
(center)

FIGURE 1–7

What three chords are shown? A chord which contains the center is *a diameter*. What two diameters are shown? Any segment with one endpoint at the center and the other endpoint on the circle is *a radius*. What five radii are shown? Note that *the* radius of a circle is a number, the measure of *a* radius. Likewise, *the* diameter of a circle is a number, the measure of *a* diameter.

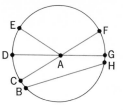

FIGURE 1–8

A *central angle* of a circle is an angle whose vertex is the center of the circle. See Figure 1–9. If a central angle, $\angle BAC$, intersects a circle at B and at C, then the set containing B, C, and all points of the circle that are in the interior of $\angle BAC$ is an arc, *minor arc $\overset{\frown}{BC}$*. The set containing B, C, and all points of the circle that are in the exterior of $\angle BAC$ is *major arc $\overset{\frown}{BC}$*. In each case B and C are endpoints of the arcs. If D and E are endpoints of a diameter of the circle, then the set which contains D, E, and all points of the circle that are on one side of $\overleftrightarrow{DE}$ is an arc, *semicircle $\overset{\frown}{DE}$*, with endpoints D and E. Note that the notations $\overset{\frown}{BC}$ and $\overset{\frown}{DE}$ are ambiguous. To avoid confusion, we select one other point on the arc. Thus, minor arc $\overset{\frown}{BC} = \overset{\frown}{BHC}$; major arc $\overset{\frown}{BC} = \overset{\frown}{BGC}$; and semicircle $\overset{\frown}{DFE}$ is the unique semicircle with endpoints D and E which also contains F. In each case the *radius of the arc* is the radius of the circle and the *center of the arc* is the center of the circle.

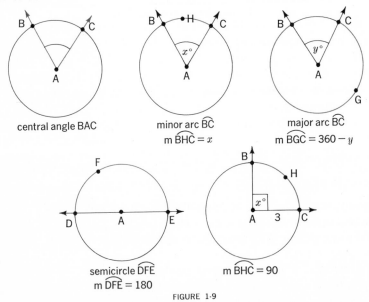

central angle BAC

minor arc $\overset{\frown}{BC}$
m $\overset{\frown}{BHC}$ = x

major arc $\overset{\frown}{BC}$
m $\overset{\frown}{BGC}$ = $360 - y$

semicircle $\overset{\frown}{DFE}$
m $\overset{\frown}{DFE}$ = 180

m $\overset{\frown}{BHC}$ = 90

FIGURE 1-9

We use $m\overset{\frown}{XY}$ to mean the degree measure of $\overset{\frown}{XY}$. Degree measures are assigned to arcs by the following scheme. See Figure 1–9.

1. m minor arc $\overset{\frown}{BC} = m\angle BAC$

2. m major arc $\overset{\frown}{BC}$ = 360 − $m\angle BAC$
3. degree measure of each circle = 360
4. degree measure of each semicircle = 180

Given a minor arc $\overset{\frown}{BC}$ and a central angle, $\angle BAC$, as in Figure 1–9, we say that the central angle $\angle BAC$ *intercepts* $\overset{\frown}{BC}$. The length of this intercepted arc is determined by its radius and its degree measure. Suppose that $AC = 3$ and $m\angle BAC = 90$. Since $AC = 3$, the circumference of the circle is 6π. Since $m\angle BAC = 90$, $\angle BAC$ intercepts $\dfrac{90}{360}$ or $\dfrac{1}{4}$ of the circle. Therefore, the length of $\overset{\frown}{BHC}$, the arc *intercepted* by $\angle BAC$, is $\dfrac{1}{4}(6\pi)$ or $\dfrac{3\pi}{2}$.

TRIANGLES

Given three points, A, B, and C, not all on the same line, the set of points on segments $\overline{AB}$, $\overline{BC}$, and $\overline{AC}$ determines a *triangle*, $\triangle ABC$. A, B, and C are the *vertices* and the three segments are the *sides* of the triangle.

TYPES OF TRIANGLES

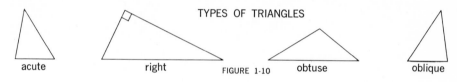

acute   right   obtuse   oblique

FIGURE 1-10

Triangles may be classified by the following scheme. We say $\triangle XYZ$ is:
1. an *acute triangle* if and only if $\angle X$, $\angle Y$, and $\angle Z$ are acute angles.
2. a *right triangle* if and only if one of $\angle X$, $\angle Y$, or $\angle Z$ is a right angle.
3. an *obtuse triangle* if and only if one of $\angle X$, $\angle Y$, or $\angle Z$ is an obtuse angle.
4. an *oblique triangle* if and only if neither $\angle X$, $\angle Y$, nor $\angle Z$ is a right angle.

You should recall that for any $\triangle XYZ$, $m\angle X + m\angle Y + m\angle Z = 180$. Can a right triangle be an obtuse triangle? Why or why not?

Right triangles are of special importance because of the Pythagorean Theorem.

PYTHAGOREAN THEOREM   For any right triangle ABC, if $\angle C$ is a right angle, then $(AC)^2 + (BC)^2 = (AB)^2$.

If $AC = 2$ and $AB = 3$, then
$$(AC)^2 + (BC)^2 = (AB)^2$$
$$2^2 + (BC)^2 = 3^2$$
$$(BC)^2 = 5$$
$$BC = \sqrt{5}$$

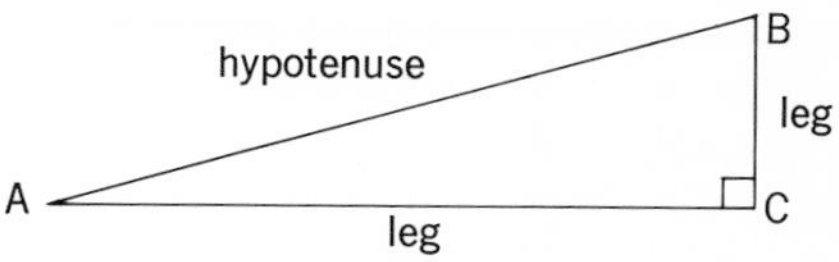

hypotenuse   leg   leg

FIGURE 1-11

The sides of a right triangle have special names. The *hypotenuse* of a right triangle is its longest side. The other two sides are the *legs*. See Figure 1–11.

Consider the isosceles right triangle *ABC* of Figure 1–12. It is a *45° right triangle.* Why? If $AC = BC = m$, then $m^2 + m^2 = (AB)^2$. Why? It follows that $AB = m\sqrt{2}$. Show this. Give the lengths of the other two sides of a 45° right triangle if the length of one leg is 3; is $4\sqrt{2}$; if the length of the hypotenuse is 5; is $8\sqrt{2}$.

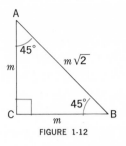

FIGURE 1-12

In Figure 1–13, $\triangle MPQ$ is equilateral and equiangular. $\overline{PR}$ is the altitude from *P*. $\triangle MPR$ is a *30°-60° right triangle.* Why? If $MP = n$, then $MR = \dfrac{n}{2}$. Why?

Thus, $(PR)^2 + \left(\dfrac{n}{2}\right)^2 = n^2$. Why? It follows that $PR = \dfrac{n\sqrt{3}}{2}$. Show all the steps in deriving this formula. Give the lengths of the other two sides of a 30°-60° right triangle whose shorter leg is three units long; whose hypotenuse is eight units long.

If in $\triangle ABC$ and $\triangle A'B'C'$,

$$m\angle A = m\angle A' \qquad m\angle B = m\angle B'$$
$$m\angle C = m\angle C'$$

the triangles are *similar* and possess the property that

$$\frac{AB}{A'B'} = \frac{BC}{B'C'} = \frac{AC}{A'C'}$$

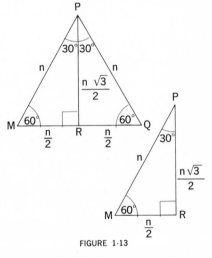

FIGURE 1-13

As an example in Figure 1–14, suppose $AB = 8$, $BC = 5$, $A'B' = 13$ and $A'C' = 17$. We can determine AC and $B'C'$ as follows:

$$\frac{8}{13} = \frac{5}{B'C'}$$
$$8(B'C') = 65$$
$$B'C' = \frac{65}{8} = 8\frac{1}{8}$$

$$\frac{AC}{17} = \frac{8}{13}$$
$$13(AC) = 136$$
$$AC = \frac{136}{13} = 10\frac{6}{13}$$

FIGURE 1-14

EXERCISES

1. Indicate whether each of the following refers to (1) a set of points or (2) a number.

   a. $\overrightarrow{MN}$ f. $\angle F$ k. $\overset{\frown}{CD}$ p. the diameter

   b. CD g. a radius   l. semicircle   q. $\triangle ABC$

   c. $\overline{CD}$ h. $m\angle B$ m. circumference   r. hypotenuse

   d. interior of $\angle K$ i. $m\overset{\frown}{CD}$ n. arc   s. $\overleftrightarrow{BC}$

   e. the radius   j. chord   o. circle   t. CM

2. Refer to the figure on the right.

   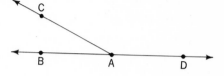

   a. List four segments whose endpoints are named in the figure.

   b. List five rays whose endpoints are labeled.

   c. What acute angle is shown in the figure?

   d. What obtuse angle is shown?

   e. Is a pair of angles in the figure supplementary or complementary?

   f. Why would it be improper to speak of $\angle A$ for this figure?

   g. Is D in the interior or exterior of $\angle BAC$?

3. Angle A is the complement of angle B and $m\angle A = 2x - 7$ and $m\angle B = 2 + 3x$. Determine x, $m\angle A$, and $m\angle B$.

4. What name is given to each of the following as it relates to circle A shown below on the left?

   a. $\overline{BD}$ g. AE

   b. $\angle DAC$ h. $2\pi(AC)$

   c. EC i. $\overline{AE}$

   d. $\overline{BC}$ j. $\overset{\frown}{BCE}$

   e. A k. $2(AE)$

   f. $\overset{\frown}{CBE}$ l. $\pi(BD)$

   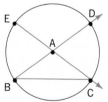

   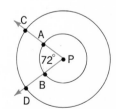

5. Given two concentric circles, centers at P, as shown above on the right with $PA = 1$ and $PC = 2$. Determine the following:

   a. m minor arc $\overset{\frown}{AB}$ and m major arc $\overset{\frown}{AB}$ e. Length of minor arc $\overset{\frown}{AB}$

   b. m minor arc $\overset{\frown}{CD}$ and m major arc $\overset{\frown}{CD}$ f. Length of minor arc $\overset{\frown}{CD}$

   c. Circumference of smaller circle   g. Length of major arc $\overset{\frown}{AB}$

   d. Circumference of larger circle   h. Length of major arc $\overset{\frown}{CD}$

6. Given two concentric circles, as shown in the figure at the right, centers at P, $PA = 1$, $PC = r$, and $m \angle CPD = x$. Determine the degree measure of each arc whose endpoints are labeled.

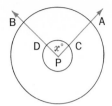

7. Determine the linear measure of each arc whose endpoints are labeled in Exercise 6.

8. The radius of the circle shown below on the right is 1, and each acute central angle is a 45° angle. Determine the length of each arc. Simplify each answer.

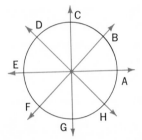

a. minor arc $\overset{\frown}{AB}$ **g.** $\overset{\frown}{ABH}$

b. $\overset{\frown}{ABC}$ **h.** $\overset{\frown}{AHF}$

c. $\overset{\frown}{ABD}$ **i.** $\overset{\frown}{AHD}$

d. $\overset{\frown}{ABE}$

e. $\overset{\frown}{ABF}$

f. $\overset{\frown}{ABG}$

9. The radius of the circle shown below on the right is 1. Each acute central angle is either a 30° angle or a 60° angle. Determine the length of each arc.

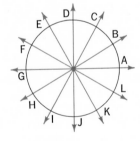

a. minor arc $\overset{\frown}{AB}$

b. $\overset{\frown}{ABC}$ **g.** $\overset{\frown}{ABH}$

c. $\overset{\frown}{ABD}$ **h.** $\overset{\frown}{ABI}$

d. $\overset{\frown}{ABE}$ **i.** $\overset{\frown}{ABJ}$

e. $\overset{\frown}{ABF}$ **j.** $\overset{\frown}{ABK}$

f. $\overset{\frown}{ABG}$ **k.** $\overset{\frown}{ABL}$

10. True or false?

a. No right triangle is acute.

b. Every obtuse triangle is also oblique.

c. In every right triangle, two of the angles are supplementary.

d. Every equilateral triangle is obtuse.

e. If a pair of angles are supplementary and equal in measure, then they are a pair of right angles.

f. Point A is in the interior of $\angle ABC$.

g. Every chord of a circle is shorter than every diameter of that circle.

h. The degree measure of each minor arc is less than 180.

i. There is a 6-8-10 right triangle.

11. For the pair of similar triangles shown below, determine BC and DF. What is the ratio of the perimeters of these triangles?

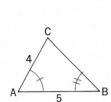
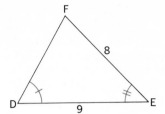

12. For $\triangle KLM$, $m \angle K = 3x - 1$, $m \angle L = 14 + x$ and $m \angle M = 2x + 7$. Determine $m \angle K$, $m \angle L$, and $m \angle M$.

13. For each rectangle $ABCD$ which has the dimensions given below, determine BD, the length of a diagonal.

a. $AB = 3$, $AD = 4$ **c.** $AB = 1$, $AD = 1$

b. $AB = 2$, $AD = 5$ **d.** $AB = 5$, $AD = 12$

14. For each rectangle, determine KL, the length of one side of rectangle $KLMN$, from the following information.

a. $KM = 6$, $LM = 1$ **c.** $KM = \sqrt{7}$, $LM = \sqrt{2}$

b. $KM = 10$, $LM = 8$ **d.** $LN = 2$, $KN = 1$

15. For each case, determine the measures of two sides of $\triangle ABC$ if the measure of the third side is as given.

a. $AB = 6$ **d.** $AB = 7$ **g.** $AB = \sqrt{5}$

b. $AC = \sqrt{3}$ **e.** $AC = 5$ **h.** $AC = 2$

c. $BC = 4$ **f.** $BC = 2$ **i.** $BC = \sqrt{2}$

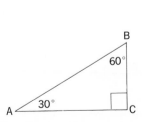
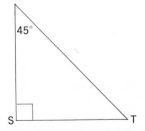

16. For each case, determine the measures of two sides of $\triangle RST$ if the measure of the third side is as given.

a. $RS = 7$ **c.** $RT = 5\sqrt{2}$ **e.** $RS = \dfrac{1}{4}$

b. $ST = 1$ **d.** $RT = \dfrac{2}{3}$ **f.** $RT = 3$

RECTANGULAR COORDINATE SYSTEM

Consider the set of points which is the entire plane. To each point of the plane we can assign a unique ordered pair of real numbers, and to each ordered pair of real numbers we can assign a unique point. Thus we can establish a *one-to-one correspondence* between all points in the plane and all ordered pairs of real numbers. We use a rectangular coordinate system to establish such a correspondence. See Figure 1–15. We place two number lines perpendicular to one another and intersecting at their zero points. Each line is an *axis* and the point of intersection is the *origin*. If one line is the x-axis and the other is the y-axis, then the ordered number pair (x, y) is associated with the point which is $|x|$ units away from the y-axis (in the positive direction if $x > 0$, in the negative direction if $x < 0$, on the y-axis if $x = 0$) and $|y|$ units away from the x-axis (in the positive direction if $y > 0$, in the negative direction if $y < 0$, on the x-axis if $y = 0$). Conversely, each point in the plane is associated with exactly one ordered pair (x, y) as suggested by Figure 1–15.

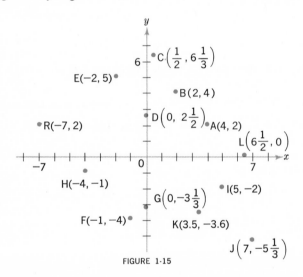

FIGURE 1-15

When a number pair (x, y) is associated with a point as described above, x is the *x-coordinate* or *abscissa* of the point and y is the *y-coordinate* or *ordinate* of the point. What are the x- and y-coordinates of the origin?

A plane with a coordinate system is called a *coordinate plane*. To *plot* a point on a coordinate plane, we use the point's coordinates to locate and mark the point. Notice the points plotted in Figure 1–15. We will use notation such as $P(3, 4)$ to mean the point P whose coordinates are $(3, 4)$ and will sometimes speak of the point $(3, 4)$ rather than the point $P(3, 4)$.

We shall often be concerned with straight lines and circles which lie on a coordinate plane. It is helpful in studying such figures to be able to graph all the points selected by an equation of the line or circle. The set of all such points is the graph of the equation.

The two axes separate the plane into four sets. See Figure 1–16. Each of the four sets of points is the interior of a right angle whose sides are the axes. Each such set is a *quadrant* and the four quadrants are numbered as shown in Figure 1–16. Does a point on an axis belong to a quadrant? Describe the *x*-

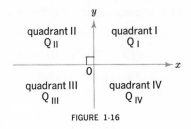

FIGURE 1-16

and *y*-coordinates of the points in quadrant I (Q_I); in Q_{II}; in Q_{III}; in Q_{IV}.

Example 1   Graph $2x + 3y = 6$.

Selecting -3, 0, 3, and 6 as values of *x*, we compute the corresponding values of *y* from $2x + 3y = 6$ and obtain the ordered pairs $(-3, 4)$, $(0, 2)$, $(3, 0)$, and $(6, -2)$. Locating and marking the four points as shown in Figure 1–17, we then draw a picture of the line through them. What is the least number of points that must be plotted in order to determine the line?

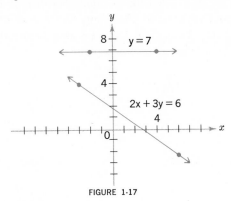

FIGURE 1-17

Example 2   Graph $y = 7$.

For the coordinate plane, the equation $y = 7$ means "$y = 7$ and *x* is a real number." Therefore, any two ordered pairs of the form $(x, 7)$, say $(-2, 7)$ and $(4, 7)$ will suffice. These points are located and marked and a picture of the line is drawn in Figure 1–17.

Before discussing circles in a coordinate plane, we shall state what is meant by distance between two points. See Figure 1–18.

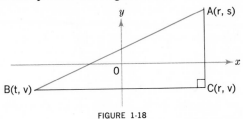

FIGURE 1-18

You will notice that we define three cases of distance between two points.

DISTANCE BETWEEN TWO POINTS ON A COORDINATE PLANE   Given $A(r, s)$ and $B(t, v)$ with $\overleftrightarrow{AB}$ oblique to both axes and point $C(r, v)$, thus making $\overleftrightarrow{AC}$ parallel to the y-axis and $\overleftrightarrow{BC}$ parallel to the x-axis.

CASE 1 $B(t, v)$ and $C(r, v)$ are on a horizontal line and $BC = |t - r|$.

CASE 2 $A(r, s)$ and $C(r, v)$ are on a vertical line and $AC = |v - s|$.
Note: $|x|$ is defined to be x for $x \geq 0$ and $-x$ for $x < 0$. Pronounce $|x|$ as "the *absolute value* of x." Pronounce $-x$ as "the *additive inverse* (or *opposite*) of x."

CASE 3 $B(t, v)$ and $A(r, s)$ are on an oblique line and
$BA = \sqrt{(t - r)^2 + (v - s)^2}$.

The equation of CASE 3 is called the *Distance Formula* and may be derived as a consequence of the Pythagorean Theorem. Show that CASE 3 can be used to determine BC and AC. Thus CASE 3 can be used to determine the distance between any two points on the coordinate plane.

Examples   Given: $A(5, 2)$, $B(5, -3)$, $C(-3, -3)$, and $D(5, -5)$ as shown in Figure 1–19.

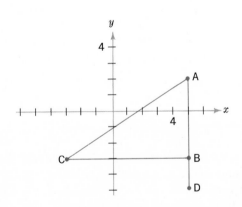

FIGURE 1-19

1. $BD = |(-3) - (-5)| = |2| = 2$
2. $CB = |(-3) - (5)| = |-8| = 8$
3. $AB = |(2) - (-3)| = |5| = 5$
4. $AC = \sqrt{[5 - (-3)]^2 + [2 - (-3)]^2}$
    $= \sqrt{8^2 + 5^2} = \sqrt{64 + 25} = \sqrt{89}$

Compute AD and CD.

On a coordinate plane, consider any circle whose center is the origin and whose radius is r. See Figure 1–20. Since this circle is the set of all points $P(x, y)$ which are at a distance r from the origin, it follows that $PO = r$.
By the distance formula

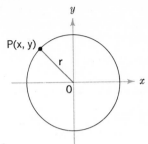

$$PO = \sqrt{(x - 0)^2 + (y - 0)^2}$$
and $\qquad PO = \sqrt{x^2 + y^2} = r$
or $\qquad\qquad x^2 + y^2 = r^2$

Thus, $x^2 + y^2 = r^2$ is an equation of a circle whose center is the origin and whose radius is r. What is the radius of the circle specified by $x^2 + y^2 = 25$? Describe how you would graph the equation $x^2 + y^2 = 49$.

EXERCISES

1. Give the coordinates of each point shown on the coordinate plane. For some answers you will have to make estimates.

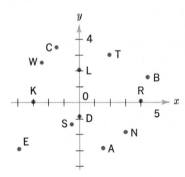

a. N	e. B	i. S
b. T	f. D	j. R
c. E	g. C	k. L
d. K	h. A	l. W

2. Establish eight coordinate systems on graph paper and graph these eight equations.

a. $3x + 4y = 12$ c. $y = -3$ e. $x^2 + y^2 = 36$ g. $y = x$

b. $5y = 3x + 10$ d. $x = 4$ f. $x^2 + y^2 = 1$ h. $y = -x$

3. Study Figure 1–18 and prove, using the Pythagorean Theorem, that

$$BA = \sqrt{(t - r)^2 + (v - s)^2}.$$

4. Use the Distance Formula and compute AB.

a. $A(-7, 0)$ and $B(2, 3)$ d. $A(14, -5)$ and $B(14, 5)$

b. $A(6, -9)$ and $B(-4, -9)$ e. $A(5, -3)$ and $B(-2, 4)$

c. $A(0, 8)$ and $B(-6, 0)$ f. $A(-7, 2)$ and $B(-3, 7)$

5. Give the radius of each of the following circles.

a. $x^2 + y^2 = 144$ b. $x^2 + y^2 = 7$ c. $2x^2 + 2y^2 = 10$

6. Give an equation of the circle whose center is the origin and which passes through the given point.

a. $A(5, 0)$

b. $B(0, -3)$

e. $E\left(\dfrac{\sqrt{3}}{2}, \dfrac{-1}{2}\right)$

g. $G\left(\dfrac{-\sqrt{3}}{2}, \dfrac{-1}{2}\right)$

c. $C(-6, 8)$

d. $D(-6, -8)$

f. $F\left(\dfrac{-1}{\sqrt{2}}, \dfrac{1}{\sqrt{2}}\right)$

h. $H\left(\dfrac{1}{\sqrt{2}}, \dfrac{-1}{\sqrt{2}}\right)$

7. Determine the circumference of each circle in Exercise 6.

8. Determine the coordinates of the two points where the line specified by $y = x$ intersects the circle whose equation is $x^2 + y^2 = 1$.

Hint: Solve the system $\begin{cases} x^2 + y^2 = 1 \\ y = x \end{cases}$ by the substitution method.

9. Repeat Exercise 8, using the line specified by $y = -x$ and the same circle.

SYMMETRY

Observe in Figure 1–21 that the y-axis is the perpendicular bisector of segments $\overline{AA'}$, $\overline{BB'}$ and $\overline{CC'}$. The coordinates of the endpoints are given in the figure. Look for a relationship between the coordinates of the endpoints of each such segment.

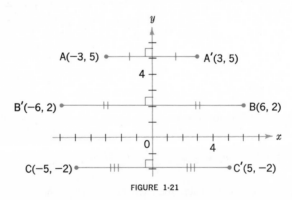

FIGURE 1-21

The points A and A' are *symmetric with respect to the y-axis*. The same is true of points B and B' and of points C and C'. In general,

    1. each point $P(x, y)$ is symmetric to the point $P'(-x, y)$ with respect to the y-axis and

    2. points P and P' are symmetric with respect to the y-axis if and only if the y-axis is the perpendicular bisector of segment $\overline{PP'}$.

With respect to the y-axis what point is symmetric to $D\left(-4\tfrac{1}{2}, 3\tfrac{1}{2}\right)$? to $E\left(5\tfrac{1}{4}, -1\right)$? to $F(-4, 0)$? to $G(0, 3)$?

In Figure 1–22 the x-axis is the perpendicular bisector of segments $\overline{RR'}$, $\overline{SS'}$ and $\overline{TT'}$. Coordinates of endpoints are given in the figure. Do you see a relation between the coordinates of the endpoints of each such segment? The points R and R' are *symmetric with respect to the x-axis*. The same is true for the points S and S' and also for T and T'. In general,

1. each point $P(x, y)$ is symmetric to the point $P'(x, -y)$ with respect to the x-axis and
2. points P and P' are symmetric with respect to the x-axis if and only if the x-axis is the perpendicular bisector of segment $\overline{PP'}$.

With respect to the x-axis what point is symmetric to $D\left(-4\frac{1}{2}, 3\frac{1}{2}\right)$? to $E\left(5\frac{1}{4}, -1\right)$? to $F(-4, 0)$? to $G(0, 3)$?

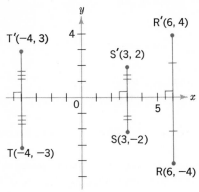

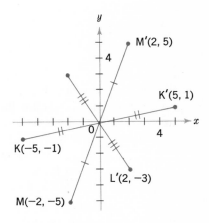

FIGURE 1-22   FIGURE 1-23

In Figure 1–23 the origin is the midpoint of segments $\overline{KK'}$, $\overline{LL'}$ and $\overline{MM'}$. Study the coordinates of the endpoints as given in the figure and look for a pattern. The points K and K' are *symmetric with respect to the origin*. This is true also for points L and L' and for M and M'. In general,

1. each point $P(x, y)$ is symmetric to the point $P'(-x, -y)$ with respect to the origin and
2. points P and P' are symmetric with respect to the origin if and only if the origin is the midpoint of segment $\overline{PP'}$.

With respect to the origin what point is symmetric to $D\left(-4\frac{1}{2}, 3\frac{1}{2}\right)$? to $E\left(5\frac{1}{4}, -1\right)$? to $F(-4, 0)$? to $G(0, 3)$? to $H(-4, -4)$?

In Figure 1–24 on page 20 the line specified by $y = x$ is the perpendicular bisector of segments $\overline{VV'}$, $\overline{WW'}$ and $\overline{ZZ'}$. The coordinates of endpoints are given in the figure. For any such segment, what is the relation of the coordinates of one endpoint to those of the other endpoint?

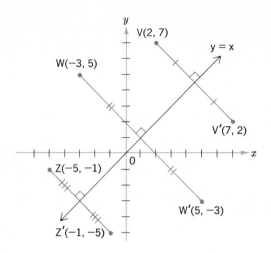

FIGURE 1-24

We say that the points V and V' are *symmetric with respect to the line specified by* $y = x$. The same is true for the points W and W' and for the points Z and Z'. In general,

1. each point $P(x, y)$ is symmetric to the point $P'(y, x)$ with respect to the line specified by $y = x$ and
2. points P and P' are symmetric with respect to the line specified by $y = x$ if and only if this line is the perpendicular bisector of segment $\overline{PP'}$.

With respect to the line specified by $y = x$ what point is symmetric to $J(9, 3)$? to $N(-7, 5)$? to $Q(-3, -4)$? to $U(6, -2)$?

EXERCISES

1. For the figure below, tell the capital letter name of the point symmetric to the given point with respect to (1) the y-axis, (2) the x-axis and (3) the origin.

a. A b. B c. C d. D e. E f. F

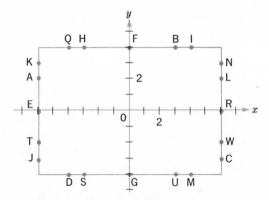

2. For the figure of Exercise 1, give the coordinates of the point symmetric to the given point with respect to (1) the y-axis, (2) the x-axis and (3) the origin.

a. $A(-6, 2)$ d. $D(-4, -4)$ g. Any point $P(m, n)$ of the rectangle

b. $B(3, 4)$ e. $E(-6, 0)$ h. Any point $V(-c, d)$ of the rectangle

c. $C(6, -3)$ f. $F(0, 4)$ i. Any point $H(t, -h)$ of the rectangle

3. The circle at the right contains pairs of points that are symmetric with respect to the origin and with respect to each axis.

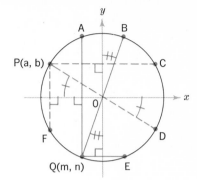

a. Give the capital letter name and coordinates of the point symmetric to $P(a, b)$ with respect to (1) the y-axis, (2) the x-axis and (3) the origin.

b. Repeat the procedure for the point $Q(m, n)$.

4. For each point $P(x, y)$ listed below, give the coordinates of P', the point symmetric to $P(x, y)$ with respect to the line specified by $y = x$.

a. $P(7, 4)$ d. $P(-2, -8)$ g. $P(-3c, 2a)$

b. $P(-6, 2)$ e. $P(a, b)$ h. $P(-c, -d)$

c. $P(3, -5)$ f. $P(m, -2n)$ i. $P(a + b, m - n)$

5. Give the coordinates of the point symmetric to the given points of Exercise 4 with respect to (1) the y-axis, (2) the x-axis, and (3) the origin.

FUNCTIONS

Sets whose members are ordered pairs were mentioned previously. Some of these sets are *functions*. Much of mathematics is concerned with the study of functions.

DEFINITION OF FUNCTION   A *function* is a set of ordered pairs no two of which have the same first component.

Examples of functions are

$$\{(3, 2), (-4, 6.5), (\pi, \sqrt{2})\}$$

$$\{(x, y) \mid y = x^2\} \qquad \{(x, y) \mid y = 2x + 3\}$$

The following sets are *not* functions since each contains at least two ordered pairs with the same first component. For each set, list two ordered pairs which will prove that it is not a function.

1. $\{(4, 3), (2, 1), (4, 7), (5, 6)\}$
2. $\{(x, y) \mid x = y^2\}$
3. $\{(x, y) \mid x^2 + y^2 = 25\}$

Associated with each function are two other sets, the *domain* and the *range* of the function.

DEFINITION OF DOMAIN AND RANGE   The *domain* of a function is the set of all first components of the ordered pairs in the function. The *range* of a function is the set of all second components of the ordered pairs in the function.

Study the following table which describes the domain and range of six functions.

function	domain	range
I $\{(2, 1), (3, 1), (4, 2)\}$	$\{2, 3, 4\}$	$\{1, 2\}$
II $\{(0, 0), (1, 3), (2, 6), (3, 9), \ldots\}$	$\{0, 1, 2, \ldots\}$	$\{0, 3, 6, \ldots\}$
III $\{(x, y) \mid y = |x|\}$	$R = \{$all real numbers$\}$	$\{y \mid y \geq 0\}$
IV $\{(x, y) \mid y = 2x + 1\}$	R	R
V $\{(x, y) \mid y = x^2\}$	R	$\{y \mid y \geq 0\}$
VI $\{(x, y) \mid xy = -2\}$	$\{x \mid x \neq 0\}$	$\{y \mid y \neq 0\}$

In the table above, the functions were specified by either the roster method or the rule method. A function may also be specified by its graph. The graphs of the six functions of the table are shown.

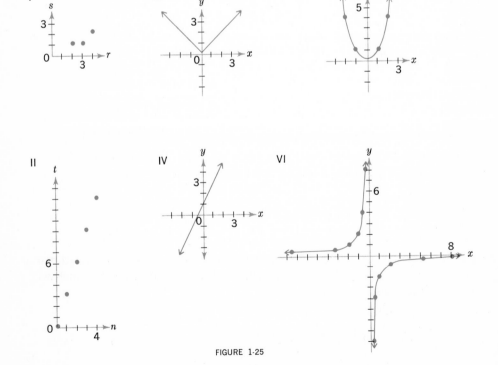

FIGURE 1-25

Determine the domain and the range of each function by observing its graph; then check the table above to verify your answers.

A function may be named by a letter. This is usually a lower case letter but could also be a capital letter or even a Greek letter. Study the following examples which introduce an important notation.

Example 1   Suppose $f = \{(2, 7), (5, 3), (-4, 1)\}$.
The function f pairs 7 from its range with 2 from the domain. The last sentence may be abbreviated to the equation $f(2) = 7$, where $f(2)$ means "the element in the range which is paired with 2 in the domain." Determine $f(-4); f(5)$.

Example 2   Suppose $g = \{(x, y) \mid y = 2x + 1\}$.
This function g pairs, for example, 9 from its range with 4 from the domain. Therefore, $g(4) = 9$. Note that $\big(4, g(4)\big)$ is an ordered pair in function g and that for any x, $y = g(x)$. We might also describe g as $\{(x, g(x)) \mid g(x) = 2x + 1\}$. Determine $g(-5); g(3a); g(5 + a)$.

Example 3   Suppose $h = \{(x, h(x)) \mid h(x) = x^2\}$.
Rather than using this notation, it is sometimes more convenient to speak of "the function h specified by $h(x) = x^2$." Determine $t(10)$ where t is specified by $t(x) = 3x^2 - 5$.

EXERCISES

1. Give the domain and the range of each of the following functions.

   a. $\{(3, 2), (2, 3), (1, 4), (5, 2)\}$

   b. $\{\ldots, (-3, 6), (-1, 0), (1, -6),$
   $(3, -12), \ldots\}$

   c. $\{(x, y) \mid y = (x - 2)^2 + 1\}$

   d. $\{(x, f(x)) \mid f(x) = -2x + 3\}$

   e. g such that $g(x) = \sqrt{x}$

   f. t such that $t(x) = 3$

g.
(incomplete graph)

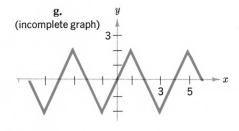

h.
(incomplete graph)

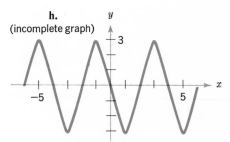

2. Given a function f such that $f(x) = x^2 + 1$, determine the following.

   a. $f(7)$ b. $f(1.1)$ c. $f(-\sqrt{3})$ d. $f(-5a)$ e. $f(c + 3)$ f. $f\left(\dfrac{\sqrt{2}}{2}\right)$

3. Tell which sets are functions and which are not.

a. $\{(5, 8), (2.3, -6.7), (5, -4)\}$

b. $\{(1, 1), (2, 4), (3, 9), \ldots\}$

c. $\{(x, y) \mid y = 5 - 2x\}$

d. $\{(a, b) \mid a = (2b - 1)^2\}$

e. $\{(m, n) \mid m^2 + n^2 = 9\}$

f. $\{(x, y) \mid x = 2\}$

g. $\{(x, y) \mid y = -4\}$

h. $\{(c, d) \mid d = |c - 3|\}$

i. $\{(x, y) \mid xy = 12\}$

j. $\{(x, y) \mid y = \sqrt{1 - x^2}\}$

VOCABULARY

Use each of the following correctly in a sentence to demonstrate that you understand its meaning. If you are not sure, refer back to the chapter.

abscissa
absolute value
central angle
complementary
coordinate plane
degree measure
Distance Formula
domain
function
infinite set
intercepted arc

irrational number
major arc
minor arc
Pythagorean Theorem
quadrant
quadratic formula
range
semicircle
similar triangles
solution set
symmetric points

REVIEW EXERCISES

1. Use the roster method to give the real number solution set of each equation.

a. $x^2 = 17$

b. $x^2 - 7x = 0$

c. $x^2 + 9 = 0$

d. $2x^2 + 3x - 1 = 0$

e. $\pi x - 2\pi = \pi$

f. $\dfrac{\pi}{3} + \dfrac{5\pi}{3} = 2x$

2. Tell whether the number is (1) rational or (2) irrational.

a. 4.632

b. $-3.\overline{29}$

c. π

d. $-5\dfrac{2}{3}$

e. 2.7373373337 . . .

f. $5 + \sqrt{2}$

3. Graph each set on the real number line.

a. $\{m \mid -2 \leq m < 2\}$

b. $\{t \mid t < -3\}$

4. Tell five ordered pairs of real numbers that belong to the set.

a. $\{(x, y) \mid 2y = 5x - 1\}$

b. $\{(x, y) \mid x^2 + y^2 = 5\}$

c. $\{(x, y) \mid x = -3\}$

d. $\{(x, y) \mid y - 1 = 0\}$

5. Describe the coordinates, x and y, for points $P(x, y)$ in Quadrant II.

6. Given the circle in a coordinate plane with center at the origin, as pictured above.

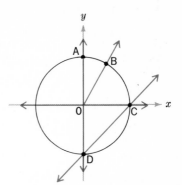

    a. Why would it be improper to speak of $\angle C$? of $\overset{\frown}{AB}$?

    b. List one pair of supplementary oblique angles. Two pairs of complementary angles.

    c. Name one diameter, five rays, and one radius.

    d. Name two minor arcs. Two major arcs.

    e. Name one chord that is not a diameter.

    f. Use three letters to name one semicircle.

    g. Name two acute central angles. One obtuse central angle. One right angle.

    h. Name one pair of non-perpendicular lines.

    i. Name one point in the interior of $\angle ADC$.

7. Given the two circles shown below with their centers at P, $PA = 2$, $PB = 3$, determine the following.

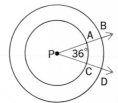

    a. m minor arc $\overset{\frown}{AC}$

    b. m major arc $\overset{\frown}{AC}$

    c. m major arc $\overset{\frown}{BD}$

    d. circumference of smaller circle

    e. length of minor arc $\overset{\frown}{AC}$

    f. length of major arc $\overset{\frown}{BD}$

    g. m minor arc $\overset{\frown}{BD}$

    h. circumference of greater circle

8. Determine BD, the length of a diagonal of rectangle $ABCD$, if $AB = 5$ and $BC = 2$.

9. Determine the lengths of the sides of a 30°-60° right triangle if the length of the hypotenuse is 8.

10. Determine the length of a diagonal of a 5-inch square.

11. Graph each equation.

    a. $5y - 3x = 2$ **b.** $x^2 + y^2 = 25$

12. Write an equation of the circle whose center is the origin and whose radius is 4.

13. Determine the distance between A and B in each case.

    a. $A(3, 17)$ and $B(-5, 17)$ **c.** $A(-6, 3)$ and $B(-6, 11)$

    b. $A(6, -2)$ and $B(-3, -4)$ **d.** $A(-2, -7)$ and $B(-7, -2)$

14. Tell the point $P(x, y)$ that is symmetric to $Q(-3, 4)$ with respect

    a. to the y-axis   **c.** to the origin

    b. to the x-axis   **d.** to the line specified by $y = x$

15. Tell whether each set is a function. If it is not, give two ordered pairs with the same first component to prove that the set is not a function.

a. $\{(-2, 4), (-3, 9), (4, -2)\}$ d. $\{(x, y) \mid x = y^2 + 2\}$

b. $\{(5, 7), (9, 11), (6, 4), (5, 7)\}$ e. $\{(x, y) \mid x = |y|\}$

c. $\{(x, y) \mid y = x^2 + 2\}$ f. $\{(x, y) \mid xy = 5\}$

16. Give the domain and the range of each of the following functions.

a. $\{(2, 7), (4, 14), (6, 21), (8, 28), \ldots\}$ d. f such that $f(x) = \sqrt{x - 2}$

b. $\{(x, y) \mid 2y = x^2 + 6\}$ e. g such that $g(x) = x + 1$

c. $\{(x, y) \mid y = |x| + 3\}$

17. Given a function k such that $k(x) = x^2 - 3$, determine the following:

a. $k(10)$ b. $k(2a)$ c. $k(\sqrt{5})$ d. $k(t - 2)$ e. $k(\pi)$

18. Use the roster method to indicate the membership of $\{5 + 3k\}$.

CHAPTER TEST

1. Give the real number solution set of each equation.

a. $2x^2 = 12$ c. $2x^2 + 8 = 0$

b. $2x^2 + 3x - 7 = 0$ d. $2\pi x - 3\pi = 5\pi$

2. Tell whether the number is rational or irrational.

a. $-\sqrt{3}$ b. π c. -3.5 d. $5.1212212221 \ldots$

3. Graph each set on the real number line.

a. $\{c \mid -3 \le c \le 2\}$ b. $\{a \mid a > 5\}$

4. If $m \angle A = 80$, give the degree measure of

a. a complement of $\angle A$.   b. a supplement of $\angle A$.

5. The measure of the hypotenuse of a $30°$-$60°$ right triangle is 6. Determine the lengths of the legs.

6. Determine the perimeter of a square whose diagonal is $7\sqrt{2}$ units long.

7. True or false?

a. Each real number has a terminating decimal numeral as one of its names.

b. The ordered pair $(8, -4)$ is a member of $\{(x, y) \mid 2y = x^2\}$.

c. The ordered pair $(-2, 7)$ corresponds to a point in quadrant **IV**.

d. The degree measure of a central angle is the same as the degree measure of its intercepted arc.

e. There is a right triangle whose sides measure $\frac{2}{3}\sqrt{5}, \frac{1}{3}$ and $\frac{1}{3}\sqrt{21}$.

f. The radius of the circle whose equation is $x^2 + y^2 = 8$ is 4.

g. $\{(2, 3), (7, 2), (3, 7)\}$ is a function.

h. $\{3 + 2k\}$ is the same set of numbers as $\{3 - 2k\}$, where k is an integer.

i. $\{(x, y) \mid y^2 = x + 1\}$ is a function.

j. $P(0.4, 0.6)$ is a point of the circle whose equation is $x^2 + y^2 = 1$.

8. Graph each equation.

   a. $2y = 3x + 4$

   b. $x^2 + y^2 = 36$

9. Determine the distance between A and B.

   a. $A(-2, 7)$ and $B(3, 9)$

   b. $A(2t, c)$ and $B(t + 3, 3c - 2)$

10. Tell the coordinates of the point that is symmetric to $P(a, b)$ with respect

   a. to the x-axis

   b. to the origin

   c. to the y-axis

   d. to the line specified by $y = x$

11. Give the domain and the range of each function.

   a. $\{(3, 1), (6, 2), (9, 3), (12, 4), \ldots\}$

   b. $\{(x, y) \mid y = x^2 + 4\}$

   c. f such that $f(x) = \sqrt{x - 5}$

12. Given a function g such that $g(x) = 3x - 2$, determine the following.

   a. $g\left(\dfrac{-2}{3}\right)$

   b. $g(-5c)$

   c. $g\left(\dfrac{\pi}{3}\right)$

   d. $g(2m - 1)$

13. Given a circle with minor arc $\overset{\frown}{AB}$ and central angle APB. $PA = 4$ and $m \angle APB = 120$. Determine each of the following.

   a. $m\overset{\frown}{AB}$

   b. The length of $\overset{\frown}{AB}$

14. Write an equation of the circle with center at the origin and passing through $P(\sqrt{2}, -\sqrt{2})$.

CHAPTER 2

PATHS AND THE WRAPPING FUNCTION

PATHS

Let us consider moves along certain geometric figures. One kind of move is along a square. Consider the square *TCRV* of Figure 2–1. Each side is two units long. Points *A*, *K*, *L*, and *M* are midpoints of the sides as shown.

The course traveled during a move will be called a *path*. The move along this square from *A* to *C* which goes through *T* and then through *K* is three units long. The direction of the move described is positive. This counterclockwise path is denoted by the ordered pair (*A*, 3) signifying the move begins at *A* and moves three units along the square in the positive direction. We call *A* the initial point and *C* the terminal point of this path. The path traversed by a move from *V* along the square for four units in the negative direction is (*V*, −4). Observe that *C* is the terminal point of this path.

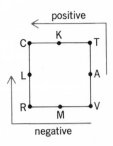

FIGURE 2·1

Describe each of the following paths by telling its
    (1) initial and terminal points, (2) length, and (3) direction.

(*A*, 8)	(*L*, 4)	$\left(C, -3\frac{1}{2}\right)$	(*R*, 0)	(*K*, 5)
(*T*, 6)	(*A*, −8)		(*R*, 8)	(*K*, −3)
(*R*, 3)	$\left(C, 3\frac{1}{2}\right)$	(*M*, 0)		(*A*, 4)
		(*M*, −8)	(*A*, −4)	

For the square of Figure 2–1, the length of a move may be greater than 8, even though the perimeter of the square is 8.

28

Observe in Figure 2–2 the part which indicates the path (A, 12).

Even though the move is on the square the marking which shows this move is drawn off the square. The path (A, 12) from A along the square for 12 units in the positive direction has L as its terminal point. Now, considering

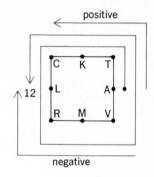

(1) initial point
(2) terminal point
(3) length and
(4) direction

FIGURE 2-2

in which respects are the following paths alike?

(A, 12) and (A, 4)   (A, −2) and (A, −10)

(A, −10) and (A, 10)   (A, 10) and (A, −14)

Let us consider a function F, defined in the following way.

> Given any path (A, d) on square TCRV, F(d) = P,
> where P is the terminal point of the path (A, d).

The domain of F is the set of all real numbers d. The range is the set of all points on square TCRV (see Figure 2–2). Observe that F(3) = C, F(−2) = M, F(10) = K, and F(−7) = T. Which point is F(5)? F(−5)? F(14)? F(−9)?

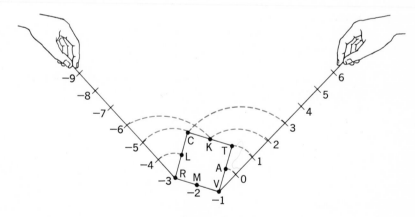

FIGURE 2-3

To interpret the function F, think of the square as a cross section of a rectangular spool and think of the real number line as a thread. The thread is wrapped around the spool without stretching so that zero goes to A. The positive portion is thus wrapped continuously in one direction, and the negative portion in the other direction. See Figure 2–3.

This function F possesses the unusual property that for each real number d and for each integer k, F(d) = F(d + 8k). Observe that point C = ... F(−13) = F(−5) = F(3) = F(11) = ... To indicate this, we write F(3 + 8k) = C. For what real numbers d is it true that F(d) = R? Determine F(18); F(−24); F(83).

In the preceding discussion we gave an intuitive description of the function F. We now consider this in a more precise way, this time using a coordinate plane. See Figure 2–4. Let $TCRV$ be a square on an x, y coordinate plane with $T(1, 1)$, $C(-1, 1)$, $R(-1, -1)$, $V(1, -1)$, and $A(1, 0)$.

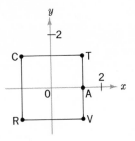

FIGURE 2·4

The function F has the set of all real numbers for its domain. Its range is the square $TCRV$. We define F so that to the real number d there corresponds P, the terminal point of the path (A, d).

1. If d is a real number such that $0 \leq d \leq 1$, then to d there corresponds the point P with coordinates $(1, d)$; that is, $F(d) = P(1, d)$.
   For example, $F\left(\frac{3}{4}\right) = P\left(1, \frac{3}{4}\right)$. Which point is $F(0.3)$?

2. If $1 \leq d \leq 3$, then $F(d) = P(2 - d, 1)$.
   For example, $F(1.5) = P(0.5, 1)$ and $F(2.5) = P(-0.5, 1)$.
   Determine $F(1.8)$ and $F(2.7)$.

3. If $3 \leq d \leq 5$, then $F(d) = P(-1, 4 - d)$.
   For example, $F(3.5) = P(-1, 0.5)$ and $F(4.5) = P(-1, -0.5)$.
   Determine $F(3.7)$ and $F(4.2)$.

4. If $5 \leq d \leq 7$, then $F(d) = P(d - 6, -1)$.
   For example, $F(5.5) = P(-0.5, -1)$ and $F(6.5) = P(0.5, -1)$.
   Determine $F(6.9)$ and $F(5.9)$.

5. If $7 \leq d < 8$, then $F(d) = P(1, d - 8)$.
   For example, $F(7.5) = P(1, -0.5)$.
   Determine $F(7.3)$.

6. If $d < 0$ or if $d \geq 8$, then $F(d) = F(d - 8k)$ where k is an integer such that $0 \leq d - 8k < 8$.
   $F(d - 8k)$, and therefore, $F(d)$ is defined by one of the above.

Examples $\quad F(19.4) = F(19.4 - 16) = F(3.4) = P(-1, 0.6)$
$F(-6.2) = F(-6.2 + 8) = F(1.8) = P(0.2, 1)$
$F(29.6) = F(29.6 - 24) = F(5.6) = P(-0.4, -1)$
$F(-14.7) = F(-14.7 + 16) = F(1.3) = P(0.7, 1)$

Determine $F(27)$ and $F(-27)$.

EXERCISES

Each exercise refers to the function F which was defined in the preceding section.

1. Determine the point $P(x, y)$ for each of the following.
   Example $\quad F\left(\frac{1}{2}\right) = P\left(1, \frac{1}{2}\right)$

a. $F(3.4)$	**c.** $F(7.5)$	**e.** $F(-1.6)$	**g.** $F(-5.1)$	**i.** $F(-15)$
b. $F(4.2)$	**d.** $F(12)$	**f.** $F(-2.7)$	**h.** $F(-6.3)$	**j.** $F(81)$

2. True or false?

a. $F(1) = F(5)$

b. $F(3) = F(-5)$

c. $F(-2.4) = F(5.6)$

d. $F(8) = F(-8)$

e. $F(12) = F(-12)$

f. $F(3) = F(-3)$

g. $F(4) = F(-4)$

h. For each real number d, $F(d) = F(-d)$.

i. For each natural number n, $F(4n) = F(4n^2)$.

j. $F(58) = F(2)$

k. $F(-69) = F(3)$

l. For each integer k and for each real number d, $F(d) = F(d + 8k)$.

m. The point $F(2.5)$ is symmetric to the point $F(5.5)$ with respect to the x-axis.

n. $F(4.5)$ and $F(-0.5)$ are symmetric points with respect to the y-axis.

o. $F(1)$ and $F(5)$ are symmetric with respect to the origin.

p. For each real number d, $F(d)$ is symmetric to $F(4 - d)$ with respect to the y-axis.

q. For each real number d, $F(d)$ and $F(d - 4)$ are symmetric with respect to the origin.

r. For each real number d, $F(d)$ and $F(-d)$ are symmetric with respect to the x-axis.

3. a. State the domain of F.

b. State the range of F.

4. Prove that if $d < 0$ or if $d \geq 8$, then there is an integer k such that $0 \leq d - 8k < 8$. *Hint:* Here d is either an integer multiple of 8 or d is between consecutive integer multiples of 8.

PATHS ON A CIRCLE

A second kind of move we will consider is along a circle. Consider the circle of Figure 2–5. Its radius is 1 and, therefore, its circumference is 2π ($C = 2\pi r$). Eight points of the circle, named by capital letters, separate it to form eight arcs, each of length $\frac{\pi}{4}$. A move along this circle from A to C, passing through K and then through T, is $\frac{3\pi}{4}$ units long. We consider the *counterclockwise* direction to be positive. This path is denoted by $\left(A, \frac{3\pi}{4}\right)$,

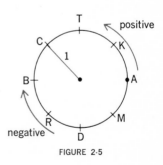

FIGURE 2-5

signifying the move which begins at A and continues for $\frac{3\pi}{4}$ units along the circle in the positive direction. The terminal point of this path is C. $\left(A, \frac{-\pi}{2}\right)$ is the path traversed by a move from A along the circle for $\frac{\pi}{2}$ units in the negative, or clockwise, direction. Note that D is the terminal point of $\left(A, \frac{-\pi}{2}\right)$.

For the circle of Figure 2–5 describe each of the following paths by telling its (1) initial and terminal points, (2) length, and (3) direction.

a. $\left(A, \dfrac{\pi}{4}\right)$ c. (A, π) e. $\left(A, \dfrac{5\pi}{4}\right)$ g. $(A, 0)$

b. $\left(A, \dfrac{-\pi}{4}\right)$ d. $(A, -\pi)$ f. $\left(A, \dfrac{-7\pi}{4}\right)$ h. $(A, -2\pi)$

For the circle of Figure 2–5, the length of a move may be greater than 2π, even though the circumference is 2π.

Observe in Figure 2–6 the part which indicates the path $\left(A, \dfrac{5\pi}{2}\right)$. This path is traversed by a move from A along the circle for $\dfrac{5\pi}{2}$ units in the positive direction. Its terminal point is X. Considering (1) initial point, (2) terminal point, (3) length, and (4) direction, in which respects are the following paths alike?

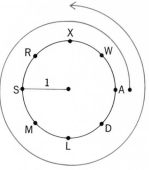

FIGURE 2-6

$\left(A, \dfrac{\pi}{4}\right)$ and $\left(A, \dfrac{9\pi}{4}\right)$

$\left(A, \dfrac{-\pi}{2}\right)$ and $\left(A, \dfrac{-5\pi}{2}\right)$ $(A, 3\pi)$ and $(A, -3\pi)$

$\left(A, \dfrac{11\pi}{4}\right)$ and $\left(A, \dfrac{-13\pi}{4}\right)$

EXERCISES

The circle P has radius 1. Eight points separate the circle into *eight* arcs, each of *equal* length. Counterclockwise moves are in the positive direction.

1. Determine the circumference of the circle.

2. Determine the length of one of the eight arcs.

3. The picture shows the path $\left(A, \dfrac{3\pi}{4}\right)$. Draw similar pictures showing the following paths.

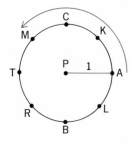

a. $\left(A, \dfrac{3\pi}{2}\right)$ c. $(A, -3\pi)$ e. $\left(A, \dfrac{-5\pi}{2}\right)$

b. $\left(A, \dfrac{-3\pi}{4}\right)$ d. $\left(A, \dfrac{5\pi}{4}\right)$ f. $\left(A, \dfrac{13\pi}{4}\right)$

4. List five other paths, three in the positive direction and two in the negative direction, that have the same initial and terminal points as does each of the following paths.

a. $\left(A, \dfrac{3\pi}{4}\right)$ b. $\left(A, \dfrac{-7\pi}{4}\right)$

5. Determine the smallest positive value of the real number θ (theta) for which the path (A, θ) will have the following terminal point.

   a. K **b.** B **c.** M **d.** R **e.** C **f.** L

The circle O has radius 1. Twelve points separate the circle into *twelve* arcs of *equal* length. Counterclockwise moves are in the positive direction.

6. Determine the circumference of the circle.

7. Determine the length of one of the twelve arcs. The picture shows the path $\left(A, \dfrac{-16\pi}{6} \right)$ which is equal to the path $\left(A, \dfrac{-8\pi}{3} \right)$. Draw similar pictures showing the following paths.

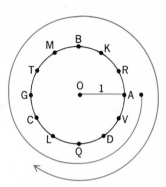

   a. $\left(A, \dfrac{5\pi}{6} \right)$ **c.** $\left(A, \dfrac{-7\pi}{6} \right)$ **e.** $\left(A, \dfrac{-17\pi}{6} \right)$

   b. $\left(A, \dfrac{-\pi}{3} \right)$ **d.** $\left(A, \dfrac{8\pi}{3} \right)$ **f.** $\left(A, \dfrac{13\pi}{6} \right)$

8. Determine the smallest positive value of θ for which the path (A, θ) will have the following terminal point.

   a. R **c.** T **e.** M **g.** C **i.** V

   b. K **d.** D **f.** Q **h.** L **j.** G

THE UNIT CIRCLE AND COTERMINAL PATHS

DEFINITION OF UNIT CIRCLE   A circle with radius 1 is a *unit circle*.

Consider the unit circle of Figure 2–7. Points A, B, C, and D separate it into four arcs of equal length, namely $\dfrac{\pi}{2}$. Observe that many paths for this circle have their initial point at A and their terminal point at B. These paths are

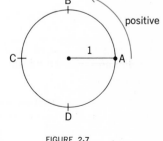

FIGURE 2-7

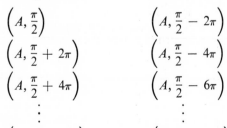

$$\left(A, \frac{\pi}{2} \right) \qquad\qquad \left(A, \frac{\pi}{2} - 2\pi \right)$$

$$\left(A, \frac{\pi}{2} + 2\pi \right) \qquad\qquad \left(A, \frac{\pi}{2} - 4\pi \right)$$

$$\left(A, \frac{\pi}{2} + 4\pi \right) \qquad\qquad \left(A, \frac{\pi}{2} - 6\pi \right)$$

$$\vdots \qquad\qquad\qquad\qquad \vdots$$

$$\left(A, \frac{\pi}{2} + 2n\pi \right) \qquad\qquad \left(A, \frac{\pi}{2} - 2n\pi \right) \quad \text{for } n = 0, 1, 2, 3, \ldots$$

$$\vdots \qquad\qquad\qquad\qquad \vdots$$

Hence, for each integer k, the path $\left(A, \dfrac{\pi}{2} + 2k\pi\right)$ has initial point A and terminal point B. Paths which share the same initial and same terminal points are called *coterminal*.

> **DEFINITION OF COTERMINAL PATHS**   Two or more paths with the same initial point and the same terminal point are *coterminal*.

In a similar manner, it is evident that

1. all paths of the form $(A, \pi + 2k\pi)$ are coterminal at C
2. all paths of the form $\left(A, \dfrac{3\pi}{2} + 2k\pi\right)$ are coterminal at D
3. in general, for any point P of this unit circle and for any real number θ, if (A, θ) has terminal point P, then all paths $(A, \theta + 2k\pi)$ are coterminal at P.

Determine the integer k for each of the three coterminal paths shown in Figure 2-8.

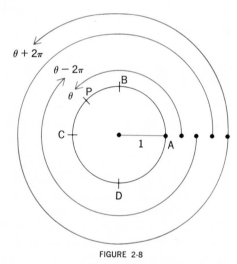

FIGURE 2-8

EXERCISES

1. Consider the unit circle O below on the right. Eight points separate the circle into eight arcs of equal length. Determine the terminal point of each path.

a. $\left(A, \dfrac{3\pi}{4} + 2k\pi\right)$

b. $\left(A, \dfrac{5\pi}{4} + 2k\pi\right)$

c. $\left(A, \dfrac{-3\pi}{4} + 2k\pi\right)$

d. $(A, \pi + 2k\pi)$

e. $(A, 0 + 2k\pi)$

f. $\left(A, \dfrac{-\pi}{2} + 2k\pi\right)$

g. $\left(A, \dfrac{\pi}{2} + 2k\pi\right)$

h. $\left(A, \dfrac{9\pi}{4} + 2k\pi\right)$

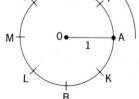

2. Consider the unit circle P on the right. Twelve points separate the circle into twelve arcs of equal length. Determine the terminal point of each path.

a. $\left(A, \dfrac{\pi}{6} + 2k\pi\right)$

e. $\left(A, \dfrac{-\pi}{6} + 2k\pi\right)$

b. $\left(A, \dfrac{\pi}{3} + 2k\pi\right)$

f. $\left(A, \dfrac{2\pi}{3} + 2k\pi\right)$

c. $\left(A, \dfrac{-5\pi}{6} + 2k\pi\right)$

g. $\left(A, \dfrac{-7\pi}{6} + 2k\pi\right)$

d. $\left(A, \dfrac{4\pi}{3} + 2k\pi\right)$

h. $\left(A, \dfrac{5\pi}{3} + 2k\pi\right)$

A WRAPPING FUNCTION

Let us consider a function W with domain the set of all real numbers θ and range a unit circle (see Figure 2–9). Eight points separate the unit circle to form eight arcs, each of length $\dfrac{\pi}{4}$. The function W pairs real numbers θ and points P in the following way.

> Given any path (A, θ) on the unit circle, $W(\theta) = P$, where P is the terminal point of the path (A, θ).

The domain of W is the set of all real numbers θ. The range is the set of all points on the unit circle. Observe that

$$W\left(\frac{\pi}{2}\right) = V, \quad W(-\pi) = M, \quad W\left(\frac{7\pi}{4}\right) = K,$$

$$W\left(\frac{-5\pi}{4}\right) = C \text{ and } W(2) \text{ is a point on minor arc } \overset{\frown}{CV}.$$

As a physical model, think of the circle as a cross-section of a spool. Imagine that the real number line is a thread. The thread is wrapped around the spool without stretching so that zero goes to A, the positive portion is wrapped continuously in a counterclockwise direction, and the negative portion in a clockwise direction.

For the unit circle, all paths $(A, \theta + 2k\pi)$ are coterminal. For this reason the wrapping function W possesses the property that for each real number θ and for each integer k, $W(\theta) = W(\theta + 2k\pi)$. Observe that

$$V = \dots = W\left(\frac{-3\pi}{2}\right) = W\left(\frac{\pi}{2}\right) = W\left(\frac{5\pi}{2}\right) = \dots$$

To indicate this we write $W\left(\dfrac{\pi}{2} + 2k\pi\right) = V$.

For what real numbers θ is it true that $W(\theta) = C$?

Determine $W(3\pi)$; $W(-4\pi)$; $W\left(\dfrac{9\pi}{4}\right)$; $W\left(\dfrac{-11\pi}{4}\right)$.

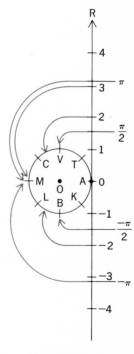

FIGURE 2-9

In the preceding discussion we gave an intuitive description of the wrapping function W. Given any real number θ, $W(\theta)$ is some point P on the unit circle. We have not stated exactly how P is determined for a given value of θ. We shall do this now.

First, consider the unit circle O shown in Figure 2–10. Let central angle AOP intercept minor arc $\overset{\frown}{AP}$ of length θ with P "above" $\overleftrightarrow{OA}$. Let $m\angle AOP = u$. Observe that the following proportion holds for any such minor arc $\overset{\frown}{AP}$ on the unit circle.

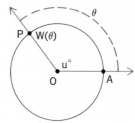

$$\frac{u}{360} = \frac{\theta}{2\pi}$$

From this proportion it follows that

$$u = \frac{180}{\pi} \cdot \theta$$

FIGURE 2-10

For example, if $\theta = \frac{3\pi}{4}$, then $u = \frac{180}{\pi} \cdot \frac{3\pi}{4} = 135$ and $\angle AOP$ is a $135°$ angle.

P is the terminal point of the path $\left(A, \frac{3\pi}{4}\right)$ and $W\left(\frac{3\pi}{4}\right) = P$. In a similar manner we may construct P "above" $\overleftrightarrow{OA}$ for any real number θ in the interval $0 < \theta < \pi$. Determine $m\angle AOP$ if θ is $\frac{\pi}{6}; \frac{2\pi}{3}; \frac{\pi}{2}; \frac{5\pi}{6}; 2; 1$.

Next, consider θ in the interval $\pi < \theta < 2\pi$. For the unit circle shown in Figure 2–11, central angle AOP intercepts minor arc AP of length $2\pi - \theta$ with P "below" $\overleftrightarrow{OA}$. Let $m\angle AOP = u$. For any θ in the interval $\pi < \theta < 2\pi$, the following proportion holds.

$$\frac{u}{360} = \frac{2\pi - \theta}{2\pi}$$

From this proportion it follows that

$$u = \frac{180}{\pi}(2\pi - \theta)$$

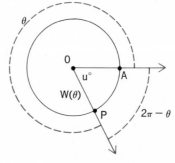

For example, if $\theta = \frac{5\pi}{3}$, then $2\pi - \theta = \frac{\pi}{3}$,

$$u = \frac{180}{\pi} \cdot \frac{\pi}{3} = 60,$$

and $\angle AOP$ is a $60°$ angle.

FIGURE 2-11

P is the terminal point of the path $\left(A, \frac{5\pi}{3}\right)$ and $W\left(\frac{5\pi}{3}\right) = P$. In a similar manner, we may construct P "below" $\overleftrightarrow{OA}$ for any real number θ in the interval $\pi < \theta < 2\pi$. Determine $m\angle AOP$ if θ is $\frac{3\pi}{2}; \frac{7\pi}{6}; \frac{4\pi}{3}; \frac{11\pi}{6}; 4; 5$.

We shall now give a precise description of the wrapping function W.

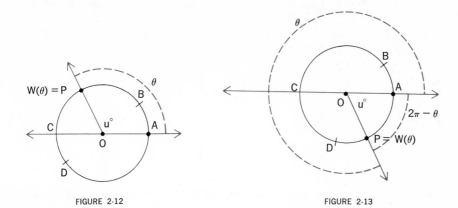

FIGURE 2-12   FIGURE 2-13

Given a unit circle, see Figures 2–12 and 2–13, with a diameter $\overline{AC}$ and center O. Let B and D be points on the circle, B on one side of $\overleftrightarrow{AC}$ and D on the other side. There is a function W with domain the set of all real numbers and range the unit circle. W is defined so that to the real number θ there corresponds P, the terminal point of path (A, θ).

1. To the real number 0 there corresponds A; that is, $W(0) = A$.
2. To the real number π there corresponds C; that is, $W(\pi) = C$.
3. If θ is in the interval $0 < \theta < \pi$, then $W(\theta) = P$, the point on semicircle $\overset{\frown}{ABC}$ for which $m \angle AOP = u = \theta \cdot \dfrac{180}{\pi}$ (see Figure 2–12).
4. If θ is in the interval $\pi < \theta < 2\pi$, then $W(\theta) = P$, the point on semicircle $\overset{\frown}{ADC}$ for which $m \angle AOP = u = (2\pi - \theta) \cdot \dfrac{180}{\pi}$ (see Figure 2–13).
5. If $\theta \geq 2\pi$ or if $\theta < 0$, then $W(\theta) = W(\theta - 2k\pi)$ where k is an integer such that $0 \leq \theta - 2k\pi < 2\pi$. $W(\theta - 2k\pi)$ and, therefore, $W(\theta)$, is defined by either 1, 2, 3 or 4 above.

Examples

$$W\left(\frac{-2\pi}{3}\right) = W\left(\frac{-2\pi}{3} + 2\pi\right) = W\left(\frac{4\pi}{3}\right)$$

$$W\left(\frac{9\pi}{4}\right) = W\left(\frac{9\pi}{4} - 2\pi\right) = W\left(\frac{\pi}{4}\right)$$

$$W(2\pi) = W(2\pi - 2\pi) = W(0)$$

$$W\left(\frac{17\pi}{2}\right) = W\left(\frac{17\pi}{2} - 8\pi\right) = W\left(\frac{\pi}{2}\right)$$

$$W(-9\pi) = W(-9\pi + 10\pi) = W(\pi)$$

$$W(8) = W(8 - 2\pi)$$

$$W(-5) = W(-5 + 2\pi)$$

EXERCISES

1. Draw a large picture of a unit circle with diameter $\overline{AC}$ and with points B and D on the circle, B on one side of $\overleftrightarrow{AC}$ and D on the other side. Use a protractor and construct $W(\theta)$, the terminal point of each of the following paths. Label each terminal point as $W(\theta)$ with the appropriate value of θ.

a. $\left(A, \dfrac{\pi}{4}\right)$ **d.** $\left(A, \dfrac{5\pi}{6}\right)$ **g.** $\left(A, \dfrac{-\pi}{3}\right)$ **j.** $\left(A, \dfrac{16\pi}{3}\right)$ **m.** $(A, 2)$

b. $\left(A, \dfrac{\pi}{6}\right)$ **e.** $\left(A, \dfrac{2\pi}{3}\right)$ **h.** $\left(A, \dfrac{-\pi}{6}\right)$ **k.** $\left(A, \dfrac{-5\pi}{4}\right)$ **n.** $(A, -1)$

c. $\left(A, \dfrac{\pi}{3}\right)$ **f.** $\left(A, \dfrac{7\pi}{6}\right)$ **i.** $\left(A, \dfrac{-\pi}{4}\right)$ **l.** $\left(A, \dfrac{-7\pi}{2}\right)$ **o.** $(A, 9)$

2. The following statements concern the function W which was defined in this section. For each statement, tell whether it is true or false.

a. $W(0) = W(2\pi)$ **e.** $W(7\pi) = W(5\pi)$

b. $W\left(\dfrac{3\pi}{4}\right) = W\left(\dfrac{-3\pi}{4}\right)$ **f.** $W(-7\pi) = W(\pi)$

                                  g. $W\left(\dfrac{13\pi}{6}\right) = W\left(\dfrac{\pi}{6}\right)$

c. $W(\pi) = W(-\pi)$

d. $W\left(\dfrac{2\pi}{3}\right) = W\left(\dfrac{-4\pi}{3}\right)$ **h.** $W\left(\dfrac{-\pi}{4}\right) = W\left(\dfrac{9\pi}{4}\right)$

i. $W\left(\dfrac{-5\pi}{6}\right) = W\left(\dfrac{7\pi}{6}\right)$

j. $W(10) = W(10 - 2\pi)$

k. For each real number θ and for each integer k, $W(\theta) = W(\theta + 2k\pi)$.

3. State the domain of W, the function defined in this section.

4. State the range of W.

5. Given a unit circle, perpendicular diameters $\overline{AC}$ and $\overline{BD}$, shown below on the left. $F = W(\theta)$ and $G = W(\pi - \theta)$. Show that $W(\theta)$ and $W(\pi - \theta)$ are symmetric points with respect to $\overline{BD}$ by showing that $\overline{BD}$ is the perpendicular bisector of $\overline{FG}$. *Hint:* Segment $\overline{BD}$ is the perpendicular bisector of $\overline{FG}$ if $FB = BG$ and $FO = OG$.

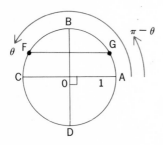 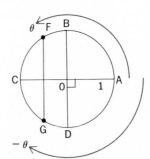

6. For the unit circle shown above on the right, prove that $W(\theta)$ and $W(-\theta)$ are symmetric points with respect to $\overline{AC}$.

7. For the unit circle shown on the right, prove that $W(\theta)$ and $W(\theta - \pi)$ are symmetric points with respect to the origin. *Hint:* Prove that $\overline{FG}$ is a diameter.

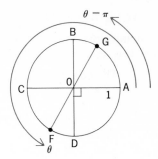

8. For each value of θ given below, determine m such that $0 \le m < 2\pi$ and $W(\theta) = W(m)$.

a. 7π

d. $\dfrac{13\pi}{6}$

g. $\dfrac{-2\pi}{3}$

j. $\dfrac{-17\pi}{6}$

m. 7

b. $\dfrac{19\pi}{4}$

e. -9π

h. $\dfrac{-3\pi}{2}$

k. $\dfrac{-7\pi}{6}$

n. 32

c. $\dfrac{17\pi}{3}$

f. -4π

i. $\dfrac{-9\pi}{4}$

l. 8π

o. -5

9. Suppose that $W(7) = P$.

a. Determine the next three positive numbers θ for which $W(\theta) = P$.

b. Determine the greatest three negative numbers θ for which $W(\theta) = P$.

10. Prove that if $\theta < 0$ or if $\theta \ge 2\pi$, then there is an integer k such that $0 \le \theta - 2k\pi < 2\pi$. *Hint:* θ is either an integer multiple of 2π or θ is between consecutive integer multiples of 2π.

THE UNIT CIRCLE ON A COORDINATE PLANE

DEFINITION OF STANDARD POSITION FOR CIRCLES   A circle with center at the origin of a coordinate plane is in *standard position*.

From this point on, we will be discussing only those paths along a unit circle in standard position which have the initial point $A(1, 0)$. Each *counter-clockwise move* is considered to be in the *positive direction*. Each move in the *clockwise direction* is *negative*. Now, for each real number θ, the terminal point of the path (A, θ) is a point P on the unit circle (see Figure 2–14). Point P is determined by W, the function discussed in the previous section. The coordinates (x, y) of P must satisfy the equation of the unit circle: $x^2 + y^2 = 1$.

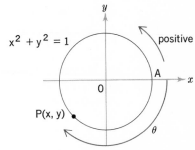

FIGURE 2·14

UNIT CIRCLE REFERENCE POINTS

The coordinates of a few terminal points are readily determined. Consider the following three cases.

CASE 1   The coordinates of four terminal points are

$$A(1, 0) \qquad B(0, 1) \qquad C(-1, 0) \qquad D(0, -1)$$

These are the points at which the axes intersect the circle (see Figure 2–15). Determine the coordinates of the terminal point for each of the following paths.

$$(A, \pi + 2k\pi) \quad \left(A, \frac{\pi}{2} + 2k\pi\right) \quad (A, 0 + 2k\pi) \quad \left(A, \frac{-\pi}{2} + 2k\pi\right)$$

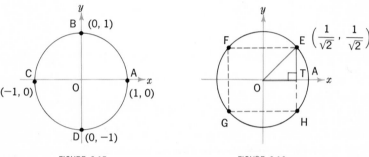

FIGURE 2-15   FIGURE 2-16

CASE 2   Examine Figure 2–16. The points E, F, G, and H bisect the arcs in their respective quadrants. Triangle EOT is a 45° right triangle. Why? $EO = 1$ and $ET = OT = \dfrac{1}{\sqrt{2}} = \dfrac{\sqrt{2}}{2}$. Why?

The coordinates of E are therefore $\left(\dfrac{1}{\sqrt{2}}, \dfrac{1}{\sqrt{2}}\right)$, which is the same as $\left(\dfrac{\sqrt{2}}{2}, \dfrac{\sqrt{2}}{2}\right)$. Use symmetry to determine the coordinates of F, G, and H. The length of minor arc $\overparen{AE}$ is $\dfrac{\pi}{4}$. Why? Determine the terminal point and its coordinates for each of the following paths.

$$\left(A, \frac{\pi}{4} + 2k\pi\right) \left(A, \frac{3\pi}{4} + 2k\pi\right) \left(A, \frac{7\pi}{4} + 2k\pi\right) \left(A, \frac{5\pi}{4} + 2k\pi\right)$$

CASE 3   In Figures 2–17 and 2–18 the points J, K, L, M, N, P, Q, and R trisect the arcs in their respective quadrants. Triangle JOV is a 30°-60° right triangle. Why? Triangle JOM is equilateral. Why? $OJ = 1$, $JV = \dfrac{1}{2}$ and $OV = \dfrac{\sqrt{3}}{2}$. Why? The coordinates of J are therefore $\left(\dfrac{\sqrt{3}}{2}, \dfrac{1}{2}\right)$. Use symmetry to determine the coordinates of

K, L, and M. The length of minor arc $\overset{\frown}{AJ}$ is $\frac{\pi}{6}$. Why? Determine the terminal point and its coordinates for each of the following paths.

$$\left(A, \frac{\pi}{6} + 2k\pi\right) \quad \left(A, \frac{5\pi}{6} + 2k\pi\right) \quad \left(A, \frac{11\pi}{6} + 2k\pi\right) \quad \left(A, \frac{7\pi}{6} + 2k\pi\right)$$

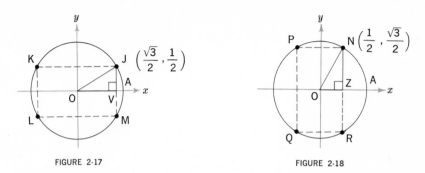

FIGURE 2-17   FIGURE 2-18

By a similar argument, show that the coordinates of N (see Figure 2–18) are $\left(\frac{1}{2}, \frac{\sqrt{3}}{2}\right)$. Use symmetry to determine the coordinates of P, Q, and R. The length of minor arc $\overset{\frown}{AN}$ is $\frac{\pi}{3}$. Why? Determine the terminal point and its coordinates for each of the following paths.

$$\left(A, \frac{\pi}{3} + 2k\pi\right) \quad \left(A, \frac{2\pi}{3} + 2k\pi\right) \quad \left(A, \frac{5\pi}{3} + 2k\pi\right) \quad \left(A, \frac{4\pi}{3} + 2k\pi\right)$$

We now know the coordinates of 16 reference points $W(\theta)$ for which θ is a multiple of $\frac{\pi}{6}$ or $\frac{\pi}{4}$. See Figure 2–19. Observe that $W\left(\frac{-\pi}{3}\right) = P\left(\frac{1}{2}, \frac{-\sqrt{3}}{2}\right)$. You will soon find it helpful to be able to recall quickly the coordinates of these 16 points. Learn them as soon as you can.

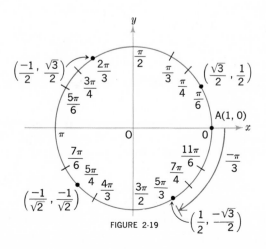

FIGURE 2-19

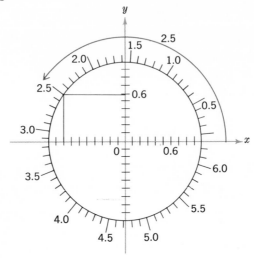

FIGURE 2-20

Recall that the domain of W is the set of all real numbers, not just those whose numerals contain the symbol π. To bring this to your attention, study Figure 2–20, where a decimal scale has been established on a unit circle in standard position. This scale goes from 0 to the number 2π, which is between 6.2 and 6.3; that is, $6.2 < 2\pi < 6.3$. Observe that $W(2.5)$ is a point whose coordinates are $(-.8, .6)$, each coordinate correct to the nearest tenth.

EXERCISES

For the unit circle shown below, $K, L, M,$ and N bisect the arcs in their respective quadrants.

1. Determine three values of θ, two positive and one negative, for the following terminal points of the path (A, θ).

   a. K **c.** N **e.** M

   b. B **d.** C **f.** L

2. Determine the coordinates of each point.

   a. K **c.** C **e.** N **g.** L

   b. B **d.** M **f.** A **h.** D

3. Determine the terminal point of each path.

   a. $(A, 8\pi)$ **c.** $\left(A, \dfrac{5\pi}{2}\right)$ **e.** $\left(A, \dfrac{-65\pi}{4}\right)$

   b. $(A, -7\pi)$ **d.** $\left(A, \dfrac{-9\pi}{4}\right)$ **f.** $(A, 321\pi)$

For the unit circle shown below, E, F, G, H, Q, R, S, and T trisect the arcs in their respective quadrants.

4. Determine three values of θ, two positive and one negative, for the following terminal points of the path (A, θ).

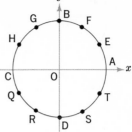

a. F c. R e. Q g. D

b. E d. T f. G h. H

5. Determine the coordinates of each point.

a. F c. E e. T g. S

b. H d. R f. G h. Q

6. Determine the terminal point of each path.

a. $\left(A, \dfrac{7\pi}{3} \right)$ c. $(A, -12\pi)$ e. $\left(A, \dfrac{-29\pi}{6} \right)$

b. $\left(A, \dfrac{-17\pi}{6} \right)$ d. $\left(A, \dfrac{23\pi}{6} \right)$ f. $\left(A, \dfrac{-7\pi}{2} \right)$

7. Use Figure 2–20 and determine the coordinates of the terminal point of each of the following paths. Express each coordinate correct to the nearest tenth.

a. $(A, 0.8)$ d. $(A, 3.9)$ g. $(A, 8.7)$

b. $(A, 6.2)$ e. $(A, 2.4)$ h. $(A, 2.2)$

c. $(A, 1.1)$ f. $(A, 4.3)$ i. $(A, 5.6)$

THE WRAPPING FUNCTION, W

You have seen that for each path (A, θ) on the unit circle in standard position, the terminal point P can be determined. In previous sections you learned ways of doing this. With this background we now define the *wrapping function*, which will be used in subsequent chapters to develop the trigonometric functions.

For each real number θ, the wrapping function W pairs θ and the point $P(x, y)$, the terminal point of the path (A, θ). See Figure 2–21. The number θ is in the domain of W; the terminal point of (A, θ) is in the range of W. Now study the following two examples.

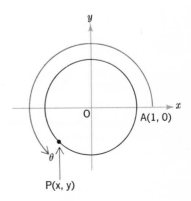

FIGURE 2-21

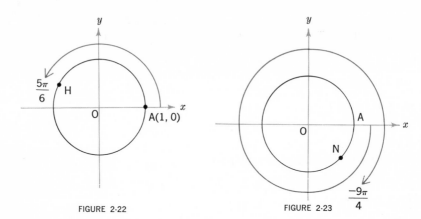

FIGURE 2-22   FIGURE 2-23

Example 1   The terminal point of $\left(A, \dfrac{5\pi}{6}\right)$ is H (see Figure 2–22). The coordinates of H are $\left(\dfrac{-\sqrt{3}}{2}, \dfrac{1}{2}\right)$. W pairs $\dfrac{5\pi}{6}$ and H and we write

$$W\left(\frac{5\pi}{6}\right) = H\left(\frac{-\sqrt{3}}{2}, \frac{1}{2}\right).$$

Example 2   The terminal point of $\left(A, \dfrac{-9\pi}{4}\right)$ is N (see Figure 2–23). The coordinates of N are $\left(\dfrac{1}{\sqrt{2}}, \dfrac{-1}{\sqrt{2}}\right)$. Thus, $W\left(\dfrac{-9\pi}{4}\right) = N\left(\dfrac{1}{\sqrt{2}}, \dfrac{-1}{\sqrt{2}}\right)$.

DEFINITION OF WRAPPING FUNCTION, W   A function is the *wrapping function* W if and only if it pairs each real number θ and $P(x, y)$, the terminal point of (A, θ) where (A, θ) is a path on the unit circle in standard position, with $A(1, 0)$.

This definition implies each of the following statements.

1. The domain of W is R, the set of all real numbers.
2. The range of W is the unit circle in standard position.
3. The coordinates (x, y) of each point in the range must satisfy $x^2 + y^2 = 1$, an equation of the unit circle.
4. W is specified by $W(\theta) = P(x, y)$.

For what values of y will $P(x, y)$ be a point on the unit circle in standard position? Since an equation of this circle is $x^2 + y^2 = 1$, x and y must satisfy this equation. This imposes a limitation on the values of y. Since $x^2 + y^2 = 1$,

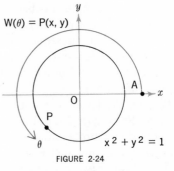

FIGURE 2-24

$$x^2 = 1 - y^2$$
$$x = \sqrt{1 - y^2} \text{ or } x = -\sqrt{1 - y^2}$$
$$1 - y^2 \geq 0 \quad \text{Why?}$$
$$y^2 \leq 1$$
$$-1 \leq y \leq 1$$

This restriction upon the values of y is also evident from a study of Figure 2-24. To what interval are the values of x restricted?

EXERCISES

1. Given the unit circle shown below, determine the coordinates of each of the points.

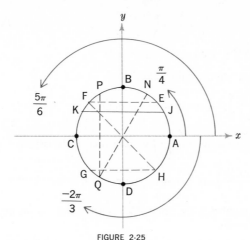

FIGURE 2-25

a. A	**c.** J	**e.** P	**g.** C	**i.** D	**k.** N
b. E	**d.** B	**f.** G	**h.** F	**j.** H	**l.** Q

2. Express each of the following in the form $P(x, y)$ with the appropriate values of x and y.

   Example $W(-\pi) = P(-1, 0)$

   a. $W\left(\dfrac{\pi}{6}\right)$ **d.** $W(\pi)$ **g.** $W(0)$ **j.** $W\left(\dfrac{-\pi}{2}\right)$ **m.** $W(-5\pi)$

   b. $W\left(\dfrac{3\pi}{4}\right)$ **e.** $W(4\pi)$ **h.** $W\left(\dfrac{-7\pi}{3}\right)$ **k.** $W\left(\dfrac{-31\pi}{2}\right)$ **n.** $W\left(\dfrac{5\pi}{4}\right)$

   c. $W\left(\dfrac{-\pi}{3}\right)$ **f.** $W\left(\dfrac{17\pi}{6}\right)$ **i.** $W\left(\dfrac{4\pi}{3}\right)$ **l.** $W\left(\dfrac{7\pi}{2}\right)$ **o.** $W\left(\dfrac{-17\pi}{6}\right)$

3. True or false?

   a. $W(-5\pi) = W(\pi)$

   b. $W\left(\dfrac{-\pi}{6}\right) = W\left(\dfrac{13\pi}{6}\right)$

   c. $W\left(\dfrac{2\pi}{3}\right) = W\left(\dfrac{8\pi}{3}\right)$

   d. $W\left(\dfrac{-5\pi}{6}\right) = W\left(\dfrac{19\pi}{6}\right)$

   e. $W(4.7 + 2\pi) = W(4.7)$

   f. For each real number θ,
   $W(\theta) = W(-\theta)$.

   g. For each natural number n,
   $W(n\pi) = W(n^2\pi)$.

   h. For each real number θ and for each integer k, $W(\theta) = W(\theta + 2k\pi)$.

i. For each integer k,
$$W\left(\frac{\pi}{2}\right) = W\left(\frac{\pi}{2} + k\pi\right).$$

j. For each integer k,
$$W\left(\frac{\pi}{6}\right) = W\left(\frac{\pi}{6} + 2k\pi\right).$$

In k–p, if a point is on the unit circle mark it true. If not, false.

k. $P(1, 1)$ **m.** $P(2, -1)$ **o.** $P(0.5, 0.7)$

l. $P\left(\frac{5}{13}, \frac{12}{13}\right)$ **n.** $P\left(\frac{-4}{5}, \frac{3}{5}\right)$ **p.** $P(0.8, 0.6)$

q. $P(-0.6, -0.8)$ is a point on the unit circle.

r. $P(x, y)$ is a point on the unit circle if $x^2 + y^2 = 1$.

s. The point $W\left(\frac{2\pi}{3}\right)$ is symmetric to the point $W\left(\frac{\pi}{3}\right)$ with respect to the y-axis.

t. $W\left(\frac{5\pi}{6}\right)$ is symmetric to $W\left(\frac{-\pi}{6}\right)$ with respect to the origin.

u. $W\left(\frac{3\pi}{4}\right)$ and $W\left(\frac{5\pi}{4}\right)$ are symmetric points with respect to the x-axis.

v. For each real number θ, the point $W(\theta)$ is symmetric to the point $W(\pi - \theta)$ with respect to the y-axis.

w. For each real number θ, $W(\theta)$ is symmetric to $W(-\theta)$ with respect to the x-axis.

x. For each real number θ, $W(\theta)$ and $W(\theta - \pi)$ are symmetric points with respect to the origin.

4. What is the domain of W?

5. What is the range of W?

6. Explain why there is no point $P(2, y)$ on the unit circle.

7. Determine two values of x for which $P\left(x, \frac{1}{4}\right)$ will be a point on the unit circle.

PERIODIC FUNCTIONS

The wrapping function possesses an unusual property. Look for a pattern in the following.

$$W\left(\frac{\pi}{6}\right) = W\left(\frac{\pi}{6} \pm 2\pi\right) = W\left(\frac{\pi}{6} \pm 4\pi\right) = W\left(\frac{\pi}{6} \pm 6\pi\right) = \ldots$$

$$W\left(\frac{\pi}{3}\right) = W\left(\frac{\pi}{3} \pm 2\pi\right) = W\left(\frac{\pi}{3} \pm 4\pi\right) = W\left(\frac{\pi}{3} \pm 6\pi\right) = \ldots$$

In general, for any real number θ and for each integer k,

$$W(\theta) = W(\theta + 2k\pi)$$

A function that possesses such a property is called a *periodic function*.

We define it formally as follows.

DEFINITION OF PERIODIC FUNCTION   Given a function f with domain D and some number $p \neq 0$, we say that f is a *periodic function* if and only if $f(x) = f(x + p)$ for every x in D. The number p is called *a period* of f.

Is 4π a period of W? In other words, is it true that for all real numbers θ, $W(\theta) = W(\theta + 4\pi)$? Is -6π a period of W? Is 3π? What is the smallest positive period of W? Study the following examples of periodic functions.

Example 1 $h = \{\ldots, (3, 1), (5, 2), (7, 1), (9, 2), (11, 1), (13, 2), \ldots\}$
Observe that $\ldots = h(3) = h(7) = h(11) = \ldots$ and that $\ldots = h(5) = h(9) = h(13) = \ldots$ and in general, for each x in the domain of h, $h(x) = h(x + 4)$. By the definition of periodic function, 4 is a period of h. Is 8 a period of h? Is 12? Is -4? Is 6? What is the smallest positive period of h?

Example 2   A periodic function g is specified by its graph in Figure 2–26.

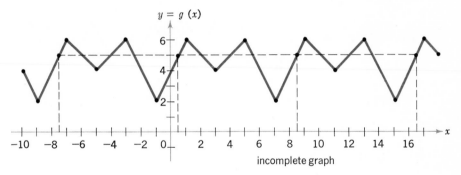

FIGURE 2-26

The graph of g is incomplete; that is, not all of the graph is shown. This is true of the graphs of most functions and certainly true whenever the domain is R, the set of real numbers. In such a case, the picture shows either an important portion or enough of the graph to establish a pattern for the part not shown.

To determine a period of g, we might proceed as follows. The fact that $g(6) = g(8)$ suggests that 2 might be a period. But $g(8) \neq g(10)$, so 2 is not a period. Also $g(3) = g(6)$ but $g(6) \neq g(9)$, therefore 3 is not a period. Observe that $g(-7.5) = g(0.5) = g(8.5) = g(16.5)$. This suggests that 8 is a period and that for each real number x, $g(x) = g(x + 8)$. If a picture of the graph of g were cut into vertical strips each eight units wide, the graphs shown on each strip would be identical figures. Is 4 a period of g? Is 16? Is -8? What is the smallest positive period of g?

If f is a periodic function with a period p, it will have many different periods, as you have seen. Among all the periods of a function, we are usually interested in the smallest positive period.

DEFINITION OF PRIMITIVE PERIOD   Given a periodic function f and all periods of f, the smallest positive period, if it exists, is called the *primitive period* of f or, simply, *the period* of f.

What is the primitive period of W, the wrapping function? What is *the* period of h in Example 1? Of g in Example 2?

EXERCISES

1. Each function specified below is a periodic function. Determine the period of each function.

   a. $\left\{\ldots, (2, 7), \left(2\frac{1}{2}, -3\right), (3, 7), \left(3\frac{1}{2}, -3\right), (4, 7), \left(4\frac{1}{2}, -3\right), \ldots\right\}$

   b. $\{\ldots, (-7, \pi), (-3, \pi), (1, \pi), (5, \pi), (9, \pi), \ldots\}$

   c. $\{\ldots, (3.2, \sqrt{2}), (3.3, \sqrt{3}), (3.4, \sqrt{2}), (3.5, \sqrt{3}), (3.6, \sqrt{2}), (3.7, \sqrt{3}), \ldots\}$

   d. $f = \{(x, y) \mid y = 8 \text{ and } (x \text{ is an even integer or } x \text{ is a multiple of } 3)\}$

e
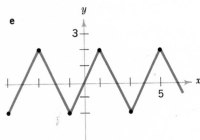

f
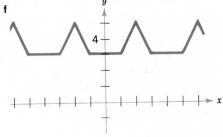

g
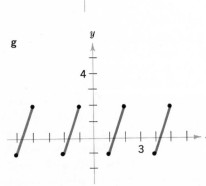

h
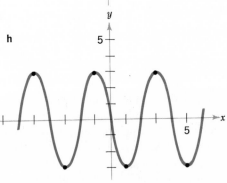

2. Consider the function f with domain R such that $f(x) = 3$.

   a. Determine $f(3)$, $f(5)$, and $f(7)$.

   b. True or false? For each x, $f(x) = f(x + 2)$.

   c. True or false? For each x, $f(x) = f(x + 0.5)$.

   d. True or false? For each x, $f(x) = f(x + 0.2)$.

   e. What is the smallest positive period of f?

PERIODIC PHENOMENA

Many events, or *phenomena*, in nature are periodic. One of the simplest examples is the four phases of the moon. At approximately one-week intervals we see the new moon, first quarter, full moon and last quarter phases. To be exact, the period from any new moon phase to the next new moon phase is 29 days, 12 hours, 44 minutes and 2.8 seconds.

The motion of a simple *pendulum* is periodic. If a weight is suspended on a string, we have a pendulum. See Figure 2–27. If the weight is pulled to *A* and released, it will swing to *B* and back to *C*. One such back and forth motion is called a vibration. The time it takes for this is called the *period of vibration*. It will then swing through more vibrations; *C* to *D* and back to *E*; *E* to *F* and back to *G* for two more vibrations. Now, although the length of each vibration is successively shorter, the period (time) of each vibration is the *same;* that is, the period is constant. The action of some clocks is based on the periodic motion of a pendulum.

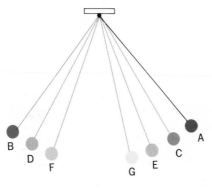

FIGURE 2-27

The time *T* for one period of a single pendulum is given by the formula

$$T = 2\pi\sqrt{\frac{l}{g}}$$ where *l* is the length of the string and *g* is the acceleration of gravity.

Notice that the period *T* of a pendulum depends upon the length of the string and not upon the weight of the bob or the length of one vibration. The number of vibrations per unit of time is called the *frequency* of vibration. For example, if a pendulum makes 20 vibrations in 30 seconds, then the time *T* for one period is $\frac{3}{2}$ seconds. The frequency of this pendulum is $\frac{2}{3}$ vibrations per second. If a pendulum makes 10 vibrations in 30 seconds, what is the time *T* for one period and the frequency *f* in vibrations per second? In general, $T = \frac{1}{f}$ where *T* is the time for one period and *f* is the frequency of vibrations per unit of time.

Wave motion is another example of periodic phenomena. *Transverse waves* are rising and falling motions which are passed on from one particle to another. See Figure 2–28. They are caused by a disturbance. If you drop a stone into a calm body of water, you see larger and larger circles appearing with their centers at the point of disturbance. The water does not move outward but simply rises and falls; this can be shown by floating a cork on the water's surface. It is the wave motion that moves outward, transferring the energy of one wave to the nearby particles of water, causing another wave. Wave motion is an important way to transfer energy from one point to another without transferring matter.

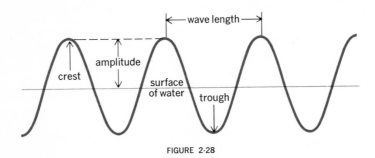

FIGURE 2-28

All wave motions which are described as electromagnetic, such as light waves, radio waves, heat waves, and X-rays, are transverse waves.

The other basic type of wave motion is *longitudinal*. Transverse waves involve rising and falling particles which send the wave motion outward and perpendicular to the up and down direction. A longitudinal wave involves back and forth motion in the same direction as the wave motion. Such a wave motion is illustrated when a long coil spring has a few of its turns compressed and then released. The next few turns will be compressed and then released, compressing the next few turns and releasing them, and so on until this wave motion reaches the end of the spring.

This type of wave motion occurs when air is disturbed. As sound waves travel through the air, the air is alternately compressed and released until the sound wave strikes an object. If you strike a tuning fork, it will vibrate and cause the surrounding air to be alternately compressed and expanded. See Figure 2–29. If this wave reaches a person, sound is received.

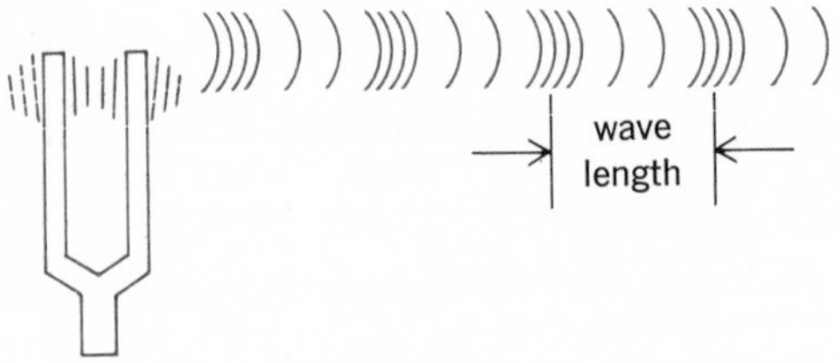

FIGURE 2-29

Periodicity, as a concept, forms a basis for much of the study of physical phenomena. For example, quantum theory is associated with the phenomenon of vibration, which is periodic. Since quantum theory is centered around the radiant energy of an atom, it is thus related to the periods of the radiant wave systems.

Periodicity of certain phenomena is known to have been instrumental in the development of modern chemistry. The known chemical elements arranged in order according to their increasing atomic weights revealed a periodicity in their properties. Thus, every element was placed in a sequence of elements in accordance with its properties. This arrangement led to the correction of atomic weights and the prediction of the existence of yet undiscovered elements. The arrangement served also as a basis for chemical reasoning and prediction in the planning of experimental work.

One of the famous mathematicians is known for his contributions to the study of periodic functions. He is Henri Poincaré, a French savant, who in the 19th century invented the so-called *elliptic* function, which is periodic.

EXERCISES

1. What is the period, approximately, of the phenomenon called sunrise?

2. What is the period of any one person's birth date celebration?

3. For the simple pendulum of Figure 2–27, suppose the weight were released from point E rather than from point A. How would the period be affected?

4. In order to double the period of a given pendulum, how should the length of the string be changed?

5. A pendulum has a period of 4.0 seconds. What is its frequency?

6. A pendulum makes 15 vibrations in 75 seconds. What is the period and frequency of the pendulum?

7. Write a formula for the frequency f of a pendulum in terms of g and l.

8. What is the length of a pendulum for which the period is 2 seconds and $g = 9.8$ meters per second per second?

9. What must be the length of a simple pendulum if it is to have a period of one second where $g = 32$ feet per second per second?

10. What is the period of a pendulum whose length is 1.4 meters where $g = 9.8$ meters per second per second?

11. In what way are transverse waves different from longitudinal waves?

12. Why can a sound wave not travel through a vacuum?

VOCABULARY

Use each of the following correctly in a sentence to demonstrate that you understand its meaning. If you are not sure, refer back to the chapter.

clockwise
coterminal paths
counterclockwise
frequency
initial point
longitudinal wave
path
period
periodic function

periodic phenomenon
primitive period
standard position
terminal point
transverse wave
unit circle
vibration
wave motion
wrapping function

REVIEW EXERCISES

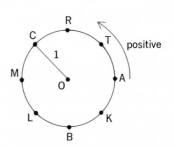

1. For the unit circle O, eight points separate the circle into eight arcs of equal length. List five paths that have initial point A and terminal point C.

2. Answer the following questions relative to a unit circle.

   a. Are the paths (A, π) and $(A, -3\pi)$ coterminal?

   b. Are $\left(A, \dfrac{2\pi}{3} \right)$ and $\left(A, \dfrac{-2\pi}{3} \right)$ coterminal?

   c. Are all paths $\left(A, \dfrac{5\pi}{6} + 2k\pi \right)$ coterminal?

3. Determine the coordinates of each point.

   a. $W\left(\dfrac{3\pi}{4} \right)$

   b. $W\left(\dfrac{-\pi}{3} \right)$

   c. $W\left(\dfrac{5\pi}{6} \right)$

   d. $W\left(\dfrac{7\pi}{3} \right)$

   e. $W\left(\dfrac{13\pi}{6} \right)$

   f. $W\left(\dfrac{-7\pi}{4} \right)$

   g. $W(-\pi)$

   h. $W\left(\dfrac{-13\pi}{6} \right)$

   i. $W\left(\dfrac{13\pi}{4} \right)$

   j. $W\left(\dfrac{3\pi}{2} \right)$

   k. $W(6\pi)$

   l. $W\left(\dfrac{5\pi}{2} \right)$

4. Determine the smallest positive value of θ which makes the equation true.

   a. $W(\theta) = P(0, -1)$

   b. $W(\theta) = P\left(\dfrac{-1}{2}, \dfrac{\sqrt{3}}{2} \right)$

   c. $W(\theta) = P\left(\dfrac{1}{\sqrt{2}}, \dfrac{-1}{\sqrt{2}} \right)$

   d. $W(\theta) = P\left(\dfrac{-\sqrt{3}}{2}, \dfrac{1}{2} \right)$

5. Determine the greatest negative value of θ which makes the equation true.

   a. $W(\theta) = P(-1, 0)$ **c.** $W(\theta) = P\left(\dfrac{-\sqrt{3}}{2}, \dfrac{-1}{2}\right)$

   b. $W(\theta) = P\left(\dfrac{-1}{\sqrt{2}}, \dfrac{1}{\sqrt{2}}\right)$ **d.** $W(\theta) = P\left(\dfrac{1}{2}, \dfrac{\sqrt{3}}{2}\right)$

6. What is the domain of W?

7. What is the range of W?

8. Write an equation of the unit circle in standard position.

9. Determine two values of y for which $P\left(\dfrac{2}{3}, y\right)$ will be a point on the unit circle in standard position.

10. What is the period of W?

11. Graph a periodic function with primitive period 6.

12. A simple pendulum makes 18 vibrations in 45 seconds. What is its frequency?

13. A simple pendulum has a period of 3.2 seconds. What is its frequency?

CHAPTER TEST

1. For the unit circle O twelve points separate the circle into twelve arcs of equal length. List three paths that have initial point A and terminal point T.

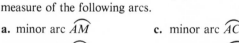

2. For the unit circle in Problem 1, give the linear measure of the following arcs.

   a. minor arc $\overarc{AM}$ **c.** minor arc $\overarc{AC}$

   b. major arc $\overarc{AV}$ **d.** semicircle $\overarc{ACB}$

3. Determine the coordinates of each point.

   a. $W\left(\dfrac{2\pi}{3}\right)$ **c.** $W\left(\dfrac{-5\pi}{6}\right)$ **e.** $W(7\pi)$

   b. $W\left(\dfrac{7\pi}{4}\right)$ **d.** $W\left(\dfrac{-3\pi}{2}\right)$ **f.** $W\left(\dfrac{-10\pi}{3}\right)$

4. Determine four values of θ, two positive and two negative, each satisfying the equation $W(\theta) = P\left(\dfrac{-1}{2}, \dfrac{\sqrt{3}}{2}\right)$.

5. Determine two values of x for which $P\left(x, \dfrac{3}{4}\right)$ is a point on the unit circle in standard position.

6. True or false?

a. $P(0.7, 0.3)$ is a point on the unit circle in standard position.

b. One period of W is 4.

c. If $P(x, y)$ is a point on the unit circle in standard position, $-1 \leq x \leq 1$.

d. $P\left(\dfrac{\sqrt{35}}{7}, \dfrac{-\sqrt{14}}{7}\right)$ is a point on the unit circle in standard position.

e. $\dfrac{5\pi}{2}$ is in the domain of W.

f. 7 is in the domain of W.

g. Every function is periodic.

h. The paths $\left(A, \dfrac{3\pi}{4}\right)$ and $\left(A, \dfrac{-3\pi}{4}\right)$ are coterminal.

i. The origin is the center of every unit circle.

j. $(1, -1)$ is a point on the unit circle in standard position.

7. a. Determine the primitive period of the periodic function whose graph is shown below.

b. Give three other periods of this function.

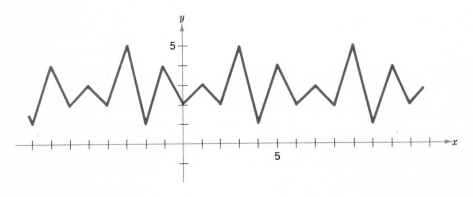

8. A simple pendulum makes 12 vibrations in 30 seconds. What is the period and frequency of the pendulum?

CHAPTER 3

COSINE
AND SINE

TWO CIRCULAR FUNCTIONS

We shall now introduce two new functions, the *cosine* and the *sine*. They are two of the six functions which are based on W, the wrapping function. For this reason they are called *circular functions*. Circular functions are of great importance in the sciences since they supply the mathematics necessary for the study of circular motion and wave motion.

COSINE AND SINE

By the definition of W, the wrapping function, we know that for each real number θ, $W(\theta)$ determines a point $P(x, y)$ on the unit circle. Two circular functions, cosine and sine, arise from W if (1) with each real number θ, we pair x and (2) with each real number θ, we pair y. The first pairing yields the cosine function and the second gives the sine.

DEFINITION OF COSINE   Given W, for which $W(\theta) = P(x, y)$, the *cosine* function is $\{(\theta, x)\}$.

Cosine is abbreviated as *cos*; thus, $\cos(\theta) = x$. Pronounce $\cos(\theta)$ as *cosine theta*.

DEFINITION OF SINE   Given W, for which $W(\theta) = P(x, y)$, the *sine* function is $\{(\theta, y)\}$.

Sine is abbreviated as *sin*; thus, $\sin(\theta) = y$. Pronounce $\sin(\theta)$ as *sine theta*.

Study the following groups of three statements. The second and third statements in each group are consequences of the first statement and of the definitions of cosine and sine.

$W(\theta) = P(x, y)$	$\cos(\theta) = x$	$\sin(\theta) = y$
$W\left(\dfrac{\pi}{6}\right) = P\left(\dfrac{\sqrt{3}}{2}, \dfrac{1}{2}\right)$	$\cos\left(\dfrac{\pi}{6}\right) = \dfrac{\sqrt{3}}{2}$	$\sin\left(\dfrac{\pi}{6}\right) = \dfrac{1}{2}$
$W\left(\dfrac{2\pi}{3}\right) = P\left(\dfrac{-1}{2}, \dfrac{\sqrt{3}}{2}\right)$	$\cos\left(\dfrac{2\pi}{3}\right) = \dfrac{-1}{2}$	$\sin\left(\dfrac{2\pi}{3}\right) = \dfrac{\sqrt{3}}{2}$
$W\left(\dfrac{7\pi}{4}\right) = P\left(\dfrac{1}{\sqrt{2}}, \dfrac{-1}{\sqrt{2}}\right)$	$\cos\left(\dfrac{7\pi}{4}\right) = \dfrac{1}{\sqrt{2}}$	$\sin\left(\dfrac{7\pi}{4}\right) = \dfrac{-1}{\sqrt{2}}$
$W(\pi) = P(-1, 0)$	$\cos(\pi) = -1$	$\sin(\pi) = 0$
$W\left(\dfrac{-\pi}{3}\right) = P\left(\dfrac{1}{2}, \dfrac{-\sqrt{3}}{2}\right)$	$\cos\left(\dfrac{-\pi}{3}\right) = \dfrac{1}{2}$	$\sin\left(\dfrac{-\pi}{3}\right) = \dfrac{-\sqrt{3}}{2}$
$W\left(\dfrac{-3\pi}{2}\right) = P(0, 1)$	$\cos\left(\dfrac{-3\pi}{2}\right) = 0$	$\sin\left(\dfrac{-3\pi}{2}\right) = 1$
$W\left(\dfrac{-5\pi}{6}\right) = P\left(\dfrac{-\sqrt{3}}{2}, \dfrac{-1}{2}\right)$	$\cos\left(\dfrac{-5\pi}{6}\right) = \dfrac{-\sqrt{3}}{2}$	$\sin\left(\dfrac{-5\pi}{6}\right) = \dfrac{-1}{2}$
$W(6\pi) = P(1, 0)$	$\cos(6\pi) = 1$	$\sin(6\pi) = 0$
$W\left(\dfrac{11\pi}{4}\right) = P\left(\dfrac{-1}{\sqrt{2}}, \dfrac{1}{\sqrt{2}}\right)$	$\cos\left(\dfrac{11\pi}{4}\right) = \dfrac{-1}{\sqrt{2}}$	$\sin\left(\dfrac{11\pi}{4}\right) = \dfrac{1}{\sqrt{2}}$
$W(-9\pi) = P(-1, 0)$	$\cos(-9\pi) = -1$	$\sin(-9\pi) = 0$

Note: It is customary to omit the parentheses from $\cos(\theta)$ and $\sin(\theta)$; thus, we usually write $\cos\theta$ and $\sin\theta$ for $\cos(\theta)$ and $\sin(\theta)$. However, whenever the additive inverse symbol $(-)$ appears, we may use parentheses, as in $\sin(-\pi)$.

What is $\cos\dfrac{7\pi}{6}$ equal to? $\sin\dfrac{7\pi}{6}$? $\cos\dfrac{-2\pi}{3}$? $\sin\dfrac{-2\pi}{3}$? $\cos(-\pi)$? $\sin(-\pi)$?

Since cosine and sine are defined on the basis of W, where $W(\theta) = P(x, y)$, it is often helpful to write and think of the coordinates (x, y) of P as $(\cos\theta, \sin\theta)$. See Figure 3–1.

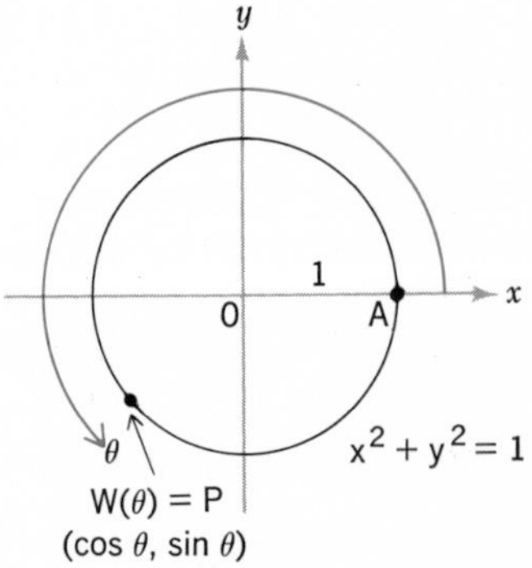

Study each of the following statements. You will notice that each is a consequence of the scheme shown in Figure 3–1 or of the definitions of cosine and sine. You should verify each of these statements to your satisfaction.

1. The domain of cosine and of sine is R, the set of all real numbers θ.
2. Since $x^2 + y^2 = 1$ is an equation of the unit circle with $\cos\theta = x$ and $\sin\theta = y$, it follows that, for each real number θ, $(\cos\theta)^2 + (\sin\theta)^2 = 1$.

$W(\theta) = P$
$(\cos\theta, \sin\theta)$

FIGURE 3-1

The symbols $\cos^2\theta$ and $\sin^2\theta$ are usually used instead of $(\cos\theta)^2$ and $(\sin\theta)^2$, respectively. Thus, for all real numbers θ,

$$\cos^2\theta + \sin^2\theta \equiv 1 \qquad [3.1]$$

Such an equation is called an *identity*. To indicate an identity, we shall use the symbol $\equiv$.

DEFINITION OF IDENTITY   An equation which is true for all permissible values of the variables is called an *identity*.

3. The range of cosine is $\{x \mid -1 \le x \le 1\}$. As you examine Figure 3–1, notice that all points on the unit circle have an x-coordinate within the range indicated. This also follows from the identity $\cos^2\theta + \sin^2\theta \equiv 1$, which can be shown as follows.

$$\sin^2\theta \equiv 1 - \cos^2\theta$$
$$\sin\theta \equiv \sqrt{1 - \cos^2\theta} \text{ or } \sin\theta \equiv -\sqrt{1 - \cos^2\theta}$$

Hence, $1 - \cos^2\theta \ge 0$
$$\cos^2\theta \le 1 \quad \text{Why not } \ge?$$
$$-1 \le \cos\theta \le 1$$

4. The range of sine is $\{y \mid -1 \le y \le 1\}$. Using the identity as was done above, determine the range of $\sin\theta$.
5. Cosine and sine are periodic functions with primitive periods of 2π. That is, $\cos\theta \equiv \cos(\theta + 2\pi)$ and $\sin\theta \equiv \sin(\theta + 2\pi)$.
6. If $W(\theta)$ is a point in Q_2, then we call θ a *second quadrant number*. In general, θ is a first, second, third, or fourth quadrant number if and only if $W(\theta)$ is a point $P(x, y)$ in Q_1, Q_2, Q_3, or Q_4. For $\theta \ne k \cdot \frac{\pi}{2}$, k is any integer, it is readily determined whether $\cos\theta$ and $\sin\theta$ are positive or negative. In summary,

For each second quadrant number θ $\cos\theta < 0$, and $\sin\theta > 0$, since $x < 0$ and $y > 0$.	For each first quadrant number θ $\cos\theta > 0$, and $\sin\theta > 0$, since $x > 0$ and $y > 0$.
For each third quadrant number θ $\cos\theta < 0$, and $\sin\theta < 0$, since $x < 0$ and $y < 0$.	For each fourth quadrant number θ $\cos\theta > 0$, and $\sin\theta < 0$, since $x > 0$ and $y < 0$.

7. For each integer k, the numbers $k \cdot \frac{\pi}{2}$ are called *quadrantal numbers*.

If $\theta = k \cdot \frac{\pi}{2}$, then $\cos\theta$ (and $\sin\theta$) is either 0, 1, or -1.

EXERCISES

1. Determine the value of each of the following.

a. $\cos\dfrac{\pi}{6}$

b. $\cos\dfrac{\pi}{4}$

c. $\sin(-\pi)$

d. $\sin\dfrac{5\pi}{6}$

e. $\cos(-\pi)$

f. $\cos\dfrac{5\pi}{6}$

g. $\sin\dfrac{\pi}{6}$

h. $\sin\dfrac{\pi}{4}$

i. $\cos\dfrac{5\pi}{4}$

j. $\cos 2\pi$

k. $\sin\dfrac{-3\pi}{4}$

l. $\sin\dfrac{7\pi}{6}$

m. $\cos \dfrac{-3\pi}{4}$

u. $\cos \dfrac{15\pi}{4}$

c'. $\sin \dfrac{3\pi}{2}$

k'. $\cos^2 \dfrac{\pi}{4}$

n. $\cos \dfrac{7\pi}{6}$

v. $\cos \dfrac{-\pi}{6}$

d'. $\sin \pi$

l'. $\cos^2 \dfrac{5\pi}{4}$

o. $\sin \dfrac{2\pi}{3}$

w. $\cos \dfrac{3\pi}{2}$

e'. $\cos \dfrac{\pi}{3}$

m'. $\sin^2 \dfrac{5\pi}{4}$

p. $\sin \dfrac{11\pi}{6}$

x. $\cos \pi$

f'. $\cos \dfrac{-13\pi}{4}$

n'. $\cos^2 (-\pi)$

q. $\cos \dfrac{2\pi}{3}$

y. $\sin \dfrac{15\pi}{4}$

g'. $\sin (-4\pi)$

o'. $\sin^2 \dfrac{-2\pi}{3}$

r. $\cos \dfrac{11\pi}{6}$

z. $\sin \dfrac{-\pi}{6}$

h'. $\sin 0$

p'. $\dfrac{\sin \dfrac{2\pi}{3}}{\cos \dfrac{2\pi}{3}}$

s. $\sin \dfrac{5\pi}{4}$

a'. $\cos (-4\pi)$

i'. $\sin \dfrac{\pi}{3}$

t. $\sin 2\pi$

b'. $\cos 0$

j'. $\sin \dfrac{-13\pi}{4}$

2. True or false?

a. $\cos \dfrac{\pi}{4} = \cos \dfrac{-\pi}{4}$

b. $\cos \dfrac{2\pi}{3} = \cos \dfrac{-2\pi}{3}$

c. For each θ, $\cos \theta = \cos (-\theta)$.

d. $\sin \pi = \sin (-\pi)$

e. $\sin 3\pi = \sin (-3\pi)$

f. For each θ, $\sin \theta = \sin (-\theta)$.

g. $\sin \dfrac{\pi}{4} = \sin \dfrac{-\pi}{4}$

h. $\sin \dfrac{-\pi}{3} = -\sin \dfrac{\pi}{3}$

i. $\sin \dfrac{-3\pi}{4} = -\sin \dfrac{3\pi}{4}$

j. For each θ, $\sin (-\theta) = -\sin \theta$.

k. $\cos \left(\dfrac{\pi}{6} + \dfrac{\pi}{3} \right) = \cos \dfrac{\pi}{6} + \cos \dfrac{\pi}{3}$

l. $\sin \left(\dfrac{\pi}{4} + \dfrac{3\pi}{4} \right) = \sin \dfrac{\pi}{4} + \sin \dfrac{3\pi}{4}$

m. For each θ, $-1 \leq \cos \theta \leq 1$.

n. For each θ, $0 \leq \sin \theta \leq 1$.

o. For each θ, $\cos \theta = \cos (\theta + 3\pi)$.

p. For each θ, $\sin \theta = \sin (\theta + 3\pi)$.

q. $\cos^2 \dfrac{2\pi}{3} + \sin^2 \dfrac{2\pi}{3} = 1$

r. $\cos^2 \dfrac{5\pi}{6} + \sin^2 \dfrac{5\pi}{6} = 1$

s. For each θ, $\cos^2 \theta + \sin^2 \theta = 1$.

t. For each θ, if $\dfrac{5\pi}{2} < \theta < 3\pi$, then $\cos \theta < 0$ and $\sin \theta > 0$.

u. For each θ, if $\dfrac{-5\pi}{2} < \theta < -2\pi$, then $\cos \theta > 0$ and $\sin \theta < 0$.

v. The number 2 is in the domain of cosine.

w. $\sin 5$ is a real number.

x. The number $\sqrt{3}$ is in the range of sine.

y. The number $\dfrac{9\pi}{2}$ is a quadrantal number.

z. If θ is a quadrantal number, then $\cos \theta$ and $\sin \theta$ are integers.

3. Given W such that $W(\theta) = P(x, y)$, which of the following is the cosine function?

a. $\{(x, y)\}$ **c.** $\{(x, \theta)\}$ **e.** $\{(y, \theta)\}$

b. $\{(\theta, P)\}$ **d.** $\{(\theta, x)\}$ **f.** $\{(\theta, y)\}$

4. Which of the following equations are identities? If an equation is not an identity, give one permissible value of the variable for which the equation is false.

a. $\cos^2 \theta + \sin^2 \theta = 1$ **f.** $2(c + 4) = 3 + 2c$

b. $\cos \theta + \sin \theta = 1$ **g.** $\cos \theta = \cos (\theta + 5\pi)$

c. $2 \cdot \cos \theta = 1$ **h.** $\sin \theta = \sin (\theta + 6\pi)$

d. $3(t + 2) = 6 + 3t$ **i.** $\cos \theta = \sin \theta$

e. $5 - (m - 2) = 2m + 1$

5. Use Figure 2–20 on page 42 to determine each of the following to the nearest tenth.

a. $\cos 0.8$ **d.** $\sin 2.2$ **g.** $\cos 5.2$

b. $\sin 3.9$ **e.** $\cos 4.3$ **h.** $\sin 3.6$

c. $\cos 1.1$ **f.** $\sin 5.6$ **i.** $\cos 8.8$

6. For each of the following intervals, tell whether (1) $\cos \theta$ and (2) $\sin \theta$ are positive or negative.

a. $0 < \theta < \dfrac{\pi}{2}$ **d.** $\dfrac{3\pi}{2} < \theta < 2\pi$ **g.** $\dfrac{-\pi}{2} < \theta < 0$

b. $\dfrac{\pi}{2} < \theta < \pi$ **e.** $\dfrac{-3\pi}{2} < \theta < -\pi$ **h.** $-2\pi < \theta < \dfrac{-3\pi}{2}$

c. $\pi < \theta < \dfrac{3\pi}{2}$ **f.** $3\pi < \theta < \dfrac{7\pi}{2}$

7. Solve $\cos^2 \theta + \sin^2 \theta = 1$ for $\cos \theta$ in terms of $\sin \theta$ and then show that $-1 \le \sin \theta \le 1$ for all θ.

8. For each interval in Exercise 6, tell whether θ is a first, second, third, or fourth quadrant number.

9. Express each of the following in terms of $\cos \theta$ or $\sin \theta$ for the interval $0 \le \theta < 2\pi$.

Example $\cos \dfrac{7\pi}{2} = \cos \left(\dfrac{7\pi}{2} - 2\pi\right) = \cos \dfrac{3\pi}{2}$

a. $\sin \dfrac{-\pi}{4}$ **d.** $\cos \dfrac{-23\pi}{3}$ **g.** $\sin 8$

b. $\cos \dfrac{25\pi}{6}$ **e.** $\sin (-7\pi)$ **h.** $\cos (-2)$

c. $\sin \dfrac{17\pi}{4}$ **f.** $\cos 15\pi$ **i.** $\cos (-3)$

10. For which quadrant numbers is $\cos \theta$ positive?

11. For which quadrant numbers is $\sin \theta$ negative?

12. Given that $\cos \theta = \dfrac{2}{3}$ and $\dfrac{3\pi}{2} < \theta < 2\pi$, determine $\sin \theta$. *Hint:* $\cos^2 \theta + \sin^2 \theta \equiv 1$.

13. Given that $\sin \theta = \dfrac{-4}{5}$ and $\pi < \theta < \dfrac{3\pi}{2}$, determine $\cos \theta$.

14. Show that each of the following equations is true by computing the value of each of the two members.

a. $\sin \dfrac{5\pi}{3} = 2 \cdot \sin \dfrac{5\pi}{6} \cdot \cos \dfrac{5\pi}{6}$

b. $\cos \left(\dfrac{5\pi}{6} - \dfrac{4\pi}{3} \right) = \cos \dfrac{5\pi}{6} \cdot \cos \dfrac{4\pi}{3} + \sin \dfrac{5\pi}{6} \cdot \sin \dfrac{4\pi}{3}$

c. $\cos \dfrac{2\pi}{3} = \cos^2 \dfrac{\pi}{3} - \sin^2 \dfrac{\pi}{3}$

d. $\sin \left(\dfrac{3\pi}{4} - \dfrac{7\pi}{4} \right) = \sin \dfrac{3\pi}{4} \cdot \cos \dfrac{7\pi}{4} - \cos \dfrac{3\pi}{4} \cdot \sin \dfrac{7\pi}{4}$

e. $\sin \dfrac{\pi}{6} = \sqrt{\dfrac{1 - \cos \dfrac{\pi}{3}}{2}}$

f. $\sin \dfrac{5\pi}{3} \cdot \cos \pi = \dfrac{1}{2} \left(\sin \dfrac{8\pi}{3} + \sin \dfrac{2\pi}{3} \right)$

g. $\cos \dfrac{-\pi}{2} = 1 - 2 \cdot \sin^2 \dfrac{-\pi}{4}$

h. $2 \cdot \sin \dfrac{\pi}{3} \cdot \cos \dfrac{5\pi}{6} = \sin \left(\dfrac{\pi}{3} + \dfrac{5\pi}{6} \right) + \sin \left(\dfrac{\pi}{3} - \dfrac{5\pi}{6} \right)$

i. $\cos \dfrac{-5\pi}{6} = - \sqrt{\dfrac{1 + \cos \dfrac{5\pi}{3}}{2}}$

j. $\cos \left(\dfrac{-4\pi}{3} \right) = 2 \cos^2 \left(\dfrac{-2\pi}{3} \right) - 1$

k. $\sin \dfrac{\pi}{2} \cdot \cos \dfrac{\pi}{4} = \dfrac{1}{2} \left[\sin \left(\dfrac{\pi}{2} + \dfrac{\pi}{4} \right) + \sin \left(\dfrac{\pi}{2} - \dfrac{\pi}{4} \right) \right]$

l. $\sin \pi + \sin \dfrac{\pi}{2} = 2 \sin \left[\dfrac{1}{2} \left(\pi + \dfrac{\pi}{2} \right) \right] \cdot \cos \left[\dfrac{1}{2} \left(\pi - \dfrac{\pi}{2} \right) \right]$

m. $\dfrac{\sin \dfrac{\pi}{2} + \sin \dfrac{\pi}{4}}{\sin \left(\dfrac{\pi}{2} + \dfrac{\pi}{4} \right)} = \dfrac{\sin \left(\dfrac{\pi}{2} - \dfrac{\pi}{4} \right)}{\sin \dfrac{\pi}{2} - \sin \dfrac{\pi}{4}}$

SYMMETRY RELATIONS

If α is not in the interval $0 \leq \alpha < 2\pi$, then cos α and sin α may be expressed in terms of cos θ and sin θ, respectively, where $0 \leq \theta \leq 2\pi$. This may always be done since cosine and sine are periodic with period 2π. For example,

$$\cos \frac{24\pi}{5} = \cos \left(\frac{24\pi}{5} - 4\pi\right) = \cos \frac{4\pi}{5} \qquad \text{What is } \alpha? \ \theta?$$

$$\sin \frac{-13\pi}{9} = \sin \left(\frac{-13\pi}{9} + 2\pi\right) = \sin \frac{5\pi}{9} \qquad \text{What is } \alpha? \ \theta?$$

Moreover, if θ is in the interval $0 \leq \theta < 2\pi$, then cos θ and sin θ may be expressed in terms of cos β and sin β, where $0 \leq \beta < \frac{\pi}{2}$. For example, sin $\frac{5\pi}{6}$ and cos $\frac{5\pi}{6}$ may be expressed in terms of functions of first quadrant numbers as sin $\frac{\pi}{6}$ and $-\cos \frac{\pi}{6}$, respectively.

The basic concept used for this is symmetry. In Chapter One, the topic of symmetry with respect to each axis and to the origin was discussed (see Figure 3–2). Recall that $P(a, b)$ is symmetric to $P'(-a, b)$ with respect to the y-axis, $Q(c, d)$ is symmetric to $Q'(-c, -d)$ with respect to the origin and $R(e, f)$ is symmetric to $R'(e, -f)$ with respect to the x-axis.

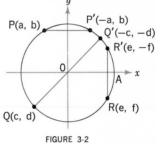

FIGURE 3-2

Suppose θ is a second, third, or fourth quadrant number. With reference to Figure 3–3 observe that

1. if θ is a second quadrant number, then $W(\theta)$ and $W(\pi - \theta)$ are symmetric with respect to the y-axis
2. if θ is a third quadrant number, then $W(\theta)$ and $W(\theta - \pi)$ are symmetric with respect to the origin
3. if θ is a fourth quadrant number, then $W(\theta)$ and $W(2\pi - \theta)$ are symmetric with respect to the x-axis.

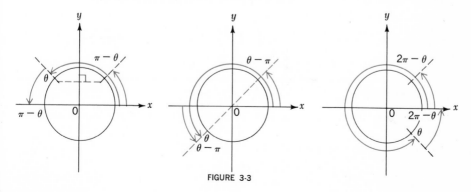

FIGURE 3-3

Observe in Figure 3–4 that if θ is a second quadrant number, then $\pi - \theta$ is a first quadrant number such that $W(\theta)$ is symmetric to $W(\pi - \theta)$ with respect to the y-axis and therefore

$$\cos \theta = -\cos (\pi - \theta) \qquad [3.2]$$
$$\sin \theta = \sin (\pi - \theta) \qquad [3.3]$$

Equations [3.2] and [3.3] are identities and hold for all θ. We will prove them in the next chapter. Thus, for any second quadrant number θ, $\cos \theta$ and $\sin \theta$ may be expressed in terms of $\cos \beta$ and $\sin \beta$, where β is a first quadrant number. For this reason, these identities are called *reduction identities*. For example,

$$\cos \frac{4\pi}{7} = -\cos \left(\pi - \frac{4\pi}{7} \right) = -\cos \frac{3\pi}{7} \qquad \cos 2 = -\cos (\pi - 2)$$

$$\sin \frac{7\pi}{9} = \sin \left(\pi - \frac{7\pi}{9} \right) = \sin \frac{2\pi}{9} \qquad \sin 3 = \sin (\pi - 3)$$

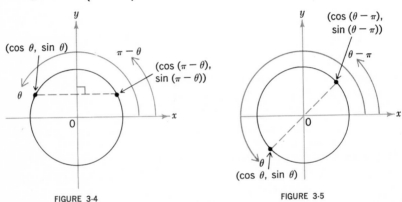

FIGURE 3-4   FIGURE 3-5

From Figure 3–5 you should note that if θ is a third quadrant number, then $\theta - \pi$ is a first quadrant number for which $W(\theta)$ is symmetric to $W(\theta - \pi)$ with respect to the origin and therefore,

$$\cos \theta = -\cos (\theta - \pi) \qquad [3.4]$$
$$\sin \theta = -\sin (\theta - \pi) \qquad [3.5]$$

Here are some examples of the use of these reduction identities.

Examples $\cos \frac{13\pi}{10} = -\cos \left(\frac{13\pi}{10} - \pi \right) = -\cos \frac{3\pi}{10}$

$\sin \frac{9\pi}{8} = -\sin \left(\frac{9\pi}{8} - \pi \right) = -\sin \frac{\pi}{8}$

$\cos 4 = -\cos (4 - \pi)$

$\sin 4.32 = -\sin (4.32 - \pi)$

You should observe from a study of Figure 3–6 that if θ is a fourth quadrant number, then $2\pi - \theta$ is a first quadrant number such that $W(\theta)$ and $W(2\pi - \theta)$ are symmetric with respect to the x-axis and therefore

$$\cos \theta = \cos (2\pi - \theta) \qquad [3.6]$$
$$\sin \theta = -\sin (2\pi - \theta) \qquad [3.7]$$

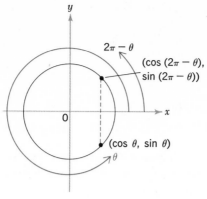

FIGURE 3-6

Here are some examples of the use of these reduction identities.

Examples $\cos \dfrac{15\pi}{8} = \cos\left(2\pi - \dfrac{15\pi}{8}\right) = \cos\dfrac{\pi}{8}$

$\sin \dfrac{12\pi}{7} = -\sin\left(2\pi - \dfrac{12\pi}{7}\right) = -\sin\dfrac{2\pi}{7}$

$\cos 5 = \cos(2\pi - 5)$

$\sin 6 = -\sin(2\pi - 6)$

Symmetry suggests two other identities (see Figures 3–7 and 3–8). For each real number θ, $W(\theta)$ and $W(-\theta)$ are symmetric with respect to the x-axis and therefore

$$\cos(-\theta) \equiv \cos\theta \qquad\qquad [3.8]$$
$$\sin(-\theta) \equiv -\sin\theta \qquad\qquad [3.9]$$

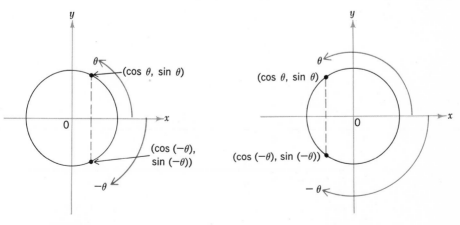

FIGURE 3-7   FIGURE 3-8

If θ is a negative number, identities [3.8] and [3.9] permit us to express $\cos\theta$ and $\sin\theta$, in terms of $\cos\beta$ and $\sin\beta$ so that β will be a positive number.

This is illustrated in the following examples.

$$\cos\frac{-5\pi}{7} = \cos\frac{5\pi}{7} \quad \text{and} \quad \sin\frac{-5\pi}{7} = -\sin\frac{5\pi}{7}$$

$$\cos\frac{-\pi}{5} = \cos\frac{\pi}{5} \quad \text{and} \quad \sin\frac{-\pi}{5} = -\sin\frac{\pi}{5}$$

$$\cos\frac{-9\pi}{8} = \cos\frac{9\pi}{8} \quad \text{and} \quad \sin\frac{-9\pi}{8} = -\sin\frac{9\pi}{8}$$

$$\cos(-2) = \cos 2 \quad \text{and} \quad \sin(-2) = -\sin 2$$

In actual practice one does not memorize the long list of reduction identities developed in this section. Rather, for a particular problem, it is better to sketch a unit circle and use symmetry to arrive at the desired expression.

Consider any two points Q and Q' that are symmetric with respect to the line specified by $y = x$. Recall that if the coordinates of Q are (a, b), then the coordinates of Q' are (b, a). See Figure 3–9. Let $W(\theta) = P$ and $W(\alpha) = P'$ where P and P' are two points symmetric with respect to the line specified by $y = x$. Observe that

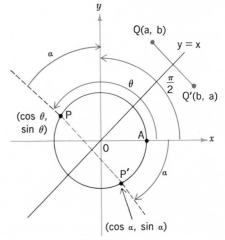

FIGURE 3-9

$$\theta + \alpha = \frac{\pi}{2},$$

$$\cos\theta = \sin\alpha,$$

and $\sin\theta = \cos\alpha$.

It will be proved in Chapter Four that for all real numbers θ and α,

If $\theta + \alpha = \frac{\pi}{2}$, then $\cos\theta = \sin\alpha$ and $\sin\theta = \cos\alpha$.

This is called the $\frac{\pi}{2}$-*sum relation*. This relation enables us to express the one function in terms of the other. Study the following examples.

Examples $\sin\frac{\pi}{8} = \cos\frac{3\pi}{8}$, since $\frac{\pi}{8} + \frac{3\pi}{8} = \frac{\pi}{2}$

$$\cos\frac{3\pi}{10} = \sin\frac{\pi}{5}, \text{ since } \frac{3\pi}{10} + \frac{\pi}{5} = \frac{\pi}{2}$$

$$\sin\left(\frac{\pi}{2} - \theta\right) = \cos\theta, \text{ since } \left(\frac{\pi}{2} - \theta\right) + \theta = \frac{\pi}{2}$$

$$\cos\left(\frac{\pi}{2} - \theta\right) = \sin\theta, \text{ since } \left(\frac{\pi}{2} - \theta\right) + \theta = \frac{\pi}{2}$$

For equations such as

$$\cos \theta = 0.4 \qquad \text{or} \qquad \sin \theta = -0.7$$

there are two values of θ between 0 and 2π which satisfy the equation. Study Figures 3–10 and 3–11. Cos θ is positive for first and fourth quadrant numbers θ.

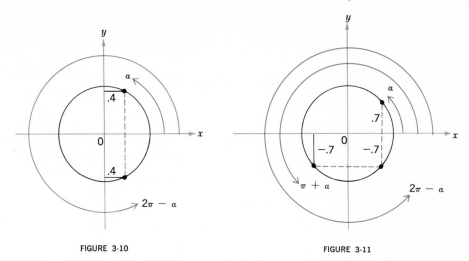

FIGURE 3-10   FIGURE 3-11

Hence, for the equation $\cos \theta = 0.4$, there is some first quadrant number α and some fourth quadrant number $2\pi - \alpha$, both satisfying the equation. Sin θ is negative for third and fourth quadrant numbers θ. Hence, for the equation $\sin \theta = -0.7$, if α is a first quadrant number for which $\sin \alpha = 0.7$, then $\pi + \alpha$ and $2\pi - \alpha$ are solutions of $\sin \theta = -0.7$.

EXERCISES

In each of the three diagrams below a symmetry and the length of $\overset{\frown}{AP'P}$ is given for a unit circle in standard position.

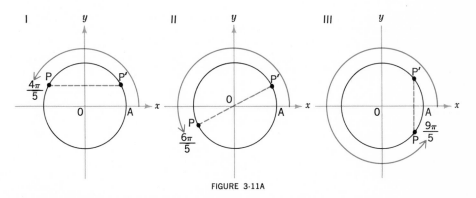

FIGURE 3-11A

1. For each diagram determine the length of minor arc $\overset{\frown}{AP'}$.

2. Express each of the following in terms of $\cos \theta$, where $0 < \theta < \dfrac{\pi}{2}$.

a. $\cos \dfrac{4\pi}{5}$ **d.** $\cos \dfrac{-4\pi}{5}$ **g.** $\cos \dfrac{13\pi}{5}$ **j.** $\cos \dfrac{9\pi}{8}$

b. $\cos \dfrac{6\pi}{5}$ **e.** $\cos \dfrac{-6\pi}{5}$ **h.** $\cos \dfrac{7\pi}{9}$ **k.** $\cos 6$

c. $\cos \dfrac{9\pi}{5}$ **f.** $\cos \dfrac{-9\pi}{5}$ **i.** $\cos \dfrac{-14\pi}{5}$ **l.** $\cos \dfrac{15\pi}{8}$

3. Express each of the following in terms of $\sin \theta$, where $0 < \theta < \dfrac{\pi}{2}$.

a. $\sin \dfrac{4\pi}{5}$ **d.** $\sin \dfrac{-4\pi}{5}$ **g.** $\sin \dfrac{13\pi}{5}$ **j.** $\sin \dfrac{9\pi}{8}$

b. $\sin \dfrac{6\pi}{5}$ **e.** $\sin \dfrac{-6\pi}{5}$ **h.** $\sin \dfrac{7\pi}{9}$ **k.** $\sin 6$

c. $\sin \dfrac{9\pi}{5}$ **f.** $\sin \dfrac{-9\pi}{5}$ **i.** $\sin \dfrac{-14\pi}{5}$ **l.** $\sin \dfrac{15\pi}{8}$

4. True or false?

a. $\cos \dfrac{-4\pi}{5} = \cos \dfrac{4\pi}{5}$ **c.** $\cos \dfrac{-6\pi}{5} = \cos \dfrac{6\pi}{5}$ **e.** $\cos \dfrac{-9\pi}{5} = \cos \dfrac{9\pi}{5}$

b. $\sin \dfrac{-4\pi}{5} = \sin \dfrac{4\pi}{5}$ **d.** $\sin \dfrac{-6\pi}{5} = \sin \dfrac{6\pi}{5}$ **f.** $\sin \dfrac{-9\pi}{5} = \sin \dfrac{9\pi}{5}$

5. Express each of the following in terms of $\cos \theta$.

a. $\sin \dfrac{\pi}{3}$ **c.** $\sin \dfrac{\pi}{5}$ **e.** $\sin \dfrac{\pi}{4}$ **g.** $\sin \dfrac{5\pi}{4}$

b. $\sin \dfrac{\pi}{6}$ **d.** $\sin \dfrac{2\pi}{5}$ **f.** $\sin \dfrac{2\pi}{3}$ **h.** $\sin 1$

6. Express each of the following in terms of $\sin \theta$.

a. $\cos 0$ **c.** $\cos \dfrac{\pi}{6}$ **e.** $\cos \dfrac{2\pi}{3}$ **g.** $\cos \dfrac{\pi}{4}$

b. $\cos \dfrac{\pi}{2}$ **d.** $\cos \dfrac{\pi}{3}$ **f.** $\cos \dfrac{\pi}{5}$ **h.** $\cos 1.4$

7. True or false?

a. $\sin \dfrac{7\pi}{6} > 0$ **c.** $-\sin \dfrac{7\pi}{6} < 0$ **e.** $\cos \dfrac{-3\pi}{4} < 0$

b. $\sin \dfrac{-7\pi}{6} < 0$ **d.** $\cos \dfrac{3\pi}{4} > 0$ **f.** $-\cos \dfrac{3\pi}{4} < 0$

g. $\cos \dfrac{3\pi}{4} = \cos \dfrac{\pi}{4}$ **n.** $\sin \dfrac{-2\pi}{3} = -\sin \dfrac{2\pi}{3}$ **u.** $\cos (-2) = \cos 2$

h. $\sin \dfrac{2\pi}{3} = \sin \dfrac{\pi}{3}$ **o.** $\cos (\pi - 1) = \cos 1$ **v.** $\sin (-2) = \sin 2$

i. $\cos \dfrac{7\pi}{6} = -\cos \dfrac{\pi}{6}$ **p.** $\sin (\pi - 1) = \sin 1$ **w.** $\cos \left(\dfrac{\pi}{2} - 3\right) = \sin 3$

j. $\sin \dfrac{7\pi}{6} = -\sin \dfrac{\pi}{6}$ **q.** $\cos (\pi + 1) = \cos 1$ **x.** $\sin \left(\dfrac{\pi}{2} - 3\right) = \cos 3$

k. $\cos \dfrac{5\pi}{3} = \cos \dfrac{\pi}{3}$ **r.** $\sin (\pi + 1) = \sin 1$ **y.** $\cos \left(4 - \dfrac{\pi}{2}\right) = \sin 4$

l. $\sin \dfrac{5\pi}{3} = \sin \dfrac{\pi}{3}$ **s.** $\cos (2\pi - 1) = \cos 1$ **z.** $\sin \left(4 - \dfrac{\pi}{2}\right) = \cos 4$

m. $\cos \dfrac{-5\pi}{4} = -\cos \dfrac{5\pi}{4}$ **t.** $\sin (2\pi - 1) = \sin 1$

8. Express each of the following in terms of either $\cos \theta$ or $\sin \theta$. Assume that θ is a first quadrant number.

a. $\cos (2\pi - \theta)$ **c.** $\cos (\pi - \theta)$ **e.** $\cos (\pi + \theta)$

b. $\sin (2\pi - \theta)$ **d.** $\sin (\pi - \theta)$ **f.** $\sin (\pi + \theta)$

9. Express each of the following in terms of either $\cos \theta$ or $\sin \theta$, where θ is any real number.

a. $\cos (-\theta)$ **c.** $\cos \left(\dfrac{\pi}{2} - \theta\right)$ **e.** $\cos \left(\theta - \dfrac{\pi}{2}\right)$

b. $\sin (-\theta)$ **d.** $\sin \left(\dfrac{\pi}{2} - \theta\right)$ **f.** $\sin \left(\theta - \dfrac{\pi}{2}\right)$

10. Determine two values of θ between θ and 2π for which the equation is true.

a. $\cos \theta = \dfrac{1}{\sqrt{2}}$ **c.** $\cos \theta = \dfrac{-\sqrt{3}}{2}$ **e.** $\cos \theta = \dfrac{-1}{2}$

b. $\sin \theta = \dfrac{1}{2}$ **d.** $\sin \theta = \dfrac{-1}{\sqrt{2}}$ **f.** $\sin \theta = \dfrac{\sqrt{3}}{2}$

11. Given a first quadrant number α for which $\cos \alpha = 0.8$, determine the two solutions of each equation between 0 and 2π. Express the answers in terms of α.

a. $\cos \theta = -0.8$ **b.** $\cos \theta = 0.8$

12. Given a first quadrant number α for which $\sin \alpha = 0.6$, determine the two solutions of each equation between 0 and 2π. Express the answers in terms of α.

a. $\sin \theta = 0.6$ **b.** $\sin \theta = -0.6$

VALUES OF COS θ AND SIN θ FROM A TABLE

Whenever the real number θ is a multiple of $\frac{\pi}{6}$ or $\frac{\pi}{4}$, we are now able to express the values of cos θ and sin θ. For some of these values of θ, cos θ and sin θ are rational numbers. For example, $\cos \frac{\pi}{3} = \frac{1}{2}$, $\sin \frac{7\pi}{2} = -1$ and $\cos \frac{-\pi}{2} = 0$. For many values of θ, cos θ and sin θ are irrational numbers; their decimal numerals are nonterminating and nonrepeating. In this case, we are able to express the values of cos θ and sin θ with accuracy to a specified number of decimal places. At this time, you should study Appendix A, which is a discussion of *accuracy*.

Given a first quadrant number θ, accurate to two decimal places, cos θ and sin θ are expressed with accuracy to four decimal places in Table I at the back of this book. A portion of Table I is reproduced in Figure 3–12.

real number θ	sin θ	cos θ
1.20	0.9320	0.3624
1.21	.9356	.3530
1.22	.9391	.3436
1.23	.9425	.3342

FIGURE 3-12

From this reproduced portion of Table I, we read that sin 1.21 ≐ 0.9356 and cos 1.22 ≐ 0.3436 (≐ means "is approximately equal to"). The statement sin 1.21 ≐ 0.9356 means that sin 1.21 is 0.9356, with accuracy to four decimal places; that is, $0.93555 < \sin 1.21 < 0.93565$. Find sin 1.20 and cos 1.23 from Figure 3–12.

Given sin θ or cos θ between 0 and 1, we can read in the table the value of θ, accurate to two decimal places, between 0 and $\frac{\pi}{2}$ $\left(\frac{\pi}{2} \doteq 1.57\right)$. For example, if sin θ ≐ 0.9391, then θ ≐ 1.22; if cos θ ≐ 0.3530, then θ ≐ 1.21. Read in Figure 3–12 the approximation of θ between 0 and $\frac{\pi}{2}$ if sin θ ≐ 0.9425; if cos θ ≐ 0.3624.

Study the following examples which show how to use Table I if θ is not a first quadrant number.

Example 1   Suppose θ is a second quadrant number, such as 2.53. Determine cos 2.53 and sin 2.53.

Using the appropriate reduction identities:

$$\cos \theta = -\cos (\pi - \theta) \qquad \sin \theta = \sin (\pi - \theta)$$
$$\cos 2.53 \doteq -\cos (3.14 - 2.53) \quad \sin 2.53 \doteq \sin (3.14 - 2.53)$$
$$= -\cos 0.61 \qquad\qquad = \sin 0.61$$
$$\doteq -0.8196 \qquad\qquad \doteq 0.5729$$

Example 2   Determine cos 3.72 and sin 3.72.
3.72 is a third quadrant number; therefore we write

$$\begin{aligned}
\cos 3.72 &= -\cos (3.72 - \pi) & \sin 3.72 &= -\sin (3.72 - \pi) \\
&\doteq -\cos (3.72 - 3.14) & &\doteq -\sin (3.72 - 3.14) \\
&= -\cos 0.58 & &= -\sin 0.58 \\
&\doteq -0.8365 & &\doteq -0.5480
\end{aligned}$$

Example 3   Determine cos 5.68 and sin 5.68.
5.68 is a fourth quadrant number; therefore we write

$$\begin{aligned}
\cos 5.68 &= \cos (2\pi - 5.68) & \sin 5.68 &= -\sin (2\pi - 5.68) \\
&\doteq \cos (6.28 - 5.68) & &\doteq -\sin (6.28 - 5.68) \\
&= \cos 0.60 & &= -\sin 0.60 \\
&\doteq 0.8253 & &\doteq -0.5646
\end{aligned}$$

Example 4   Suppose θ is a negative number, such as -0.62. Determine cos (-0.62) and sin (-0.62).
Recall that $\cos (-\theta) \equiv \cos \theta$ and $\sin (-\theta) \equiv -\sin \theta$.

$$\begin{aligned}
\cos (-0.62) &= \cos 0.62 & \sin (-0.62) &= -\sin 0.62 \\
&\doteq 0.8139 & &\doteq -0.5810
\end{aligned}$$

Given an equation such as

$$\sin \theta \doteq 0.8624$$

there are two values of θ between 0 and 2π which are solutions of this equation. Table I shows that 1.04 is one such value. Another value is $\pi - 1.04 \doteq 3.14 - 1.04 = 2.10$.
Given an equation such as

$$\cos \theta \doteq -0.4357$$

there are two solutions between 0 and 2π, a second and a third quadrant number. From Table I we find that

$$\cos 1.12 \doteq 0.4357$$

The second quadrant number is $\pi - 1.12 \doteq 3.14 - 1.12 = 2.02$.
The third quadrant number is $\pi + 1.12 \doteq 3.14 + 1.12 = 4.26$.
    You may occasionally be given the number θ to three decimal places. You would be able to determine an approximation of sin θ and of cos θ using Table I and the technique of *interpolation*. This is illustrated for you in Appendix B.
    You may be wondering how the approximations in Table I were determined. It is proved in calculus that for each real number θ,

$$\text{I} \qquad \sin \theta = \theta - \frac{\theta^3}{3!} + \frac{\theta^5}{5!} - \frac{\theta^7}{7!} + \frac{\theta^9}{9!} - \cdots$$

$$\text{II} \qquad \cos \theta = 1 - \frac{\theta^2}{2!} + \frac{\theta^4}{4!} - \frac{\theta^6}{6!} + \frac{\theta^8}{8!} - \cdots$$

where $n!$ (read: n factorial) is defined for n, a natural number, as $1 \times 2 \times 3 \times \ldots \times (n - 1) \times n$. Equations I and II show infinite series which converge.

Using equation I we may approximate sin 1 to as many decimal places as desired.

$$\sin 1 = 1 - \frac{1}{3!} + \frac{1}{5!} - \frac{1}{7!} + \frac{1}{9!} - \cdots$$

$$= 1 - \frac{1}{6} + \frac{1}{120} - \frac{1}{5040} + \frac{1}{362,880} - \cdots$$

$$= 1 - (0.1666666 \ldots) + (0.0083333 \ldots) - (0.0001984 \ldots)$$
$$+ (0.0000027 \ldots) - \cdots$$

$$= 0.84147 \ldots$$

The inclusion of more terms will not alter the first five decimal places. Why not? Electronic computers are used to carry out such computations.

EXERCISES

1. Use Table I and determine each of the following to four decimal places.

   a. sin 0.62   e. sin 2.04   i. sin 4.98

   b. cos 0.43   f. cos 3.02   j. cos 5.23

   c. sin 1.46   g. sin 3.51   k. sin (−0.34)

   d. cos 1.33   h. cos 3.78   l. cos (−1.46)

2. Determine two solutions between 0 and 2π for each equation. Express answers to two decimal places.

   a. $\sin \theta \doteq 0.3616$ e. $\sin \theta \doteq -0.8866$

   b. $\cos \theta \doteq 0.9171$ f. $\cos \theta \doteq -0.4267$

   c. $\sin \theta \doteq 0.9086$ g. $\sin \theta \doteq -0.4529$

   d. $\cos \theta \doteq 0.2867$ h. $\cos \theta \doteq -0.9131$

3. Determine each of the following to four decimal places using Table I and the technique of interpolation.

   a. sin 0.863   b. cos 1.274   c. sin (−0.378)   d. cos (−1.312)

4. Interpolate and determine to three decimal places a first quadrant number θ for which the equation is true.

   a. $\sin \theta \doteq 0.5843$ c. $\sin \theta \doteq 0.7734$

   b. $\cos \theta \doteq 0.9263$ d. $\cos \theta \doteq 0.5111$

5. Use the example shown at the top of the page for approximating sin 1 to help you approximate each of the following to four decimal places.

   a. sin 0.1   b. sin 0.2

6. Examine the infinite series for sin θ and tell why, for very small values of θ, sin $\theta \doteq \theta$. Verify this in Table I for θ in the interval $0 < \theta < 0.29$.

LINE VALUES AND VARIATION

For any real number θ, the values of $\sin \theta$ and $\cos \theta$ may be shown as directed lengths of segments. Values of $\sin \theta$ and $\cos \theta$ shown in this way are called *line values*. Line values help us to study the changes, or variation, in $\sin \theta$ and in $\cos \theta$ that correspond to specified changes in θ.

Given θ_1 and θ_2 determining points B and D, respectively, as shown in Figure 3–13, the line values of $\sin \theta_1$ and $\sin \theta_2$ are given the directed lengths of $\overline{AB}$ and $\overline{CD}$, respectively. These segments are parallel to the y-axis with A and C on the x-axis. The line values are as follows: $\sin \theta_1 = AB$ and $\sin \theta_2 = -CD$. Point B is above the x-axis, showing that $\sin \theta_1$ is positive. Point D is below the x-axis, showing that $\sin \theta_2$ is negative. The line value of $\sin \pi$ is given by the point J; thus, $\sin \pi = 0$.

Consider θ_3 and θ_4, determining points F and H, respectively, as shown in Figure 3–14. The line values of $\cos \theta_3$ and $\cos \theta_4$ are given by the directed lengths of $\overline{EF}$ and $\overline{GH}$, respectively. These segments are parallel to the x-axis with E and G on the y-axis. We have that $\cos \theta_3 = EF$ and $\cos \theta_4 = -GH$. Point F is to the right of the y-axis, showing that $\cos \theta_3$ is positive. Point H is to the left of the y-axis, showing that $\cos \theta_4$ is negative. The line value of $\cos \frac{3\pi}{2}$ is given by the point K; thus, $\cos \frac{3\pi}{2} = 0$.

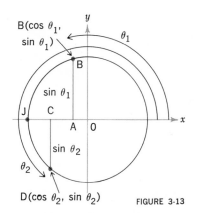

FIGURE 3-13

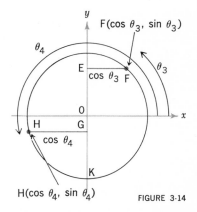

FIGURE 3-14

As the value of θ increases from 0 to 2π, how do the line values of $\sin \theta$ vary? See Figure 3–15. As θ increases from 0 to $\frac{\pi}{2}$, $\sin \theta$ increases from 0 to 1. As θ increases from $\frac{\pi}{2}$ to π, $\sin \theta$ decreases from 1 to 0. As θ increases from π to $\frac{3\pi}{2}$, does $\sin \theta$ increase or decrease? From what value to what value? Describe the variation of $\sin \theta$ as θ increases from $\frac{3\pi}{2}$ to 2π.

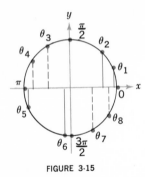

FIGURE 3-15

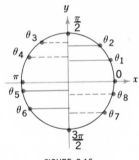

FIGURE 3-16

Consider the variation of $\cos \theta$ as θ increases from 0 to 2π (see Figure 3–16). In what intervals does $\cos \theta$ increase as θ increases? Describe the variation in $\cos \theta$ as θ increases from 0 to $\frac{\pi}{2}$; from $\frac{\pi}{2}$ to π; from π to $\frac{3\pi}{2}$; from $\frac{3\pi}{2}$ to 2π. What is the maximum value of $\cos \theta$? the minimum value?

In the calculus of circular (trigonometric) functions it is important to consider the variation of $\frac{\sin \theta}{\theta}$ as θ decreases from $\frac{\pi}{2}$ to 0.

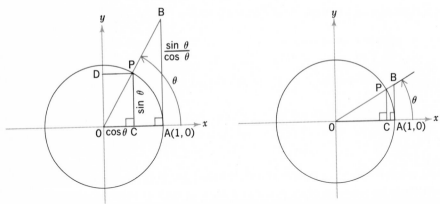

FIGURE 3-17

Figure 3–17 shows $W(\theta) = P$ for $0 < \theta < \frac{\pi}{2}$. Let PC be the line value of $\sin \theta$ and let DP, or OC, be the line value of $\cos \theta$. Now, right $\triangle OPC$ is similar to right $\triangle OBA$. Why? Therefore,

$$\frac{AB}{CP} = \frac{OA}{OC} \quad \text{Why?} \qquad\qquad \frac{AB}{\sin \theta} = \frac{1}{\cos \theta} \quad \text{Why?} \qquad\qquad AB = \frac{\sin \theta}{\cos \theta} \quad \text{Why?}$$

Observe in the two successive diagrams that

θ is decreasing from $\frac{\pi}{2}$ to 0 $\qquad\qquad$ $\cos \theta$ is increasing from 0 to 1

$\sin \theta$ is decreasing from 1 to 0 $\qquad\qquad$ $\frac{\sin \theta}{\cos \theta}$ is decreasing to 0

Notice at $\theta = 0$: $\sin \theta = 0$, $\cos \theta = 1$, $\dfrac{\sin \theta}{\cos \theta} = 0$ but $\dfrac{\sin \theta}{\theta}$ is undefined. Why?

$$\sin \theta < \theta < \frac{\sin \theta}{\cos \theta} \text{ for } 0 < \theta < \frac{\pi}{2}$$

Dividing by $\sin \theta$, $\theta \neq 0$, we obtain

$$1 < \frac{\theta}{\sin \theta} < \frac{1}{\cos \theta} \qquad \left[\text{If } 0 < a < b < c, \text{ then } 0 < 1 < \frac{b}{a} < \frac{c}{a}. \right]$$

Taking the reciprocal of each term and reversing the order of inequality,

$$1 > \frac{\sin \theta}{\theta} > \cos \theta \qquad \left[\text{If } 0 < m < n < p, \text{ then } \frac{1}{m} > \frac{1}{n} > \frac{1}{p}. \right]$$

Thus, we have $\dfrac{\sin \theta}{\theta}$ "squeezed" between $\cos \theta$ and 1. But as θ decreases from $\dfrac{\pi}{2}$ to 0, $\cos \theta$ increases to 1.

Hence, $\dfrac{\sin \theta}{\theta}$ increases to 1 as a *limit*, though $\dfrac{\sin \theta}{\theta}$ is undefined at $\theta = 0$.

EXERCISES

1. Describe the variation of $\cos \theta$ for each variation of θ.

a. θ increases from 0 to $\dfrac{\pi}{2}$.

d. θ increases from $\dfrac{3\pi}{2}$ to 2π.

b. θ increases from $\dfrac{\pi}{2}$ to π.

e. θ decreases from $\dfrac{3\pi}{2}$ to π.

c. θ increases from π to $\dfrac{3\pi}{2}$.

f. θ decreases from $\dfrac{\pi}{2}$ to 0.

2. Give the minimum and maximum values of each of the following.

a. $\cos \theta$

b. $\sin \theta$

3. Give all θ such that $0 \leq \theta \leq 2\pi$ and each of the following is true.

a. $\cos \theta = 0$

b. $\cos \theta = 1$

c. $\cos \theta = -1$

d. $\sin \theta = 0$

e. $\sin \theta = 1$

f. $\sin \theta = -1$

g. $\cos \theta > 0$

h. $\cos \theta < 0$

i. $\sin \theta > 0$

4. Tell the range of the cosine function.

5. Tell the range of the sine function.

6. Construct an argument similar to that of the text to show that the *limit* of the variation of $\dfrac{\sin \theta}{\theta}$ is 1 as θ increases from $\dfrac{-\pi}{2}$ to 0. Begin by drawing an appropriate figure such as Figure 3–17 with $W(\theta) = P$, a point in Q_4.

7. True or false?

a. If $\dfrac{\pi}{2} < \theta_1 < \theta_2 < \pi$,

then $0 < \sin \theta_1 < \sin \theta_2 < 1$.

b. If $\pi < \theta_1 < \theta_2 < \dfrac{3\pi}{2}$,

then $-1 < \cos \theta_1 < \cos \theta_2 < 0$.

c. As θ increases from 0 to $\dfrac{\pi}{4}$, $\sin \theta$ increases from 0 to 1.

d. If $\dfrac{\pi}{2} > \theta_1 > \theta_2 > 0$,

then $1 > \sin \theta_1 > \sin \theta_2 > 0$.

e. As θ increases from 0 to $\dfrac{\pi}{4}$, $\cos \theta$ decreases from 1 to $\dfrac{1}{\sqrt{2}}$.

f. $\dfrac{\theta}{\cos \theta}$ is defined for $\theta = 0$.

GRAPHS OF SINE AND COSINE

You have no doubt had the experience of gaining insight into a mathematical concept by means of a graph. For this purpose we shall now introduce the graphs of sine and cosine.

First, recall that sine $= \{(\theta, y)\}$ for which $W(\theta) = P(x, y)$. To construct the graph of sine, we project line values of $\sin \theta$ into points of another rectangular coordinate plane. Study Figures 3–18 and 3–19.

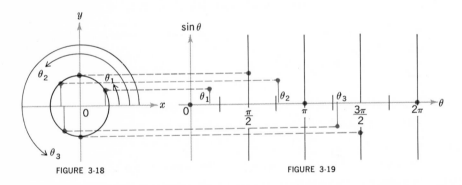

FIGURE 3-18   FIGURE 3-19

In Figure 3–18 we have determined seven points for which $W(\theta) = P(x, y)$. Then, by projecting from the unit circle into the θ, $\sin \theta$ plane, we constructed eight points (θ, y) in Figure 3–19. These eight points of the θ, $\sin \theta$ plane are on the graph of the sine function. Figure 3–20 shows the completed graph of sine for $0 \le \theta \le 2\pi$.

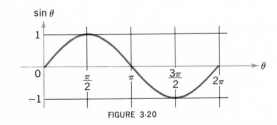

FIGURE 3-20

Since the sine function is periodic with period 2π, we can easily extend the picture for one or more periods in either direction (see Figure 3–21).

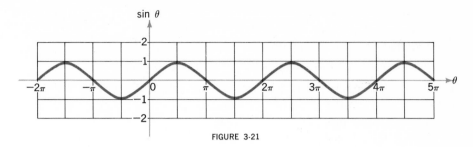

FIGURE 3-21

From the incomplete graph of sine shown in Figure 3–21, verify these observations

> The domain of sine is R, the set of all real numbers.
> The range of sine is $\{y \mid -1 \leq y \leq 1\}$.
> Sine is a periodic function with primitive period 2π.
> The *amplitude*, or maximum value, of sine is 1.

DEFINITION OF AMPLITUDE OF PERIODIC FUNCTION

Given a periodic function f with its greatest and least values equal in absolute value, the *amplitude* of f is the maximum value of f.

The graphs of certain functions are related in a special way. For example, let us consider the functions f, g, and h, such that

$$f(x) = x \qquad\qquad g(x) = x - 2 \qquad\qquad h(x) = x + 3$$

Their graphs are shown in Figure 3–22. Observe that

> For each real number a, $g(a) = f(a - 2)$ and a "shift" of 2 units to the right "moves" the graph of f onto the graph of g.

> For each real number a, $h(a) = f(a + 3)$ and a "shift" of 3 units to the left "moves" the graph of f onto the graph of h.

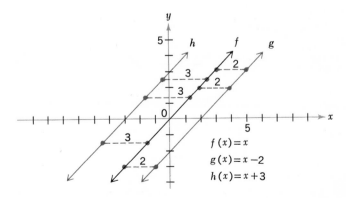

$$f(x) = x$$
$$g(x) = x - 2$$
$$h(x) = x + 3$$

FIGURE 3-22

Given functions r, s and t, such that

$$r(x) = |x|$$
$$s(x) = |x - 4|$$
$$t(x) = |x + 2|$$

Observe that for each real number a,

$$s(a) = r(a - 4) \qquad t(a) = r(a + 2)$$

Predict the horizontal "shift" that "moves" the graph of r onto the graph of s; the graph of r onto the graph of t. Graph r, s and t on one coordinate system to verify your predictions.

The graph of sine may be "shifted" horizontally to obtain the graph of cosine. Recall that

$$\cos(-\theta) \equiv \sin\left(\theta + \frac{\pi}{2}\right)$$

is an identity according to the $\frac{\pi}{2}$-sum relation.

Since $\cos(-\theta) \equiv \cos\theta$ is an identity, it follows that

$$\cos\theta \equiv \sin\left(\theta + \frac{\pi}{2}\right)$$

is also an identity. Now let us consider the graphs of f and g, such that

$$f(\theta) = \sin\theta$$
$$g(\theta) = \cos\theta = \sin\left(\theta + \frac{\pi}{2}\right)$$

The graph of f, the sine function, is "moved" onto the graph of g, the cosine function, by "shifting" the graph of sine to the left $\frac{\pi}{2}$ units. See Figure 3–23.

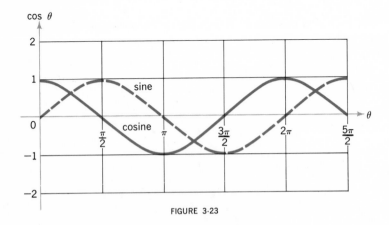

FIGURE 3-23

From the incomplete graph of cosine shown in Figure 3–23, tell the domain, range, primitive period and amplitude of cosine.

EXERCISES

1. The scheme shown below gives a method of projecting the line value of $\sin \dfrac{3\pi}{8}$ onto the point $\left(\dfrac{3\pi}{8},\ \sin \dfrac{3\pi}{8}\right)$ on the θ, $\sin \theta$ coordinate plane.

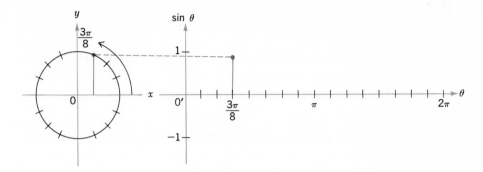

Draw a larger picture of the above scheme and project each line value of $\sin \theta$, where θ is a multiple of $\dfrac{\pi}{8}$ between 0 and 2π, onto a point of the θ, $\sin \theta$ coordinate plane.

2. The scheme shown below gives a method of projecting the line value of $\cos \dfrac{\pi}{8}$ onto the point $\left(\dfrac{\pi}{8},\ \cos \dfrac{3\pi}{8}\right)$ on the θ, $\cos \theta$ coordinate plane. Observe that we use the line value of $\sin \dfrac{5\pi}{8}$ for the value of $\cos \dfrac{\pi}{8}$. This is based on the identity $\cos \theta \equiv \sin \left(\theta + \dfrac{\pi}{2}\right)$, which also tells us that $\cos \dfrac{\pi}{4} = \sin \dfrac{3\pi}{4}$, $\cos \dfrac{3\pi}{8} = \sin \dfrac{7\pi}{8}$, $\cos \dfrac{\pi}{2} = \sin \pi$, etc.

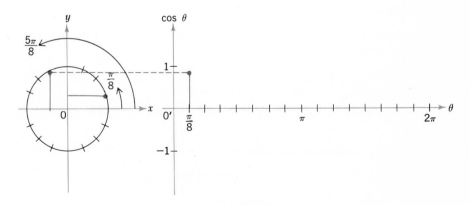

Draw a larger picture of the above scheme and project each line value of $\cos \theta$, where θ is a multiple of $\dfrac{\pi}{8}$ between 0 and 2π, onto a point of the θ, $\cos \theta$ coordinate plane.

3. Sketch the graphs of $y = \sin \theta$ and $y = \cos \theta$ on the same coordinate system for the interval $0 \leq \theta < 2\pi$. Use these graphs to answer the following questions.

   a. How many solutions does the equation $\sin \theta = \cos \theta$ have in the interval $0 \leq \theta < 2\pi$?

   b. For what values of θ, in the interval $0 \leq \theta < 2\pi$, is it true that $\cos \theta < \sin \theta$?

   c. For what values of θ, in the interval $0 \leq \theta < 2\pi$, is it true that $|\cos \theta| < |\sin \theta|$?

   d. How many solutions does the equation $\sin \theta = 0.8$ have in the interval $0 \leq \theta < 2\pi$?

4. Given functions r, s and t such that $r(x) = |x|$, $s(x) = |x - 4|$ and $t(x) = |x + 2|$.

   a. Graph r, s and t on one coordinate system.

   b. Describe the horizontal "move" that would "shift" the graph of r onto the graph of s.

   c. Describe the horizontal "move" that would "shift" the graph of r onto the graph of t.

5. Given functions f, g, and h such that $f(x) = x$, $g(x) = x + 5$ and $h(x) = x - 7$.

   a. Describe the horizontal "move" that "shifts" the graph of f onto the graph of g.

   b. Describe the horizontal "move" that "shifts" the graph of f onto the graph of h.

6. Given functions f and g, such that $f(x) = 2x$ and $g(x) = 2x + 7$.

   a. Is the graph of f "moved" onto the graph of g by a "shift" of seven units to the left?

   b. Is the graph of f "moved" onto the graph of g by a "shift" of $3\frac{1}{2}$ units to the left?

   c. May g be expressed as $g(x) = 2\left(x + 3\frac{1}{2}\right)$?

   d. Of the two equations, $g(x) = 2x + 7$ and $g(x) = 2\left(x + 3\frac{1}{2}\right)$, which provides the better means of telling the "move" that "shifts" the graph of f onto the graph of g without graphing f and g?

7. Given function f, such that $f(x) = 3x$, tell the "move" that "shifts" the graph of f onto the graph of g, for each function g specified below.

   a. $g(x) = 3x + 12$ b. $g(x) = 3x - 6$ c. $g(x) = 3x + 5$

8. Given function f, such that $f(x) = \frac{1}{4}x$, tell the "move" that "shifts" the graph of f onto the graph of h for each function h specified below.

   a. $h(x) = \frac{1}{4}x + 4$ b. $h(x) = \frac{1}{4}x - 8$ c. $h(x) = \frac{1}{4}x + 2$

9. Given function f such that $f(x) = mx$, $(m > 0)$, tell the "move" that "shifts" the graph of f onto the graph of g, if $g(x) = mx + b$, $(b > 0)$.

GRAPH OF $y = a \sin b(\theta + c)$

The graph of sine is the basis for obtaining sketches of the graphs of functions specified by equations, such as

$$y = 2 \sin \theta \qquad [2 \sin \theta \text{ means } 2 \cdot \sin \theta]$$
$$y = \sin 3\theta \qquad [\sin 3\theta \text{ means } \sin (3\theta)]$$
$$y = \sin \left(\theta + \frac{\pi}{4}\right)$$
$$y = 2 \sin 3\left(\theta + \frac{\pi}{4}\right)$$

The letter y in these equations should *not* be interpreted as the second component of (x, y) where $x = \cos \theta$ and $y = \sin \theta$. In the first equation, y is the second component of (x, y) where $x = \theta$ and $y = 2 \sin \theta$.

Consider the problem of graphing $y = a \sin \theta$, $a \neq 0$. For each θ, we multiply $\sin \theta$ by a to obtain $(\theta, a \sin \theta)$, a member of the function specified by $y = a \sin \theta$. Study Figure 3–24.

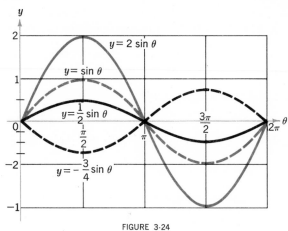

FIGURE 3·24

What is the amplitude and the period of the function specified by $y = 2 \sin \theta$? by $y = \sin \theta$? by $y = \frac{1}{2} \sin \theta$? by $y = \frac{-3}{4} \sin \theta$? by $y = a \sin \theta$?

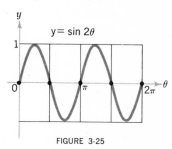

FIGURE 3-25

Let us now develop the pattern involved in graphing $y = \sin b\theta$ ($b > 0$). We first graph $y = \sin 2\theta$ (see Figure 3–25). Observe that if 0, $\frac{\pi}{2}$, π, $\frac{3\pi}{\pi}$, and 2π are values of θ, then values of 2θ are 0, π, 2π, 3π, and 4π at which $\sin 2\theta = 0$.

Figure 3-26 shows the graph of $y = \sin \frac{1}{3}\theta$. Note that if 0, 3π and 6π are values

of θ, then 0, π, and 2π are values of $\frac{1}{3}\theta$ at which $\sin \frac{1}{3}\theta = 0$.

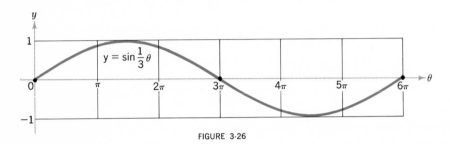

FIGURE 3-26

What is the period of the function specified by $y = \sin \theta$? by $y = \sin 2\theta$? by

$y = \sin \frac{1}{3}\theta$? by $y = \sin b\theta$?

We have considered the graph of $y = a \sin \theta$ and the graph of $y = \sin b\theta$. In general, the amplitude of the function specified by $y = a \sin b\theta$ $(b > 0)$ is $|a|$

and the period is $\frac{1}{b} \cdot 2\pi$. This information will be valuable in sketching the graph

of $y = a \sin b\theta$.

The graphs of $y = \sin(\theta + c)$ and $y = \sin(\theta - c)$ are also related to the

graph of $y = \sin \theta$. Study the graphs of $y = \sin\left(\theta + \frac{\pi}{4}\right)$ and $y = \sin\left(\theta - \frac{\pi}{4}\right)$

shown in Figure 3-27 and compare them with the graph of $y = \sin \theta$.

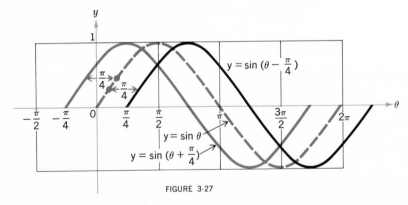

FIGURE 3-27

Describe the "move" that would "shift" the graph of $y = \sin \theta$ onto the graph

of $y = \sin\left(\theta + \frac{\pi}{4}\right)$. Describe the "move" that would "shift" the graph of sine

onto the graph of $y = \sin\left(\theta - \frac{\pi}{4}\right)$. These moves are described by the *phase number* of the function.

DEFINITION OF PHASE NUMBER   Given the function f specified by either $y = a \sin b(\theta + c)$ or $y = a \cos b(\theta + c)$ for real numbers a, b, and c (where $a \neq 0$, $b > 0$), c is called the *phase number* of f.

The phase number c describes the length and direction of the horizontal "move" which "shifts" the graph of $y = a \sin b\theta$ onto the graph of $y = a \sin b(\theta + c)$; the "move" is $|c|$ units, to the left if c is positive, to the right if c is negative. Examine Figure 3–27 to be sure that you understand the role of c.

Let us summarize our discussion of the graph of $y = a \sin b(\theta + c)$, $b > 0$.

    1. The *amplitude* is given by $|a|$.

    2. The *period* is determined by the expression $\dfrac{1}{b} \cdot 2\pi$.

    3. The *phase number* is c.

When these three things are known, the graph can be sketched by the techniques shown in the following examples. If an equation is given in the form

$$y = a \sin (b\theta + d),$$ it should be changed to the equivalent equation

$$y = a \sin b\left(\theta + \frac{d}{b}\right).$$ Notice that the phase number in this case is $\dfrac{d}{b}$.

Example 1   Sketch the graph of $y = 2 \sin 3\theta$ for one period.

Solution   The amplitude is 2 and the period is $\dfrac{1}{3} \cdot 2\pi = \dfrac{2\pi}{3}$. As an aid to sketching the graph for one period, we first draw a picture of a rectangle whose length is the period and whose width is twice the amplitude. On a θ, y coordinate system, draw pictures of horizontal lines $y = 2$ and $y = -2$. Draw pictures of vertical lines at quarter-periods of $\dfrac{1}{4} \cdot \dfrac{2\pi}{3} = \dfrac{\pi}{6}$, beginning at 0. Plot $(0, 0)$, $\left(\dfrac{\pi}{6}, 2\right)$, $\left(\dfrac{\pi}{3}, 0\right)$, $\left(\dfrac{\pi}{2}, -2\right)$, and $\left(\dfrac{2\pi}{3}, 0\right)$. Draw a picture of a "sine-like" curve containing the five points.

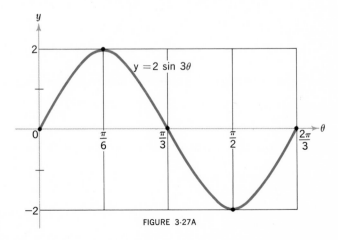

FIGURE 3-27A

Example 2   Sketch the graph of $y = \dfrac{3}{4} \sin \left(\theta - \dfrac{\pi}{3} \right)$ for one period.

Solution   The amplitude is $\dfrac{3}{4}$, the period is 2π, and the phase number is $\dfrac{-\pi}{3}$. On a θ, y coordinate system, draw pictures of horizontal lines $y = \dfrac{3}{4}$ and $y = \dfrac{-3}{4}$. Draw pictures of vertical lines at quarter-periods of $\dfrac{\pi}{2}$, beginning at $\dfrac{\pi}{3}$, that is, at $\dfrac{\pi}{3}$, $\left(\dfrac{\pi}{3} + \dfrac{\pi}{2} \right)$, $\left(\dfrac{\pi}{3} + \pi \right)$, $\left(\dfrac{\pi}{3} + \dfrac{3\pi}{2} \right)$, and $\left(\dfrac{\pi}{3} + 2\pi \right)$. Why? What connection does this have with the phase number? Plot the points $\left(\dfrac{\pi}{3}, 0 \right)$, $\left(\dfrac{5\pi}{6}, \dfrac{3}{4} \right)$, $\left(\dfrac{4\pi}{3}, 0 \right)$, $\left(\dfrac{11\pi}{6}, \dfrac{-3}{4} \right)$ and $\left(\dfrac{7\pi}{3}, 0 \right)$. Draw a picture of a "sine-like" curve containing the five points.

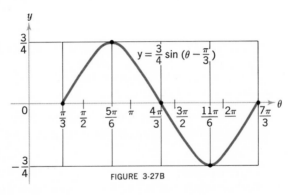

FIGURE 3-27B

Example 3   Sketch the graph of $y = \sin \dfrac{1}{2} \left(\theta + \dfrac{2\pi}{3} \right)$ for one period.

Solution   The amplitude is 1, the period is $2 \cdot 2\pi = 4\pi$ and the phase number is $\dfrac{2\pi}{3}$. On a θ, y coordinate system draw pictures of horizontal lines $y = 1$ and $y = -1$. Draw pictures of vertical lines at quarter-periods of $\dfrac{1}{4} \cdot 4\pi = \pi$, beginning at $\dfrac{-2\pi}{3}$, that is, at $\dfrac{-2\pi}{3}$, $\left(\dfrac{-2\pi}{3} + \pi \right)$, $\left(\dfrac{-2\pi}{3} + 2\pi \right)$, $\left(\dfrac{-2\pi}{3} + 3\pi \right)$, and $\left(\dfrac{-2\pi}{3} + 4\pi \right)$. Why? What connection does this have with the phase number? Plot the five points $\left(\dfrac{-2\pi}{3}, 0 \right)$, $\left(\dfrac{\pi}{3}, 1 \right)$, $\left(\dfrac{4\pi}{3}, 0 \right)$, $\left(\dfrac{7\pi}{3}, -1 \right)$, and $\left(\dfrac{10\pi}{3}, 0 \right)$. Draw a picture of a "sine-like" curve containing them.

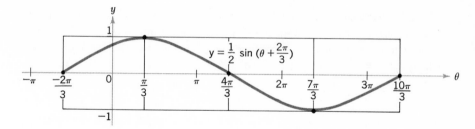

$$y = \frac{1}{2} \sin \left(\theta + \frac{2\pi}{3}\right)$$

Example 4   Sketch the graph of $y = 3 \sin (2\theta + \pi)$ for one period.

Solution   This equation is not in the form $y = a \sin b(\theta + c)$. An equivalent

equation is $y = 3 \sin 2\left(\theta + \frac{\pi}{2}\right)$, which is in the desired form with

$a = 3, b = 2$ and $c = \frac{\pi}{2}$. Use the equivalent equation and proceed

as in Example 3. What is the amplitude? the period? the phase
number?

Example 5   Sketch the graph of $y = \frac{2}{3} \sin \left(\frac{1}{3}\theta - \frac{2\pi}{5}\right)$ for one period.

Solution   An equivalent equation of the form $y = a \sin b(\theta + c)$ is $y = \frac{2}{3}$

$\sin \frac{1}{3}\left(\theta - \frac{6\pi}{5}\right)$ with $a = \frac{2}{3}, b = \frac{1}{3}$ and $c = \frac{-6\pi}{5}$. Use the equiv-

alent equation and proceed as in Example 3. What is the amplitude? the period? the phase number?

Example 6   Sketch the graph of $y = -3 \sin \pi\theta$ for
one period.

Solution   The amplitude is $|-3|$, which is equal to

3, and the period is $\frac{1}{\pi} \cdot 2\pi$, which is equal

to 2. Draw pictures of vertical lines at

quarter-periods of $\frac{1}{4} \cdot 2 = \frac{1}{2}$, beginning at

0. Draw pictures of horizontal lines $y = 3$
and $y = -3$. Draw a picture of a "sine-

like" curve containing $(0, 0)$, $\left(\frac{1}{2}, -3\right)$,

$(1, 0)$, $\left(1\frac{1}{2}, 3\right)$, and $(2, 0)$.

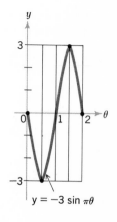

$y = -3 \sin \pi\theta$

In our discussion, we have been concerned with sketching the graphs of functions specified by $y = a \sin b(\theta + c)$ for real numbers a, b, and c ($a \neq 0$, $b > 0$). The discussion of $y = a \cos b(\theta + c)$ would be similar in all respects. Hence, questions concerning $y = a \cos b(\theta + c)$ are included in the exercises.

EXERCISES

1. For each function specified below, determine (1) the amplitude, (2) the period, and (3) the phase number.

a. $y = \dfrac{2}{3} \sin 4\theta$

f. $y = \cos \dfrac{1}{2}\left(\theta - \dfrac{\pi}{6}\right)$

b. $y = -3 \cos \dfrac{1}{3}\theta$

g. $y = \sin \pi\left(\theta + \dfrac{2}{3}\right)$

c. $y = 2 \sin \pi\theta$

h. $y = 3 \sin \left(\dfrac{2}{3}\theta - \dfrac{\pi}{6}\right)$

d. $y = \dfrac{4}{3} \cos 2\pi\theta$

i. $y = -2 \cos \left(\dfrac{4}{3}\theta + \dfrac{\pi}{2}\right)$

e. $y = 2 \sin 3\left(\theta + \dfrac{\pi}{4}\right)$

j. $y = \sin \left(\pi\theta - \dfrac{3\pi}{4}\right)$

2. Sketch the graph of each function specified below for one period. Use a separate coordinate system for each graph.

a. $y = 3 \sin \theta$

f. $y = \sin \pi\theta$

b. $y = 2 \cos \theta$

g. $y = \cos \dfrac{1}{3}\theta$

c. $y = -2 \sin \theta$

h. $y = \sin \dfrac{1}{2}\theta$

d. $y = \sin 4\theta$

i. $y = \cos 2\pi\theta$

e. $y = \cos 2\theta$

j. $y = \sin \dfrac{\pi\theta}{2}$

3. Sketch the graph of each function specified below for the interval given. Use a separate coordinate system for each graph.

a. $y = 2 \sin 2\theta$ \qquad $0 \leq \theta \leq 2\pi$

d. $y = \dfrac{1}{2} \cos \dfrac{1}{2}\theta$ \qquad $0 \leq \theta \leq 4\pi$

b. $y = \dfrac{3}{2} \cos 3\theta$ \qquad $0 \leq \theta \leq 2\pi$

e. $y = 2 \sin 2\pi\theta$ \qquad $0 \leq \theta \leq 2$

c. $y = 3 \sin \dfrac{2}{3}\theta$ \qquad $0 \leq \theta \leq 3\pi$

f. $y = \dfrac{1}{2} \cos \pi\theta$ \qquad $0 \leq \theta \leq 2$

4. Sketch the graph of each function specified below for one period. Use a separate coordinate system for each graph.

a. $y = \sin \left(\theta - \dfrac{3\pi}{4}\right)$

b. $y = \cos \left(\theta + \dfrac{\pi}{4}\right)$

c. $y = \sin 2\left(\theta + \dfrac{\pi}{3}\right)$

g. $y = \sin \left(\dfrac{2}{3}\theta - \dfrac{\pi}{6}\right)$

d. $y = \cos \dfrac{1}{2}\left(\theta - \dfrac{2\pi}{3}\right)$

h. $y = \cos \left(\dfrac{4}{3}\theta + \dfrac{2\pi}{3}\right)$

e. $y = 2 \sin \left(2\theta + \dfrac{\pi}{2}\right)$

i. $y = 2 \sin \left(\pi\theta - \dfrac{\pi}{2}\right)$

f. $y = -2 \cos (3\theta - \pi)$

5. Graph $y = 2 \sin 2\theta$ and $y = \cos 3\theta$ on the same coordinate system for the interval $0 \le \theta < 2\pi$. Use these graphs to determine the number of solutions each of the following equations has in the interval $0 \le \theta < 2\pi$.

a. $2 \sin 2\theta = \cos 3\theta$ **b.** $2 \sin 2\theta = 1$ **c.** $\cos 3\theta = -\dfrac{1}{2}$

UNIFORM CIRCULAR MOTION

Consider again the motion of a point P along a unit circle in standard position (see Figure 3–28). Suppose that $A(1, 0)$ is the initial position of P and that P moves at a constant speed of ω (omega) units per second. We can thus tabulate the following information about the motion of P and conclude that, after t seconds, P is at an arc-distance of ωt units from A.

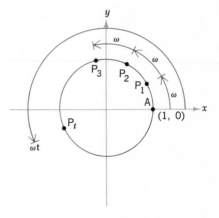

after t seconds	position of P	length of $\overset{\frown}{AP}$
1	P_1	ω
2	P_2	2ω
3	P_3	3ω
$\vdots$	$\vdots$	$\vdots$
t	P_t	ωt

FIGURE 3-28

As is shown in Figure 3–29, the coordinates (x, y) of P_t, the position of P at the end of t seconds, are given by

$$x = \cos \omega t$$

$$y = \sin \omega t$$

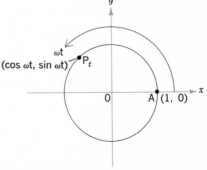

FIGURE 3-29

In order to visualize the displacement of the point P from the t-axis, study the graphs of $y = \sin \omega t$ as shown in Figure 3–30 for various values of ω. Notice ω is in terms of π in each case. From these graphs it is evident why motion of this type is called *wave motion*.

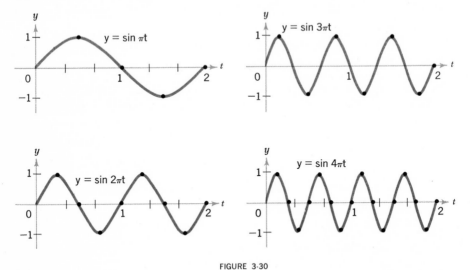

FIGURE 3-30

The motion of the point through one period is called a *cycle*. Recall from the previous section that the period of $y = \sin \omega t$ is $\frac{1}{\omega} \cdot 2\pi$. The number of cycles occurring in a unit of time is called the *frequency*. For the wave motions shown in Figure 3–30, the frequencies are $\frac{1}{2}$, 1, $1\frac{1}{2}$, and 2 cycles per second, respectively.

In general, the frequency of the motion specified by $y = \sin \omega t$ is $\frac{\omega}{2\pi}$. Do you see that the frequency is the reciprocal of the period?

The alternating electrical current used in our homes is called 60 cycle current. The current builds from 0 to a maximum, returns to 0, builds to a maximum in the other direction and again returns to 0. It does this periodically, 60 times a second, hence the expression *60 cycle*.

EXERCISES

1. Graph the wave motions specified by the equations below for the interval $0 \le t \le 2$, t given in seconds. What is ω in each case?

   a. $y = 2 \sin 5\pi t$ **c.** $y = 2 \cos 2\pi t$

   b. $y = 3 \sin \pi t$ **d.** $y = \frac{1}{2} \cos 3\pi t$

2. For the wave motions specified in Exercise 1, determine (1) the time for one cycle and (2) the frequency of the motion.

3. a. The point $P(x, y)$ moves along a unit circle from $A(1, 0)$ with a constant speed of $\omega = \dfrac{\pi}{12}$ units per second. Determine the coordinates of P at the end of 2, 3, 4, and 20 seconds.

b. What is the displacement of P from the x-axis at the end of 2, 3, 4, 6, 8, 9_x and 10 seconds?

c. Does the displacement of P from the x-axis vary directly with time?

d. At what times will the point P reach its maximum displacements from the x-axis?

e. What is the period (in seconds) of this motion?

f. What is the frequency (in cycles per second) of this motion?

SIMPLE HARMONIC MOTION

Consider the motions exhibited by the following moving objects.

> A weight suspended on a spring is pulled down and then released
> A piston in a cylinder of an automobile engine which is idling
> A child on a swing   A buoy in rough water
> A simple pendulum   An atom in a crystal

Each of the above is an example of back and forth or up and down motion which is repeated at regular time intervals. Such a motion is called *simple harmonic motion*. Each harmonic motion may be studied in terms of a circular function.

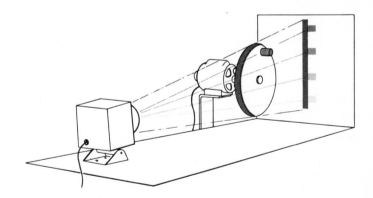

Uniform circular motion may be projected to show simple harmonic motion along a line. The figure above shows a wheel, mounted vertically, with a knob on its rim. A light casts a shadow of the wheel and knob as a segment and a point, respectively, on a screen. As the wheel rotates at a constant speed, the knob exhibits *uniform circular motion* while its shadow shows simple harmonic motion up and down the segment. The point with simple harmonic motion accelerates as it moves toward the midpoint of the segment and decelerates as it moves toward an endpoint.

We may obtain an equation of this simple harmonic motion in the following way. In the figure below, the point P moves along the unit circle at a constant speed of ω units per second. The point P' moves up and down the segment so as to be directly across from P. The vertical displacement of P from the x-axis, which is also the displacement of P' from A', is given by $d = \sin \omega t$

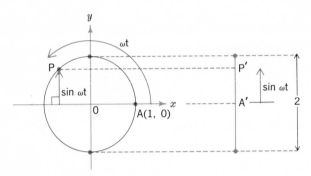

Example   Suppose P moves along the unit circle at a constant speed of $\frac{\pi}{3}$ units per second. At the end of 4 seconds, P has moved $\frac{4\pi}{3}$ units from A along the circle. The displacement of P from the x-axis and the displacement of P' from A' is $\sin \frac{4\pi}{3}$ or $\frac{-\sqrt{3}}{2}$. What is the displacement of P' from A' at the end of $2\frac{1}{2}$ seconds? In general, the displacement of P' from A' at the end of t seconds is given by

$$d = \sin \frac{\pi}{3}t$$

The example above illustrates a simple harmonic motion whose period is 6 seconds, since 6 seconds are needed for P to complete one revolution at the rate of $\frac{\pi}{3}$ units per second and 6 seconds are needed for P' to complete one cycle. In one second $\left(\frac{1}{6}\text{ period}\right)$, the point P' has completed $\frac{1}{6}$ cycle. We say that P' oscillates (vibrates) at a rate of $\frac{1}{6}$ cycle per second or 10 cycles per minute. The maximum displacement of P' from A', called the amplitude, is 1 unit, up or down, and occurs at each $1\frac{1}{2} + 6n$ seconds and at each $4\frac{1}{2} + 6n$ seconds, where n is any natural number. When does P' have its minimum displacement (zero) from A'? What is the displacement of P' from A' at the end of 5 seconds? $8\frac{1}{2}$ seconds? $\frac{2}{3}$ period? $\frac{1}{12}$ period? $2\frac{1}{3}$ periods?

EXERCISES

1. In the diagram at the right, point A is the midpoint of a segment which is 2 inches long. A point moves along this segment with a simple harmonic motion that has an 8-second period. When $t = 0$, the displacement from A is zero. Determine the

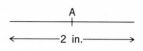

displacement (negative to the left of A and positive to the right) from A at the end of the following time intervals.

a. $\frac{1}{2}$ period

b. $1\frac{1}{3}$ seconds

c. 4 periods

d. $2\frac{2}{3}$ seconds

e. $\frac{3}{4}$ period

f. 3 seconds

g. $\frac{5}{8}$ period

h. 5 seconds

i. $2\frac{1}{3}$ periods

j. $9\frac{1}{3}$ seconds

k. $\frac{7}{6}$ periods

l. 6 seconds

m. $1\frac{7}{8}$ periods

n. 15 seconds

o. $3\frac{1}{2}$ periods

p. 1 minute

2. For the harmonic motion described in Exercise 1, answer the following questions.

a. When does the point have maximum displacement from A?

b. When does the point have minimum displacement from A?

3. A point P moves along a unit circle with uniform speed of $\frac{3\pi}{4}$ units per second beginning at $A(1, 0)$. Determine the displacement of P from the horizontal axis at the end of the following time intervals.

a. 3 seconds

b. $4\frac{1}{3}$ seconds

c. 6 seconds

d. $5\frac{2}{3}$ seconds

e. $\frac{1}{3}$ period

f. $\frac{5}{8}$ period

g. $\frac{3}{4}$ period

h. $6\frac{1}{2}$ periods

4. For Exercise 3 when does P have maximum displacement from the x-axis? minimum displacement from the x-axis?

5. A wheel revolves at a constant speed of 10 revolutions, or cycles, per second. What is the period of this circular motion?

6. A wheel revolves so that its period is $\frac{1}{12}$ second. What is its frequency in revolutions (or cycles) per second?

7. A simple harmonic motion is described by the equation $d = \sin \frac{5\pi}{6}t$. Determine the period and the frequency of the harmonic motion, where t is in seconds.

8. If T is the period in seconds and f is the frequency in cycles per second for a simple harmonic motion, express T in terms of f and express f in terms of T.

SUMS OF FUNCTIONS

Some phenomena in science may be described by a function which is defined as the sum of simpler functions. Examples of such sums are functions specified by the following equations.

$$y = \frac{\theta}{2} + 2 \sin \theta \qquad\qquad y = \theta - \sin \theta$$

$$y = \sin \theta - \cos \theta \qquad\qquad y = 2 \sin \theta + \cos 2\theta$$

The graph of a sum may be drawn by graphing each simpler function and then, at intervals, adding the second coordinates of the simpler functions. On the graph this addition may be accomplished by the use of a ruler, compass, or dividers. Study the following examples.

Example 1   Given the graph of the parabola $u = \frac{1}{4}x^2$ and the graph of the angle $v = 4 - |x|$ as shown in Figure 3–31, construct the graph of $y = \left(\frac{1}{4}x^2\right) + (4 - |x|)$ for $-7 \leq x \leq 7$.

Observe in Figure 3–31 that for $x = -6$, the following are true: $u = AB$, $v = -AC = -BD$, and $y = AB - BD = AD$. For $x = -2$, the following hold: $u = EF = GH$, $v = EG$ and $y = EG + GH = EH$. Thus, two points on the graph are D and H. Repeating this procedure at frequent intervals produces enough points to sketch the graph of $y = \frac{1}{4}x^2 + 4 - |x|$ for $-7 \leq x \leq 7$.

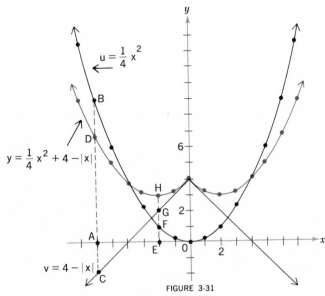

FIGURE 3-31

Example 2   Graph $y = \frac{\theta}{2} + 2 \sin \theta$ for $0 \leq \theta \leq 2\pi$.

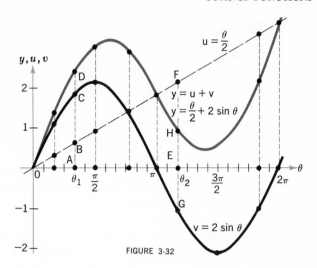

FIGURE 3-32

Sketch lightly the graphs of $u = \dfrac{\theta}{2}$ and $v = 2 \sin \theta$. Observe in Figure 3-32 that for θ_1, $y = AB + AC = AC + CD = AD$. For θ_2, $y = EF - EG = EF - FH = EH$. Thus, D and H are two points on the graph of $y = \dfrac{\theta}{2} + 2 \sin \theta$. Similar constructions are made at enough intervals between 0 and 2π to draw a picture of a smooth curve. Note that the sum is not a periodic function.

Example 3   Graph $y = 2 \sin \theta + \cos 2\theta$ for one period.

Graph $u = 2 \sin \theta$ for one period and graph $v = \cos 2\theta$ for two periods (see Figure 3–33).

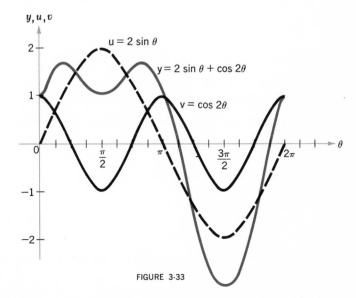

FIGURE 3-33

At intervals of approximately $\frac{\pi}{8}$ on the θ-axis, construct $P(\theta, y)$ so that $y = u + v = 2 \sin \theta + \cos 2\theta$. Is the sum a periodic function? If so, what is the period?

In Example 3, two "simple" periodic functions, $u = 2 \sin \theta$ and $v = \cos 2\theta$, were added to obtain a "non-simple" periodic function, $y = 2 \sin \theta + \cos 2\theta$. Suppose we were given a non-simple periodic function. Is it possible to express this function as the sum of simple periodic functions? The answer is "yes" and such a process is the subject of *harmonic analysis*. Given a function or wave, the physicist seeks to approximate it as a sum of sines and cosines over a specified interval. That this may be done was proved by Jean-Baptiste-Joseph Fourier (1768–1830), a famous French mathematician and physicist. *Fourier's Theorem* says that, given a "smooth" continuous periodic function f with period 2π, f can be expressed as the infinite series

$$
\begin{aligned}
f(\theta) = a_0 &+ (a_1 \cos \theta + b_1 \sin \theta) \\
&+ (a_2 \cos 2\theta + b_2 \sin 2\theta) \\
&+ (a_3 \cos 3\theta + b_3 \sin 3\theta) \\
&+ \ldots \\
&+ (a_n \cos n\theta + b_n \sin n\theta) + \ldots
\end{aligned}
$$

where the coefficients $a_0, a_1, a_2, \ldots, b_1, b_2, b_3, \ldots$ are real numbers. The theory by which these coefficients are determined is called *harmonic analysis*.

The infinite series given above is known as a *Fourier Series*. Over a specified interval of values of θ, the coefficients may be chosen by harmonic analysis so as to approximate f. The greater the number of terms used in the series, the closer the approximation is to f. Applications of *Fourier Analysis* are found in most branches of modern physics, especially in the analysis of wave motion. It would be well worth your time to read about the life of Fourier in E. T. Bell's *Men of Mathematics*.

EXERCISES

1. Graph each function specified by the equations below for $0 \leq \theta \leq 2\pi$.

a. $y = \sin \theta + \cos \theta$ **d.** $y = -2 + \sin \theta$ **g.** $y = \sin 2\theta + \frac{1}{2} \cos \theta$

b. $y = \sin \theta - \cos \theta$ **e.** $y = \sin 2\theta + 2 \cos \theta$ **h.** $y = \theta - \cos \theta$

c. $y = 2 + \cos \theta$ **f.** $y = \sin 2\theta - \cos \theta$ **i.** $y = \cos \theta + \cos 2\theta + \cos 3\theta$

2. Which sum in Exercise 1 is not periodic?

3. Give the period of each sum specified below.

Example $y = \sin 2\theta + \cos 3\theta$
The points at which $u = \sin 2\theta$ begins to repeat are at π, 2π, 3π, etc. The points at which $v = \cos 3\theta$ begins repeating are at $\frac{2\pi}{3}, \frac{4\pi}{3}, \frac{6\pi}{3} = 2\pi, \frac{8\pi}{3}$, etc. We see then that both u and v begin

to repeat at 2π, 4π, 6π, etc. The period of $y = \sin 2\theta + \cos 3\theta$ is 2π, the least common multiple of $\dfrac{2\pi}{3}$ and π.

a. $y = \sin \theta + \cos \theta$

b. $y = \sin 2\theta + \cos \theta$

c. $y = \sin 2\theta + \cos 2\theta$

d. $y = \sin 3\theta + \cos 2\theta$

e. $y = \sin 5\theta + \cos 3\theta$

f. $y = \sin \pi\theta + \cos \pi\theta$

g. $y = \sin \dfrac{\pi}{2}\theta + \cos 2\pi\theta$

h. $y = \sin \dfrac{2\pi\theta}{3} + \cos \pi\theta$

i. $y = \sin \dfrac{3\pi\theta}{4} + \cos \dfrac{2\pi\theta}{3}$

j. $y = \sin 3\theta + \sin 5\theta + \sin 7\theta$

4. Graph each sum specified by the equations below for one period.

a. $y = \sin \pi\theta + \cos \pi\theta$

b. $y = \sin \pi\theta + \cos 2\pi\theta$

c. $y = \sin \dfrac{\pi\theta}{2} + \cos \dfrac{\pi\theta}{2}$

d. $y = \sin \dfrac{\pi\theta}{2} + \cos \pi\theta$

VOCABULARY

Use each of the following correctly in a sentence to demonstrate that you understand its meaning. If you are not sure of the meaning of any word refer back to the chapter.

circular function
cosine
cycle
Fourier, Joseph
Fourier analysis
Fourier series
Fourier Theorem
frequency
harmonic analysis
identity
interpolation
limit

line value
quadrantal numbers
reduction identity
second quadrant number
sine
variation
wave motion
$n!$
θ, theta
α, alpha
β, beta
ω, omega

REVIEW EXERCISES

1. Determine the value of each of the following:

a. $\cos \dfrac{2\pi}{3}$

b. $\sin \dfrac{5\pi}{6}$

c. $\cos \dfrac{5\pi}{4}$

d. $\sin \dfrac{4\pi}{3}$

e. $\cos \dfrac{11\pi}{6}$

f. $\sin \dfrac{7\pi}{4}$

g. $\cos \dfrac{-5\pi}{6}$

h. $\sin \dfrac{-5\pi}{4}$

i. $\cos \dfrac{13\pi}{6}$

j. $\sin \dfrac{5\pi}{2}$

k. $\cos 5\pi$

l. $\sin (-3\pi)$

2. What is the domain of sine?

3. What is the range of cosine?

4. List five quadrantal numbers.

5. For each of the four intervals, $0 < \theta < \dfrac{\pi}{2}, \dfrac{\pi}{2} < \theta < \pi, \pi < \theta < \dfrac{3\pi}{2}$, and $\dfrac{3\pi}{2} < \theta < 2\pi$, tell whether $\cos \theta$ is positive or negative.

6. Repeat Exercise 5 for $\sin \theta$.

7. Given W such that $W(\theta) = P(x, y)$, cosine is $\{(\theta, x)\}$. Define *sine*.

8. Which of the following are identities?

    a. $a + 2 = 5$

    b. $\cos^2 \theta + \sin^2 \theta = 1$

    c. $\sin \theta = \sin (\theta + \pi)$

    d. $\cos \theta + \sin \theta = 1$

    e. $\cos \theta = \cos (\theta + 2\pi)$

    f. $\cos (-\theta) = \cos \theta$

    g. $\sin \left(\dfrac{\pi}{2} - \theta \right) = \sin \theta$

    h. $\cos \left(\dfrac{\pi}{2} - \theta \right) = \sin \theta$

9. Use Table I and determine each of the following with accuracy to four decimal places. Interpolate for **e** and **f**.

    a. $\sin 1.42$ **c.** $\sin 2.79$ **e.** $\sin 1.342$

    b. $\cos 0.56$ **d.** $\cos 1.82$ **f.** $\cos 0.816$

10. For each equation, determine two values of θ between 0 and 2π which are solutions of the equation. Use Table I and express θ with accuracy to two decimal places.

    a. $\sin \theta \doteq 0.5972$ **c.** $\sin \theta \doteq -0.4078$

    b. $\cos \theta \doteq 0.7452$ **d.** $\cos \theta \doteq -0.2385$

11. For each equation, use Table I and interpolate to determine a first quadrant number θ, with accuracy to three decimal places, which is a solution of the equation.

    a. $\sin \theta \doteq 0.8342$ **b.** $\cos \theta \doteq 0.7139$

12. Given that $\sin \theta = \dfrac{-3}{5}$ and $\pi < \theta < \dfrac{3\pi}{2}$, determine $\cos \theta$.

13. Compute the value of each expression.

    a. $\cos \dfrac{5\pi}{6} \cdot \cos \dfrac{2\pi}{3} + \sin \dfrac{5\pi}{6} \cdot \sin \dfrac{2\pi}{3}$ **c.** $\cos^2 \dfrac{3\pi}{4} - \sin^2 \dfrac{3\pi}{4}$

    b. $\cos^2 \dfrac{7\pi}{6} + \sin^2 \dfrac{7\pi}{6}$ **d.** $1 - 2 \sin^2 \dfrac{-\pi}{6}$

14. Express each of the following in terms of $\cos \theta$, where $0 < \theta < \dfrac{\pi}{2}$.

a. $\cos \dfrac{3\pi}{5}$ **c.** $\cos \dfrac{9\pi}{5}$ **e.** $\cos \dfrac{-4\pi}{5}$

b. $\cos \dfrac{6\pi}{5}$ **d.** $\cos \dfrac{-\pi}{7}$ **f.** $\sin \dfrac{\pi}{7}$

15. Express each of the following in terms of $\sin \theta$, where $0 < \theta < \dfrac{\pi}{2}$.

a. $\sin \dfrac{4\pi}{5}$ **c.** $\sin \dfrac{8\pi}{5}$ **e.** $\sin \dfrac{-6\pi}{5}$

b. $\sin \dfrac{7\pi}{5}$ **d.** $\sin \dfrac{-\pi}{7}$ **f.** $\cos \dfrac{3\pi}{8}$

16. Express each of the following in terms of either $\cos \theta$ or $\sin \theta$. Assume that θ is a first quadrant number.

a. $\cos (\pi + \theta)$ **b.** $\sin (\pi - \theta)$ **c.** $\cos (2\pi - \theta)$

17. Express each of the following in terms of either $\cos \theta$ or $\sin \theta$, where θ is any real number.

a. $\cos (-\theta)$ **b.** $\sin \left(\dfrac{\pi}{2} - \theta \right)$ **c.** $\cos \left(\theta - \dfrac{\pi}{2} \right)$

18. Graph each function for one period.

a. $y = 2 \sin \theta$ **d.** $y = \cos \pi\theta$ **g.** $y = \sin 2\left(\theta + \dfrac{2}{\pi 3} \right)$

b. $y = \cos 2\theta$ **e.** $y = \cos \left(\theta + \dfrac{\pi}{4} \right)$ **h.** $y = \cos \left(3\theta + \dfrac{\pi}{2} \right)$

c. $y = \dfrac{1}{2} \sin \dfrac{1}{2}\theta$ **f.** $y = \sin \left(\theta - \dfrac{\pi}{3} \right)$

19. Describe the variation of $\cos \theta$ as θ increases from 0 to 2π.

20. Repeat Exercise 19 for $\sin \theta$.

21. For each function specified below, give the amplitude, period and phase number.

a. $y = -2 \cos 2\theta$ **c.** $y = \pi \cos \pi(\theta + 3)$

b. $y = \dfrac{2}{3} \sin 4\left(\theta - \dfrac{\pi}{3} \right)$ **d.** $y = \sin \left(2\theta + \dfrac{\pi}{4} \right)$

22. For each wave motion specified below, give (1) the time for one cycle and (2) the frequency. The time t is in seconds.

a. $y = \sin 3\pi t$ **b.** $y = 2 \cos 4\pi t$

23. Graph $y = \sin 3\theta$ and determine the number of solutions for the equation $\sin 3\theta = \dfrac{1}{2}$ in the interval $0 \le \theta < 2\pi$.

24. For what values of θ in the interval $0 \leq \theta < 2\pi$ is it true that $\cos \theta < \frac{1}{2}$?

25. A point moves along a 2-inch segment with simple harmonic motion so that at $t = 0$ seconds, the displacement from the midpoint is zero. The period of the motion is 12 seconds.

    a. What is the displacement from the midpoint at the end of 5 seconds?

    b. What is the displacement from the midpoint at the end of $\frac{1}{3}$ period?

    c. When does the maximum displacement occur?

    d. When does the minimum displacement occur?

    e. What is the frequency of the motion in cycles per minute?

CHAPTER TEST

1. Determine the value of each expression.

    a. $\sin \dfrac{5\pi}{6}$ **c.** $\sin \dfrac{-\pi}{3}$ **e.** $\sin \dfrac{9\pi}{4}$

    b. $\cos \dfrac{3\pi}{4}$ **d.** $\cos \dfrac{-3\pi}{2}$ **f.** $\cos \dfrac{23\pi}{6}$

2. True or false?

    a. There is a real number θ, for which $\cos \theta < 0$ and $\sin \theta > 0$.

    b. $\cos (\pi - 2) = \cos 2$

    c. $\sin 4 = \sin (\pi + 4)$

    d. $\cos \dfrac{-4\pi}{7} = -\cos \dfrac{3\pi}{7}$

    e. $\sin 2 = \cos \left(\dfrac{\pi}{2} - 2 \right)$

    f. $\sin (-5) = \sin 5$

    g. As θ decreases from π to $\dfrac{\pi}{2}$, $\sin \theta$ increases from 0 to 1.

    h. If θ is a quadrantal number, then $\cos \theta$ and $\sin \theta$ are integers.

    i. If θ is a third quadrant number, then $\cos \theta < 0$ and $\sin \theta < 0$.

    j. The phase number of the function specified by $y = 2 \sin \left(3\theta + \dfrac{\pi}{4} \right)$ is $\dfrac{\pi}{4}$.

    k. There are two values of θ between 0 and 2π for which $\cos \theta = -0.43$.

    l. There are two values of θ between 0 and 2π for which $\sin \theta = 1.27$.

3. Given that $\cos \theta = \dfrac{2}{3}$ and $\dfrac{3\pi}{2} < \theta < 2\pi$, determine $\sin \theta$.

4. Compute the value of each expression.

    a. $\cos \dfrac{\pi}{6} \cdot \sin \dfrac{3\pi}{4} + \sin \dfrac{\pi}{6} \cdot \cos \dfrac{3\pi}{4}$ **b.** $1 - 2 \sin^2 \dfrac{2\pi}{3}$

5. Express the following in terms of cos θ, where $0 \leq \theta \leq \frac{\pi}{2}$.

   a. $\cos \frac{9\pi}{8}$ **b.** $\sin \frac{3\pi}{10}$ **c.** $\cos \frac{-3\pi}{7}$

6. Express the following in terms of sin θ, where $0 \leq \theta \leq \frac{\pi}{2}$.

   a. $\sin \frac{3\pi}{5}$ **b.** $\cos \frac{\pi}{8}$ **c.** $\sin \frac{-4\pi}{5}$

7. Describe the variation of sin θ as θ increases from π to $\frac{3\pi}{2}$.

8. For the function specified by each equation, give (1) the amplitude, (2) the period, and (3) the phase number.

   a. $y = -3 \sin 2\left(\theta - \frac{\pi}{6}\right)$ **b.** $y = \frac{1}{2} \cos \left(\frac{1}{2}\theta + \frac{\pi}{4}\right)$

9. Given sin $1.25 \doteq 0.9490$ and sin $1.26 \doteq 0.9521$, interpolate to determine sin 1.257, with accuracy to four decimal places.

10. Graph each equation for one period of the function.

    a. $y = \frac{1}{2} \cos 2\theta$ **b.** $y = -2 \sin \pi\theta$ **c.** $y = 2 \sin 2\left(\theta - \frac{\pi}{4}\right)$

11. Given that $P(x, y)$ moves along a unit circle from $A(1, 0)$ with a constant speed of $\omega = \frac{2\pi}{3}$ units per second. Determine the coordinates of P at the end of 5 seconds.

12. Draw a picture of a unit circle in standard position and plot some point $A = W(\theta)$ such that $\frac{\pi}{2} < \theta < \pi$. Then sketch pictures of $\overline{AB}$ and $\overline{AC}$ which determine the line values of cos θ and sin θ, respectively.

13. Determine the number of solutions for cos $2\theta = \frac{1}{3}$ in the interval $0 \leq \theta < 2\pi$.

14. A simple harmonic motion is described by the equation $d = \sin \frac{\pi}{8}t$. Determine the period and the frequency of the harmonic motion, where t is in seconds.

CHAPTER 4

IDENTITIES AND EQUATIONS FOR REAL NUMBERS

TRIGONOMETRIC IDENTITIES

In this chapter we shall discuss two types of trigonometric equations. One type consists of equations called *identities*. Identity was defined in Chapter Three on page 57. In this definition, we agree that the *permissible values* of the variables are all those real numbers for which each expression in an identity is defined. To indicate an identity, we used the symbol $\equiv$. For example, $(x + 2)^2 \equiv x^2 + 4x + 4$ is an identity since $(x + 2)^2 = x^2 + 4x + 4$ is true for all permissible values of x. Study the following three examples of identities.

Example 1 $x^2 - 1 \equiv (x - 1)(x + 1)$

Each real number is a permissible value of x in this identity, since the expressions $x^2 - 1$ and $(x - 1)(x + 1)$ are defined for every real number x.

Example 2 $\dfrac{x^2 - 4}{x - 2} \equiv x + 2$

The number 2 is not a permissible value of x, since no denominator may have the value 0. Explain why this is so. Thus, the permissible values of x for this identity are all real numbers except 2.

Example 3 $\sqrt{4x} \equiv 2\sqrt{x}$

No negative number is a permissible value of x, since $\sqrt{4x}$ is not defined in the set of real numbers for negative values of x. What kind of numbers does $\sqrt{4x}$ yield for negative values of x?

You can see that not all real numbers are permissible values in some identities. You should develop a habit of stating which real numbers are excluded in the cases of such identities.

Consider the equation $\sin \theta = 1$. It is true for an infinite number of values of θ, namely $\frac{\pi}{2} + 2k\pi$. However this equation is *not* an identity, since there exist permissible values of θ for which $\sin \theta = 1$ is not true. Give one permissible value of θ for which $\sin \theta = 1$ is not true.

One trigonometric identity is a consequence of the definitions of cosine and sine. Recall that for each real number θ, $W(\theta) = P(x, y)$ such that $x^2 + y^2 = 1$. Since $\cos \theta = x$ and $\sin \theta = y$, it follows that

$$\cos^2 \theta + \sin^2 \theta \equiv 1$$

Do you see that each real number is a permissible value of θ in this identity? This identity is important enough to memorize at this time. You will find many opportunities to recognize and use this identity in your work.

FUNDAMENTAL IDENTITY

We shall now derive a very powerful trigonometric identity from which many other trigonometric identities will follow. Consider the unit circle of Figure 4–1. For any two real numbers θ and α such that $W(\theta) \neq W(\alpha)$, let $W(0) = A(1, 0)$, $W(\theta) = D(x_1, y_1)$, $W(\alpha) = B(x_2, y_2)$ and $W(\theta - \alpha) = C(x_3, y_3)$. By the definitions of cosine and sine, each of the following is true. Check each equation in relation to Figure 4–1.

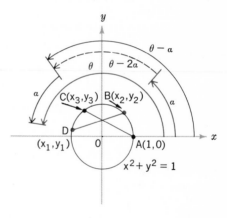

FIGURE 4-1

$$x_1 = \cos \theta \qquad y_1 = \sin \theta$$
$$x_2 = \cos \alpha \qquad y_2 = \sin \alpha$$
$$x_3 = \cos (\theta - \alpha) \quad y_3 = \sin (\theta - \alpha)$$
$$1 = \cos 0 \qquad 0 = \sin 0$$

Now study the following proof and justify each step. Refer to Figure 4–1. Since the length of $\overset{\frown}{ABC}$ = length of $\overset{\frown}{DCB}$, we know the length of $\overline{AC}$ = length of $\overline{DB}$; that is, $AC = DB$.

Now, using the Distance Formula, we obtain the following:

$$\sqrt{(x_3 - 1)^2 + (y_3 - 0)^2} = \sqrt{(x_1 - x_2)^2 + (y_1 - y_2)^2}$$
$$x_3^2 - 2x_3 + 1 + y_3^2 = x_1^2 - 2x_1x_2 + x_2^2 + y_1^2 - 2y_1y_2 + y_2^2$$
$$(x_3^2 + y_3^2) + 1 - 2x_3 = (x_1^2 + y_1^2) + (x_2^2 + y_2^2) - 2x_1x_2 - 2y_1y_2$$
$$1 + 1 - 2x_3 = 1 + 1 - 2x_1x_2 - 2y_1y_2$$
$$x_3 = x_1x_2 + y_1y_2$$
$$\cos (\theta - \alpha) \equiv \cos \theta \cdot \cos \alpha + \sin \theta \cdot \sin \alpha$$

The last equation is an identity. Its proof was independent of the picture, which served only to organize the procedure. Figure 4–1 showed θ and α as positive numbers with $\theta > 2\alpha$. But because of the generality of the Distance Formula, these restrictions do not need to be imposed on θ and α. This proof, however, did not cover the case for θ and α in which $W(\theta) = W(\alpha)$. Prove that this identity is also true in the case of $W(\theta) = W(\alpha)$.

The identity which we have just proved is called the *Fundamental Identity*. It will be used to prove other identities and should be committed to memory at this time.

FUNDAMENTAL IDENTITY

$$\cos(\theta - \alpha) \equiv \cos\theta \cdot \cos\alpha + \sin\theta \cdot \sin\alpha$$

The *Fundamental Identity* has many applications. Two of these are illustrated in the following examples.

Example 1   Determine $\cos\dfrac{\pi}{12}$.

Solution   Since we know the sine and the cosine of $\dfrac{\pi}{4}$ and of $\dfrac{\pi}{6}$, we use the following equation.

$$\cos\left(\frac{\pi}{12}\right) = \cos\left(\frac{\pi}{4} - \frac{\pi}{6}\right) \qquad \left[\frac{\pi}{12} = \frac{3\pi}{12} - \frac{2\pi}{12} = \frac{\pi}{4} - \frac{\pi}{6}\right]$$

$$= \cos\frac{\pi}{4} \cdot \cos\frac{\pi}{6} + \sin\frac{\pi}{4} \cdot \sin\frac{\pi}{6} \quad \text{[Fundamental Identity]}$$

$$= \frac{1}{\sqrt{2}} \cdot \frac{\sqrt{3}}{2} + \frac{1}{\sqrt{2}} \cdot \frac{1}{2} = \frac{\sqrt{3}+1}{2\sqrt{2}} = \frac{\sqrt{6}+\sqrt{2}}{4}$$

Example 2   Prove that $\cos\left(\dfrac{3\pi}{2} - \theta\right) \equiv -\sin\theta$.

$$\cos\left(\frac{3\pi}{2} - \theta\right) \equiv \cos\frac{3\pi}{2} \cdot \cos\theta + \sin\frac{3\pi}{2} \cdot \sin\theta \qquad \text{Why?}$$

$$\equiv 0 \cdot \cos\theta + (-1) \cdot \sin\theta \equiv -\sin\theta$$

SEVEN TRIGONOMETRIC IDENTITIES

We have said that the Fundamental Identity can lead to other identities. We shall now derive seven identities and show some of their applications. Study the derivations carefully and be prepared to justify each step.

1. In the Fundamental Identity, let $\theta = 0$ and then simplify the result.

$$\cos(0 - \alpha) \equiv \cos 0 \cdot \cos\alpha + \sin 0 \cdot \sin\alpha$$
$$\cos(-\alpha) \equiv 1 \cdot \cos\alpha + 0 \cdot \sin\alpha$$
$$\cos(-\alpha) \equiv \cos\alpha$$

You will recognize this identity as one of the symmetry relations of Chapter 3. Is $\cos(-3\theta - 4) = \cos(3\theta + 4)$ true for all θ? Why or why not?

2. In the Fundamental Identity, let $\theta = \frac{\pi}{2}$ and then simplify the result.

$$\cos\left(\frac{\pi}{2} - \alpha\right) \equiv \cos\frac{\pi}{2} \cdot \cos\alpha + \sin\frac{\pi}{2} \cdot \sin\alpha$$
$$\equiv 0 \cdot \cos\alpha + 1 \cdot \sin\alpha$$
$$\cos\left(\frac{\pi}{2} - \alpha\right) \equiv \sin\alpha$$

This identity is a $\frac{\pi}{2}$-*sum relation*, which was introduced earlier. It has now been proved for all real numbers α. Is $\cos(\pi - 3\theta) = \sin\left(3\theta - \frac{\pi}{2}\right)$ true for all θ?

3. Apply the symmetric property of equality to the previous identity, let $\alpha = \frac{\pi}{2} - \theta$, and simplify.

$$\sin\alpha \equiv \cos\left(\frac{\pi}{2} - \alpha\right)$$
$$\sin\left(\frac{\pi}{2} - \theta\right) \equiv \cos\left[\frac{\pi}{2} - \left(\frac{\pi}{2} - \theta\right)\right]$$
$$\sin\left(\frac{\pi}{2} - \theta\right) \equiv \cos\theta$$

Thus, we have established another $\frac{\pi}{2}$-sum relation.

4. In the identity $\sin\alpha \equiv \cos\left(\frac{\pi}{2} - \alpha\right)$, let $\alpha = -\theta$ and simplify the result.

$$\sin(-\theta) \equiv \cos\left[\frac{\pi}{2} - (-\theta)\right]$$
$$\equiv \cos\left(\frac{\pi}{2} + \theta\right)$$
$$\equiv \cos\left(\frac{-\pi}{2} - \theta\right) \qquad \text{Why?}$$
$$\equiv \cos\frac{-\pi}{2} \cdot \cos\theta + \sin\frac{-\pi}{2} \cdot \sin\theta \qquad \text{Why?}$$
$$\equiv 0 \cdot \cos\theta + (-1) \cdot \sin\theta$$

Hence, $\sin(-\theta) \equiv -\sin\theta$.

This establishes another symmetry relation as an identity.

Is $\sin\left(\frac{\pi}{6} - \alpha\right) = \sin\left(\alpha - \frac{\pi}{6}\right)$ an identity? Why or why not?

Is $\sin(3\alpha - 5) = -\sin(5 - 3\alpha)$ an identity? Why or why not?

5. In the Fundamental Identity, let $\alpha = -\beta$ and simplify the result.

$$\cos[\theta - (-\beta)] \equiv \cos\theta \cdot \cos(-\beta) + \sin\theta \cdot \sin(-\beta)$$
$$\cos(\theta + \beta) \equiv \cos\theta \cdot \cos\beta - \sin\theta \cdot \sin\beta \qquad \text{Why?}$$

Use this identity for cos $(\theta + \beta)$ to expand and simplify cos $\left(\dfrac{3\pi}{2} + \theta\right)$.

6. In the $\dfrac{\pi}{2}$-sum relation, sin $\beta \equiv$ cos $\left(\dfrac{\pi}{2} - \beta\right)$, let $\beta = \theta + \alpha$ and simplify the result.

$$\sin (\theta + \alpha) \equiv \cos \left[\frac{\pi}{2} - (\theta + \alpha)\right]$$

$$\equiv \cos \left[\left(\frac{\pi}{2} - \theta\right) - \alpha\right]$$

$$\equiv \cos \left(\frac{\pi}{2} - \theta\right) \cdot \cos \alpha + \sin \left(\frac{\pi}{2} - \theta\right) \cdot \sin \alpha$$

Hence, sin $(\theta + \alpha) \equiv$ sin $\theta \cdot$ cos $\alpha +$ cos $\theta \cdot$ sin α Why?

This identity may be used to simplify an expression such as sin $3t \cdot$ cos $2v$ + cos $3t \cdot$ sin $2v$ to the equivalent expression sin $(3t + 2v)$. Simplify sin $2\theta \cdot$ cos 3θ + cos $2\theta \cdot$ sin 3θ.

7. In the previous identity, let $\alpha = -\beta$ and simplify.

$$\sin [\theta + (-\beta)] \equiv \sin \theta \cdot \cos (-\beta) + \cos \theta \cdot \sin (-\beta)$$
Thus, sin $(\theta - \beta) \equiv$ sin $\theta \cdot$ cos $\beta -$ cos $\theta \cdot$ sin β Why?

At this point we list, for easy reference, nine identities which have been established so far.

$\cos^2 \theta + \sin^2 \theta \equiv 1$	[4.1]
$\cos (-\theta) \equiv \cos \theta$	[4.2]
$\sin (-\theta) \equiv -\sin \theta$	[4.3]
$\cos \left(\dfrac{\pi}{2} - \theta\right) \equiv \sin \theta$	[4.4]
$\sin \left(\dfrac{\pi}{2} - \theta\right) \equiv \cos \theta$	[4.5]
$\cos (\theta - \alpha) \equiv \cos \theta \cdot \cos \alpha + \sin \theta \cdot \sin \alpha$	[4.6]
$\cos (\theta + \alpha) \equiv \cos \theta \cdot \cos \alpha - \sin \theta \cdot \sin \alpha$	[4.7]
$\sin (\theta + \alpha) \equiv \sin \theta \cdot \cos \alpha + \cos \theta \cdot \sin \alpha$	[4.8]
$\sin (\theta - \alpha) \equiv \sin \theta \cdot \cos \alpha - \cos \theta \cdot \sin \alpha$	[4.9]

Identity 4.1 is easily recalled from the equation of the unit circle. Identities 4.2 and 4.3 are best recalled through symmetry with respect to the x-axis as shown in Chapter 3. Identities 4.4 and 4.5 are the $\dfrac{\pi}{2}$-sum relations and you need only to recall that, if $\alpha + \beta = \dfrac{\pi}{2}$, then cos $\alpha =$ sin β. The last four identities can be recalled by observing the scheme:

$$\cos (\theta \pm \alpha) \equiv \cos \theta \cdot \cos \alpha \mp \sin \theta \cdot \sin \alpha$$
$$\sin (\theta \pm \alpha) \equiv \sin \theta \cdot \cos \alpha \pm \cos \theta \cdot \sin \alpha$$

EXERCISES

1. The following reduction identities were given in Chapter 3 for certain values of θ. Prove that these identities are true for all values of α.

   a. $\cos(\pi - \alpha) \equiv -\cos\alpha$
   Hint: Begin with identity [4.6] and let $\theta = \pi$.

   b. $\sin(\pi - \alpha) \equiv \sin\alpha$

   c. $\cos(\pi + \alpha) \equiv -\cos\alpha$

   d. $\sin(\pi + \alpha) \equiv -\sin\alpha$

   e. $\cos(2\pi - \alpha) \equiv \cos\alpha$

   f. $\sin(2\pi - \alpha) \equiv -\sin\alpha$

   g. $\cos(\alpha - \pi) \equiv -\cos\alpha$

   h. $\sin(\alpha - \pi) \equiv -\sin\alpha$

2. Given $\sin\theta = \dfrac{-2}{3}$ and $\pi < \theta < \dfrac{3\pi}{2}$; $\cos\alpha = \dfrac{1}{4}$ and $\dfrac{3\pi}{2} < \alpha < 2\pi$.
   Determine each of the following.

   a. $\cos\theta$ *Hint:* Use [4.1]

   b. $\sin\alpha$

   c. $\cos(\theta - \alpha)$

   d. $\cos(\theta + \alpha)$

   e. $\sin(\theta + \alpha)$

   f. $\sin(\theta - \alpha)$

3. Use identities [4.2] and [4.3] to simplify each of the following.

   a. $\dfrac{\sin(-\theta)}{\cos(-\theta)}$

   b. $\dfrac{-\sin(-\theta)}{\cos\theta}$

   c. $\dfrac{-\sin(-\theta)}{-\cos(-\theta)}$

   d. $\cos(-7 - \theta)$

   e. $\sin(-2\theta - 5)$

   f. $-\sin(3 - \theta)$

4. Simplify, using appropriate identities.

   a. $\cos^2 3\theta + \sin^2 3\theta$

   b. $\sin\left(\dfrac{\pi}{2} - 5\theta\right)$

   c. $\cos\left(\dfrac{\pi}{2} - 3\theta\right)$

   d. $\sin\left(\dfrac{\pi}{2} + 2\theta\right)$

   e. $\cos 3\theta \cdot \cos 2\alpha + \sin 3\theta \cdot \sin 2\alpha$

   f. $\sin 5\theta \cdot \cos 4\alpha + \cos 5\theta \cdot \sin 4\alpha$

   g. $\cos 8\theta \cdot \cos 3\theta - \sin 8\theta \cdot \sin 3\theta$

   h. $\sin 2\theta \cdot \cos\theta - \cos 2\theta \cdot \sin\theta$

   i. $\cos\left(\theta - \dfrac{\pi}{2}\right)$

   j. $\sin\left(\theta - \dfrac{\pi}{2}\right)$

   k. $\cos\left(\dfrac{\pi}{2} + \theta\right)$

   l. $\sin\left(\dfrac{\pi}{2} + \theta\right)$

   m. $\dfrac{\sin(-\theta)}{-\cos\theta} \cdot \dfrac{\cos(\pi + \theta)}{\sin(\pi - \theta)}$

   n. $\dfrac{\sin(\pi + \theta)}{\cos(\theta - \pi)} \cdot \dfrac{\cos(-\theta)}{\sin(\theta - \pi)}$

   o. $\sin(\theta + \alpha) + \sin(\theta - \alpha)$

   p. $\cos(\theta + \alpha) + \cos(\theta - \alpha)$

   q. $\sin\dfrac{2\theta}{7} \cdot \cos\dfrac{5\theta}{7} + \cos\dfrac{2\theta}{7} \cdot \sin\dfrac{5\theta}{7}$

   r. $\sin(\theta + \alpha) - \sin(\theta - \alpha)$

   s. $\cos(\theta - \alpha) - \cos(\theta + \alpha)$

5. Compute each of the following.

Example   Compute $\cos \dfrac{13\pi}{12}$.

Solution $\cos \dfrac{13\pi}{12} = \cos \left(\dfrac{9\pi}{12} + \dfrac{4\pi}{12}\right) = \cos \left(\dfrac{3\pi}{4} + \dfrac{\pi}{3}\right)$

$$= \cos \dfrac{3\pi}{4} \cdot \cos \dfrac{\pi}{3} - \sin \dfrac{3\pi}{4} \cdot \sin \dfrac{\pi}{3}$$

$$= \dfrac{-1}{\sqrt{2}} \cdot \dfrac{1}{2} - \dfrac{1}{\sqrt{2}} \cdot \dfrac{\sqrt{3}}{2}$$

$$= \dfrac{-1 - \sqrt{3}}{2\sqrt{2}} = \dfrac{-\sqrt{2} - \sqrt{6}}{4}$$

a. $\sin \dfrac{5\pi}{12}$ **c.** $\cos \dfrac{11\pi}{12}$ **e.** $\sin \dfrac{19\pi}{12}$

b. $\cos \dfrac{\pi}{12}$ **d.** $\cos \dfrac{17\pi}{12}$ **f.** $\cos \dfrac{23\pi}{12}$

6. Prove that each of the following equations is not an identity by supplying a value(s) of the variable(s) for which the resulting statement is false.

a. $(m + n)^2 = m^2 + n^2$

b. $\cos (\theta + \alpha) = \cos \theta + \cos \alpha$

c. $\cos \theta = -1$

d. $\cos \left(\dfrac{\pi}{2} + \theta\right) = \sin \theta$

e. $\dfrac{\sin (-\theta)}{-\cos \theta} = \dfrac{-\sin \theta}{\cos (-\theta)}$

7. For each expression, state which real numbers are not permissible values of θ.

a. $\dfrac{\cos \theta}{\sin \theta}$ **c.** $\dfrac{\cos \theta}{1 - \sin \theta}$ **e.** $\dfrac{2}{\sin \theta \cdot \cos \theta}$

b. $\dfrac{2}{\cos \theta}$ **d.** $\dfrac{\sin \theta}{\cos \theta} + \dfrac{3}{1 - \cos \theta}$ **f.** $\dfrac{\cos \theta}{\sin \theta \, (1 - \sin \theta)}$

8. Use identity [4.8] to determine $\sin (\theta + \alpha)$ for each set of conditions.

a. $\sin \theta = \dfrac{2}{3}$ and $\dfrac{\pi}{2} < \theta < \pi$; $\cos \alpha = \dfrac{-1}{3}$ and $\pi < \alpha < \dfrac{3\pi}{2}$

b. $\cos \theta = 0.6$ and $\dfrac{3\pi}{2} < \theta < 2\pi$; $\cos \alpha = -0.8$ and $\dfrac{\pi}{2} < \alpha < \pi$

9. Express $\sin 2\theta$ in terms of $\sin \theta$ and $\cos \theta$. Begin with $\sin 2\theta \equiv \sin (\theta + \theta)$.

10. Express $\cos 2\theta$ in terms of $\sin \theta$ and $\cos \theta$. *Hint:* $\cos 2\theta \equiv \cos (\theta + \theta)$.

11. Express $\cos 2\theta$ in terms of $\sin \theta$. *Hint:* Use the result of Exercise 10 and identity [4.1].

12. Express $\cos 2\theta$ in terms of $\cos \theta$.

OPERATIONS ON TRIGONOMETRIC EXPRESSIONS

In algebra courses you have learned to determine pairs of equivalent expressions such as the following. Verify the equivalence of each pair of expressions.

$$\frac{m}{3t} + \frac{c}{d} \text{ and } \frac{md + 3ct}{3td}$$

$$a + \frac{b}{c} \text{ and } \frac{ac + b}{c}$$

$$\frac{a}{bc} + \frac{n}{c} \text{ and } \frac{a + bn}{bc}$$

$$a\left(1 + \frac{b}{a}\right) \text{ and } a + b$$

$$2(3x \cdot y) \cdot x \text{ and } 6x^2y$$

$$(x - m)(x + m) \text{ and } x^2 - m^2$$

You also learned to factor expressions such as the following. Verify the factoring in each.

$3x^2 - x$	obtaining	$x(3x - 1)$
$x^2 - y^2$	obtaining	$(x + y)(x - y)$
$x^2 - 7x + 12$	obtaining	$(x - 3)(x - 4)$
$4x^3 - x$	obtaining	$x(2x + 1)(2x - 1)$
$2c^2 + 7c - 4$	obtaining	$(2c - 1)(c + 4)$

Similar operations are often performed on expressions containing trigonometric functions. Study the following examples and notice the similarity to the algebraic expressions above.

Example 1   SHOWING A SUM AS ONE FRACTIONAL EXPRESSION

a. $\dfrac{3}{\sin \theta} + \dfrac{2}{\cos \theta} \equiv \dfrac{3 \cos \theta + 2 \sin \theta}{\sin \theta \cdot \cos \theta}$

b. $\sin \theta + \dfrac{a}{\cos \theta} \equiv \dfrac{\sin \theta \cdot \cos \theta + a}{\cos \theta}$

c. $\dfrac{a}{\sin \theta} + \dfrac{c}{\sin \theta \cdot \cos \theta} \equiv \dfrac{a \cos \theta + c}{\sin \theta \cdot \cos \theta}$

Example 2   EXPANDING PRODUCTS

a. $5(\sin \theta \cdot \cos \theta) \cdot \sin \theta \equiv 5 \sin^2 \theta \cdot \cos \theta$

b. $\sin \theta\left(1 + \dfrac{\cos \theta}{\sin \theta}\right) \equiv \sin \theta + \cos \theta$

c. $(2 - \sin \theta)(3 + \sin \theta) \equiv 6 - \sin \theta - \sin^2 \theta$

Example 3   FACTORING EXPRESSIONS

a. $2 \cos^2 \theta - \cos \theta \equiv \cos \theta(2 \cos \theta - 1)$

b. $2 \sin^2 \theta + 7 \sin \theta - 4 \equiv (2 \sin \theta - 1)(\sin \theta + 4)$

c. $4 \sin^2 \theta - 1 \equiv (2 \sin \theta + 1)(2 \sin \theta - 1)$

d. $9 \cos^3 \theta - \cos \theta \equiv \cos \theta(3 \cos \theta + 1)(3 \cos \theta - 1)$

EXERCISES

1. Show each of the following as one fractional expression.

a. $\dfrac{2 + \sin \theta}{\cos \theta} + \dfrac{3}{\sin \theta}$

c. $\dfrac{1}{\sin \theta \cdot \cos \theta} + \dfrac{3}{2 \sin \theta}$

b. $\sin \theta + \dfrac{\cos \theta}{\sin \theta}$

d. $\dfrac{\sin \theta}{1 - \cos \theta} + \dfrac{2}{1 + \cos \theta}$

2. Factor each expression.

a. $\cos \theta - \cos \theta \cdot \sin \theta$

d. $\cos^2 \theta - 3 \cos \theta \cdot \sin \theta$

b. $\sin^2 \theta - 7 \sin \theta + 12$

e. $\cos^3 \theta + \sin^2 \theta \cdot \cos \theta$

c. $\cos^4 \theta - \sin^4 \theta$

f. $2 \cos^2 \theta + \cos \theta - 1$

3. Expand each product.

a. $\sin \theta \left(\sin \theta - \dfrac{2}{\sin \theta} \right)$

e. $(2 + \sin \theta)(3 - \sin \theta)$

b. $3 \sin \theta \, (2 \cos \theta \cdot \sin \theta)$

f. $(\sin \theta + \cos \theta)^2$

c. $3 \sin \theta \, (2 \cos \theta + \sin \theta)$

g. $(1 - \cos^2 \theta)^2$

d. $(1 - \cos \theta)(1 + \cos \theta)$

h. $4(1 - \cos \theta) \cdot \sin \theta$

PROVING TRIGONOMETRIC IDENTITIES

Given a trigonometric expression, such as $\cos \theta + \dfrac{\sin^2 \theta}{\cos \theta}$, it can be simplified by using the techniques of algebra and the identities of trigonometry. Observe that the numbers $\dfrac{\pi}{2} + k\pi$, for all integers k, are not permissible values of θ in this expression. Explain. Study the following development.

$$\cos \theta + \frac{\sin^2 \theta}{\cos \theta} \equiv \frac{\cos \theta}{1} + \frac{\sin^2 \theta}{\cos \theta}$$

$$\equiv \frac{\cos^2 \theta + \sin^2 \theta}{\cos \theta}$$

$$\equiv \frac{1}{\cos \theta}$$

Thus, if asked to simplify $\cos \theta + \dfrac{\sin^2 \theta}{\cos \theta}$, we obtain the result $\dfrac{1}{\cos \theta}$, remembering that $\dfrac{\pi}{2} + k\pi$ are not permissible values of θ.

To *prove an identity* means to prove that an equation is true for all permissible values of the variables. Study the following examples in which some identities are proved.

Example 1   Prove the identity $\dfrac{1 + \cos \theta}{\sin \theta} + \dfrac{\sin \theta}{\cos \theta} \equiv \dfrac{\cos \theta + 1}{\sin \theta \cdot \cos \theta}$

Proof
$$\frac{1 + \cos \theta}{\sin \theta} + \frac{\sin \theta}{\cos \theta} \equiv \frac{(1 + \cos \theta)\cos \theta}{\sin \theta \cdot \cos \theta} + \frac{\sin \theta \cdot \sin \theta}{\cos \theta \cdot \sin \theta}$$

$$\equiv \frac{\cos \theta + \cos^2 \theta + \sin^2 \theta}{\sin \theta \cdot \cos \theta}$$

$$\equiv \frac{\cos \theta + 1}{\sin \theta \cdot \cos \theta}$$

Did you remember to check what values of θ are not permissible?
Notice that above we have proved an identity in the form $A \equiv D$, by proving
$A \equiv B$, $B \equiv C$ and $C \equiv D$. The work was arranged in the form

$$A \equiv B$$
$$\equiv C$$
$$\equiv D$$

Example 2   Prove the identity $\dfrac{1}{\sin \theta \cdot \cos \theta} - \dfrac{\cos \theta}{\sin \theta} \equiv \dfrac{\sin \theta}{1 - \sin^2 \theta} \cdot \cos \theta.$

Proof
$$\frac{1}{\sin \theta \cdot \cos \theta} - \frac{\cos \theta}{\sin \theta} \equiv \frac{\sin \theta}{1 - \sin^2 \theta} \cdot \cos \theta$$

$$\frac{1}{\sin \theta \cdot \cos \theta} - \frac{\cos \theta \cdot \cos \theta}{\sin \theta \cdot \cos \theta} \equiv \frac{\sin \theta}{1 - \sin^2 \theta} \cdot \frac{\cos \theta}{1}$$

$$\frac{1 - \cos^2 \theta}{\sin \theta \cdot \cos \theta} \equiv \frac{\sin \theta \cdot \cos \theta}{\cos^2 \theta}$$

$$\frac{\sin^2 \theta}{\sin \theta \cdot \cos \theta} \equiv \frac{\sin \theta \cdot \cos \theta}{\cos^2 \theta}$$

$$\frac{\sin \theta}{\cos \theta} \equiv \frac{\sin \theta}{\cos \theta}$$

Notice that here we proved an identity in the form $K \equiv L$ by proving $K \equiv M$
and $L \equiv M$. The work was arranged in the form

$$K \equiv L$$
$$\downarrow \;\; \equiv \;\; \downarrow$$
$$M \equiv M$$

Either of the methods shown in Examples 1 and 2 may be used since both are
based on properties of equality. You are cautioned not to use equation properties
which create expressions that are not equivalent to the members of the identity
being proved. For example, in proving the identity

$$\frac{1 - \cos^2 \theta}{\sin \theta} \equiv \sin \theta$$

you should *not* multiply both members by $\sin \theta$ to obtain

$$1 - \cos^2 \theta \equiv \sin^2 \theta$$

since the last identity is also true for values which are not permissible in
$\dfrac{1 - \cos^2 \theta}{\sin \theta}$, namely $\theta = 0, \pi, -\pi, 2\pi, -2\pi, 3\pi, \ldots$

Example 3   Prove the identity
$$2 \sin^4 \theta - \sin^2 \theta \cdot \cos^2 \theta - 3 \cos^4 \theta \equiv 2 - 5 \cos^2 \theta.$$

Proof $2 \sin^4 \theta - \sin^2 \theta \cdot \cos^2 \theta - 3 \cos^4 \theta$

$\equiv (\sin^2 \theta + \cos^2 \theta)(2 \sin^2 \theta - 3 \cos^2 \theta)$ [Factoring]

$\equiv 1 \cdot [2(1 - \cos^2 \theta) - 3 \cos^2 \theta]$ $[\sin^2 \theta + \cos^2 \theta \equiv 1;$
$\qquad \qquad \qquad \qquad \qquad \qquad \qquad \qquad \sin^2 \theta \equiv 1 - \cos^2 \theta]$

$\equiv 2 - 2 \cos^2 \theta - 3 \cos^2 \theta$

$\equiv 2 - 5 \cos^2 \theta$

Observe that the skills of adding rational forms, of factoring, and of recognizing the best identity to employ were necessary in proving the identities above.

EXERCISES

1. Simplify each expression. In each case, state which real numbers are not permissible values of θ.

   a. $\dfrac{\sin \theta}{\cos \theta} + \dfrac{\cos \theta}{\sin \theta}$

   b. $\sin \theta + \dfrac{\cos^2 \theta}{\sin \theta}$

   c. $\dfrac{1 - \sin^2 \theta}{\sin \theta} \cdot \dfrac{1}{\cos \theta}$

   d. $\sin \theta \left(\sin \theta - \dfrac{1}{\sin \theta} \right)$

   e. $\dfrac{1}{\sin \theta \cdot \cos \theta} - \dfrac{\cos \theta}{\sin \theta}$

   f. $\cos \theta \left(\dfrac{1}{\cos \theta} - \cos \theta \right)$

   g. $\dfrac{\sin \theta}{\cos \theta} \cdot \dfrac{1 + \dfrac{\cos \theta}{\sin \theta}}{1 + \dfrac{\sin \theta}{\cos \theta}}$

   h. $(1 - \cos \theta)\left(\dfrac{1 + \cos \theta}{\sin \theta} \right)$

   i. $\dfrac{\sin \theta}{1 + \cos \theta} + \dfrac{\sin \theta}{1 - \cos \theta}$

   j. $\sin^4 \theta - \sin^2 \theta \cdot \cos^2 \theta - 2 \cos^4 \theta$

   k. $\dfrac{2 \cos^2 \theta - \sin^2 \theta + 1}{\cos \theta}$

   l. $\cos^3 \theta + \sin^2 \theta \cdot \cos \theta$

2. Prove each identity.

   a. $(1 - \sin \theta)(1 + \sin \theta) \equiv \cos^2 \theta$

   b. $(\cos \theta + \sin \theta)^2 \equiv 1 + 2 \sin \theta \cdot \cos \theta$

   c. $\cos^4 \theta - \sin^4 \theta \equiv \cos^2 \theta - \sin^2 \theta$

   d. $\dfrac{1 + \sin \theta}{\cos \theta} + \dfrac{\cos \theta}{\sin \theta} \equiv \dfrac{1 + \sin \theta}{\cos \theta \cdot \sin \theta}$

   e. $\dfrac{\sin^2 \theta}{\cos \theta} + \cos \theta \equiv \dfrac{1}{\cos \theta}$

   f. $\sin \theta \left(\dfrac{1}{\sin \theta} - \sin \theta \right) \equiv \cos^2 \theta$

   g. $\sin^4 \theta - 2 \sin^2 \theta \cdot \cos^2 \theta - 3 \cos^4 \theta$
   $\equiv 1 - 4 \cos^2 \theta$

   h. $\dfrac{2 \sin^2 \theta - \cos^2 \theta + 1}{\sin \theta} \equiv 3 \sin \theta$

   i. $1 - 2 \cos^2 \theta + \cos^4 \theta \equiv \sin^4 \theta$

   j. $\dfrac{\sin \theta}{1 - \cos \theta} - \dfrac{\cos \theta}{\sin \theta} \equiv \dfrac{1}{\sin \theta}$

   k. $\dfrac{1}{\sin^2 \theta} + \dfrac{1}{\cos^2 \theta} \equiv \dfrac{1}{\sin^2 \theta} \cdot \dfrac{1}{\cos^2 \theta}$

   l. $\dfrac{1}{\cos^2 \theta} + 1 + \dfrac{\sin^2 \theta}{\cos^2 \theta} \equiv \dfrac{2}{\cos^2 \theta}$

   m. $\cos (\pi - \theta) \equiv \cos (\pi + \theta)$

IDENTITIES INVOLVING 2θ OR $\frac{\theta}{2}$

Identities which express $\sin 2\theta$, $\cos 2\theta$, $\sin \frac{\theta}{2}$ and $\cos \frac{\theta}{2}$ in terms of $\cos \theta$ and $\sin \theta$ may be derived from identities proved earlier. In identity 4.8 let $\alpha = \theta$. Then,

$$\sin (\theta + \alpha) \equiv \sin \theta \cdot \cos \alpha + \cos \theta \cdot \sin \alpha$$

becomes $\sin (\theta + \theta) \equiv \sin \theta \cdot \cos \theta + \cos \theta \cdot \sin \theta$

Thus,

$$\sin 2\theta \equiv 2 \sin \theta \cdot \cos \theta \qquad [4.10]$$

In a similar manner, in identity 4.7, let $\alpha = \theta$. Then,

$$\cos (\theta + \alpha) \equiv \cos \theta \cos \alpha - \sin \theta \sin \alpha$$

becomes $\cos (\theta + \theta) \equiv \cos \theta \cos \theta - \sin \theta \sin \theta$

Thus,

$$\cos 2\theta \equiv \cos^2 \theta - \sin^2 \theta \qquad [4.11]$$

Since $\cos^2 \theta + \sin^2 \theta \equiv 1$, it follows that $\sin^2 \theta \equiv 1 - \cos^2 \theta$ and $\cos^2 \theta \equiv 1 - \sin^2 \theta$. By making appropriate substitutions in $\cos 2\theta \equiv \cos^2 \theta - \sin^2 \theta$, we obtain two more identities for $\cos 2\theta$.

$$\cos 2\theta \equiv 2 \cos^2 \theta - 1 \qquad [4.12]$$
$$\cos 2\theta \equiv 1 - 2 \sin^2 \theta \qquad [4.13]$$

The identity for $\cos \frac{\theta}{2}$ is derived from the identity $\cos 2\alpha \equiv 2 \cos^2 \alpha - 1$. Solving for $\cos^2 \alpha$,

$$2 \cos^2 \alpha \equiv 1 + \cos 2\alpha$$
$$\cos^2 \alpha \equiv \frac{1 + \cos 2\alpha}{2}$$

Let $\alpha = \frac{\theta}{2}$. Then, $\cos^2 \frac{\theta}{2} \equiv \frac{1 + \cos \theta}{2}$. Solving for $\cos \frac{\theta}{2}$,

$$\cos \frac{\theta}{2} \equiv \sqrt{\frac{1 + \cos \theta}{2}}, \text{ for } \cos \frac{\theta}{2} \geq 0 \qquad \text{and} \qquad [4.14]$$

$$\cos \frac{\theta}{2} \equiv -\sqrt{\frac{1 + \cos \theta}{2}}, \text{ for } \cos \frac{\theta}{2} < 0$$

Is $\frac{1 + \cos \theta}{2}$ negative for some value of θ? Is $\sqrt{\frac{1 + \cos \theta}{2}}$ a real number for each value of θ?

In a similar manner, the identity for $\sin \frac{\theta}{2}$ is derived from the identity $\cos 2\alpha \equiv 1 - 2 \sin^2 \alpha$. You will be asked to derive this in the exercises. Here we state the final results.

$$\sin \frac{\theta}{2} \equiv \sqrt{\frac{1 - \cos \theta}{2}}, \text{ for } \sin \frac{\theta}{2} \geq 0 \qquad \text{and} \qquad [4.15]$$

$$\sin \frac{\theta}{2} \equiv -\sqrt{\frac{1 - \cos \theta}{2}}, \text{ for } \sin \frac{\theta}{2} < 0$$

The identities derived in this section are listed and numbered below.

$$\sin 2\theta \equiv 2 \sin \theta \cdot \cos \theta \qquad\qquad [4.10]$$
$$\cos 2\theta \equiv \cos^2 \theta - \sin^2 \theta \qquad\qquad [4.11]$$
$$\cos 2\theta \equiv 2 \cos^2 \theta - 1 \qquad\qquad [4.12]$$
$$\cos 2\theta \equiv 1 - 2 \sin^2 \theta \qquad\qquad [4.13]$$
$$\cos \frac{\theta}{2} \equiv \pm\sqrt{\frac{1 + \cos \theta}{2}} \qquad\qquad [4.14]$$
$$\sin \frac{\theta}{2} \equiv \pm\sqrt{\frac{1 - \cos \theta}{2}} \qquad\qquad [4.15]$$

In identities [4.14] and [4.15], the value of the right-hand member is chosen to be positive, negative, or zero to agree with the left-hand member. This is indicated by the symbol $\pm$, which means that a choice is to be made.

The identities above may be used to prove other identities. Study the example.

Example   Prove the identity $\dfrac{\sin 2\theta}{1 + \cos 2\theta} \equiv \dfrac{\sin \theta}{\cos \theta}$.

Proof
$$\frac{\sin 2\theta}{1 + \cos 2\theta} \equiv \frac{2 \sin \theta \cdot \cos \theta}{1 + 2 \cos^2 \theta - 1}$$
$$\equiv \frac{2 \sin \theta \cdot \cos \theta}{2 \cos^2 \theta}$$
$$\equiv \frac{\sin \theta}{\cos \theta}$$

Did you mentally list the values of θ that are not permissible?

EXERCISES

1. Derive each identity below by using the two identities $\cos 2\theta \equiv \cos^2 \theta - \sin^2 \theta$ and $\cos^2 \theta + \sin^2 \theta \equiv 1$.

   a. $\cos 2\theta \equiv 2 \cos^2 \theta - 1$ b. $\cos 2\theta \equiv 1 - 2 \sin^2 \theta$

2. For each interval given below, determine whether (1) $\cos \dfrac{\theta}{2}$ and (2) $\sin \dfrac{\theta}{2}$ are positive or negative.

   Example $\pi < \theta < \dfrac{3\pi}{2}$

   Since θ is in the interval $\pi < \theta < \dfrac{3\pi}{2}$, it follows that $\dfrac{\theta}{2}$ is in the interval $\dfrac{\pi}{2} < \theta < \dfrac{3\pi}{4}$. Hence,

   (1) $\cos \dfrac{\theta}{2} < 0$ and   (2) $\sin \dfrac{\theta}{2} > 0$.

   a. $0 < \theta < \dfrac{\pi}{2}$ b. $\dfrac{\pi}{2} < \theta < \pi$ c. $\dfrac{3\pi}{2} < \theta < 2\pi$ d. $2\pi < \theta < \dfrac{5\pi}{2}$

3. Study the derivation of the identity for $\cos \dfrac{\theta}{2}$ as given in the text. Then derive the identity for $\sin \dfrac{\theta}{2}$ from the identity $\cos 2\alpha \equiv 1 - 2 \sin^2 \alpha$.

4. For each set of conditions, determine (1) $\sin 2\theta$, (2) $\cos 2\theta$, (3) $\sin \dfrac{\theta}{2}$, and (4) $\cos \dfrac{\theta}{2}$.

Example $\sin \theta = \dfrac{-1}{3}$ and $\pi < \theta < \dfrac{3\pi}{2}$

Solution $\cos^2 \theta + \sin^2 \theta \equiv 1$

$$\cos^2 \theta + \left(\frac{-1}{3} \right)^2 = 1$$

$$\cos^2 \theta = \frac{8}{9}$$

$$\cos \theta = \frac{2\sqrt{2}}{3} \text{ or } \cos \theta = \frac{-2\sqrt{2}}{3}$$

We conclude that $\cos \theta = \dfrac{-2\sqrt{2}}{3}$, because θ is in the interval $\pi < \theta < \dfrac{3\pi}{2}$.

(1) $\sin 2\theta \equiv 2 \sin \theta \cdot \cos \theta$

$$= 2 \left(\frac{-1}{3} \right) \left(\frac{-2\sqrt{2}}{3} \right) = \frac{4\sqrt{2}}{9}$$

(2) $\cos 2\theta \equiv 1 - 2 \sin^2 \theta$

$$= 1 - 2 \left(\frac{-1}{3} \right)^2 = 1 - \frac{2}{9} = \frac{7}{9}$$

(3) $\sin \dfrac{\theta}{2} \equiv \sqrt{\dfrac{1 - \cos \theta}{2}}$ $\left(\text{since } \sin \dfrac{\theta}{2} > 0 \right)$

$$= \sqrt{\frac{1 - \dfrac{-2\sqrt{2}}{3}}{2}} = \sqrt{\frac{3 + 2\sqrt{2}}{6}}$$

(4) $\cos \dfrac{\theta}{2} \equiv -\sqrt{\dfrac{1 + \cos \theta}{2}}$ $\left(\text{since } \cos \dfrac{\theta}{2} < 0 \right)$

$$= -\sqrt{\frac{1 + \dfrac{-2\sqrt{2}}{3}}{2}} = -\sqrt{\frac{3 - 2\sqrt{2}}{6}}$$

a. $\cos \theta = \dfrac{2}{5}$ and $\dfrac{3\pi}{2} < \theta < 2\pi$

b. $\sin \theta = \dfrac{1}{2}$ and $\dfrac{\pi}{2} < \theta < \pi$

c. $\cos \theta = \dfrac{-2}{3}$ and $\pi < \theta < \dfrac{3\pi}{2}$

d. $\sin \theta = 0.6$ and $0 < \theta < \dfrac{\pi}{2}$

e. $\cos \theta = -0.8$ and $\pi < \theta < \dfrac{3\pi}{2}$

f. $\sin \theta = \dfrac{-3}{5}$ and $\dfrac{3\pi}{2} < \theta < 2\pi$

5. Express sin 3θ in terms of sin θ. *Hint:* sin $3\theta \equiv \sin(2\theta + \theta)$

6. Express cos 3θ in terms of cos θ.

7. Use the identities for $\sin \dfrac{\theta}{2}$ and $\cos \dfrac{\theta}{2}$ to compute each of the following.

$$\textit{Example} \quad \cos \frac{5\pi}{8} = -\sqrt{\frac{1 + \cos \dfrac{5\pi}{4}}{2}} = -\sqrt{\frac{1 + \dfrac{-1}{\sqrt{2}}}{2}} = \frac{-\sqrt{2 - \sqrt{2}}}{2}$$

a. $\sin \dfrac{\pi}{8}$

c. $\sin \dfrac{13\pi}{12}$

e. $\cos \dfrac{15\pi}{8} \cdot \sin \dfrac{15\pi}{8}$

b. $\cos \dfrac{9\pi}{8}$

d. $\cos \dfrac{7\pi}{12} \cdot \sin \dfrac{7\pi}{12}$

f. $\sin \dfrac{7\pi}{8} \cdot \cos \dfrac{3\pi}{8} - \cos \dfrac{7\pi}{8} \cdot \sin \dfrac{3\pi}{8}$

8. Simplify each of the following.

a. $\cos^2 \dfrac{\theta}{2} - \sin^2 \dfrac{\theta}{2}$

d. $1 - 2 \sin^2 \dfrac{\theta}{2}$

g. $\dfrac{1 + \cos 2\theta}{\sin 2\theta}$

b. $\dfrac{\sin 2\theta}{2 \sin \theta}$

e. $\dfrac{\cos 2\theta}{\cos \theta - \sin \theta}$

h. $\dfrac{2}{\sin 2\theta}$

c. $2 \sin \dfrac{\theta}{2} \cdot \cos \dfrac{\theta}{2}$

f. $2 \sin^2 \dfrac{\theta}{2} + \cos \theta$

i. $2 \cos^2 \dfrac{\theta}{2}$

9. True or false?

a. $2 \sin \dfrac{\theta}{2} \equiv \sin \theta$

b. $\cos 3\theta + \cos 2\theta \equiv \cos 5\theta$

c. $\sin (2\theta + 2\alpha) \equiv \sin 2\theta + \sin 2\alpha$

d. $\sin (-2 - 3\theta) \equiv \sin (-2) - \sin 3\theta$

e. $\sin (-4 - 5\alpha) \equiv - \sin (4 + 5\alpha)$

f. $2 \sin^2 \dfrac{\theta}{2} \equiv 1 - \cos \theta$

g. $1 - \cos \theta \cdot \cos \alpha - \sin \theta \cdot \sin \alpha \equiv 1 - (\cos \theta \cdot \cos \alpha + \sin \theta \cdot \sin \alpha)$

h. $1 - \sin \theta \cdot \cos \alpha + \cos \theta \cdot \sin \alpha \equiv 1 - \sin (\theta - \alpha)$

10. Prove each of the following identities.

a. $(\sin \theta + \cos \theta)^2 \equiv 1 + \sin 2\theta$

b. $1 - \cos 5\theta \cdot \cos 3\theta - \sin 5\theta \cdot \sin 3\theta$
$\equiv 2 \sin^2 \theta$

c. $\dfrac{1 - \cos 2\theta}{\sin 2\theta} \equiv \dfrac{\sin \theta}{\cos \theta}$

d. $2 \sin \theta \cdot \cos^3 \theta + 2 \sin^3 \theta \cdot \cos \theta$
$\equiv \sin 2\theta$

e. $\dfrac{\sin 2\theta + \sin \theta}{\cos 2\theta + \cos \theta + 1} \equiv \dfrac{\sin \theta}{\cos \theta}$

f. $(\sin \theta - \cos \theta)^2 \equiv 1 - \sin 2\theta$

g. $2 \sin^2 \theta \equiv 1 - \cos 2\theta$

h. $\dfrac{\sin \theta \cdot \sin 2\theta}{\cos \theta} \equiv 2 \sin^2 \theta$

i. $\dfrac{\cos 2\theta}{\cos \theta - \sin \theta} \equiv \cos \theta + \sin \theta$

j. $2 \cos^2 \dfrac{\theta}{2} - \cos \theta \equiv 1$

k. $4 \sin^2 \theta \cdot \cos^2 \theta \equiv 1 - \cos^2 2\theta$

l. $\cos^4 \theta - \sin^4 \theta \equiv \cos 2\theta$

m. $\dfrac{\sin 2\theta}{\sin \theta} - \dfrac{\cos 2\theta}{\cos \theta} \equiv \dfrac{1}{\cos \theta}$

n. $\cos 4\theta \equiv 8 \cos^4 \theta - 8 \cos^2 \theta + 1$

o. $2 \cos \left(\theta + \dfrac{\alpha}{2} \right) \cdot \sin \dfrac{\alpha}{2}$
$\equiv \sin (\theta + \alpha) - \sin \theta$

EXPRESSING PRODUCTS AS SUMS AND SUMS AS PRODUCTS

We discussed periodic phenomena at the end of Chapter 2. In the analysis of periodic phenomena, the product of two circular functions often occurs. Sometimes it is necessary to express this product as the sum or difference of two circular functions. Observe how this may be done for $\cos \theta$ and $\sin \alpha$.

Consider the four identities which we previously established.

$$\cos (\theta - \alpha) \equiv \cos \theta \cdot \cos \alpha + \sin \theta \cdot \sin \alpha \qquad [4.6]$$
$$\cos (\theta + \alpha) \equiv \cos \theta \cdot \cos \alpha - \sin \theta \cdot \sin \alpha \qquad [4.7]$$
$$\sin (\theta + \alpha) \equiv \sin \theta \cdot \cos \alpha + \cos \theta \cdot \sin \alpha \qquad [4.8]$$
$$\sin (\theta - \alpha) \equiv \sin \theta \cdot \cos \alpha - \cos \theta \cdot \sin \alpha \qquad [4.9]$$

Adding or subtracting a pair of these identities and then simplifying leads to the following four identities.

$$\cos \theta \cdot \cos \alpha \equiv \frac{1}{2}[\cos (\theta + \alpha) + \cos (\theta - \alpha)] \qquad [4.16]$$

$$\sin \theta \cdot \sin \alpha \equiv -\frac{1}{2}[\cos (\theta + \alpha) - \cos (\theta - \alpha)] \qquad [4.17]$$

$$\cos \theta \cdot \sin \alpha \equiv \frac{1}{2}[\sin (\theta + \alpha) - \sin (\theta - \alpha)] \qquad [4.18]$$

$$\sin \theta \cdot \cos \alpha \equiv \frac{1}{2}[\sin (\theta + \alpha) + \sin (\theta - \alpha)] \qquad [4.19]$$

Identities 4.16 through 4.19 do not need to be memorized. It is more important that you be able to derive them and apply them so as to express a product as a sum. For illustrations of these procedures, study the examples below.

Example 1   Derive [4.16], $\cos \theta \cdot \cos \alpha \equiv \dfrac{1}{2} [\cos (\theta + \alpha) + \cos (\theta - \alpha)]$.

To do this we use two previously proved identities.
$$\cos (\theta - \alpha) \equiv \cos \theta \cdot \cos \alpha + \sin \theta \cdot \sin \alpha$$
$$\cos (\theta + \alpha) \equiv \cos \theta \cdot \cos \alpha - \sin \theta \cdot \sin \alpha$$
$$\cos (\theta + \alpha) + \cos (\theta - \alpha) \equiv 2 \cos \theta \cdot \cos \alpha \qquad \text{[Adding]}$$
Multiplying by $\dfrac{1}{2}$ we obtain

$$\cos \theta \cdot \cos \alpha \equiv \frac{1}{2}[\cos (\theta + \alpha) + \cos (\theta - \alpha)]$$

Example 2   Express sin 5β · cos 2β as a sum or a difference.
By using identity [4.19],

$$\sin \theta \cdot \cos \alpha \equiv \frac{1}{2}[\sin (\theta + \alpha) + \sin (\theta - \alpha)]$$

$$\sin 5\beta \cdot \cos 2\beta \equiv \frac{1}{2}[\sin (5\beta + 2\beta) + \sin (5\beta - 2\beta)]$$

$$\equiv \frac{1}{2}[\sin 7\beta + \sin 3\beta]$$

Product identities [4.16] through [4.19] may be used to derive so-called *addition identities*. They permit us to express the sum or difference of sines or cosines as a product. The four addition identities are the following:

$$\sin u + \sin v \equiv 2 \sin \frac{u + v}{2} \cdot \cos \frac{u - v}{2} \qquad\qquad [4.20]$$

$$\sin u - \sin v \equiv 2 \cos \frac{u + v}{2} \cdot \sin \frac{u - v}{2} \qquad\qquad [4.21]$$

$$\cos u + \cos v \equiv 2 \cos \frac{u + v}{2} \cdot \cos \frac{u - v}{2} \qquad\qquad [4.22]$$

$$\cos u - \cos v \equiv -2 \sin \frac{u + v}{2} \cdot \sin \frac{u - v}{2} \qquad\qquad [4.23]$$

Identities [4.20] through [4.23] do not need to be memorized. You should be able to derive them and apply them as shown by the following examples.

Example 1   Derive identity [4.20] from identity [4.19].

Solution   Let $u = \theta + \alpha$
and $v = \theta - \alpha$

Then $u + v = 2\theta$ and, hence, $\theta = \dfrac{u + v}{2}$;

and $u - v = 2\alpha$ and, hence, $\alpha = \dfrac{u - v}{2}$.

Making these substitutions for θ and α in identity [4.19],

$$\sin \frac{u + v}{2} \cdot \cos \frac{u - v}{2} \equiv \frac{1}{2}[\sin u + \sin v].$$

Solving for sin u + sin v, we obtain

$$\sin u + \sin v \equiv 2 \sin \frac{u + v}{2} \cdot \cos \frac{u - v}{2}.$$

Example 2   Express sin 8θ + sin 2θ as a product.

Solution   Using identity [4.20],

$$\sin 8\theta + \sin 2\theta \equiv 2 \sin \frac{8\theta + 2\theta}{2} \cdot \cos \frac{8\theta - 2\theta}{2}$$

$$\equiv 2 \sin 5\theta \cdot \cos 3\theta$$

EXERCISES

1. Derive each of the following identities.

    a. Identity [4.17]   **b.** Identity [4.18]   **c.** Identity [4.19]

2. Express each product as a sum or a difference.

    a. $\cos 7\theta \cdot \sin 3\alpha$ **e.** $\cos \dfrac{2\pi}{5} \cdot \cos \dfrac{\pi}{5}$

    b. $\cos 6\theta \cdot \cos 3\alpha$ **f.** $\sin \dfrac{\pi}{5} \cdot \sin \dfrac{\pi}{8}$

    c. $2 \sin 8\theta \cdot \cos 3\theta$ **g.** $\cos 0.8 \cdot \cos 0.3$

    d. $\sin 7\alpha \cdot \sin 4\alpha$ **h.** $\sin 7 \cdot \cos 2$

3. Derive each of the following identities.

    a. Identity [4.21]   **b.** Identity [4.22]   **c.** Identity [4.23]

4. Express each sum or difference as a product.

    a. $\sin 7\theta - \sin 3\theta$ **f.** $\sin \dfrac{\pi}{5} - \sin \dfrac{\pi}{7}$

    b. $\cos 6\theta + \cos 4\alpha$ **g.** $\cos \dfrac{3\pi}{5} + \cos \dfrac{3\pi}{7}$

    c. $\cos 5\alpha - \cos 3\alpha$ **h.** $\cos \dfrac{3\pi}{5} - \cos \dfrac{3\pi}{7}$

    d. $\sin (4\theta + 6\alpha) + \sin (4\theta - 6\alpha)$ **i.** $\sin 6 - \sin 2$

    e. $\sin \dfrac{\pi}{5} + \sin \dfrac{\pi}{7}$ **j.** $\sin (\theta + \alpha) - \sin \theta$

TRIGONOMETRIC EQUATIONS

Here are five examples of *trigonometric equations*.

$$2 \sin \theta = 1 \qquad 4 \cos^2 \theta = 3 \qquad 2 \cos 2\theta = -1$$

$$2 \sin^2 \theta + \sin \theta = 1 \qquad 5 + 5 \cos \theta = 3 \cos \theta + 4$$

To solve a trigonometric equation, such as one of the above, means to find all values of θ which satisfy the equation. Such values of θ are called *solutions* or *roots* of the equation. The set of all solutions of a trigonometric equation is called the *solution set* of the equation. Thus, you see that there is nothing different in the meaning of *trigonometric equations* from the equations you encountered in algebra. The difference lies in the fact that trigonometric equations involve trigonometric functions.

    Study the following examples as we explore various techniques for solving trigonometric equations.

Example 1   Solve $2 \sin \theta = 1$.

Solution $2 \sin \theta = 1$

$$\sin \theta = \frac{1}{2}$$

From your work with the sine function, you know that there are two values of θ in the interval $0 \leq \theta < 2\pi$ for which $\sin \theta = \frac{1}{2}$. These values are $\frac{\pi}{6}$ and $\frac{5\pi}{6}$. Since sine is a periodic function, there are infinitely many values of θ for which $\sin \theta = \frac{1}{2}$ (see the figure).

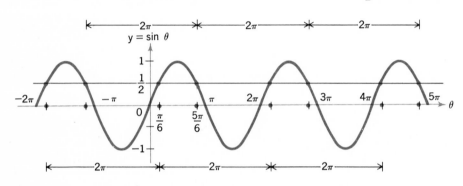

The complete solution set of $\sin \theta = \frac{1}{2}$ is $\left\{\frac{\pi}{6} + 2k\pi, \frac{5\pi}{6} + 2k\pi\right\}$, but for the interval $0 \leq \theta < 2\pi$ the solution set is $\left\{\frac{\pi}{6}, \frac{5\pi}{6}\right\}$.

Example 2   Solve $4 \cos^2 \theta = 3$ for $0 \leq \theta < 2\pi$.

Solution $4 \cos^2 \theta = 3$

$$\cos^2 \theta = \frac{3}{4}$$

$$\cos \theta = \frac{\sqrt{3}}{2} \text{ or } \cos \theta = \frac{-\sqrt{3}}{2} \quad \begin{array}{l}\text{[If } x^2 = k \text{ and } k \geq 0, \text{ then}\\ x = \sqrt{k} \text{ or } x = -\sqrt{k}.\text{]}\end{array}$$

There are two values of θ, namely $\frac{\pi}{6}$ and $\frac{11\pi}{6}$, in the interval $0 \leq \theta < 2\pi$ for which $\cos \theta = \frac{\sqrt{3}}{2}$. Also, there are two values of θ, $\frac{5\pi}{6}$ and $\frac{7\pi}{6}$, in this interval for which $\cos \theta = \frac{-\sqrt{3}}{2}$. The solution set of $4 \cos^2 \theta = 3$ for $0 \leq \theta < 2\pi$ is $\left\{\frac{\pi}{6}, \frac{5\pi}{6}, \frac{7\pi}{6}, \frac{11\pi}{6}\right\}$. Observe that the complete solution set of $4 \cos^2 \theta = 3$ is $\left\{\frac{\pi}{6} + k\pi, \frac{5\pi}{6} + k\pi\right\}$, which has an infinite number of members.

Example 3   Solve $2 \sin^2 \theta + \sin \theta = 1$ for $0 \le \theta < 2\pi$.

Solution   Observe that the equation is quadratic. We could solve for $\sin \theta$ by the quadratic formula but, in this case, factoring is easier.

$$2 \sin^2 \theta + \sin \theta = 1$$
$$2 \sin^2 \theta + \sin \theta - 1 = 0$$
$$(2 \sin \theta - 1)(\sin \theta + 1) = 0$$
$$(2 \sin \theta - 1 = 0) \text{ or } (\sin \theta + 1 = 0) \qquad \text{Why?}$$
$$\left(\sin \theta = \frac{1}{2}\right) \text{ or } (\sin \theta = -1)$$
$$\left(\theta = \frac{\pi}{6} \text{ or } \theta = \frac{5\pi}{6}\right) \text{ or } \left(\theta = \frac{3\pi}{2}\right)$$

The solution set for the specified interval is $\left\{\frac{\pi}{6}, \frac{5\pi}{6}, \frac{3\pi}{2}\right\}$.

Example 4   Solve $2 \sin 2\theta = 1$ for $0 \le \theta < 2\pi$.

Solution   Let $\alpha = 2\theta$. Then substituting we obtain $2 \sin \alpha = 1$.

Thus, $\sin \alpha = \frac{1}{2}$.

Values of α are $\frac{\pi}{6}, \frac{5\pi}{6}, \frac{\pi}{6} + 2\pi, \frac{5\pi}{6} + 2\pi$. Hence, values of θ are

$\frac{\pi}{12}, \frac{5\pi}{12}, \frac{13\pi}{12}, \frac{17\pi}{12}$. Observe that since θ is in the interval $0 \le \theta < 2\pi$, we consider 2θ in the interval $0 \le 2\theta < 4\pi$.

The solution set is $\left\{\frac{\pi}{12}, \frac{5\pi}{12}, \frac{13\pi}{12}, \frac{17\pi}{12}\right\}$

Example 5   Determine the solutions of $3 \cos \theta + 2 = 0$ to two decimal places for $0 \le \theta < 2\pi$.

Solution $$3 \cos \theta + 2 = 0$$
$$\cos \theta = \frac{-2}{3}$$
$$\cos \theta \doteq -0.6667$$

Since $\cos \theta < 0$, θ is a second or a third quadrant number.
From Table I, $\cos 0.84 \doteq 0.6667$
Hence, $\theta = \pi - 0.84 \doteq 3.14 - 0.84 = 2.30$
or $\theta = \pi + 0.84 \doteq 3.14 + 0.84 = 3.98$
The approximate solutions are 2.30 and 3.98.

Example 6   Solve $4 \cos \theta + 2 \sin \theta = 3$ for θ in the interval $0 \le \theta < 2\pi$.

Solution $$4 \cos \theta + 2 \sin \theta = 3$$
$$4 \cos \theta = 3 - 2 \sin \theta$$
Squaring both members, $16 \cos^2 \theta = 9 - 12 \sin \theta + 4 \sin^2 \theta$
Substituting $1 - \sin^2 \theta$ for $\cos^2 \theta$, we obtain
$$16 - 16 \sin^2 \theta = 9 - 12 \sin \theta + 4 \sin^2 \theta$$
and $20 \sin^2 \theta - 12 \sin \theta - 7 = 0$.

The equation $20 \sin^2 \theta - 12 \sin^2 \theta - 7 = 0$ is quadratic. Using the quadratic formula to solve for $\sin \theta$,

$$\sin \theta = \frac{12 \pm \sqrt{144 + 560}}{40} = \frac{12 \pm \sqrt{704}}{40}$$

$$\doteq \frac{12 \pm 26.5330}{40}$$

Hence, $(\sin \theta \doteq 0.9633)$ or $(\sin \theta \doteq -0.3633)$. Thus, $(\theta \doteq 1.30$ or $\theta \doteq \pi - 1.30 \doteq 1.84)$ or $(\theta \doteq \pi + 0.37 \doteq 3.51$ or $\theta \doteq 2\pi - 0.37 \doteq 5.91)$.

In squaring both members, the new equation may have more solutions than the given equation. In fact, this equation is a good illustration. Checking each of these four values of θ in the given equation shows that two of the solutions do not satisfy the original equation. The correct solutions are 1.30 and 5.91, accurate to two decimal places.

EXERCISES

1. For each equation, tell the number of solutions it has in the interval $0 \leq \theta < 2\pi$.

   a. $\cos \theta = \dfrac{1}{\sqrt{2}}$

   b. $\sin \theta = 2$

   c. $\cos \theta = -1$

   d. $2 \sin^2 \theta = 1$

   e. $2 \cos 2\theta = 1$

   f. $\sin 3\theta = \dfrac{\sqrt{3}}{2}$

   g. $(3 \sin \theta - 2)(2 \cos \theta + 1) = 0$

   h. $8 \cos^2 \theta - 4 \cos \theta - 1 = 0$

2. For each equation, determine all solutions in the interval $0 \leq \theta < 2\pi$.

   a. $\sin \theta = 1$

   b. $\cos \theta = -1$

   c. $2 \cos^2 \theta = 1$

   d. $\cos 2\theta = \dfrac{1}{2}$

   e. $4 \sin \theta + \sqrt{12} = 0$

   f. $\sin 3\theta = 1$

   g. $2 \cos \theta + \sin \theta = 1$

   h. $\dfrac{1}{\sin \theta} - 2 = 0$

   i. $4 \cos^2 \theta = 1$

   j. $2 \cos^2 \theta - \sqrt{3} \cos \theta = 0$

   k. $2 \sin^2 \theta + \sin \theta = 0$

   l. $4 \sin^3 \theta - \sin \theta = 0$

   m. $2 \sin^2 \theta + 7 \sin \theta - 4 = 0$

   n. $2 \sin^2 \theta - 5 \sin \theta + 2 = 0$

   o. $\sin \theta \cdot \cos \theta + \sin \theta + \cos \theta + 1 = 0$

   p. $\sin^2 \theta - \cos^2 \theta = 0$

   q. $\cos \theta + 3 \sin \theta = 2$

   r. $\sin^2 \theta + \dfrac{1}{2} = \cos^2 \theta$

   s. $\sin \theta = 0$

   t. $\cos 2\theta = 0$

   u. $\sin^2 \theta = 1$

3. Determine the solutions of each equation to two decimal places for $0 \leq \theta < 2\pi$.

   a. $3 \sin \theta = 1$

   b. $5 \cos^2 \theta = 4$

   c. $5 \sin \theta + 2 = 0$

   d. $9 \sin^2 \theta - 3 \sin \theta - 2 = 0$

   e. $9 \cos^2 \theta + 6 \cos \theta - 2 = 0$

   f. $3 \cos \theta + 4 \cos^2 \theta = 0$

SIMPLIFYING TRIGONOMETRIC EQUATIONS

The identities of the first part of this chapter may be used to simplify the solving of some trigonometric equations. This is best illustrated by examples.

Example 1   Solve $\sin 2\theta - \cos \theta = 0$ for $0 \le \theta < 2\pi$.

Solution
$$\sin 2\theta - \cos \theta = 0$$
$$2 \sin \theta \cdot \cos \theta - \cos \theta = 0 \qquad [\sin 2\theta \equiv 2 \sin \theta \cdot \cos \theta]$$
$$(2 \sin \theta - 1) \cdot \cos \theta = 0 \qquad [\text{Factoring}]$$
$$\left(\sin \theta = \frac{1}{2}\right) \text{ or } (\cos \theta = 0) \qquad \begin{array}{l} [\text{If } A \cdot B = 0, \text{ then } A = 0 \\ \text{ or } B = 0.] \end{array}$$
$$\left(\theta = \frac{\pi}{6} \text{ or } \theta = \frac{5\pi}{6}\right) \text{ or } \left(\theta = \frac{\pi}{2} \text{ or } \theta = \frac{3\pi}{2}\right)$$

Thus, the solution set in the given interval is $\left\{\dfrac{\pi}{6}, \dfrac{\pi}{2}, \dfrac{5\pi}{6}, \dfrac{3\pi}{2}\right\}$.

Example 2   Solve $\sin 5\theta \cdot \cos 2\theta - \cos 5\theta \cdot \sin 2\theta = \dfrac{1}{\sqrt{2}}$ for $0 \le \theta < 2\pi$.

Solution
$$\sin 5\theta \cdot \cos 2\theta - \cos 5\theta \cdot \sin 2\theta = \frac{1}{\sqrt{2}}$$
$$\sin (5\theta - 2\theta) = \frac{1}{\sqrt{2}} \qquad\qquad by\ 4.9$$
$$\sin 3\theta = \frac{1}{\sqrt{2}}$$

Values of 3θ are $\dfrac{\pi}{4}, \dfrac{\pi}{4} + 2\pi, \dfrac{\pi}{4} + 4\pi, \dfrac{3\pi}{4}, \dfrac{3\pi}{4} + 2\pi$, and $\dfrac{3\pi}{4} + 4\pi$.

Values of θ are $\dfrac{\pi}{12}, \dfrac{3\pi}{4}, \dfrac{17\pi}{12}, \dfrac{\pi}{4}, \dfrac{11\pi}{12}$, and $\dfrac{19\pi}{12}$.

In this example, why did we consider the interval $0 \le 3\theta < 6\pi$ for 3θ?

EXERCISES

Solve each equation for the interval $0 \le \theta < 2\pi$.

1. $\sin 2\theta \cdot \sin \theta - \cos \theta = 0$

2. $\sin^2 \theta - \cos^2 \theta + 1 = 0$

3. $\cos 2\theta + \sin \theta - 1 = 0$

4. $2 \sin^2 \theta + 3 \cos \theta - 3 = 0$

5. $\sin 2\theta + \sin \theta = 0$

6. $\cos 2\theta - \sin \theta = 0$

7. $\cos^2 \theta + \sin \theta + 1 = 0$

8. $2 \cos^2 \theta + 2 \cos 2\theta = 1$

9. $\cos 2\theta + 2 \cos^2 \dfrac{\theta}{2} = 1$

10. $\cos 2\theta \cdot \cos \theta + \sin 2\theta \cdot \sin \theta = 1$

11. $\sin 2\theta \cdot \cos \theta - \cos 2\theta \cdot \sin \theta + 1 = 0$

12. $\cos^2 \theta - \sin^2 \theta = \sin \theta$

13. $5 \cos^2 \theta - 5 \sin^2 \theta + 1 = 0$

14. $2 \cos^2 2\theta - 2 \sin^2 2\theta = 1$

15. $\sin 2\theta = 2 \sin \theta$

SOLVING EQUATIONS OF THE FORM A COS θ + B SIN θ = C

Equations of the form

$$\text{I} \qquad A \cos \theta + B \sin \theta = C$$

occur frequently in mathematics and science. We will present a generalized method for solving all such equations where $A^2 + B^2 \geq C^2$. In equation I, multiply each member by $\dfrac{1}{\sqrt{A^2 + B^2}}$ to obtain

$$\frac{A}{\sqrt{A^2 + B^2}} \cos \theta + \frac{B}{\sqrt{A^2 + B^2}} \sin \theta = \frac{C}{\sqrt{A^2 + B^2}}.$$

In this equation make the following substitutions

$$\text{II} \qquad \sin \alpha = \frac{A}{\sqrt{A^2 + B^2}} \quad \text{and}$$

$$\cos \alpha = \frac{B}{\sqrt{A^2 + B^2}},$$

resulting in

$$\text{III} \qquad \sin \alpha \cdot \cos \theta + \cos \alpha \cdot \sin \theta = \frac{C}{\sqrt{A^2 + B^2}},$$

which is equivalent to

$$\text{IV} \qquad \sin (\theta + \alpha) = \frac{C}{\sqrt{A^2 + B^2}}. \qquad\qquad \textit{by 4.8}$$

Hence, any equation of the form I, where $A^2 + B^2 \geq C^2$, is equivalent to equation IV, where α is specified by equations II. Study the following example which illustrates this technique of solution.

Example   Solve $4 \cos \theta + 2 \sin \theta = 3$ for $0 \leq \theta < 2\pi$.

Solution $4 \cos \theta + 2 \sin \theta = 3$ is in the form $A \cos \theta + B \sin \theta = C$, where $A = 4$, $B = 2$, and $C = 3$. From equations II above we first determine α.

$$\sin \alpha = \frac{4}{\sqrt{20}} = \frac{4}{2\sqrt{5}} = \frac{2\sqrt{5}}{5} \doteq 0.8944$$

$$\text{and } \cos \alpha = \frac{2}{\sqrt{20}} = \frac{2}{2\sqrt{5}} = \frac{\sqrt{5}}{5} \doteq 0.4472$$

Hence $\alpha \doteq 1.11$ (Why is $\pi - 1.11$ not a value of α?)
From equation IV above we now determine θ.
$\sin (\theta + \alpha) \doteq \sin (\theta + 1.11)$

$$= \frac{3}{\sqrt{20}} = \frac{3}{2\sqrt{5}} = \frac{3\sqrt{5}}{10} \doteq 0.6708$$

Hence $\theta + 1.11 \doteq 0.74$ or $\theta + 1.11 \doteq \pi - 0.74$
and $\qquad\qquad \theta \doteq -0.37$ or $\theta \doteq 1.29$
The solutions in the interval $0 \leq \theta < 2\pi$ are 1.29 and $2\pi - 0.37$ or 5.91, with accuracy to two decimal places. Compare this technique of solution with the procedure shown in Example 6 on page 117 where the same equation was solved.

EXERCISES

1. Prove that there is a real number α such that

$$\sin \alpha = \frac{A}{\sqrt{A^2 + B^2}} \text{ and } \cos \alpha = \frac{B}{\sqrt{A^2 + B^2}}. \text{ Hint: use identity [4.1].}$$

2. Solve each equation for θ in the interval $0 \leq \theta < 2\pi$. Use Table II to determine n^2 or $\sqrt{n}$ for any natural number less than 100.

a. $2 \cos \theta + 2 \sin \theta = \sqrt{6}$ **d.** $2 \cos \theta + 5 \sin \theta = 3$

b. $\sqrt{2} \cos \theta - \sqrt{2} \sin \theta = 2$ **e.** $\cos \theta - 3 \sin \theta = 2$

c. $2 \cos \theta + 2 \sin \theta = \sqrt{2}$ **f.** $2 \cos \theta - \sin \theta = 1$

VOCABULARY

Use each of the following correctly in a sentence to demonstrate that you understand its meaning. If you are not sure of the meaning of any word, refer back to the chapter.

Fundamental Identity   solution set

permissible value   trigonometric equation

root   trigonometric identity

solution

                                        $\frac{\pi}{2}$-sum relation

REVIEW EXERCISES

1. Given $\sin \theta = \frac{1}{4}$ and $\frac{\pi}{2} < \theta < \pi$; $\cos \alpha = \frac{-2}{5}$ and $\pi < \alpha < \frac{3\pi}{2}$, determine each of the following.

a. $\cos \theta$ **e.** $\cos (\theta - \alpha)$ **i.** $\cos (-\alpha)$

b. $\sin \alpha$ **f.** $\sin (\theta + \alpha)$ **j.** $\cos 2\alpha$

c. $\sin (\pi - \theta)$ **g.** $\cos^2 \theta + \sin^2 \theta$ **k.** $\sin 2\theta$

d. $\cos (\pi + \alpha)$ **h.** $\sin (-\theta)$ **l.** $\sin \frac{\theta}{2}$

2. Simplify each of the following as much as possible.

a. $\dfrac{\sin (-\theta)}{\cos (-\theta)}$ **g.** $\cos 5\theta \cdot \cos 3\alpha + \sin 5\theta \cdot \sin 3\alpha$

                               h. $\sin 3\theta \cdot \cos 4\theta + \cos 3\theta \cdot \sin 4\theta$

b. $\cos (-\theta - 4)$

c. $\sin (-3\theta - 2)$ **i.** $\dfrac{\cos \theta}{\sin \theta} + \dfrac{\sin \theta}{\cos \theta}$

d. $\cos \left(\dfrac{\pi}{2} - 3 \right)$ **j.** $\dfrac{1 - \cos^2 \theta}{2} \cdot \dfrac{6}{\sin \theta}$

e. $\sin \left(\dfrac{\pi}{2} + 2 \right)$ **k.** $\sin^3 \theta + \sin \theta \cdot \cos^2 \theta$

f. $\cos^2 2\theta + \sin^2 2\theta$ **l.** $\dfrac{1 + \cos 2\theta}{\cos \theta}$

m. $\dfrac{\sin 2\theta}{2 \cos \theta}$

o. $2 \cos^2 \dfrac{\pi}{12} - 1$

n. $2 \sin \dfrac{\pi}{8} \cos \dfrac{\pi}{8}$

p. $\sin \dfrac{\pi}{8} - \cos \dfrac{3\pi}{8}$

3. Compute each of the following.

a. $\cos \dfrac{5\pi}{12}$ **b.** $\sin \dfrac{11\pi}{12}$ **c.** $\sin \dfrac{3\pi}{8}$ **d.** $\cos \dfrac{5\pi}{8}$

4. Prove each of the following identities.

a. $\sin^4 \theta - \cos^4 \theta \equiv - \cos 2\theta$

c. $\cos \theta \left(\dfrac{1}{\cos \theta} - \cos \theta \right) \equiv \sin^2 \theta$

b. $\dfrac{\cos^2 \theta}{\sin \theta} + \sin \theta \equiv \dfrac{1}{\sin \theta}$

d. $\cos^4 \theta - 3 \cos^2 \theta \cdot \sin^2 \theta - 4 \sin^4 \theta \equiv 1 - 5 \sin^2 \theta$

5. Express $\cos 4\theta$ in terms of $\cos \theta$.

6. Prove each of the following identities. In each case specify which values of θ are not permissible.

a. $(\cos \theta - \sin \theta)^2 \equiv 1 - \sin 2\theta$

d. $\dfrac{\cos 3\theta \cdot \cos \theta + \sin 3\theta \cdot \sin \theta + 1}{1 - \sin^2 \theta} \equiv 2$

b. $\dfrac{\sin 2\theta}{\cos 2\theta + 1} \equiv \dfrac{\sin \theta}{\cos \theta}$

e. $2 \cos^2 \dfrac{\theta}{2} - 1 \equiv \cos \theta$

c. $\dfrac{\cos^2 \theta - 2 \cos^2 \theta \cdot \sin^2 \theta}{1 - \sin^2 \theta} \equiv \cos 2\theta$

7. Express each product as a sum or a difference.

a. $\cos 5\theta \cdot \cos 4\theta$

b. $2 \sin 3 \cdot \cos 2$

8. Express each sum as a product.

a. $\cos 4\alpha + \cos 2\alpha$

b. $\sin 6.2 + \sin 4.2$

9. Solve each equation for θ in the interval $0 \leq \theta < 2\pi$.

a. $2 \sin \theta - 3 = 4 \sin \theta - 2$

e. $\cos \theta + \sin \theta = 1$

b. $4 \cos^2 \theta = 3$

f. $2 \sin^2 \theta + \sin \theta = 1$

c. $\sin 3\theta = 1$

g. $\sin 2\theta + \cos \theta = 0$

d. $2 \sin^2 \theta - \sin \theta = 0$

h. $\sin^2 \theta - 3 \cos^2 \theta = 0$

10. Determine the solutions of each equation to two decimal places for $0 \leq \theta < 2\pi$.

a. $3 \cos \theta = 2$ **b.** $5 \sin \theta + 3 = 0$ **c.** $\cos \theta + 2 \sin \theta = 1$

CHAPTER TEST

1. Given $\cos \theta = \dfrac{-3}{4}$ and $\dfrac{\pi}{2} < \theta < \pi$; $\sin \alpha = \dfrac{-1}{4}$ and $\dfrac{3\pi}{2} < \alpha < 2\pi$, determine each of the following.

   a. $\sin \theta$ **d.** $\sin (-\alpha)$ **g.** $\sin 2\theta$

   b. $\cos \alpha$ **e.** $\cos (\theta + \alpha)$ **h.** $\cos 2\alpha$

   c. $\cos (\pi + \theta)$ **f.** $\sin (\theta + \alpha)$ **i.** $\cos \dfrac{\theta}{2}$

2. Simplify as much as possible.

   a. $\dfrac{\sin (-\theta)}{-\cos (-\theta)}$

   b. $\sin (-2 - 3\alpha)$

   c. $\cos \left(\dfrac{\pi}{2} - 2 \right)$

   d. $1 - \sin^2 \theta$

   e. $\sin 5 \cdot \cos 3 - \cos 5 \cdot \sin 3$

   f. $\dfrac{\cos \theta}{4} \cdot \dfrac{2 \sin 2\theta}{1 - \sin^2 \theta}$

   g. $\dfrac{\cos 2\theta + 1}{2 \cos \theta}$

3. Given $\cos \dfrac{\theta}{2} \equiv \pm \sqrt{\dfrac{1 + \cos \theta}{2}}$ and $\sin \dfrac{\theta}{2} \equiv \pm \sqrt{\dfrac{1 - \cos \theta}{2}}$, determine each of the following.

   a. $\cos \dfrac{7\pi}{8}$ **b.** $\sin \dfrac{5\pi}{8}$

4. Prove each identity. State in each case which values of θ are not permissible.

   a. $\dfrac{1 - \cos^2 \theta}{\sin \theta} \cdot 2 \cos \theta \equiv \sin 2\theta$

   b. $\sin \theta + \dfrac{\cos^2 \theta}{\sin \theta} \equiv \dfrac{1}{\sin \theta}$

   c. $1 + \cos 4\theta \cdot \cos 2\theta + \sin 4\theta \cdot \sin 2\theta \equiv 2 \cos^2 \theta$

5. Express $\sin 3\theta$ in terms of $\sin \theta$.

6. Solve each equation for θ in the interval $0 \le \theta < 2\pi$.

   a. $4 \cos \theta + 2 = 0$ **d.** $4 \sin^2 \theta = 3$

   b. $2 \sin^2 \theta - \sin \theta = 0$ **e.** $\cos^2 \theta - 2 \cos \theta = 3$

   c. $2 \cos 2\theta = \sqrt{3}$

7. Given that $A \cos \theta + B \sin \theta = C$ is equivalent to $\sin (\theta + \alpha) = \dfrac{C}{\sqrt{A^2 + B^2}}$ where

   $$\sin \alpha = \dfrac{A}{\sqrt{A^2 + B^2}} \text{ and } \cos \alpha = \dfrac{B}{\sqrt{A^2 + B^2}}$$

   Solve $\sqrt{2} \cos \theta + \sqrt{2} \sin \theta = 2$ for θ in the interval $0 \le \theta < 2\pi$.

CUMULATIVE REVIEW
CHAPTERS 1–4

1. For each of the following, tell whether it is (1) rational or (2) irrational.

   a. $\dfrac{\pi}{6}$ **c.** $\dfrac{\sqrt{2}}{2}$ **e.** $\sin\dfrac{\pi}{3}$

   b. $\sin\dfrac{\pi}{6}$ **d.** $\cos\dfrac{5\pi}{6}$ **f.** $\cos^2\dfrac{\pi}{4}$

2. Given the point $P(x, y)$, determine two values of y so that P is on the unit circle in standard position.

   a. $P\left(\dfrac{-2}{3}, y\right)$ **b.** $P(0.8, y)$

3. Determine the lengths of the sides of a 30°–60° right triangle, in which the hypotenuse is 10 units long.

4. Determine the distance, in terms of c and m, between $A(c, -m)$ and $B(-3c, 2m)$.

5. Determine the coordinates of the point symmetric to $P(2, -5)$ with respect

   a. to the x-axis   **c.** to the origin

   b. to the y-axis   **d.** to the line specified by $y = x$

6. Give the domain, range and period of each of the following functions.

   a. W, the wrapping function   **b.** cosine   **c.** sine

7. List two positive and two negative numbers which belong to the set $\left\{\dfrac{\pi}{3} + 2k\pi\right\}$, where k is any integer.

8. Determine the coordinates of each of the following points. W is the wrapping function.

   a. $W\left(\dfrac{5\pi}{6}\right)$ **b.** $W\left(\dfrac{3\pi}{2}\right)$ **c.** $W\left(\dfrac{-2\pi}{3}\right)$ **d.** $W\left(\dfrac{13\pi}{4}\right)$

9. Determine three values of θ for which the paths (A, θ) and $\left(A, \dfrac{-\pi}{3}\right)$ are coterminal paths on a unit circle.

10. For each real number θ, determine the point symmetric to the point $W(\theta)$ with respect to each of the following.

   Example   With respect to the y-axis, $W(\pi - \theta)$ is symmetric to $W(\theta)$.

   a. the x-axis   **b.** the origin   **c.** the line specified by $y = x$

11. A simple pendulum makes 15 vibrations in 45 seconds. What is the period and frequency of the pendulum?

12. Which of the following equations are identities?

a. $\cos^2 2\theta + \sin^2 2\theta = 1$

b. $\cos \theta = \cos (\theta + \pi)$

c. $\sin \theta = \sin (\theta + 2k\pi)$, for any integer k

d. $\cos \left(\theta + \dfrac{\pi}{2}\right) = \sin (-\theta)$

e. $\sin (-3\theta) = -\sin 3\theta$

f. $\cos 5\theta \cdot \cos 2\theta - \sin 5\theta \cdot \sin 2\theta = \cos 3\theta$

g. $\sin 2\theta = 2 \sin \theta$

h. $\cos 4\theta = 2 \cos^2 2\theta - 1$

13. Determine the value of each of the following.

a. $\cos \dfrac{3\pi}{4}$

b. $\sin \dfrac{2\pi}{3}$

c. $\cos \dfrac{-5\pi}{6}$

d. $\sin \dfrac{-3\pi}{4}$

e. $\cos \dfrac{5\pi}{3}$

f. $\sin \dfrac{11\pi}{6}$

14. Determine each of the following, accurate to four decimal places.

a. $\cos 2.78$

b. $\sin 3.79$

c. $\cos 1.342$

15. Interpolate and determine θ in the interval $0 < \theta < \dfrac{\pi}{2}$, with accuracy to three decimal places, so that $\sin \theta \doteq 0.5362$.

16. Given a second quadrant number θ for which $\sin \theta = \dfrac{5}{13}$, determine $\cos \theta$.

17. Express $\cos \left(\dfrac{3\pi}{8} + \alpha\right)$ in terms of the sine function.

18. Simplify and express each of the following in terms of $\cos \theta$.

a. $\cos (\theta + 6\pi)$

b. $\cos (4\pi - \theta)$

c. $\cos (\theta - 3\pi)$

d. $\cos (5\pi + \theta)$

e. $\cos (-\theta)$

f. $1 - \sin^2 \theta$

g. $\sin \left(\dfrac{\pi}{2} - \theta\right)$

h. $\sin \left(\dfrac{\pi}{2} + \theta\right)$

19. Express each of the following in terms of $\sin \theta$, where $0 < \theta < \dfrac{\pi}{2}$.

a. $\sin \dfrac{7\pi}{10}$

b. $\sin \dfrac{11\pi}{8}$

c. $\cos \dfrac{\pi}{5}$

d. $\sin 3$

e. $\sin \dfrac{-2\pi}{7}$

f. $\sin 4$

20. For each function specified below, give its amplitude, period, and phase number.

a. $y = -2 \sin \dfrac{\theta}{2}$

b. $y = \dfrac{1}{2} \cos 3\theta$

c. $y = \sin \pi\theta$

d. $y = 2 \cos \dfrac{1}{2}\left(\theta + \dfrac{\pi}{4}\right)$

e. $y = \sin (2\theta - \pi)$

21. Describe the variation of $\cos \theta$ as θ increases from $\dfrac{\pi}{2}$ to π.

22. Prove each of the following identities.

    a. $\cos^4 \theta - \sin^4 \theta \equiv \cos 2\theta$

    b. $\dfrac{2 \cos \theta}{\sin \theta} - \dfrac{2 \cos^3 \theta}{\sin \theta} \equiv \sin 2\theta$

    c. $1 + (3 \sin \theta - \cos \theta)(\sin \theta + \cos \theta) \equiv 4 \sin^2 \theta + \sin 2\theta$

    d. $\sin 3\theta \equiv 3 \sin \theta - 4 \sin^3 \theta$

23. Graph each function of Exercise 20 for one period.

24. For the wave motion specified by $y = 3 \sin \pi t$, where the time t is in seconds, give (1) the period and (2) the frequency of the motion.

25. Graph $y = \cos 2\theta$ and $y = \dfrac{2}{3}$ on the same coordinate system to show that the equation $\cos 2\theta = \dfrac{2}{3}$ has four solutions in the interval $0 \le \theta < 2\pi$.

26. A point moves along a 2-cm. segment with simple harmonic motion so that at $t = 0$ seconds, the displacement from the midpoint is zero. The period of the motion is 2 seconds.

    a. Write an equation of the motion.

    b. What is the displacement at the end of $\dfrac{3}{4}$ second? at the end of $\dfrac{1}{6}$ period?

    c. When (in seconds) does the maximum displacement occur?

    d. What is the frequency of the motion in cycles per minute?

27. Given $\sin \theta = \dfrac{2}{3}$ and $\dfrac{\pi}{2} < \theta < \pi$; $\cos \alpha = \dfrac{-1}{5}$ and $\pi < \alpha < \dfrac{3\pi}{2}$, determine each of the following.

    a. $\cos (\theta + \alpha)$ **b.** $\sin 2\theta$ **c.** $\cos 2\alpha$ **d.** $\cos \dfrac{\alpha}{2}$

28. Simplify each of the following as much as possible.

    a. $(1 - \cos \theta)(1 + \cos \theta)$

    b. $-\sin (-\theta)$

    c. $\cos (-\theta - \pi)$

    d. $\sin \left(\dfrac{\pi}{2} - 2 \right)$

    e. $\cos^2 2\theta + \sin^2 2\theta$

    f. $\sin 4\alpha \cdot \cos 2\alpha + \cos 4\alpha \cdot \sin 2\alpha$

    g. $\dfrac{\sin \theta}{2 \cos \theta} + \dfrac{\cos \theta}{2 \sin \theta}$

    h. $\dfrac{1 - \cos 2\theta}{2 \sin \theta}$

    i. $\cos \theta \sin^2 \theta + \cos^3 \theta$

    j. $(\cos \theta + \sin \theta)(\cos \theta - \sin \theta)$

CHAPTER 5

THE TANGENT FUNCTION

ANOTHER CIRCULAR FUNCTION

Up to this point we have studied two circular functions, cosine and sine. Now we introduce a third circular function, the *tangent*.

DEFINITION OF TANGENT   Given W for which $W(\theta) = P(x, y)$, the *tangent* function is $\left\{\left(\theta, \dfrac{y}{x}\right)\right\}$, $x \neq 0$.

Tangent is abbreviated as *tan;* thus, $\tan \theta = \dfrac{y}{x}$. Pronounce $\tan \theta$ as *tangent theta.*

Study the ten pairs of statements on the following page. The second statement in each pair is a consequence of the first statement and of the definition of *tangent*. That is,

if $W(\theta) = P(x, y)$, then $\tan \theta = \dfrac{y}{x}$.

Use Figure 5–1 to verify each pair of statements which is listed at the top of the following page.

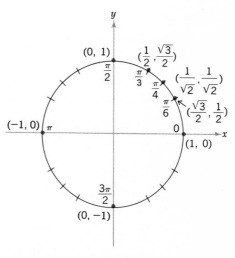

FIGURE 5-1

If	*then*
$W\left(\dfrac{\pi}{6}\right) = P\left(\dfrac{\sqrt{3}}{2}, \dfrac{1}{2}\right)$	$\tan\dfrac{\pi}{6} = \dfrac{1}{\sqrt{3}} = \dfrac{\sqrt{3}}{3}$
$W\left(\dfrac{2\pi}{3}\right) = P\left(\dfrac{-1}{2}, \dfrac{\sqrt{3}}{2}\right)$	$\tan\dfrac{2\pi}{3} = -\sqrt{3}$
$W\left(\dfrac{7\pi}{4}\right) = P\left(\dfrac{1}{\sqrt{2}}, \dfrac{-1}{\sqrt{2}}\right)$	$\tan\dfrac{7\pi}{4} = -1$
$W(\pi) = P(-1, 0)$	$\tan\pi = 0$
$W\left(\dfrac{\pi}{2}\right) = P(0, 1)$	$\tan\dfrac{\pi}{2}$ is undefined. Why?
$W\left(\dfrac{7\pi}{3}\right) = P\left(\dfrac{1}{2}, \dfrac{\sqrt{3}}{2}\right)$	$\tan\dfrac{7\pi}{3} = \sqrt{3}$
$W\left(\dfrac{-5\pi}{4}\right) = P\left(\dfrac{-1}{\sqrt{2}}, \dfrac{1}{\sqrt{2}}\right)$	$\tan\dfrac{-5\pi}{4} = -1$
$W\left(\dfrac{-5\pi}{6}\right) = P\left(\dfrac{-\sqrt{3}}{2}, \dfrac{-1}{2}\right)$	$\tan\dfrac{-5\pi}{6} = \dfrac{1}{\sqrt{3}} = \dfrac{\sqrt{3}}{3}$
$W(0) = P(1, 0)$	$\tan 0 = 0$
$W\left(\dfrac{3\pi}{2}\right) = P(0, -1)$	$\tan\dfrac{3\pi}{2}$ is undefined. Why?

What is $\tan\dfrac{3\pi}{4}$ equal to? $\tan\dfrac{4\pi}{3}$? $\tan(-\pi)$? $\tan\dfrac{5\pi}{2}$?

Let us determine the domain of tangent, that is, the set of all values of θ for which $\tan\theta$ exists. By the definition of tangent, $\tan\theta = \dfrac{y}{x}$, where $W(\theta) = P(x, y)$. However, $\dfrac{y}{x}$ is undefined if $x = 0$. Why? Observe in Figure 5–1 that $x = 0$ and $\theta = \dfrac{\pi}{2} + k\pi$ if and only if $W(\theta)$ is $P(0, 1)$ or $Q(0, -1)$. Therefore, the domain of tangent is the set of all real numbers $\theta \neq \dfrac{\pi}{2} + k\pi$.

Is there an identity which relates $\tan\theta$ to $\sin\theta$ and $\cos\theta$? To answer this question recall that, given $W(\theta) = P(x, y)$, we know that $\sin\theta = y$ and $\cos\theta = x$. We also know that $\tan\theta = \dfrac{y}{x}$. It follows then that

$$\tan\theta \equiv \frac{\sin\theta}{\cos\theta} \qquad\qquad [5.1]$$

Which values of θ are not permissible for this identity?

EXERCISES

1. Determine the value of each of the following if it is defined.

a. $\tan \dfrac{\pi}{3}$

b. $\tan \dfrac{\pi}{4}$

c. $\tan (-\pi)$

d. $\tan \dfrac{5\pi}{6}$

e. $\tan \dfrac{4\pi}{3}$

f. $\tan \dfrac{5\pi}{4}$

g. $\tan 2\pi$

h. $\tan \dfrac{-3\pi}{4}$

i. $\tan \dfrac{7\pi}{6}$

j. $\tan \dfrac{5\pi}{3}$

k. $\tan \dfrac{11\pi}{6}$

l. $\tan \dfrac{15\pi}{4}$

m. $\tan \dfrac{-\pi}{6}$

n. $\tan \dfrac{5\pi}{2}$

o. $\tan \dfrac{14\pi}{3}$

p. $\tan (-3\pi)$

q. $\tan \dfrac{-\pi}{2}$

r. $\tan \dfrac{-3\pi}{2}$

s. $-\tan \dfrac{3\pi}{4}$

t. $-\tan \dfrac{-4\pi}{3}$

2. True or false?

a. $\tan \dfrac{\pi}{4} = \tan \dfrac{3\pi}{4}$

b. $\tan \dfrac{\pi}{4} = -\tan \dfrac{3\pi}{4}$

c. $\tan \dfrac{\pi}{4} = \tan \dfrac{-3\pi}{4}$

d. $\tan \dfrac{\pi}{6} = \tan \dfrac{7\pi}{6}$

e. $\tan \dfrac{2\pi}{3} = \tan \dfrac{5\pi}{3}$

f. $\tan \dfrac{\pi}{3} = \tan \left(\dfrac{\pi}{3} + \pi \right)$

g. $\tan \dfrac{3\pi}{4} = \tan \left(\dfrac{3\pi}{4} + \pi \right)$

h. $\tan \dfrac{7\pi}{6} = \tan \left(\dfrac{7\pi}{6} + 3\pi \right)$

i. $\tan \dfrac{5\pi}{3} = \tan \left(\dfrac{5\pi}{3} - \pi \right)$

j. $\tan \pi = 0$

k. $\tan 0 = 0$

l. $\tan (-5\pi) = 0$

m. For every integer k, $\tan k\pi = 0$

n. For every integer k,
$$\tan \left(\dfrac{\pi}{2} + k\pi \right) = 0$$

o. $\dfrac{\sin \dfrac{3\pi}{4}}{\cos \dfrac{3\pi}{4}} = \tan \dfrac{3\pi}{4}$

p. $\dfrac{\sin 3\pi}{\cos 3\pi} = \tan 3\pi$

q. $\dfrac{\sin \theta}{\cos \theta} \equiv \tan \theta$

r. For each θ, $-1 \le \tan \theta \le 1$

s. For every integer k,
$$\tan \left(\dfrac{\pi}{4} + k\pi \right) = 1$$

t. 2π is a period of tangent.

u. If $\theta = \dfrac{\pi}{2} + k\pi$, then $\tan \theta$ is undefined.

v. The domain of tangent is the set of all real numbers.

w. $\tan \left(\dfrac{\pi}{3} + \dfrac{\pi}{3} \right) = \tan \dfrac{\pi}{3} + \tan \dfrac{\pi}{3}$

x. For each θ in the interval $\pi < \theta < \dfrac{3\pi}{2}$, $\tan \theta > 0$

3. For each interval, determine whether $\tan \theta$ is positive or negative.

a. $0 < \theta < \dfrac{\pi}{2}$
                          c. $\pi < \theta < \dfrac{3\pi}{2}$

b. $\dfrac{\pi}{2} < \theta < \pi$
                          d. $\dfrac{3\pi}{2} < \theta < 2\pi$

4. For each of the following values of θ, determine (1) $\cos \theta$, (2) $\sin \theta$, and (3) $\tan \theta$.

a. $\dfrac{\pi}{3}$ **c.** $\dfrac{5\pi}{6}$ **e.** $\dfrac{\pi}{2}$ **g.** $\dfrac{2\pi}{3}$

b. π **d.** $\dfrac{-\pi}{4}$ **f.** 0 **h.** $\dfrac{3\pi}{2}$

5. Show that each of the following is true by computing the value of each member of the equation.

a. $\tan \dfrac{11\pi}{6} = \dfrac{\tan \dfrac{2\pi}{3} + \tan \dfrac{7\pi}{6}}{1 - \tan \dfrac{2\pi}{3} \cdot \tan \dfrac{7\pi}{6}}$
          d. $\tan \dfrac{\pi}{3} = \dfrac{1 - \cos \dfrac{2\pi}{3}}{\sin \dfrac{2\pi}{3}}$

b. $\tan \dfrac{5\pi}{3} = \dfrac{2 \tan \dfrac{5\pi}{6}}{1 - \tan^2 \dfrac{5\pi}{6}}$
          e. $\tan \dfrac{5\pi}{6} = \dfrac{\sin \dfrac{5\pi}{3}}{1 + \cos \dfrac{5\pi}{3}}$

c. $\tan \dfrac{7\pi}{6} = \dfrac{\tan \dfrac{4\pi}{3} - \tan \dfrac{\pi}{6}}{1 + \tan \dfrac{4\pi}{3} \cdot \tan \dfrac{\pi}{6}}$
          f. $\tan \dfrac{3\pi}{4} = \dfrac{\sin \dfrac{5\pi}{4}}{\cos \dfrac{7\pi}{4}}$

6. Tell whether $\tan \theta$ is positive or negative, given that θ is a

a. first quadrant number   **c.** third quadrant number

b. second quadrant number   **d.** fourth quadrant number

7. For each equation, give two solutions in the interval $0 \le \theta < 2\pi$.

a. $\tan \theta = 1$ **e.** $\tan \theta = \sqrt{3}$

b. $\tan \theta = -1$

c. $\tan \theta = 0$ **f.** $\tan \theta = \dfrac{\sqrt{3}}{3}$

d. $\tan \theta = \dfrac{-1}{\sqrt{3}}$ **g.** $\tan \theta = -\sqrt{3}$

8. For what values of θ is the expression $\dfrac{2}{1 - \tan \theta}$ undefined?

TWO VALUES FROM ONE

Given the value of either cos θ, sin θ, or tan θ, it is possible to determine the values of the other two. The methods for doing this are illustrated in the following two examples.

Example 1   Given $\cos \theta = \dfrac{-2}{5}$ and $\dfrac{\pi}{2} < \theta < \pi$, determine sin θ and tan θ.

Solution

$$\cos^2 \theta + \sin^2 \theta \equiv 1$$

$$\left(\frac{-2}{5}\right)^2 + \sin^2 \theta = 1$$

$$\sin^2 \theta = \frac{21}{25}$$

$$\sin \theta = \frac{\sqrt{21}}{5} \text{ or } \sin \theta = \frac{-\sqrt{21}}{5}$$

$$\sin \theta = \frac{\sqrt{21}}{5} \text{ only, because } \frac{\pi}{2} < \theta < \pi$$

Using $\tan \theta \equiv \dfrac{\sin \theta}{\cos \theta}$

$$\tan \theta = \frac{\dfrac{\sqrt{21}}{5}}{\dfrac{-2}{5}} = \frac{\sqrt{21}}{-2}$$

Example 2   Given $\tan \theta = \dfrac{\sqrt{5}}{6}$ and $\pi < \theta < \dfrac{3\pi}{2}$, determine cos θ and sin θ.

Solution

$$\tan \theta \equiv \frac{\sin \theta}{\cos \theta}$$

$$\frac{\sin \theta}{\cos \theta} = \frac{\sqrt{5}}{6}$$

$$\sin \theta = \frac{\sqrt{5}}{6} \cos \theta$$

Using $\cos^2 \theta + \sin^2 \theta \equiv 1$

$$\cos^2 \theta + \left(\frac{\sqrt{5}}{6} \cos \theta\right)^2 = 1$$

$$\cos^2 \theta + \frac{5}{36} \cos^2 \theta = 1$$

$$\frac{41}{36} \cos^2 \theta = 1$$

$$\cos^2 \theta = \frac{36}{41}$$

$$\cos \theta = \frac{6}{\sqrt{41}} \text{ or } \cos \theta = \frac{-6}{\sqrt{41}}$$

$$\cos \theta = \frac{-6}{\sqrt{41}} \text{ only, since } \pi < \theta < \frac{3\pi}{2}$$

$$\text{Hence } \sin \theta = \frac{\sqrt{5}}{6} \cdot \cos \theta = \frac{\sqrt{5}}{6} \cdot \frac{-6}{\sqrt{41}} = \frac{-\sqrt{5}}{\sqrt{41}}$$

EXERCISES

1. For each given set of conditions, determine the values of the remaining two of cos θ, sin θ, and tan θ.

a. $\sin \theta = \frac{-5}{13}, \quad \frac{3\pi}{2} < \theta < 2\pi$

f. $\tan \theta = \frac{12}{5}, \quad \pi < \theta < \frac{3\pi}{2}$

b. $\cos \theta = -0.8, \quad \frac{\pi}{2} < \theta < \pi$

g. $\cos \theta = \frac{\sqrt{7}}{3}, \quad 0 < \theta < \frac{\pi}{2}$

c. $\tan \theta = \frac{3}{4}, \quad \pi < \theta < \frac{3\pi}{2}$

h. $\sin \theta = \frac{-\sqrt{6}}{4}, \quad \pi < \theta < \frac{3\pi}{2}$

d. $\cos \theta = \frac{-3}{8}, \quad \frac{\pi}{2} < \theta < \pi$

i. $\tan \theta = -2, \quad \frac{3\pi}{2} < \theta < 2\pi$

e. $\sin \theta = \frac{1}{3}, \quad \frac{\pi}{2} < \theta < \pi$

j. $\cos \theta = \frac{4}{\sqrt{30}}, \quad \frac{3\pi}{2} < \theta < 2\pi$

2. Given $\sin \theta = \frac{\sqrt{5}}{3}$ and $\cos \theta < 0$, determine $\tan \theta$.

3. Given $\tan \theta = \frac{-3}{\sqrt{2}}$ and $\sin \theta < 0$, determine $\cos \theta$.

LINE VALUES AND GRAPH OF TANGENT

The line values of tan θ help us to determine the variation of tan θ as well as the graph, primitive period and range of tangent. Observe in Figure 5–2a that θ is a first quadrant number and $\theta + \pi$ is a third quadrant number. Line $\overleftrightarrow{AB}$ is perpendicular to the x-axis at $A(1, 0)$. Recall that the slope of the line through $P(x, y)$, the origin and $P'(-x, -y)$ is $\frac{y}{x}$ $(x \neq 0)$. Since this line passes through the point $B(1, n)$, the slope of this line can be shown as n or $\frac{n}{1}$. Hence,

$n = \frac{y}{x} = \frac{-y}{-x} = AB$. It follows that

$\tan \theta = \frac{y}{x} = AB$ and

$\tan (\theta + \pi) = \frac{-y}{-x} = AB$.

Note that B is above the x-axis and that AB is a positive number.

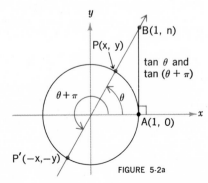

FIGURE 5-2a

Observe in Figure 5–2b that θ is a second quadrant number and $\theta + \pi$ is a fourth quadrant number. The slope of the line through $Q(x, y)$, the origin, and $Q'(-x, -y)$ is $\dfrac{y}{x}$ ($x \neq 0$). Since this line passes through the point $C(1, n)$, the slope of this line can also be shown as $\dfrac{n}{1}$ or n. Hence, $n = \dfrac{y}{x} = \dfrac{-y}{-x} = -AC$. It follows that

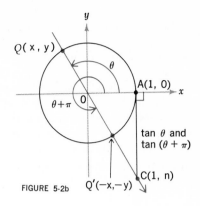

FIGURE 5-2b

$$\tan \theta = \frac{y}{x} = -AC \qquad \text{and} \qquad \tan (\theta + \pi) = \frac{-y}{-x} = -AC.$$

Note that C is below the x-axis and that $\tan \theta$, which is equal to $-AC$, is negative.

It follows that $\overline{AB}$ (or $\overline{AC}$) gives the line value of $\tan \theta$ and of $\tan (\theta + \pi)$. Furthermore, you should observe that, for any integer k,

$$\tan \theta \equiv \tan (\theta + k\pi) \qquad\qquad [5.2]$$

This identity tells us that the *primitive period* of tangent is π.

Consider the line value variation of $\tan \theta$ in Figure 5–3a as θ increases from 0 to $\dfrac{\pi}{2}$. If $\theta = 0$, then B is at A and $\tan \theta = 0$. As θ increases from 0 to $\dfrac{\pi}{2}$; that is, $0 < \theta_1 < \theta_2 < \theta_3 < \dfrac{\pi}{2}$, the point B is positioned successively higher above A. Therefore, $\tan \theta$, which is equal to AB, increases from 0 *without upper limit*.

$$0 < AB_1 < AB_2 < AB_3$$

FIGURE 5-3a

If $\theta = \dfrac{\pi}{2}$, then $\tan \dfrac{\pi}{2}$ is undefined, since the line through the origin and the point $P(0, 1)$ does not intersect the vertical line through A. Describe the variation of $\tan \theta$ as θ increases from π to $\dfrac{3\pi}{2}$. Is there a segment, $\overline{AB}$, which gives the line value of $\tan \dfrac{3\pi}{2}$? Why?

Observe in Figure 5–3b that, as θ increases from $\dfrac{\pi}{2}$ to π; that is, $\dfrac{\pi}{2} < \theta_1 < \theta_2 < \theta_3 < \pi$, the point C is positioned below A and successively higher. Therefore, $\tan \theta$, which is equal to $-AC$, is negative and increases to 0. Notice that, in this case, $\tan \theta$ has no *lower limit*.

$$-AC_1 < -AC_2 < -AC_3 < 0$$

Describe the variation of $\tan \theta$ as θ increases from $\dfrac{3\pi}{2}$
to 2π; from $\dfrac{-\pi}{2}$ to $\dfrac{\pi}{2}$; from $\dfrac{\pi}{2}$ to $\dfrac{3\pi}{2}$.

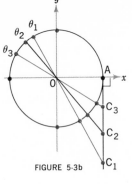

The line value scheme helps us to determine the range of tangent (see Figures 5–3a and 5–3b). Given any real number n, there is a line through the origin and the point $P(1, n)$ which is on the vertical line through $A(1, 0)$. This line intersects the circle at two points, $W(\theta)$ and $W(\theta + \pi)$, such that

$$n = \tan \theta = \tan (\theta + \pi).$$

FIGURE 5-3b

Hence the range of tangent is R, the set of all real numbers.

In Figure 5–3a tell how to construct a point $W(\theta)$ such that $\tan \theta = 3$. In Figure 5–3b tell how to construct a point $W(\theta)$ such that $\tan \theta = -7$.

To construct the graph of tangent, we project line values of $\tan \theta$ into points of another rectangular coordinate plane. Study Figure 5–4.

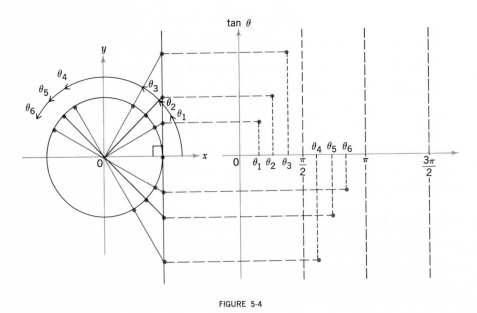

FIGURE 5-4

In Figure 5–4 we have constructed six points $(\theta, \tan \theta)$ by projecting line values from the x, y plane into the $\theta, \tan \theta$ plane. Figure 5–5 shows the completed graph of tangent for $\dfrac{-3\pi}{2} < \theta < \dfrac{3\pi}{2}$. Imagining that the graph in Figure 5–5 would be continued beyond the domain values shown, give the domain, the range and the primitive period of tangent.

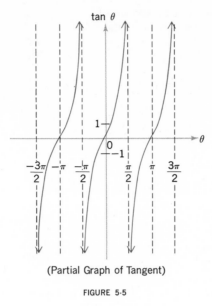

(Partial Graph of Tangent)

FIGURE 5·5

EXERCISES

1. The scheme shown on page 134 gives a method for projecting line values into a point on the θ, $\tan \theta$ coordinate plane. We use this method to project the line value of $\tan \dfrac{3\pi}{8}$ into the point $\left(\dfrac{3\pi}{8}, \tan \dfrac{3\pi}{8}\right)$ as illustrated below.

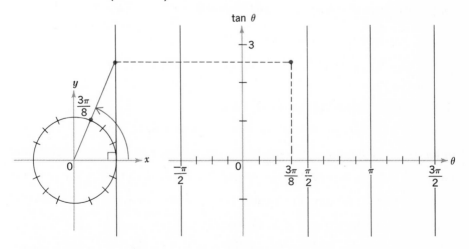

Draw a larger picture of the scheme above and project each line value of $\tan \theta$, where θ is a multiple of $\dfrac{\pi}{8}$ in the interval $\dfrac{-\pi}{2} < \theta < \dfrac{3\pi}{2}$, $\theta \neq \dfrac{\pi}{2}$, into a point of the θ, $\tan \theta$ coordinate plane.

2. In the adjoining figure, give the segments which determine the line values of the following.

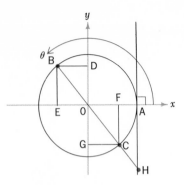

a. $\sin \theta$

e. $\tan \theta$

b. $\sin (\theta + \pi)$

f. $\tan (\theta + \pi)$

c. $\cos \theta$

g. $\tan (\theta - \pi)$

d. $\cos (\theta + \pi)$

h. $\sin (\theta - \pi)$

3. Describe the variations of $\tan \theta$ for the following variations of θ.

a. θ increases from 0 to $\frac{\pi}{2}$.

d. θ increases from $\frac{3\pi}{2}$ to 2π.

b. θ increases from $\frac{\pi}{2}$ to π.

e. θ increases from $\frac{\pi}{2}$ to $\frac{3\pi}{2}$.

c. θ increases from π to $\frac{3\pi}{2}$.

f. θ increases from $\frac{-\pi}{2}$ to $\frac{\pi}{2}$.

4. Determine all θ in the interval $0 \leq \theta < 2\pi$ such that the following are true.

a. $\tan \theta = 0$ **c.** $\tan \theta = -1$ **e.** $\tan \theta > 0$

b. $\tan \theta = 1$ **d.** $\tan \theta < 0$ **f.** $\tan \theta$ is undefined

5. Tell the domain of sine, of cosine, and of tangent.

6. Tell the range of sine, of cosine, and of tangent.

7. Tell the primitive period of sine, of cosine, and of tangent.

8. For what values of θ is the expression $\dfrac{1}{3 - \tan^2 \theta}$ undefined?

REDUCTION IDENTITIES FOR TAN θ

You have seen that, for any real number α, we were able to express $\sin \alpha$ or $\cos \alpha$ in terms of $\sin \theta$ and $\cos \theta$, respectively, where $0 \leq \theta \leq \frac{\pi}{2}$. The situation with tangent is similar. Recall that the period of tangent is π; that is, $\tan \alpha \equiv \tan (\alpha + k\pi)$. Hence, for any real number $\alpha \neq \frac{\pi}{2} + k\pi$, $\tan \alpha$ may be expressed in terms of $\tan \theta$, where $0 \leq \theta < \pi$. For example,

$$\tan \frac{17\pi}{3} = \tan \left(\frac{17\pi}{3} - 5\pi \right) = \tan \frac{2\pi}{3}$$
$$\tan \frac{-9\pi}{4} = \tan \left(\frac{-9\pi}{4} + 3\pi \right) = \tan \frac{3\pi}{4}$$

Furthermore, for θ in the interval $\frac{\pi}{2} < \theta < \pi$, tan θ may be expressed in terms of

tan β, where $0 < \beta < \frac{\pi}{2}$. This is accomplished by using the identity

$$\tan \theta \equiv -\tan (\pi - \theta). \qquad [5.3]$$

Here is a proof of this identity.

Proof $\tan \theta \equiv \dfrac{\sin \theta}{\cos \theta}$ *by 5.1*

$\qquad\qquad \equiv \dfrac{\sin (\pi - \theta)}{-\cos (\pi - \theta)}$ $[\sin \theta \equiv \sin (\pi - \theta)$

$\qquad\qquad\qquad\qquad\qquad\qquad \cos \theta \equiv -\cos (\pi - \theta)]$

$\qquad\qquad \equiv -\dfrac{\sin (\pi - \theta)}{\cos (\pi - \theta)}$

$\qquad\qquad \equiv -\tan (\pi - \theta)$ *by 5.1*

Using this reduction identity is quite simple.

Examples $\tan \dfrac{6\pi}{7} = -\tan \left(\pi - \dfrac{6\pi}{7}\right) = -\tan \dfrac{\pi}{7}$ $\tan 2 = -\tan (\pi - 2)$

Another identity

$$\tan (-\theta) \equiv -\tan \theta \qquad [5.4]$$

may be used to express the tangent of a negative number in terms of the tangent of a positive number.

Examples $\tan \dfrac{-\pi}{6} = -\tan \dfrac{\pi}{6}$ $\qquad\qquad \tan \dfrac{-5\pi}{7} = -\tan \dfrac{5\pi}{7}$

$\qquad\qquad\qquad\qquad \tan (-1.02) = -\tan 1.02$

You will be asked to prove identity 5.4 in the exercises.

Study the following examples which illustrate the use of identities discussed in this section.

Example 1   Express (1) tan $\dfrac{7\pi}{5}$, (2) tan $\dfrac{5\pi}{9}$, (3) tan $\dfrac{-3\pi}{8}$, (4) tan 4 and (5) tan $\dfrac{12\pi}{7}$

in terms of tan θ where $0 \le \theta < \dfrac{\pi}{2}$.

(1) $\tan \dfrac{7\pi}{5} = \tan \left(\dfrac{7\pi}{5} - \pi\right) = \tan \dfrac{2\pi}{5}$

(2) $\tan \dfrac{5\pi}{9} = -\tan \left(\pi - \dfrac{5\pi}{9}\right) = -\tan \dfrac{4\pi}{9}$

(3) $\tan \dfrac{-3\pi}{8} = -\tan \dfrac{3\pi}{8}$

(4) $\tan 4 = \tan (4 - \pi)$

(5) $\tan \dfrac{12\pi}{7} = \tan \left(\dfrac{12\pi}{7} - \pi\right) = \tan \dfrac{5\pi}{7} = -\tan \dfrac{2\pi}{7}$

Example 2   Use Table I and determine (1) tan 1.23, (2) tan 2.32, and
(3) tan 0.862 with accuracy to four digits.
(1) In Table I we read directly that tan 1.23 ≐ 2.820.
(2) tan 2.32 = −tan (π − 2.32) ≐ −tan 0.82 ≐ −1.072.
(3) Since 0.862 has three decimal places, we interpolate.

Thus, $\dfrac{.002}{.01} = \dfrac{n}{.023}$ or $\dfrac{2}{10} = \dfrac{n}{.023}$

which yields $10n = 2(.023)$ and $n = .0046 \doteq .005$.

Hence,   tan 0.862 ≐ 1.162 + .005 = 1.167.

EXERCISES

1. Express each of the following in terms of tan θ, where $0 \le \theta < \dfrac{\pi}{2}$.

   a. tan $\dfrac{9\pi}{8}$ **e.** tan $\dfrac{-2\pi}{7}$ **i.** tan $\dfrac{4\pi}{5}$

   b. tan $\dfrac{9\pi}{5}$ **f.** tan $\dfrac{-6\pi}{5}$ **j.** tan $\dfrac{14\pi}{5}$

   c. tan 7π **g.** tan 6   **k.** tan 7

   d. tan (-3π) **h.** tan 3   **l.** tan 4.5

2. Prove identity [5.4], tan $(-\theta) \equiv -\tan \theta$.

3. Use Table I and determine each of the following to four digits. Interpolate for **h** and **i.**

   a. tan 0.67   **e.** tan 5.61   **i.** tan 0.825

   b. tan 1.32   **f.** tan (-0.51) **j.** tan 7

   c. tan 2.02   **g.** tan (-1.23) **k.** tan (-3)

   d. tan 3.68   **h.** tan 1.342   **l.** tan 8

4. Determine two values of θ between 0 and 2π for each of the following. Express answers to two decimal places.

   a. tan $\theta \doteq 0.2236$ **c.** tan $\theta \doteq -0.4586$ **e.** tan $\theta \doteq 92.62$

   b. tan $\theta \doteq 0.7139$ **d.** tan $\theta \doteq -1.185$ **f.** tan $\theta \doteq 16.43$

5. Interpolate and determine a first or a second quadrant number θ to three decimal places for each of the following.

a. $\tan \theta \doteq 2.152$ **b.** $\tan \theta \doteq 0.5280$ **c.** $\tan \theta \doteq -1.324$

IDENTITIES INVOLVING TANGENT

Four identities involving $\tan \theta$ have already been established.

$$\tan \theta \equiv \frac{\sin \theta}{\cos \theta} \quad [5.1] \qquad\qquad \tan \theta = -\tan (\pi - \theta) \quad [5.3]$$

$$\tan \theta \equiv \tan (\theta + k\pi) \quad [5.2] \qquad\qquad \tan (-\theta) \equiv -\tan \theta \quad [5.4]$$

We shall derive five more identities involving tangent and study their applications. From identity [5.1] it follows that

$$\tan (\theta + \alpha) \equiv \frac{\sin (\theta + \alpha)}{\cos (\theta + \alpha)}$$

$$\equiv \frac{\sin \theta \cdot \cos \alpha + \cos \theta \cdot \sin \alpha}{\cos \theta \cdot \cos \alpha - \sin \theta \cdot \sin \alpha}$$

$$\equiv \frac{\dfrac{\sin \theta \cdot \cos \alpha}{\cos \theta \cdot \cos \alpha} + \dfrac{\cos \theta \cdot \sin \alpha}{\cos \theta \cdot \cos \alpha}}{\dfrac{\cos \theta \cdot \cos \alpha}{\cos \theta \cdot \cos \alpha} - \dfrac{\sin \theta \cdot \sin \alpha}{\cos \theta \cdot \cos \alpha}}$$

$$\equiv \frac{\dfrac{\sin \theta}{\cos \theta} + \dfrac{\sin \alpha}{\cos \alpha}}{1 - \dfrac{\sin \theta}{\cos \theta} \cdot \dfrac{\sin \alpha}{\cos \alpha}}$$

Thus, we have proved the identity

$$\tan (\theta + \alpha) \equiv \frac{\tan \theta + \tan \alpha}{1 - \tan \theta \cdot \tan \alpha} \qquad\qquad [5.5]$$

Substituting $-\beta$ for α in identity [5.5], we can derive another identity.

$$\tan (\theta - \beta) \equiv \frac{\tan \theta - \tan \beta}{1 + \tan \theta \cdot \tan \beta} \qquad\qquad [5.6]$$

You will be asked to prove this identity in the exercises.
To derive an identity for $\tan 2\theta$, let $\alpha = \theta$ in identity [5.5].

$$\tan (\theta + \theta) \equiv \frac{\tan \theta + \tan \theta}{1 - \tan \theta \cdot \tan \theta}$$

resulting in the identity

$$\tan 2\theta \equiv \frac{2 \tan \theta}{1 - \tan^2 \theta} \qquad\qquad [5.7]$$

There are two identities for $\tan \dfrac{\theta}{2}$. From identity [5.1], it follows that

$$\tan \alpha \equiv \frac{\sin \alpha}{\cos \alpha} \cdot \frac{2 \sin \alpha}{2 \sin \alpha}$$

Hence, $\tan \alpha \equiv \dfrac{2 \sin^2 \alpha}{2 \sin \alpha \cos \alpha}$ or $\tan \alpha \equiv \dfrac{1 - \cos 2\alpha}{\sin 2\alpha}$

In the last identity, let $\alpha = \dfrac{\theta}{2}$ (then $2\alpha = \theta$) to obtain the identity

$$\tan \frac{\theta}{2} \equiv \frac{1 - \cos \theta}{\sin \theta} \qquad [5.8]$$

In a similar manner, we can derive the identity

$$\tan \frac{\theta}{2} \equiv \frac{\sin \theta}{1 + \cos \theta} \qquad [5.9]$$

These identities may be used to prove other identities and to determine $\tan \theta$ for special values of θ as is shown by the following examples. You should make a list of identities involving tangent for easy reference.

Example 1   Determine $\tan \dfrac{7\pi}{12}$.

Solution   Since $\dfrac{7\pi}{12} = \dfrac{\pi}{3} + \dfrac{\pi}{4}$, we use identity [5.5] to obtain

$$\tan \frac{7\pi}{12} = \tan \left(\frac{\pi}{3} + \frac{\pi}{4} \right)$$

$$= \frac{\tan \dfrac{\pi}{3} + \tan \dfrac{\pi}{4}}{1 - \tan \dfrac{\pi}{3} \cdot \tan \dfrac{\pi}{4}}$$

$$= \frac{\sqrt{3} + 1}{1 - \sqrt{3} \cdot 1} = \frac{1 + \sqrt{3}}{1 - \sqrt{3}} \cdot \frac{1 + \sqrt{3}}{1 + \sqrt{3}}$$

$$= \frac{1 + 2\sqrt{3} + 3}{1 - 3} = \frac{4 + 2\sqrt{3}}{-2} = -2 - \sqrt{3}$$

Example 2   Determine $\tan \dfrac{3\pi}{8}$.

Solution   Since $\dfrac{3\pi}{8} = \dfrac{1}{2}\left(\dfrac{3\pi}{4}\right)$, we use identity [5.8] to obtain

$$\tan \frac{3\pi}{8} = \frac{1 - \cos \dfrac{3\pi}{4}}{\sin \dfrac{3\pi}{4}} = \frac{1 - \left(\dfrac{-1}{\sqrt{2}}\right)}{\dfrac{1}{\sqrt{2}}}$$

$$= \frac{1 + \dfrac{1}{\sqrt{2}}}{\dfrac{1}{\sqrt{2}}} \cdot \frac{\sqrt{2}}{\sqrt{2}} = \sqrt{2} + 1$$

Example 3   Prove the identity $\dfrac{\sin \theta}{\tan \theta} \equiv \cos \theta.$

Solution $\dfrac{\sin \theta}{\tan \theta} \equiv \dfrac{\sin \theta}{\dfrac{\sin \theta}{\cos \theta}}$

$$\equiv \frac{\sin \theta}{1} \cdot \frac{\cos \theta}{\sin \theta} \equiv \cos \theta$$

Example 4   Simplify $\dfrac{\sin (-\theta)}{-\cos \theta}.$

Solution $\dfrac{\sin (-\theta)}{-\cos \theta} \equiv \dfrac{-\sin \theta}{-\cos \theta} \equiv \dfrac{\sin \theta}{\cos \theta} \equiv \tan \theta$

Example 5   Prove the identity $\sin \theta \cdot \tan \theta + \cos \theta \equiv \dfrac{1}{\cos \theta}.$

Solution $\sin \theta \cdot \tan \theta + \cos \theta \equiv \sin \theta \cdot \dfrac{\sin \theta}{\cos \theta} + \cos \theta$

$$\equiv \frac{\sin^2 \theta + \cos^2 \theta}{\cos \theta}$$

$$\equiv \frac{1}{\cos \theta}$$

Example 6   Prove the identity $\tan \theta \equiv \dfrac{\sin 2\theta}{1 + \cos 2\theta}.$

Solution $\dfrac{\sin 2\theta}{1 + \cos 2\theta} \equiv \dfrac{2 \sin \theta \cdot \cos \theta}{1 + 2 \cos^2 \theta - 1}$

$$\equiv \frac{2 \sin \theta \cdot \cos \theta}{2 \cos^2 \theta}$$

$$\equiv \frac{\sin \theta}{\cos \theta} \equiv \tan \theta$$

EXERCISES

1. Prove identity [5.6], $\tan (\theta - \alpha) \equiv \dfrac{\tan \theta - \tan \alpha}{1 + \tan \theta \cdot \tan \alpha}.$

2. Prove identity [5.9], $\tan \dfrac{\theta}{2} \equiv \dfrac{\sin \theta}{1 + \cos \theta}.$

3. Prove each reduction identity listed below.

    a. $\tan (\pi + \theta) \equiv \tan \theta$ **b.** $\tan \theta \equiv -\tan (2\pi - \theta)$

4. Given $\tan \theta = \dfrac{4}{3}$ and $\tan \alpha = \dfrac{-5}{2}$, determine each of the following.

    a. $\tan (\theta + \alpha)$ **b.** $\tan (\theta - \alpha)$ **c.** $\tan 2\theta$

5. Simplify each of the following.

a. $\dfrac{\sin(-\theta)}{\cos(-\theta)}$

e. $\dfrac{\tan 3\theta + \tan 5\theta}{1 - \tan 3\theta \cdot \tan 5\theta}$

i. $\tan(\pi - 1)$

j. $\tan(\pi + 1)$

b. $\dfrac{\sin\theta}{\cos(-\theta)}$

f. $\dfrac{\tan 5\alpha - \tan 2\alpha}{1 + \tan 5\alpha \cdot \tan 2\alpha}$

k. $\tan(-1)$

l. $-\tan(3 - \theta)$

c. $\dfrac{\sin(-\theta)}{\cos\theta}$

g. $\dfrac{\tan\theta}{\sin\theta}$

m. $\dfrac{1 - \cos 8\theta}{\sin 8\theta}$

d. $\dfrac{-\sin(-\theta)}{-\cos(-\theta)}$

h. $\dfrac{2\tan 3\theta}{1 - \tan^2 3\theta}$

n. $\dfrac{\sin 6\theta}{1 + \cos 6\theta}$

6. Compute each of the following.

a. $\tan\dfrac{5\pi}{12}$ **b.** $\tan\dfrac{\pi}{12}$ **c.** $\tan\dfrac{19\pi}{12}$ **d.** $\tan\dfrac{-7\pi}{12}$

7. What real numbers are not permissible values of θ in the expression

$$\frac{2}{1 - \tan^2\theta} + \frac{3}{\tan\theta}?$$

8. Express $\tan 3\theta$ in terms of $\tan\theta$.

9. For each set of conditions, determine (1) $\tan 2\theta$ and (2) $\tan\dfrac{\theta}{2}$.

a. $\sin\theta = \dfrac{2}{3}$ and $\dfrac{\pi}{2} < \theta < \pi$

c. $\tan\theta = \dfrac{5}{3}$ and $0 < \theta < \dfrac{\pi}{2}$

b. $\cos\theta = \dfrac{-1}{4}$ and $\pi < \theta < \dfrac{3\pi}{2}$

d. $\sin\theta = \dfrac{-2}{5}$ and $\pi < \theta < \dfrac{3\pi}{2}$

10. Use identity [5.8] or identity [5.9] to compute each of the following.

a. $\tan\dfrac{\pi}{8}$ **b.** $\tan\dfrac{7\pi}{12}$ **c.** $\tan\dfrac{13\pi}{12}$ **d.** $\tan\dfrac{5\pi}{8}$

11. Prove each of the following identities.

a. $\tan\theta \cdot \cos\theta \equiv \sin\theta$

f. $\dfrac{1}{\sin\theta \cdot \cos\theta} - \dfrac{1}{\tan\theta} \equiv \tan\theta$

b. $\dfrac{\sin\theta + \cos\theta \cdot \tan\theta}{\cos\theta} \equiv 2\tan\theta$

g. $\dfrac{\cos^4\theta - \sin^4\theta}{1 - \tan^4\theta} \equiv \cos^4\theta$

c. $\dfrac{1}{\cos^2\theta} - 1 \equiv \tan^2\theta$

h. $\dfrac{\tan\theta + \sin\theta}{2\tan\theta} \equiv \cos^2\dfrac{\theta}{2}$

d. $\dfrac{\cos\theta}{\tan\theta} + \sin\theta \equiv \dfrac{1}{\sin\theta}$

i. $(1 + \tan^2\theta)\sin^2\theta \equiv \tan^2\theta$

e. $\tan\theta + \dfrac{1}{\tan\theta} \equiv \dfrac{1}{\sin\theta \cdot \cos\theta}$

j. $\dfrac{\cos\theta \cdot \tan\theta + \sin\theta}{\tan\theta} \equiv 2\cos\theta$

k. $\dfrac{1 - \tan^2 \theta}{1 + \tan^2 \theta} \equiv \cos 2\theta$

n. $\dfrac{\tan 3\theta - \tan \theta}{1 + \tan 3\theta \cdot \tan \theta} \equiv \dfrac{2 \tan \theta}{1 - \tan^2 \theta}$

l. $\dfrac{1 - \cos 2\theta}{2 \sin \theta \cdot \cos \theta} \equiv \tan \theta$

o. $\left(\dfrac{1 + \tan \theta}{1 - \tan \theta}\right)^2 \equiv \dfrac{1 + \sin 2\theta}{1 - \sin 2\theta}$

m. $\dfrac{1 - \tan^2 \theta}{2 \tan \theta} \equiv \dfrac{\cos 2\theta}{2 \sin \theta \cdot \cos \theta}$

p. $\tan \dfrac{\theta}{2} \cdot (1 + \cos \theta) \equiv \sin \theta$

EQUATIONS INVOLVING TAN θ

Earlier you learned to solve trigonometric equations which involved $\sin \theta$ or $\cos \theta$ or both. In this section you will solve equations involving $\tan \theta$. Study the methods illustrated by the following examples.

Example 1   Solve $\tan^2 \theta + \sqrt{3} \tan \theta = 0$ for θ in the interval $0 \le \theta < 2\pi$.

Solution $\tan^2 \theta + \sqrt{3} \tan \theta = 0$
$\tan \theta (\tan \theta + \sqrt{3}) = 0$
$(\tan \theta = 0)$ or $(\tan \theta = -\sqrt{3})$
$(\theta = 0$ or $\theta = \pi)$ or $\left(\theta = \dfrac{2\pi}{3}$ or $\theta = \dfrac{5\pi}{3}\right)$

The solution set is $\left\{0, \dfrac{2\pi}{3}, \pi, \dfrac{5\pi}{3}\right\}$.

Example 2   Solve $4 \tan \theta = 3$ for θ, with accuracy to two decimal places, in the interval $0 \le \theta < 2\pi$.

Solution $4 \tan \theta = 3$

$\tan \theta = \dfrac{3}{4} = 0.7500$

From Table I, $\theta \doteq 0.64$ or $\theta \doteq \pi + 0.64 \doteq 3.78$. The solutions are 0.64 and 3.78, accurate to two decimal places.

EXERCISES

1. Solve each equation for θ in the interval $0 \le \theta < 2\pi$.

a. $\tan^2 \theta = 3$

b. $3 \tan^2 \theta - 1 = 0$

c. $\tan^2 \theta - \tan \theta = 0$

d. $\tan \theta - \sin \theta = 0$

e. $\tan^2 \theta = 1$

f. $2 \sin \theta \cdot \tan \theta + \tan \theta = 0$

g. $\tan 2\theta = 1$

h. $3 \tan^3 \theta - \tan \theta = 0$

i. $4 \tan^2 \theta - \dfrac{3}{\cos^2 \theta} = 0$

$\left[Hint: \tan \theta \equiv \dfrac{\sin \theta}{\cos \theta} \right]$

j. $\tan \theta - \sin 2\theta = 0$

k. $\tan 3\theta = -1$

l. $\sqrt{3} \tan^2 \theta + 2 \tan \theta - \sqrt{3} = 0$

2. Determine the solutions of each equation to two decimal places for $0 \leq \theta < 2\pi$.

    a. $2 \tan \theta = 3$ **b.** $4 \tan \theta + 5 = 0$ **c.** $4 \tan^2 \theta = 1$

3. What values of θ are not permissible in the expression $\dfrac{2}{1 - 3 \tan^2 \theta}$?

VOCABULARY

Use each of the following correctly in a sentence to demonstrate that you understand its meaning. If you are not sure of the meaning of any word, refer back to the chapter.

    domain of tangent   primitive period of tangent
    line value of tan θ range of tangent
    period of tangent

REVIEW EXERCISES

1. Determine each of the following, if it exists.

    a. $\tan \dfrac{\pi}{4}$ **d.** $\tan \pi$ **g.** $\tan \dfrac{2\pi}{3}$ **j.** $\tan \dfrac{-\pi}{4}$

    b. $\tan \dfrac{\pi}{3}$ **e.** $\tan \dfrac{\pi}{2}$ **h.** $\tan \dfrac{7\pi}{4}$ **k.** $\tan \dfrac{-5\pi}{3}$

    c. $\tan \dfrac{\pi}{6}$ **f.** $\tan 0$ **i.** $\tan \dfrac{7\pi}{6}$ **l.** $\tan \dfrac{-7\pi}{6}$

2. State the domain, range and primitive period of tangent.

3. Given $\sin \theta = \dfrac{-2}{3}$ and $\pi < \theta < \dfrac{3\pi}{2}$, determine $\tan \theta$.

4. Given $\tan \theta = \dfrac{-5}{3}$ and $\dfrac{\pi}{2} < \theta < \pi$, determine $\cos \theta$ and $\sin \theta$.

5. Sketch the graph of tangent for the interval $-\pi < \theta < 2\pi$.

6. Which of the following are identities?

    a. $\tan \theta = \dfrac{\cos \theta}{\sin \theta}$ **f.** $\tan \theta = \tan (\theta + k\pi)$

    b. $\tan \theta = \tan (\theta - \pi)$ **g.** $\tan (\theta + \alpha) = \dfrac{\tan \theta + \tan \alpha}{1 + \tan \theta \cdot \tan \alpha}$

    c. $\tan (-\theta) = -\tan \theta$

    d. $\tan \theta = -\tan (\pi - \theta)$ **h.** $\tan \dfrac{\theta}{2} = \dfrac{\sin \theta}{1 - \cos \theta}$

    e. $\tan \theta = \tan (\theta + \pi)$ **i.** $\tan (2\pi - \theta) = -\tan \theta$

7. Simplify.

    a. $\dfrac{\sin (-\theta)}{-\cos \theta}$ **b.** $\dfrac{\tan 3\theta + \tan 2\theta}{1 - \tan 3\theta \cdot \tan 2\theta}$ **c.** $\tan \theta \cdot \cos \theta$ **d.** $\tan (\pi + 3)$

8. Given $\tan \theta = \dfrac{1}{2}$ and $\tan \alpha = \dfrac{-3}{2}$, determine the following.

   a. $\tan (\theta + \alpha)$ **b.** $\tan (\theta - \alpha)$ **c.** $\tan 2\theta$

9. Determine each value.

   a. $\tan \dfrac{7\pi}{12}$ **b.** $\tan \dfrac{5\pi}{8}$

10. Given $\sin \theta = \dfrac{3}{4}$ and $\dfrac{\pi}{2} < \theta < \pi$, determine $\tan \dfrac{\theta}{2}$ and $\tan 2\theta$.

11. Prove each identity.

   a. $2 \tan \theta \cdot \cos^2 \theta \equiv \sin 2\theta$ **b.** $\tan \theta + \dfrac{1}{\tan \theta} \equiv \dfrac{1}{\cos \theta \cdot \sin \theta}$

12. Solve each equation for θ in the interval $0 \le \theta < 2\pi$.

   a. $3 \tan^2 \theta = 1$ **c.** $\tan 2\theta = 0$

   b. $2 \cos \theta \cdot \tan \theta - \tan \theta = 0$ **d.** $5 \tan \theta = 3$

CHAPTER TEST

1. Determine each of the following, if it exists.

   a. $\tan \dfrac{3\pi}{4}$ **b.** $\tan \dfrac{7\pi}{6}$ **c.** $\tan \pi$ **d.** $\tan \dfrac{-\pi}{3}$

2. What values of θ are not permissible for the expression $\dfrac{1}{\tan \theta}$?

3. Given $\cos \theta = \dfrac{2}{5}$ and $\dfrac{3\pi}{2} < \theta < 2\pi$, determine $\tan \theta$.

4. Given $\tan \theta = -2$ and $\dfrac{\pi}{2} < \theta < \pi$, determine $\sin \theta$ and $\cos \theta$.

5. Sketch the graph of tangent for the interval $\dfrac{-\pi}{2} < \theta < \dfrac{3\pi}{2}$.

6. Simplify.

   a. $\tan (\pi - 4)$ **b.** $\tan (\pi + 2)$ **c.** $\dfrac{\sin (-\theta)}{\cos (-\theta)}$ **d.** $\dfrac{\sin \theta}{\tan \theta}$

7. Given $\tan (\theta + \alpha) \equiv \dfrac{\tan \theta + \tan \alpha}{1 - \tan \theta \cdot \tan \alpha}$, $\tan \theta = \dfrac{3}{2}$ and $\tan \alpha = \dfrac{-3}{4}$, determine the following.

   a. $\tan (\theta + \alpha)$ **b.** $\tan (\theta - \alpha)$ **c.** $\tan 2\theta$

8. Solve for θ in the interval $0 \le \theta < 2\pi$.

   a. $\tan^2 \theta = 1$ **c.** $3 \tan \theta = \sqrt{3}$

   b. $2 \sin \theta \cdot \tan \theta + \tan \theta = 0$ **d.** $\tan 2\theta = 1$

CHAPTER 6

TRIGONOMETRIC FUNCTIONS OF ANGLE MEASURES

GENERATED ANGLES AND DEGREE MEASURE

In defining an angle as the set of points consisting of two noncollinear rays with a common endpoint, we limited the degree measures of such angles to the interval between 0° and 180°. In continuing our study of trigonometry, we shall consider the concept of an angle from a different point of view.

For the unit circle with center O shown in Figure 6–1, consider the path $\left(A, \dfrac{8\pi}{3} \right)$ with terminal point P. The point P determines ray $\overrightarrow{OP}$ which with ray $\overrightarrow{OA}$ forms $\angle AOP$. We say that $\angle AOP$ is generated by the path $\left(A, \dfrac{8\pi}{3} \right)$ and that $\angle AOP$ is a *generated angle* with *initial side* $\overrightarrow{OA}$ and *terminal side* $\overrightarrow{OP}$.

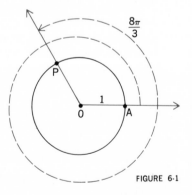

FIGURE 6-1

For the unit circle with center O shown in Figure 6–2, the six paths

$$\left(A, \frac{\pi}{4} \right) \quad \left(A, \frac{2\pi}{3} \right) \quad (A, \pi) \quad \left(A, \frac{7\pi}{6} \right) \quad \left(A, \frac{-\pi}{3} \right) \quad (A, 0)$$

have terminal points B, C, D, E, F and A, respectively. Figure 6–3 shows the six angles $\qquad \angle AOB \quad \angle AOC \quad \angle AOD \quad \angle AOE \quad \angle AOF \quad \angle AOA$

which are generated, respectively, by the six paths above. Ray $\overrightarrow{OA}$ is the initial side of each of these generated angles. Which ray is the terminal side of $\angle AOE$? Which ray is both the initial and terminal side of $\angle AOA$?

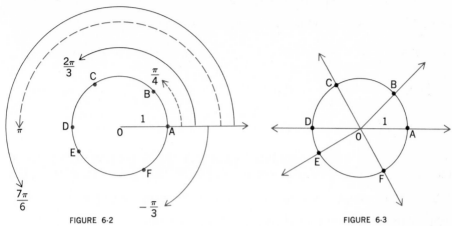

FIGURE 6-2   FIGURE 6-3

In general, given a unit circle with center O and any path (A, θ) with terminal point P on the circle, the angle AOP is a *generated angle* with *initial side* $\overrightarrow{OA}$ and *terminal side* $\overrightarrow{OP}$.

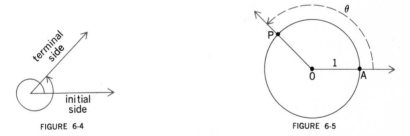

FIGURE 6-4   FIGURE 6-5

For convenience we shall often speak of "angle" rather than "generated angle." Observe in Figure 6–4 a picture of the angle generated by the path $\left(A, \dfrac{9\pi}{4}\right)$. A directed spiral around the vertex begins on the initial side, ends on the terminal side, and indicates the direction and magnitude of the path which generates the angle. The spiral thus indicates an amount of "rotation" around the vertex which would take a ray from the initial side to the terminal side of the angle.

To measure generated angles, we may use a *degree* as the unit of measure. A central angle of 1 degree intercepts $\dfrac{1}{360}$th of its circle. Observe in Figures 6–2 and 6–3 that the path (A, π) generates an angle of 180° which intercepts a semicircle. The path $\left(A, \dfrac{\pi}{4}\right)$ generates an angle of 45°.

Determining the Real Number Degree Measure of a Generated Angle. For each path (A, θ) with terminal point P on a unit circle, the real number degree measure of $\angle AOP$ is $\left(\dfrac{180}{\pi} \cdot \theta\right)^{\circ}$. See Figure 6–5.

Thus, for Figures 6–2 and 6–3 the degree measure of

$\angle AOB$ is $\left(\dfrac{180}{\pi} \cdot \dfrac{\pi}{4}\right)^{\circ}$ or 45° $\angle AOE$ is $\left(\dfrac{180}{\pi} \cdot \dfrac{7\pi}{6}\right)^{\circ}$ or 210°

$\angle AOC$ is $\left(\dfrac{180}{\pi} \cdot \dfrac{2\pi}{3}\right)^{\circ}$ or 120° $\angle AOF$ is $\left(\dfrac{180}{\pi} \cdot \dfrac{-\pi}{3}\right)^{\circ}$ or $-60°$

$\angle AOD$ is $\left(\dfrac{180}{\pi} \cdot \pi\right)^{\circ}$ or 180° $\angle AOA$ is $\left(\dfrac{180}{\pi} \cdot 0\right)^{\circ}$ or 0°

Observe that we no longer limit degree measures to the interval between 0° and 180°. A real number degree measure may be 0°, 180°, greater than 360° or less than 0°. For example, in Figure 6–6 consider the many paths $\left(A, \dfrac{2\pi}{3} + 2k\pi\right)$. Each of these paths has terminal point C and generates $\angle AOC$. According to the rule above, the degree measures of $\angle AOC$ are $\dfrac{180}{\pi} \left(\dfrac{2\pi}{3} + 2k\pi\right)^{\circ}$ or $(120 + 360k)°$. Some of these degree measures are 120°, 480° and $-240°$ as shown in Figure 6–6.

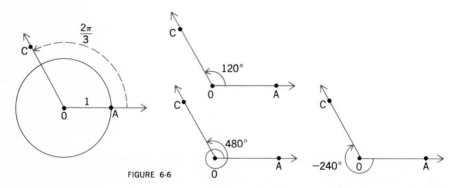

FIGURE 6·6

List two positive and one negative degree measures that may be assigned to the angle generated by the paths $\left(A, \dfrac{\pi}{4} + 2k\pi\right)$; by the paths $(A, \pi + 2k\pi)$; by the paths $\left(A, \dfrac{-\pi}{3} + 2k\pi\right)$.

We now consider generated angles on a coordinate plane and classify them according to the position of their terminal sides.

DEFINITION OF STANDARD POSITION FOR GENERATED ANGLES.   A generated angle is said to be in *standard position* if and only if (1) the angle is on a coordinate plane, (2) its vertex is at the origin, and (3) its initial side passes through the point (1, 0).

Figures 6–7 and 6–8 show angles *AOP* and *AOQ* in standard position. Check whether each of these angles satisfies the three conditions stated.

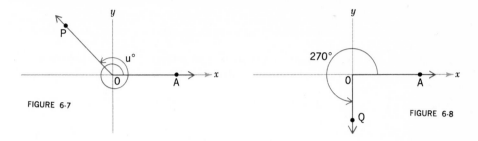

FIGURE 6-7

FIGURE 6-8

Angles in standard position may be classified according to the position of their terminal side in the following ways.

1. An angle is called a *first* (second, third, fourth) *quadrant angle* if and only if its terminal side is in quadrant I (II, III, IV), respectively. Likewise, the degree measure of a first (second, third, fourth) quadrant angle is called a *first* (second, third, fourth) *quadrant number*, respectively.

2. An angle is called a *quadrantal angle* if and only if the terminal side is on an axis. The degree measures of quadrantal angles are the integer multiples of 90°, that is, $90k°$, and are called *quadrantal numbers*.

3. Two or more angles are called *coterminal* if and only if the angles have the same terminal side.

We shall use variables such as $u°$, $v°$ and $w°$ for degree measures of angles. Figure 6–7 shows a second quadrant angle of $u°$. In this case, we say that $u°$ is a second quadrant number. Figure 6–8 shows a quadrantal angle of 270°.

What are the quadrantal numbers between −100° and 400°?

Three angles in standard position with measures of 50°, 410° and −310° are coterminal (see Figure 6-9). Note that, in standard position, an angle of $u°$ and any angle of $(u + 360k)°$ are coterminal.

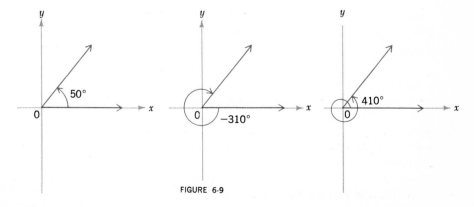

FIGURE 6-9

EXERCISES

1. Draw pictures of generated angles with the following degree measures as in Figure 6–6.

 a. 150°   **c.** 225°   **e.** 270°   **g.** 720°

 b. −120°   **d.** −360°   **f.** −330°   **h.** −540°

2. Determine the degree measure of the angle AOP generated by each of the following paths (A, θ). In each case the terminal point P is on a unit circle with center O.

 a. $\left(A, \dfrac{\pi}{2}\right)$ **d.** $\left(A, \dfrac{-3\pi}{4}\right)$ **g.** $(A, 5\pi)$ **j.** $(A, 0)$

 b. $\left(A, \dfrac{7\pi}{12}\right)$ **e.** $\left(A, \dfrac{-7\pi}{10}\right)$ **h.** $\left(A, \dfrac{7\pi}{6}\right)$ **k.** $\left(A, \dfrac{9\pi}{5}\right)$

 c. $(A, 4\pi)$ **f.** $(A, -3\pi)$ **i.** $\left(A, \dfrac{-4\pi}{3}\right)$ **l.** $\left(A, \dfrac{-4\pi}{9}\right)$

3. Draw pictures of angles in standard position with their terminal sides passing through the points given below. In each case, determine the distance from the origin to the point P.

 a. $P(-3, -4)$ **c.** $P(-2, 5)$ **e.** $P(-3, 0)$

 b. $P(0, 2)$ **d.** $P(4, 5)$ **f.** $P(6, -2)$

4. For each angle of Exercise 3 give its quadrant number or state that it is a quadrantal angle.

5. Construct the angle in standard position for each degree measure given below. Use a spiral to indicate the measure on each drawing as in Figure 6–9.

 a. 135°   **c.** 450°   **e.** 210°

 b. −60°   **d.** −180°   **f.** −120°

6. For each angle of Exercise 5, give the degree measures of two other coterminal angles, one positive and one negative.

7. Given the following degree measures, tell whether the number is a first, second, third, or fourth quadrant number or a quadrantal number.

 a. 200°   **c.** 90°   **e.** −20°   **g.** 460°   **i.** 0°

 b. 50°   **d.** 290°   **f.** −180°   **h.** 140°   **j.** −220°

8. What are the degree measures of all angles coterminal with a −20° angle?

9. Determine the degree measure of the angle generated by the minute hand of a clock if it is on the initial side at 3:00 p.m. and on the terminal side at 4:50 p.m. the same afternoon.

10. Repeat Exercise 9 for the hour hand of the clock.

11. Give a positive and a negative degree measure for each of the following generated angles as shown below on the left. The dashed lines indicate symmetry of points with respect to an axis.

a. ∠AOB   **c.** ∠AOD   **e.** ∠AOF   **g.** ∠AOH

b. ∠AOC   **d.** ∠AOE   **f.** ∠AOG   **h.** ∠AOA

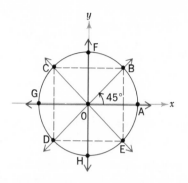
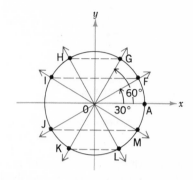

12. Give a positive and a negative degree measure for each of the following generated angles as shown above on the right. The dashed lines indicate symmetry of points with respect to the y-axis.

a. ∠AOF   **c.** ∠AOH   **e.** ∠AOJ   **g.** ∠AOL

b. ∠AOG   **d.** ∠AOI   **f.** ∠AOK   **h.** ∠AOM

13. Determine the degree measure of the angle generated during 20 seconds by a spoke of a wheel which rotates at a speed of 1200 revolutions per minute.

RADIAN MEASURE OF ANGLES

The *radian* is used as the unit of measure in the radian system of angle measurement. In Figure 6–10, ∠AOP is generated by the path (A, 1) on the unit circle. Angle AOP has a measure of 1 radian.

Observe in Figure 6–11 that the measure of each central angle, ∠AOB, ∠BOC, and ∠COP is 1 radian. Hence, the measure of ∠AOP is 3 radians and ∠AOP is generated by the path (A, 3) on a unit circle.

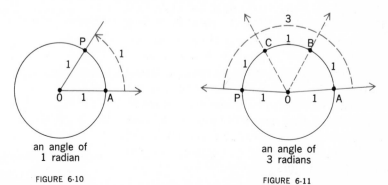

an angle of
1 radian

FIGURE 6-10

an angle of
3 radians

FIGURE 6-11

In general, the path (A, θ) generates an angle of θ radians on a unit circle. See Figure 6–12.

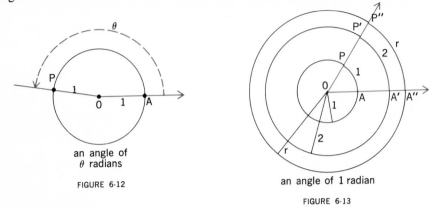

an angle of
θ radians

FIGURE 6-12

an angle of 1 radian

FIGURE 6-13

Recall that, for concentric circles, the lengths of arcs intercepted by a central angle are proportional to the lengths of the radii of the circles. In Figure 6–13 an angle of 1 radian intercepts an arc of length 2 on the circle of radius 2 and, in general, intercepts an arc of length r on the circle of radius r. For this reason, we define 1 *radian* in the following way.

DEFINITION OF RADIAN   The measure of an angle is 1 *radian* if and only if it is a central angle intercepting an arc of length r on a circle of radius r.

Let us decide now how the *radian measure* of any angle may be determined. Observe in Figure 6–14 that the measure of each central angle, $\angle AOB$, $\angle BOC$, and $\angle COP$, is 1 radian since each of the angles intercepts an arc whose length is equal to the radius of the circle. Thus, the measure of $\angle AOP$ is 3 radians and $\angle AOP$ intercepts an arc of length 15 on a circle of radius 5. We say that the path $(A, 15)$ generates $\angle AOP$, an angle of 3 radians, on a circle of radius 5.

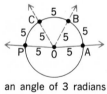

an angle of 3 radians

FIGURE 6-14

Observe in Figure 6–13 that an angle of 1 radian is generated by either the path $(A, 1)$ on a unit circle or the path (A, r) on a circle of radius r. Observe in Figures 6–11 and 6–14 that an angle of 3 radians is generated by either the path $(A, 3)$ on a unit circle or the path $(A, 15)$ on a circle of radius 5. In general, an angle of θ radians is generated by either the path (A, θ) on a unit circle or the path $(A, r\theta)$ on a circle of radius r (see Figures 6–12 and 6–15). Hence, we define *radian measure* in the following way (see Figure 6–16).

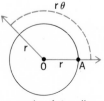

an angle of θ radians

FIGURE 6-15

DEFINITION OF RADIAN MEASURE OF A GENERATED ANGLE · Given a circle of radius r with center O and given any real number α, let P be the terminal point of the path (A, α) along the circle.

The *radian measure* θ of generated angle AOP is given by $\theta = \dfrac{\alpha}{r}$.

As a consequence of the above definition, it follows that, if a central angle of θ radians intercepts an arc of length α on a circle of radius r as shown in Figure 6–16, then

$$\alpha = r\theta$$

Study the following examples which involve radian measure of angles.

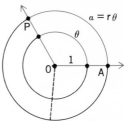

an angle of θ radians

FIGURE 6·16

Example 1   Central angle AOP intercepts an arc of length $\dfrac{4\pi}{3}$ units on a circle of radius 2 as shown. Determine θ, the radian measure of $\angle AOP$.

Solution   The radian measure, θ, of $\angle AOP$

is given by $\theta = \dfrac{\alpha}{r} = \dfrac{4\pi}{3} \div 2$ or $\dfrac{2\pi}{3}$

radians. Note: $\dfrac{2\pi}{3}$, the radian measure of the angle, is the same number as the length of arc intercepted by $\angle AOP$ on a unit circle.

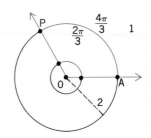

Example 2   Central angle AOP is generated by the path $\left(A, \dfrac{-9\pi}{4}\right)$ on a circle of radius 3 as shown at the right. Determine θ, the radian measure of $\angle AOP$.

Solution   The radian measure, θ, of $\angle AOP$

is given by $\theta = \dfrac{\alpha}{r} = \dfrac{-9\pi}{4} \div 3$ or

$\dfrac{-3\pi}{4}$ radians.

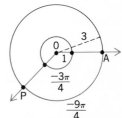

Example 3   Determine α, the length of arc intercepted by a central angle of $\dfrac{5\pi}{6}$ radians on a circle of radius $\dfrac{3}{2}$.

Solution   The length, α, is given by $\alpha = r\theta =$

$\dfrac{3}{2} \cdot \dfrac{5\pi}{6}$ or $\dfrac{5\pi}{4}$ units.

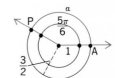

Observe in Figure 6–17 four examples of generated angles. The radian measure θ of each angle is determined by the path (A, θ) which generates the angle on a unit circle. Observe that the radian measure of the angle is indicated near its directed spiral.

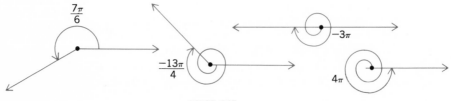

FIGURE 6-17

Degree measure is related to radian measure in the following way. Observe in Figure 6–18 that the radian measure of $\angle AOP$ is π and that the degree measure of $\angle AOP$ is 180°.

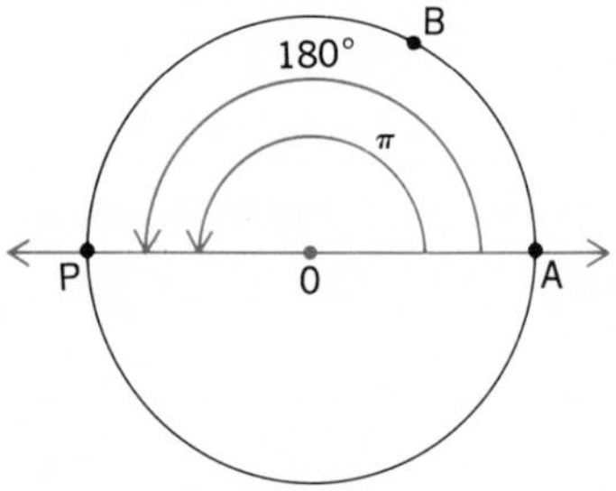

Hence,

$$\pi \text{ radians} = 180°$$

$$1 \text{ radian} = \left(\frac{180}{\pi}\right)° \qquad 1 \text{ degree} = \frac{\pi}{180} \text{ radian}$$

Tell how you would convert x radians to its equivalent degree measure. Tell how you would convert y degrees to its equivalent radian measure.

FIGURE 6-18

You should learn to convert degrees to radians and radians to degrees mentally for certain values. Study the following examples where some conversions are shown. We adopt the common convention that if no unit of measure is stated, then the unit is the radian. Thus, $\frac{\pi}{6}$ means $\frac{\pi}{6}$ radians and 2 means 2 radians.

Example 1   Since π radians $= 180°$, it follows that

$$\frac{\pi}{3} = \left(\frac{180}{3}\right)° = 60° \text{ and } \frac{5\pi}{3} = 5(60)° = 300°$$

$$\frac{\pi}{2} = \left(\frac{180}{2}\right)° = 90° \text{ and } \frac{-3\pi}{2} = -3(90)° = -270°$$

$$\frac{\pi}{4} = \left(\frac{180}{4}\right)° = 45° \text{ and } \frac{5\pi}{4} = 5(45)° = 225°$$

Example 2   Since $180° = \pi$ radians, it follows that

$$30° = \left(\frac{180}{6}\right)° = \frac{\pi}{6} \text{ and } -210° = -7(30)° = \frac{-7\pi}{6}$$

$$45° = \left(\frac{180}{4}\right)° = \frac{\pi}{4} \text{ and } 135° = 3(45)° = \frac{3\pi}{4}$$

We now introduce some terms to be used when referring to angles in standard position.

1. The radian measure of a first (second, third, fourth) quadrant angle is called a *first* (second, third, fourth) *quadrant number,* respectively.

2. The radian measure of a quadrantal angle is called a *quadrantal number.* The quadrantal numbers in the system of radian measure are the integer multiples of $\frac{\pi}{2}$, that is, $\frac{k\pi}{2}$.

   What are the quadrantal numbers between $\frac{-2\pi}{3}$ and $\frac{7\pi}{3}$?

3. Any angle of θ radians is *coterminal* with an angle of $\theta + 2k\pi$ radians.

   For example, three angles in standard position with radian measures of $\frac{\pi}{3}$, $\frac{7\pi}{3}$, and $\frac{-5\pi}{3}$ are coterminal (see Figure 6–19).

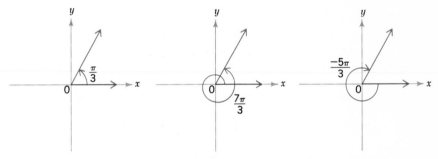

FIGURE 6-19

   For each of these three angle measures, determine the integer k which shows that the measure is of the form $\frac{\pi}{3} + 2k\pi$.

4. We shall use variables such as θ, α, and β for radian measure and $u°$, $v°$, and $w°$ for degree measure of angles.

EXERCISES

1. Draw pictures of generated angles with the following radian measures as in Figure 6–17.

a. $\dfrac{-\pi}{6}$ d. $\dfrac{2\pi}{3}$ g. $\dfrac{7\pi}{4}$ j. 1

b. $\dfrac{3\pi}{2}$ e. $-\pi$ h. -5π k. -2

c. $\dfrac{-3\pi}{4}$ f. $\dfrac{13\pi}{6}$ i. $\dfrac{5\pi}{2}$ l. 6

2. Convert each radian measure to its equivalent degree measure.

a. $\dfrac{7\pi}{6}$ d. $\dfrac{-5\pi}{6}$ g. $\dfrac{17\pi}{6}$ j. $\dfrac{5\pi}{12}$ m. $\dfrac{-7\pi}{5}$

b. $\dfrac{2\pi}{3}$ e. $\dfrac{-5\pi}{3}$ h. $\dfrac{7\pi}{3}$ k. $\dfrac{3\pi}{10}$ n. $\dfrac{2\pi}{9}$

c. $\dfrac{-3\pi}{2}$ f. $\dfrac{5\pi}{2}$ i. 3π l. $\dfrac{7\pi}{18}$ o. 0

3. Convert each degree measure to its equivalent radian measure.

a. $240°$ d. $-120°$ g. $300°$ j. $-420°$ m. $144°$

b. $-30°$ e. $210°$ h. $390°$ k. $10°$ n. $-72°$

c. $90°$ f. $-270°$ i. $1080°$ l. $15°$ o. $105°$

4. Construct the angle in standard position for each radian measure given below. Use a spiral to indicate the measure on each drawing as in Figure 6–19.

a. -3π b. $\dfrac{7\pi}{6}$ c. $\dfrac{-2\pi}{3}$ d. $\dfrac{3\pi}{2}$ e. $\dfrac{7\pi}{3}$

5. For each angle of Exercise 4, give the radian measures of two other coterminal angles, one positive and one negative.

6. What are the radian measures of all angles coterminal with an angle of $\dfrac{3\pi}{7}$ radians?

7. Express 1 radian in degree measure, correct to the nearest minute.

8. Express 1 degree in radian measure, correct to four decimal places.

9. Given the following radian measures, tell whether the number is a first (second, third, fourth) quadrant number or a quadrantal number.

a. $\dfrac{3\pi}{5}$ c. $\dfrac{9\pi}{7}$ e. 1 g. 3.2

b. $\dfrac{-\pi}{9}$ d. $\dfrac{5\pi}{2}$ f. 2.5 h. 6

10. Determine the radian measure of the angle generated by the minute hand of a clock if it is on the initial side at 1:00 p.m. and on the terminal side at 3:00 p.m. the next afternoon.

11. Given a circle of radius 5, determine (1) the radian measure and (2) the degree measure of a central angle which intercepts an arc of the length given below.

a. $\dfrac{5\pi}{3}$ c. $\dfrac{5\pi}{6}$ e. $\dfrac{5\pi}{4}$ g. $\dfrac{7\pi}{4}$

b. π d. 2π f. 3π h. $\dfrac{23\pi}{12}$

12. Given a circle of radius 4, determine the length of the arc intercepted by the central angle whose radian measure is given below.

a. $\dfrac{2\pi}{3}$ **c.** $\dfrac{5\pi}{6}$ **e.** $\dfrac{3\pi}{4}$

b. $\dfrac{\pi}{10}$ **d.** $\dfrac{7\pi}{12}$ **f.** $\dfrac{4\pi}{5}$

13. Given a circle of radius 3, determine the length of arc intercepted by each central angle whose degree measure is given below.

a. $60°$ **c.** $135°$ **e.** $10°$

b. $45°$ **d.** $150°$ **f.** $108°$

14. A circle of radius r has a central angle of θ radians or m degrees which intercepts an arc s units long. Determine those not given of r, θ, m, and s, accurate to one decimal place, for each of the following.

a. $r = 1.8 \quad s = 0.6$ **d.** $s = 14 \quad \theta = \dfrac{7\pi}{10}$ **g.** $r = 2.4 \quad \theta = \dfrac{5\pi}{8}$

b. $r = 12 \quad \theta = \dfrac{3\pi}{4}$ **e.** $s = 2.5 \quad m = 36°$ **h.** $s = 2.1 \quad m = 105°$

c. $r = 2.2 \quad m = 75°$ **f.** $r = 1.6 \quad s = 2.4$

15. Give a positive and a negative radian measure for each of the following generated angles. The dashed lines indicate symmetry of points with respect to an axis.

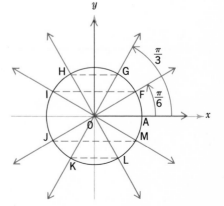

a. $\angle AOB$ **e.** $\angle AOF$

b. $\angle AOC$ **f.** $\angle AOG$

c. $\angle AOD$ **g.** $\angle AOH$

d. $\angle AOE$ **h.** $\angle AOA$

16. Give a positive and a negative radian measure for each of the following generated angles. The dashed lines indicate the symmetry of points with respect to the y-axis.

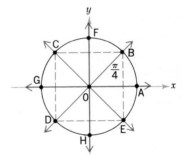

a. $\angle AOF$ **e.** $\angle AOJ$

b. $\angle AOG$ **f.** $\angle AOK$

c. $\angle AOH$ **g.** $\angle AOL$

d. $\angle AOI$ **h.** $\angle AOM$

17. Show that the area A of a circular sector (shaded region at the right) determined by a central angle of θ radians in a circle of radius r is given by

$$A = \frac{1}{2}r^2\theta$$

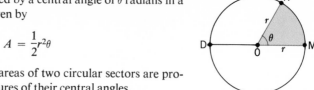

Hint: In a circle, the areas of two circular sectors are proportional to the measures of their central angles.

18. Determine the area of the following circular sectors, given the radius r of the circle and the measure of the central angle as follows.

a. $r = 6$ in., $\theta = \dfrac{5\pi}{9}$

b. $r = 2$ cm., $u° = 15°$

c. $r = 5$ ft., $\theta = \dfrac{2\pi}{5}$

d. $r = 4$ yd., $u° = 135°$

19. A spotlight has a range of 100 yards and can rotate through an angle of 150°. Find the area of the ground which can be covered by the spotlight.

20. For the figure at the right below determine the area of the shaded region for the following data.

a. $r = 6$, $\theta = \dfrac{\pi}{4}$

b. $r = 4$, $\theta = \dfrac{\pi}{6}$

c. $r = 12$, $\theta = \dfrac{\pi}{3}$

d. $r = 6$, $\theta = \dfrac{\pi}{2}$

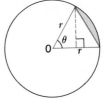

21. For the figure at the right below, determine the area of the shaded region for the following data.

a. $r = 6$, $\theta = \dfrac{\pi}{3}$

b. $r = 2.4$, $\theta = \dfrac{5\pi}{8}$

c. $r = 5$, $\theta = \dfrac{7\pi}{10}$

d. $r = 3$, $\theta = 2$

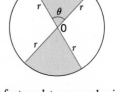

22. A windshield wiper blade is 14 inches long. Its midpoint is fastened to an endpoint of a rocker arm which is 10 inches long and oscillates through an angle of 150°. Determine the area of the surface which may be swept by the blade.

THE SIX TRIGONOMETRIC FUNCTIONS

In this section we shall define and discuss each of the trigonometric functions for real number angle measures. These six functions are

sine	cosecant
cosine	secant
tangent	cotangent

For any generated angle in standard position, let its measure be $u°$ or θ radians. Select any point $P(x, y)$ on the terminal side at a distance r $(r > 0)$ from the origin as shown in Figure 6–20. Three of the trigonometric functions are defined as follows.

For u°	*For θ radians*
$\sin u° = \dfrac{y}{r}$	$\sin \theta = \dfrac{y}{r}$
$\cos u° = \dfrac{x}{r}$	$\cos \theta = \dfrac{x}{r}$
$\tan u° = \dfrac{y}{x}\,(x \neq 0)$	$\tan \theta = \dfrac{y}{x}\,(x \neq 0)$

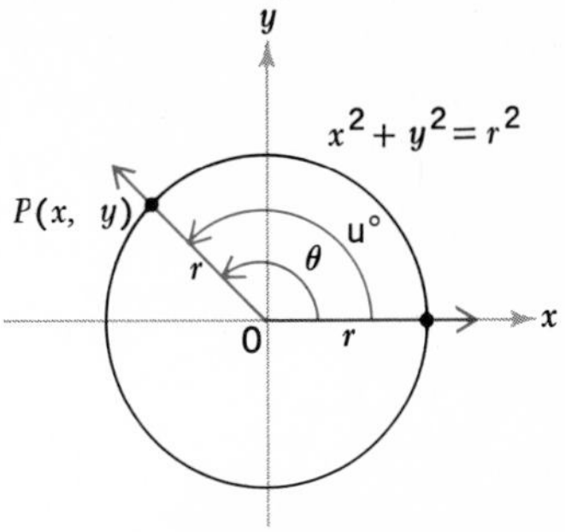

$$x^2 + y^2 = r^2$$

FIGURE 6-20

The three remaining functions are defined as the reciprocals of the functions above.

$\csc u° = \dfrac{r}{y}\,(y \neq 0)$	$\csc \theta = \dfrac{r}{y}\,(y \neq 0)$
$\sec u° = \dfrac{r}{x}\,(x \neq 0)$	$\sec \theta = \dfrac{r}{x}\,(x \neq 0)$
$\cot u° = \dfrac{x}{y}\,(y \neq 0)$	$\cot \theta = \dfrac{x}{y}\,(y \neq 0)$

Pronounce csc $u°$ as *cosecant $u°$*, sec $u°$ as *secant $u°$* and cot $u°$ as *cotangent $u°$*.

Since the definitions above refer to sets of ordered pairs, sin, cos, tan, etc., are called *functions*, $\{(u°, \sin u°)\}$, $\{(u°, \cos u°)\}$, $\{(u°, \tan u°)\}$, etc.

You should memorize these six definitions. As an aid to recalling them, observe that there are three reciprocal identities which follow from the definitions.

$$\csc u° \equiv \frac{1}{\sin u°}, \text{ since } \frac{r}{y} \equiv \frac{1}{\dfrac{y}{r}} \tag{6.1}$$

$$\sec u° \equiv \frac{1}{\cos u°}, \text{ since } \frac{r}{x} \equiv \frac{1}{\dfrac{x}{r}} \tag{6.2}$$

$$\cot u° \equiv \frac{1}{\tan u°}, \text{ since } \frac{x}{y} \equiv \frac{1}{\dfrac{y}{x}} \tag{6.3}$$

The following examples illustrate how trigonometric values can be determined by using the definitions.

Example 1   Given an angle of $u°$ with $P(-3, 4)$ on the terminal side, determine the six trigonometric functions of $u°$.

Solution   Since $x = -3$, $y = 4$ and $x^2 + y^2 = r^2$, it follows that $r = 5$. From the definitions we have that

$$\sin u° = \frac{y}{r} = \frac{4}{5}$$ $$\csc u° = \frac{r}{y} = \frac{5}{4}$$

$$\cos u° = \frac{x}{r} = -\frac{3}{5}$$ $$\sec u° = \frac{r}{x} = -\frac{5}{3}$$

$$\tan u° = \frac{y}{x} = -\frac{4}{3}$$ $$\cot u° = \frac{x}{y} = -\frac{3}{4}$$

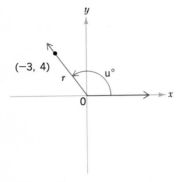
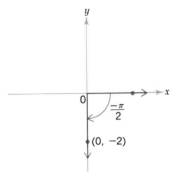

Example 2   Given an angle of $\frac{-\pi}{2}$ radians, determine the six trigonometric functions of $\frac{-\pi}{2}$.

Solution   Choose a point, say $P(0, -2)$, on the terminal side. Then $x = 0$, $y = -2$, and $r = 2$. From the definitions, we have

$$\sin \frac{-\pi}{2} = \frac{-2}{2} = -1$$

$$\cos \frac{-\pi}{2} = \frac{0}{2} = 0$$

$$\tan \frac{-\pi}{2} \text{ is undefined since } \frac{-2}{0} \text{ is undefined}$$

$$\csc \frac{-\pi}{2} = \frac{2}{-2} = -1$$

$$\sec \frac{-\pi}{2} \text{ is undefined since } \frac{2}{0} \text{ is undefined}$$

$$\cot \frac{-\pi}{2} = \frac{0}{-2} = 0$$

Example 3   Given $\sin u° = \frac{2}{3}$ and $90° < u° < 180°$, determine the other five trigonometric functions of $u°$.

Solution   Since $\sin u° = \dfrac{y}{r} = \dfrac{2}{3}$, let $y = 2$, $r = 3$, and determine x. Because $x^2 + y^2 = r^2$, it follows that $x = \sqrt{5}$ or $x = -\sqrt{5}$. Since $90° < u° < 180°$, it follows that $x = -\sqrt{5}$ only.

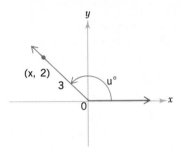

From the definitions, we find that $\csc u° = \dfrac{3}{2}$ and

$$\cos u° = -\frac{\sqrt{5}}{3} \qquad\qquad \sec u° = -\frac{3}{\sqrt{5}}$$

$$\tan u° = -\frac{2}{\sqrt{5}} \qquad\qquad \cot u° = -\frac{\sqrt{5}}{2}$$

For each function, the domain is the set of all real number angle measures *except* for the following.

1. For tan and for sec, $x \neq 0$; therefore, $u° \neq (90 + 180k)°$ and $\theta \neq \dfrac{\pi}{2} + k\pi$.

2. For csc and for cot, $y \neq 0$; therefore, $u° \neq (0 + 180k)°$ and $\theta \neq 0 + k\pi$.

If $u°$ is not a quadrantal number, then it is readily determined whether a given trigonometric function of $u°$ is positive or negative. For a second quadrant angle of $u°$ (see Figure 6–20) with $P(x, y)$ on the terminal side, we know that $x < 0$, $y > 0$ and $r > 0$.

Hence, $\sin u° > 0$, $\csc u° > 0$ since $y > 0$, $r > 0$
$\cos u° < 0$, $\sec u° < 0$ since $x < 0$, $r > 0$
$\tan u° < 0$, $\cot u° < 0$ since $y > 0$, $x < 0$

Study the following summary and be prepared to justify each entry in the table.

quadrant number *of* u°	*sin* u° *csc* u°	*cos* u° *sec* u°	*tan* u° *cot* u°
1st	positive	positive	positive
2nd	positive	negative	negative
3rd	negative	negative	positive
4th	negative	positive	negative

For the 60° angle shown in Figure 6–21, $P(1, \sqrt{3})$, and $P'(2, 2\sqrt{3})$ are two points on the terminal side at distances of 2 and 4, respectively, from the origin. Observe that, whether we select P or P', $\sin 60° = \dfrac{\sqrt{3}}{2}$, $\cos 60° = \dfrac{1}{2}$, $\tan 60° = \sqrt{3}$, etc. The trigonometric functions of 60°, evidently, do not depend upon the point selected on the terminal side. We shall now prove this for all angle measures.

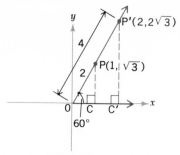

FIGURE 6·21

Given any angle of $u°$ ($u° \neq 90k°$) in standard position as shown in Figures 6–22 and 6–23, let P and P' be two distinct points on the terminal side at distances of r and r', respectively, from the origin. Right triangles OPB and $OP'B'$ are similar. Why? Consequently, the numbers x, y, and r are proportional to the numbers x', y', and r'. Hence,

$$\sin u° = \frac{y}{r} = \frac{y'}{r'} \qquad \cos u° = \frac{x}{r} = \frac{x'}{r'} \qquad \tan u° = \frac{y}{x} = \frac{y'}{x'} \qquad \text{etc.}$$

Therefore, a trigonometric function depends only upon $u°$ and not upon the point selected on the terminal side. Show that this is true also for any quadrantal angle.

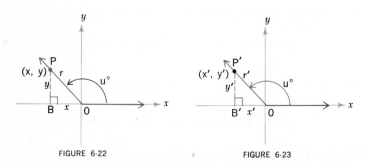

FIGURE 6·22   FIGURE 6·23

Since coterminal angles have the same terminal side, we have the following *period identities.*

$$\begin{array}{ll}
\sin \theta \equiv \sin (\theta + 2k\pi) & \sin u° \equiv \sin (u + 360k)° \quad [6.4] \\
\cos \theta \equiv \cos (\theta + 2k\pi) & \cos u° \equiv \cos (u + 360k)° \quad [6.5] \\
\quad \text{etc.} & \quad \text{etc.}
\end{array}$$

That is, each trigonometric function is periodic with a period of 2π radians (360°).

Examples $\sin 390° = \sin (390 - 360)° = \sin 30°$
$\cos (-420°) = \cos (-420 + 720)° = \cos 300°$

We shall show later that π radians or 180° is *the* period of tangent and cotangent.

EXERCISES

1. Given the point $P(x, y)$ on the terminal side of an angle of $u°$ in standard position, determine the six trigonometric functions of $u°$.

   a. $P(2, 3)$ **c.** $P(-5, -12)$ **e.** $P(-2, 0)$

   b. $P(-4, 4)$ **d.** $P(5, -2)$ **f.** $P(0, -3)$

2. For each angle measure, tell which of the six trigonometric functions are not defined.

   a. $90°$ **b.** 2π **c.** $270°$ **d.** $-180°$

3. For each interval tell which of the six trigonometric functions of $u°$ or of θ are positive.

   a. $90° < u° < 180°$ **e.** $0 < \theta < \dfrac{\pi}{2}$

   b. $270° < u° < 360°$ **f.** $\dfrac{\pi}{2} < \theta < \pi$

   c. $0° < u° < 90°$ **g.** $\pi < \theta < \dfrac{3\pi}{2}$

   d. $180° < u° < 270°$ **h.** $\dfrac{3\pi}{2} < \theta < 2\pi$

4. For each set of conditions, determine the other five trigonometric functions.

   a. $\cos u° = \dfrac{-4}{5}$ and $90° < u° < 180°$ **d.** $\sec \alpha = \dfrac{5}{3}$ and $\dfrac{3\pi}{2} < \alpha < 2\pi$

   b. $\tan \theta = \dfrac{3}{2}$ and $0 < \theta < \dfrac{\pi}{2}$ **e.** $\cot w° = 1$ and $180° < w° < 270°$

   c. $\sin v° = \dfrac{-2}{5}$ and $180° < v° < 270°$ **f.** $\sin \beta = 1$

5. Use a period identity to express each of the following as the same trigonometric function of $u°$, where $0° \le u° < 360°$.

   a. $\sin 400°$ **c.** $\tan (-310°)$ **e.** $\sec 1200°$

   b. $\cos (-20°)$ **d.** $\csc 740°$ **f.** $\cot (-380°)$

6. For each quadrantal angle measure, determine the six trigonometric functions (if they exist) of the measure.

   a. $0°$ **b.** $\dfrac{\pi}{2}$ **c.** $180°$ **d.** $270°$

7. Choose $P(0, 2)$ and $P'(0, 3)$, two distinct points on the terminal side of a $90°$ angle, and show that the six trigonometric functions of $90°$ do not depend upon the point selected on the terminal side.

TRIGONOMETRIC FUNCTIONS OF 30°, 45° AND 60°

You will recall our studying relations involving the lengths of the sides in some special right triangles (see Figure 6–24).

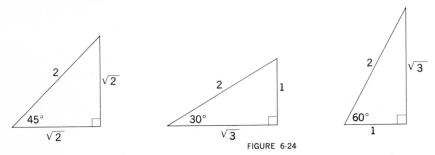

FIGURE 6-24

We shall use these relations to express the trigonometric functions of multiples of 30° or 45°. Observe in Figure 6–25 that

$$m \angle AOP = 45° \qquad m \angle AOQ = 135° \qquad m \angle AOR = 225° \qquad m \angle AOS = 315°$$

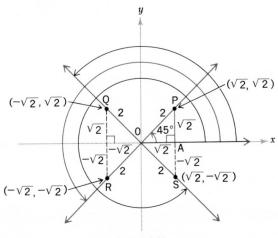

FIGURE 6-25

From the definitions and by symmetry we obtain the following values.

$$\sin 45° = \frac{y}{r} = \frac{\sqrt{2}}{2} \text{ and } \sin 135° = \frac{\sqrt{2}}{2}$$

$$\cos 45° = \frac{x}{r} = \frac{\sqrt{2}}{2} \text{ and } \cos 225° = \frac{-\sqrt{2}}{2}$$

$$\tan 45° = \frac{y}{x} = \frac{\sqrt{2}}{\sqrt{2}} = 1 \text{ and } \tan 315° = -1$$

$$\sec 45° = \frac{r}{x} = \frac{2}{\sqrt{2}} = \sqrt{2} \text{ and } \sec 135° = -\sqrt{2}$$

$$\csc 135° = \frac{r}{y} = \csc (135 + 360k)° = \frac{2}{\sqrt{2}} = \sqrt{2}$$

What is cot 45° equal to? cot 315°?

In Figure 6–26, some angle measures are

$$m\angle AOK = 30° \quad m\angle AOL = 150° \quad m\angle AOM = 210° \quad m\angle AON = 330°$$

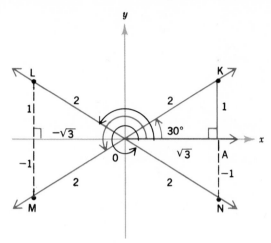

FIGURE 6-26

We are able to determine the following values.

$$\cos 30° = \frac{x}{r} = \frac{\sqrt{3}}{2} \text{ and } \sec 30° = \frac{r}{x} = \frac{2}{\sqrt{3}} = \frac{2\sqrt{3}}{3}$$

$$\tan 150° = \frac{y}{x} = \frac{-1}{\sqrt{3}} \text{ and } \cot 150° = \frac{x}{y} = -\sqrt{3}$$

$$\sin 210° = \frac{y}{r} = \frac{-1}{2} \text{ and } \csc 210° = \frac{r}{y} = -2$$

$$\cos 330° = \frac{x}{r} = \frac{\sqrt{3}}{2} \text{ and } \sec 330° = \frac{r}{x} = \frac{2}{\sqrt{3}} = \frac{2\sqrt{3}}{3}$$

$$\sec 210° = \frac{r}{x} = \sec (210 + 360k)° = -\frac{2}{\sqrt{3}} = -\frac{2\sqrt{3}}{3}$$

What is sin 150° equal to? csc 150°?

Some measures of angles shown in Figure 6–27 are

$$m\angle AOE = 60° \quad m\angle AOF = 120° \quad m\angle AOG = 240° \quad m\angle AOH = 300°$$

We can now determine these values.

$$\sin 60° = \frac{y}{r} = \frac{\sqrt{3}}{2} \text{ and } \csc 240° = -\frac{2}{\sqrt{3}} = -\frac{2\sqrt{3}}{3}$$

$$\cos 60° = \frac{x}{r} = \frac{1}{2} \text{ and } \sec 300° = 2$$

$$\tan 60° = \frac{y}{x} = \sqrt{3} \text{ and } \cot 120° = -\frac{1}{\sqrt{3}} = -\frac{\sqrt{3}}{3}$$

$$\cot 120° = \frac{x}{y} = \cot (120 + 180k)° = -\frac{1}{\sqrt{3}} = -\frac{\sqrt{3}}{3}$$

What is tan 240° equal to? cot 240°?

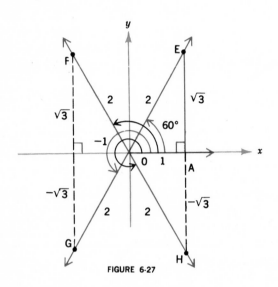

FIGURE 6-27

EXERCISES

1. Determine the six trigonometric functions (if they exist) of each angle measure.

a. 30°	**d.** 210°	**g.** −135°	**j.** 90°
b. 45°	**e.** 315°	**h.** −30°	**k.** 180°
c. 60°	**f.** 120°	**i.** −120°	**l.** −90°

2. Determine each value, if it exists.

a. $\sec \dfrac{3\pi}{4}$	**f.** $\cot \dfrac{11\pi}{6}$	**k.** $\csc \pi$
b. $\csc \dfrac{7\pi}{6}$	**g.** $\sec \dfrac{5\pi}{3}$	**l.** $\cot \left(\dfrac{-\pi}{2}\right)$
c. $\cot \dfrac{2\pi}{3}$	**h.** $\csc \dfrac{2\pi}{3}$	**m.** $\sec 0$
d. $\sec \dfrac{5\pi}{6}$	**i.** $\cot \dfrac{7\pi}{4}$	**n.** $\csc 2\pi$
e. $\csc \dfrac{5\pi}{4}$	**j.** $\sec \dfrac{\pi}{2}$	**o.** $\cot (-\pi)$

3. Compute each value.

a. $\dfrac{1}{2} \csc \dfrac{5\pi}{4} \cdot \sec \dfrac{5\pi}{4}$

b. $\cos 120° \cdot \cos 150° - \sin 120° \cdot \sin 150°$

c. $2 \cos^2 225° - 1$

d. $\sin 315° \cdot \cos 210° + \cos 315° \cdot \sin 210°$

e. $1 + \tan^2 150°$

f. $1 + \cot^2 (-30°)$

g. $\dfrac{2 \tan 210°}{1 - \tan^2 210°}$

h. $\dfrac{\tan 60° + \tan 135°}{1 - \tan 60° \cdot \tan 135°}$

i. $\dfrac{1 - \cos \dfrac{5\pi}{6}}{\sin \dfrac{5\pi}{6}}$

j. $\dfrac{\sin 240°}{1 + \cos 240°}$

REDUCTION IDENTITIES

Given any angle of $w°$, each trigonometric function of $w°$ may be expressed in terms of that same trigonometric function of $v°$, where $0° \le v° \le 90°$. The basic concept involved is that of symmetry.

With reference to Figure 6–28 observe that for a second quadrant angle of $u°$, there is a first quadrant angle of $(180 - u)°$ such that

$P(x, y)$ is symmetric to $P'(-x, y)$ with respect to the y-axis

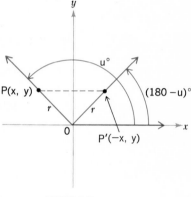

FIGURE 6-28

and therefore

$$\sin u° \equiv \sin (180 - u)° \text{ since each of these is equal to } \frac{y}{r} \qquad [6.6]$$

$$\csc u° \equiv \csc (180 - u)° \text{ since each of these is equal to } \frac{r}{y} \qquad [6.7]$$

$$\cos u° \equiv -\cos (180 - u)° \text{ since } \frac{x}{r} \equiv -\left(\frac{-x}{r}\right) \qquad [6.8]$$

$$\sec u° \equiv -\sec (180 - u)° \text{ since } \frac{r}{x} \equiv -\left(\frac{r}{-x}\right) \qquad [6.9]$$

$$\tan u° \equiv -\tan (180 - u)° \text{ since } \frac{y}{x} \equiv -\left(\frac{y}{-x}\right) \qquad [6.10]$$

$$\cot u° \equiv -\cot (180 - u)° \text{ since } \frac{x}{y} \equiv -\left(\frac{-x}{y}\right) \qquad [6.11]$$

These identities are called *reduction identities* for second quadrant angle measures.

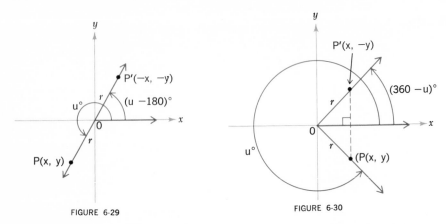

FIGURE 6-29   FIGURE 6-30

From Figure 6–29, note that for a third quadrant angle of $u°$, there is a first quadrant angle of $(u - 180)°$ such that

$P(x, y)$ is symmetric to $P'(-x, -y)$ with respect to the origin and therefore

$$\sin u° \equiv -\sin (u - 180)° \text{ since } \frac{y}{r} \equiv -\left(\frac{-y}{r}\right) \qquad [6.12]$$

$$\csc u° \equiv -\csc (u - 180)° \text{ since } \frac{r}{y} \equiv -\left(\frac{r}{-y}\right) \qquad [6.13]$$

$$\cos u° \equiv -\cos (u - 180)° \text{ since } \frac{x}{r} \equiv -\left(\frac{-x}{r}\right) \qquad [6.14]$$

$$\sec u° \equiv -\sec (u - 180)° \text{ since } \frac{r}{x} \equiv -\left(\frac{r}{-x}\right) \qquad [6.15]$$

$$\tan u° \equiv \tan (u - 180)° \text{ since } \frac{y}{x} \equiv \frac{-y}{-x} \qquad [6.16]$$

$$\cot u° \equiv \cot (u - 180)° \text{ since } \frac{x}{y} \equiv \frac{-x}{-y} \qquad [6.17]$$

These identities are reduction identities for third quadrant angle measures. As a consequence of [6.16] and [6.17], we have that 180° (or π radians) is the primitive period of tangent and of cotangent; that is,

$$\tan u° \equiv \tan (u + 180k)° \qquad [6.18]$$
$$\cot u° \equiv \cot (u + 180k)° \qquad [6.19]$$

From a study of Figure 6–30, you should observe that for a fourth quadrant angle of $u°$, there is a first quadrant angle of $(360 - u)°$ such that

$P(x, y)$ is symmetric to $P'(x, -y)$ with respect to the x-axis and therefore

$$\sin u° \equiv -\sin (360 - u)° \text{ since } \frac{y}{r} \equiv -\left(\frac{-y}{r}\right) \qquad [6.20]$$

$$\csc u° \equiv -\csc (360 - u)° \text{ since } \frac{r}{y} \equiv -\left(\frac{r}{-y}\right) \qquad [6.21]$$

$$\cos u° \equiv \cos (360 - u)° \text{ since each of these is equal to } \frac{x}{r} \qquad [6.22]$$

$$\sec u° \equiv \sec (360 - u)° \text{ since each of these is equal to } \frac{r}{x} \qquad [6.23]$$

$$\tan u° \equiv -\tan (360 - u)° \text{ since } \frac{y}{x} = -\left(\frac{-y}{x}\right) \qquad [6.24]$$

$$\cot u° \equiv -\cot (360 - u)° \text{ since } \frac{x}{y} \equiv -\left(\frac{x}{-y}\right) \qquad [6.25]$$

These identities are reduction identities for fourth quadrant angle measures.

Now, for any angle of $w°$, we are able to express $\sin w°$, $\cos w°$, etc., in terms of $\sin u°$, $\cos u°$, etc., where $0° \leq u° < 360°$. This follows from the fact that $360°$ is a period of each trigonometric function. Furthermore, $\sin u°$, $\cos u°$, etc., may be expressed in terms of $\sin v°$, $\cos v°$, etc., where $0° \leq v° \leq 90°$ by using the appropriate reduction identities.

given function	reduction	function of $v°$
sin 400°	sin (400 − 360)°	sin 40°
cos (−350)°	cos (−350 + 360)°	cos 10°
tan 140°	−tan (180 − 140)°	−tan 40°
csc 230°	−csc (230 − 180)°	−csc 50°
sec 312°	sec (360 − 312)°	sec 48°
cot 215°	cot (215 − 180)°	cot 35°

In actual practice one does not memorize the list of reduction identities developed in this section. Rather, for a particular problem, it is better to sketch the angle in standard position and use symmetry to obtain the answer.

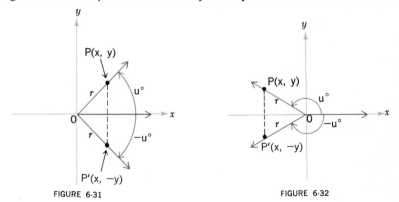

FIGURE 6-31   FIGURE 6-32

Symmetry suggests another set of identities (see Figures 6–31 and 6–32). For any angle of $u°$, there is an angle of $-u°$ such that $P(x, y)$ is symmetric to $P'(x, -y)$ with respect to the x-axis.

Therefore

$$\sin(-u°) \equiv -\sin u° \text{ since } \frac{-y}{r} \equiv -\left(\frac{y}{r}\right) \qquad [6.26]$$

$$\cos(-u°) \equiv \cos u° \text{ since each of these is equal to } \frac{x}{r} \qquad [6.27]$$

$$\tan(-u°) \equiv -\tan u° \text{ since } \frac{-y}{x} \equiv -\left(\frac{y}{x}\right) \qquad [6.28]$$

$$\csc(-u°) \equiv -\csc u° \text{ since } \frac{r}{-y} \equiv -\left(\frac{r}{y}\right) \qquad [6.29]$$

$$\sec(-u°) \equiv \sec u° \text{ since each of these is equal to } \frac{r}{x} \qquad [6.30]$$

$$\cot(-u°) \equiv -\cot u° \text{ since } \frac{x}{-y} \equiv -\left(\frac{x}{y}\right) \qquad [6.31]$$

These identities permit us to express a trigonometric function of a negative measure in terms of that same trigonometric function of a positive measure. Study the following examples.

Examples $\sin(-20°) = -\sin 20°$ and $\csc(-110°) = -\csc 110°$
$\cos(-100°) = \cos 100°$ and $\sec(-50°) = \sec 50°$
$\tan(-40°) = -\tan 40°$ and $\cot(-200°) = -\cot 200°$

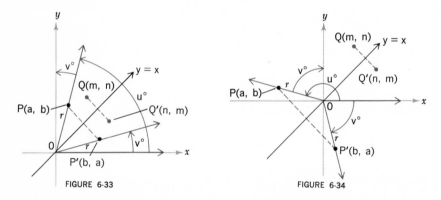

FIGURE 6-33   FIGURE 6-34

You have probably observed that three trigonometric functions, cosine, cosecant, and cotangent, are named by preceding the names of sine, secant, and tangent, respectively, with the prefix "co". Therefore, we say that for sin and cos, either is the *co-name* of the other. Similar statements hold for sec and csc and for tan and cot. The reason for this will be shown while deriving the *complementary angles relation*, which we shall do next. First, recall that a pair of angles is called *complementary* if and only if the sum of their degree measures is 90°. For the pair of angles shown in Figure 6–33 and for the pair in Figure 6–34, $u° + v° = 90°$. Hence, each pair of angles is complementary. Recall that any point $Q(m, n)$ is symmetric to $Q'(n, m)$ with respect to the line specified by $y = x$. In each figure note that $r = OP = OP'$ and that $P(a, b)$ is symmetric to $P'(b, a)$ with respect to the line specified by $y = x$.

Observe that

    1. $u° + v° = 90°$

    2. $\dfrac{b}{r} = \sin u° = \cos v°$

       $\dfrac{r}{a} = \sec u° = \csc v°$

       $\dfrac{b}{a} = \tan u° = \cot v°$

We summarize the above in the following statement.

    COMPLEMENTARY ANGLES RELATION   If $u° + v° = 90°$, that is, if an angle of $u°$ and an angle of $v°$ are *complementary*, then any trigonometric function of $u°$ is equal to that *co*-named trigonometric function of $v°$.

Hence, the name "cosine" is an abbreviation of "complementary sine" and we say that sine and cosine are co-named, or complementary, functions. Study the following examples which illustrate how a trigonometric function of $u°$ is changed to the co-named function of $(90 - u)°$.

    $\sin 40° = \cos 50°$ since $40° + 50° = 90°$
    $\sec 110° = \csc (-20°)$ since $110° + (-20°) = 90°$
    $\tan (-70°) = \cot 160°$ since $(-70°) + 160° = 90°$
    $\cos (90 - u)° = \sin u°$ since $(90 - u)° + u° = 90°$

EXERCISES

1. Express each of the following in terms of the same trigonometric function of $u°$, where $0° < u° < 90°$.

  a. $\sin 160°$ **e.** $\sec 320°$ **i.** $\tan 220°$ **m.** $\tan (-70°)$

  b. $\cos 140°$ **f.** $\cot 260°$ **j.** $\csc 170°$ **n.** $\sin (-100°)$

  c. $\tan 110°$ **g.** $\sin 212°$ **k.** $\sin (-20°)$ **o.** $\cos (-170°)$

  d. $\csc 320°$ **h.** $\cos 310°$ **l.** $\cos (-40°)$ **p.** $\tan (-140°)$

2. For each angle measure given below, determine the measure of the angle's complement.

  a. $20°$ **c.** $90°$ **e.** $-40°$ **g.** $0°$ **i.** $(90 - u)°$

  b. $80°$ **d.** $110°$ **f.** $45°$ **h.** $37°20'$ **j.** $\dfrac{\pi}{8}$

3. Express each of the following in terms of its co-named function.

  a. $\cos 20°$ **c.** $\tan 27°$ **e.** $\cot 100°$ **g.** $\sec 31°$

  b. $\sin 40°$ **d.** $\cos 140°$ **f.** $\csc 82°$ **h.** $\cos (-50°)$

i. $\sin(-20°)$ **k.** $\cos(90-c)°$ **m.** $\sin(c-90)°$

o. $\tan\dfrac{7\pi}{10}$

j. $\sin(90-c)°$ **l.** $\sin\dfrac{3\pi}{8}$ **n.** $\cos\dfrac{2\pi}{5}$

p. $\csc 1$

4. Express each of the following in terms of the same function of $u°$. Assume that $0° < u° < 90°$.

a. $\cos(360-u)°$ **e.** $\csc(180-u)°$

b. $\sin(360-u)°$ **f.** $\sin(180+u)°$

c. $\tan(180-u)°$ **g.** $\cot(180+u)°$

d. $\sec(180-u)°$ **h.** $\cos(180+u)°$

5. Determine two values of $u°$, between $0°$ and $360°$, for which the equation is true.

a. $\cos u° = \dfrac{\sqrt{2}}{2}$ **d.** $\sec u° = -2$ **g.** $\cos u° = \dfrac{-\sqrt{3}}{2}$

b. $\sin u° = \dfrac{1}{2}$ **e.** $\csc u° = \sqrt{2}$ **h.** $\sin u° = \dfrac{-\sqrt{2}}{2}$

c. $\tan u° = -\sqrt{3}$ **f.** $\cot u° = 1$ **i.** $\tan u° = \dfrac{1}{\sqrt{3}}$

6. State the primitive period of each trigonometric function.

TRIGONOMETRIC VALUES FROM A TABLE

For a first quadrant angle of $u°$, the six trigonometric functions of $u°$ are listed in Table III at the back of this book. A portion of Table III is reproduced in Figure 6–35.

$u°$		$sin\ u°$	$csc\ u°$	$tan\ u°$	$cot\ u°$	$sec\ u°$	$cos\ u°$		$u°$
31° 0′	.5411	.5150	1.942	.6009	1.664	1.167	.8572	1.0297	59° 0′
10′	440	175	932	048	653	169	557	268	50′
20′	469	200	923	088	643	171	542	239	40′
30′	.5498	.5225	1.914	.6128	1.632	1.173	.8526	1.0210	30′
40′	527	250	905	168	621	175	511	181	20′
50′	556	275	896	208	611	177	496	152	10′
32° 0′	.5585	.5299	1.887	.6249	1.600	1.179	.8480	1.0123	58° 0′
10′	614	324	878	289	590	181	465	094	50′
20′	643	348	870	330	580	184	450	065	40′
30′	.5672	.5373	1.861	.6371	1.570	1.186	.8434	1.0036	30′
40′	701	398	853	412	560	188	418	1.0007	20′
50′	730	422	844	453	550	190	403	.9977	10′
33° 0′	.5760	.5446	1.836	.6494	1.540	1.192	.8387	.9948	57° 0′
10′	789	471	828	536	530	195	371	919	50′
20′	818	495	820	577	520	197	355	890	40′
		$cos\ u°$	$sec\ u°$	$cot\ u°$	$tan\ u°$	$csc\ u°$	$sin\ u°$		$u°$

Figure 6–35

Observe that degree measures are given for each multiple of 10 minutes (10'). Recall that 1 degree (1°) = 60 minutes (60'). Sin $u°$ and cos $u°$ are given with accuracy to four decimal places in Table III. The other four trigonometric functions are given with accuracy to four digits.

In Figure 6–35 you should read the following.

$$\sin 31°20' \doteq 0.5200$$
$$\cot 31°40' \doteq 1.621$$
$$\cos 32°10' \doteq 0.8465$$

From Table III and a reduction identity we can determine two values of $u°$ between 0° and 360° for which

$$\csc u° \doteq 1.905.$$

One value is $u° \doteq 31°40'$.
The other is $u° \doteq 180° - 31°40' = 179°60' - 31°40' = 148°20'$

The complementary angles relation allows Table III to be half the expected size. The left-hand column of Table III lists values of $u°$ from 0° to 45°. Values of $u°$ from 45° to 90° are listed *from bottom to top* in the right-hand column and are to be used with the co-named functions listed at the *bottom* of the page. For example, in Figure 6–35 we read the following.

$$\sin 58°20' \doteq 0.8511 \qquad\qquad \tan 58°40' \doteq 1.643$$

Check these values in Figure 6–35.

Study the following examples which show how to use the table in case $u°$ is not between 0° and 90°.

Example 1   Determine tan 124°20'.

Solution   Using the appropriate reduction identity,
$$\tan 124°20' = -\tan (180° - 124°20')$$
$$= -\tan 55°40'$$
$$\doteq -1.464$$

Example 2   Determine sin 211°40'.

Solution $\sin 211°40' = -\sin (211°40' - 180°)$
$$= -\sin 31°40'$$
$$\doteq -.5250$$

Example 3   Determine cos 309°30'.

Solution $\cos 309°30' = \cos (360° - 309°30')$
$$= \cos 50°30'$$
$$\doteq .6361$$

Example 4   Determine csc (−12°50').

Solution   Using the identity csc $(-u°) \equiv -\csc u°$,
$$\csc (-12°50') = -\csc 12°50'$$
$$\doteq -4.502$$

If $u°$ is given to the nearest 1 minute, we use Table III and interpolate to determine a trigonometric function of $u°$. The technique of interpolation is discussed in *Appendix B*. Study the following examples.

Example 1   Determine tan 31°36′, with accuracy to four digits.

Solution   We copy appropriate portions of Table III and interpolate.

$$
\begin{array}{c c c}
 & u° & tan\ u° \\
10'\left[\ 6'\left[\begin{array}{c} 31°30' \\ 31°36' \end{array}\right.\right. & & \left.\left.\begin{array}{c} .6128 \\ ? \end{array}\right]\ n\ \right]\ .0040 \\
 & 31°40' & .6168
\end{array}
$$

$$\frac{6}{10} = \frac{n}{.0040}$$

$$n = \frac{6(.0040)}{10} = .0024$$

$$\text{tan } 31°36' \doteq .6128 + .0024 = .6152$$

Example 2   Determine cos 31°44′, with accuracy to four decimal places.

Solution   Observe that cosine is a decreasing function when moving from 0° to 90°.

$$
\begin{array}{c c c}
 & u° & cos\ u° \\
10'\left[\ 4'\left[\begin{array}{c} 31°40' \\ 31°44' \end{array}\right.\right. & & \left.\left.\begin{array}{c} .8511 \\ ? \end{array}\right]\ n\ \right]\ -.0015 \\
 & 31°50' & .8496
\end{array}
$$

$$\frac{4}{10} = \frac{n}{-.0015}$$

$$n = \frac{4(-.0015)}{10} = -.0006$$

$$\text{cos } 31°44' \doteq .8511 - .0006 = .8505$$

For a given value of a trigonometric function, we can determine $u°$ to the nearest minute by interpolating. The next example shows how this is done.

Example 3   Determine $u°$, with accuracy to the nearest minute, if sin $u° \doteq$ .5261 and 0° $< u° <$ 90°.

Solution

$$u° \qquad\qquad\qquad sin\ u°$$

$$10' \left[\begin{array}{c} n' \left[\begin{array}{c} 31°40' \\ \\ ? \\ \\ 31°50' \end{array} \right. \end{array} \right. \begin{array}{c} .5250 \\ \\ .5261 \\ \\ .5275 \end{array} \left. \begin{array}{c} \\ .0011 \\ \\ \end{array} \right] \right] .0025$$

$$\frac{n}{10} = \frac{.0011}{.0025} = \frac{11}{25}$$

$$n = 10\left(\frac{11}{25}\right) \doteq 4$$

$$u° \doteq 31°40' + 4' = 31°44'$$

EXERCISES

1. Use Table III and determine the following with accuracy to either four decimal places or four digits.

   a. sin 27°40'   **d.** cos 72°50'   **g.** sec 37°30'   **j.** cot 53°20'

   b. cos 35°20'   **e.** tan 13°20'   **h.** csc 72°40'   **k.** cos 82°20'

   c. sin 47°30'   **f.** tan 62°40'   **i.** cot 31°10'   **l.** sin 67°50'

2. Determine the following from Table III.

   a. sin 129°30'   **d.** sec (−14°10')   **g.** sin 286°50'

   b. cos 243°50'   **e.** csc (−56°40')   **h.** cos 172°20'

   c. tan 312°20'   **f.** cot (−74°30')   **i.** tan 212°40'

3. Interpolate and determine the following with accuracy to either four decimal places or four digits.

   a. sin 37°23'   **c.** tan 18°12'   **e.** csc 39°54'

   b. cos 28°46'   **d.** sec 32°37'   **f.** sin 80°28'

4. In each case, determine two values of $u°$ between 0° and 360° for which the given equation is true. Express answers with accuracy to the nearest 10 minutes.

   a. sin $u°$ ≐ .4436   **d.** sec $u°$ ≐ 1.175   **g.** cot $u°$ ≐ −.1733

   b. cos $u°$ ≐ .7844   **e.** sin $u°$ ≐ −.4514   **h.** csc $u°$ ≐ −1.410

   c. tan $u°$ ≐ 3.647   **f.** cos $u°$ ≐ −.6383

5. For each of the following equations, interpolate and determine $u°$, between 0° and 90°, with accuracy to the nearest minute.

   a. sin $u°$ ≐ .4782   **c.** tan $u°$ ≐ .2543

   b. cos $u°$ ≐ .7398   **d.** cot $u°$ ≐ 1.314

GRAPHS OF TRIGONOMETRIC FUNCTIONS

In Chapters Three and Five we constructed the graphs of the sine, cosine and tangent functions which were defined for real numbers θ (see Figures 3–20, 3–23 and 5–5). In redefining these functions for angle measures, the real number θ corresponds to an angle measure of θ radians (see Figure 6–36). Also, an angle measure of θ radians is readily converted to an angle measure of $u°$, using the relation $u° = \theta\left(\dfrac{180}{\pi}\right)°$.

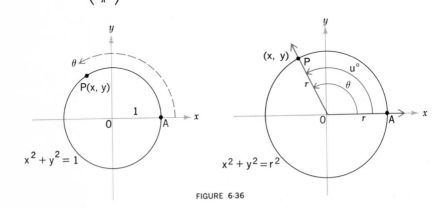

FIGURE 6-36

The graphs of sine, cosine and tangent are reproduced in Figures 6–37, 6–38 and 6–39 with the conversion from real numbers θ to the corresponding values of $u°$. Since each of these functions is periodic, the pictures of their graphs can easily be extended for one or more periods in either direction.

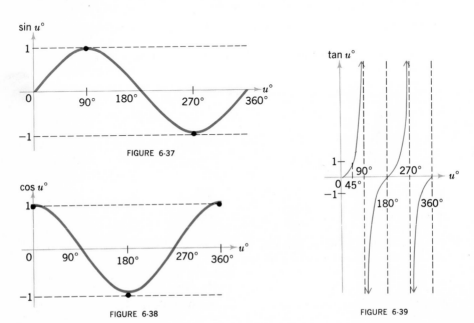

FIGURE 6-37

FIGURE 6-38

FIGURE 6-39

From a study of the portion of the graph of sine shown in Figure 6–37, one can tell that

1. the domain of sine is the set of all real number degree measures.
2. the range of sine is $\{b \mid -1 \leq b \leq 1\}$.
3. the period of sine is 360°.
4. the variation in sin $u°$ corresponds to variation in $u°$ as given by the following table:

variation in u°	variation in sin u°
from 0° to 90°	increases from 0 to 1
from 90° to 180°	decreases from 1 to 0
from 180° to 270°	decreases from 0 to −1
from 270° to 360°	increases from −1 to 0

Study the portion of the graph of cosine shown in Figure 6–38. Then determine (1) the domain, (2) the range, and (3) the period of cosine and (4) state the variation in cos $u°$ as $u°$ varies from 0° to 360°.

Study the portion of the graph of tangent shown in Figure 6–39. Note that tan $u°$ increases without upper limit as $u°$ increases from 0° to 90° and that tan $u°$ is undefined at $u° = (90 + 180k)°$. Repeat (1), (2), (3), and (4) as above for the tangent function.

The graphs of cosecant, secant, and cotangent are sketched by plotting some values for multiples of 15° as given in Table III. Portions of their graphs are shown in Figures 6–40, 6–41 and 6–42 for the interval $0° \leq u° \leq 360°$.

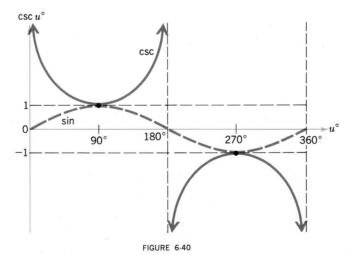

FIGURE 6-40

A portion of the graph of cosecant is shown in Figure 6–40. This graph is compared with the graph of sine for one period. You know that sine and cosecant are reciprocals of each other; observe how this is reflected in the graph of csc where sin $u°$ is equal to 0, 1 or -1. The domain of csc is the set of all real number degree measures except $180k°$. The range of csc is $\{b \mid b \geq 1 \text{ or } b \leq -1\}$.

A portion of the graph of secant is shown in Figure 6–41. This graph is compared with its reciprocal, the cosine function, for one period. State the domain and the range of secant.

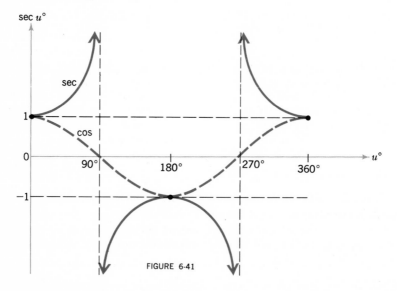

FIGURE 6-41

A portion of the graph of cotangent is shown in Figure 6–42. It is for the interval $0° < u° < 360°$.

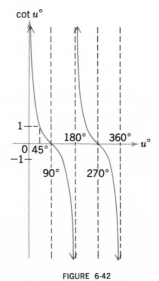

FIGURE 6-42

State the domain, range and period of cotangent.

EXERCISES

1. Study the portion of the graph of cosine shown in Figure 6–38. Then state the (1) domain, (2) range, and (3) period of cosine.

2. Describe the variation in $\cos u°$

   a. as $u°$ increases from 0° to 90°   **c.** as $u°$ increases from 180° to 270°

   b. as $u°$ increases from 90° to 180°   **d.** as $u°$ increases from 270° to 360°

3. Study the portion of the graph of tangent shown in Figure 6–39. Then state the (1) domain, (2) range, and (3) period of tangent.

4. Describe the variation in $\tan u°$

   a. as $u°$ increases from 0° to 90°

   b. as $u°$ increases from 90° to 180°

   c. as $u°$ increases from 90° to 270°

5. Study the graphs of (a) cosecant, (b) secant, and (c) cotangent. Then give the domain and range of each function.

6. Sketch the graphs of sine and its reciprocal, cosecant, on one coordinate system for the interval $0° < u° < 360°$.

7. Sketch the graphs of cosine and its reciprocal, secant, on one coordinate system for the interval $0° < u° < 360°$.

8. Sketch the graphs of tangent and its reciprocal, cotangent, on one coordinate system for the interval $0° < u° < 180°$.

9. Sketch the graphs of sine and cosine on the same coordinate system for the interval $0° \le u° < 360°$. Use these graphs to answer the following questions.

   a. How many solutions does the equation $\sin u° = \cos u°$ have in this interval?

   b. For what values of $u°$, in this interval, is it true that $\sin u° < \frac{1}{2}$?

   c. For what values of $u°$, in this interval, is it true that $\sin u° < \cos u°$?

   d. For what values of $u°$, in this interval, is it true that $|\sin u°| < |\cos u°|$?

   e. How many solutions does the equation $\cos u° = 0.3$ have in this interval?

GRAPHING $y = a \sin b (u + c)°$

In Chapter Three we presented the graphs of functions specified by $y = a \sin b(\theta + c)$ whose domain was the set of all *real numbers* θ. We shall now be concerned with the graphs of functions specified by $y = a \sin b(u + c)°$ whose domain is the set of all real number *degree measures*. Converting from real numbers, θ, to degree measures, $u°$, we state the following for functions specified by $y = a \sin b(u + c)°$.

1. The *amplitude* of the function is $|a|$.

2. The *period* of the function is $\frac{1}{b}(360)°$.

3. The *phase number c* describes the horizontal move that shifts the graph of $y = a \sin bu°$ onto the graph of $y = a \sin b(u + c)°$. The move is $|c|$ units, to the right if $c < 0$ and to the left if $c > 0$.

Study the following example.

Example   Sketch the graph of $y = 2 \sin 3(u - 40)°$ for one period.

The amplitude is $|2| = 2$, the period is $\frac{1}{3}(360)° = 120°$ and the phase number is $(-40)°$. As an aid to sketching the graph, we draw a picture of a rectangle which will contain one period of the graph. The length of this rectangle is the period, 120°. The width is twice the amplitude, or 4. The rectangle is shifted 40° to the right of the origin. Separate the rectangle into four vertical strips and draw a "sine-like" curve inside the rectangle. See Figure 6–43.

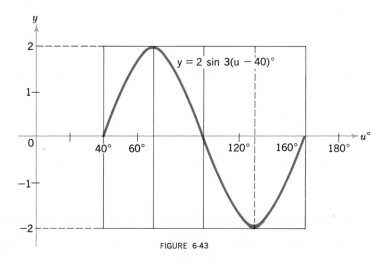

FIGURE 6-43

EXERCISES

1. For each function specified below, determine (1) the amplitude, (2) the period, and (3) the phase number.

a. $y = \frac{3}{4} \sin 3u°$

b. $y = -3 \cos \frac{1}{2}u°$

c. $y = 2 \sin 2(u + 45)°$

d. $y = \cos \frac{1}{3}(u - 30)°$

e. $y = \sin (2u + 60)°$

f. $y = \cos \left(\frac{1}{2}u - 120\right)°$

2. Sketch the graph of each function specified below for one period. Use a separate coordinate system for each graph.

a. $y = 3 \sin u°$

b. $y = -2 \cos u°$

c. $y = \sin \frac{1}{2}u°$

d. $y = \cos 2u°$

e. $y = 2 \sin 3(u - 45)°$

f. $y = \frac{1}{2}\cos \frac{1}{2}(u + 60)°$

g. $y = \sin (2u - 60)°$

h. $y = \cos \left(\frac{1}{2}u + 90\right)°$

3. Graph $y = \sin 3u°$ and $y = 2 \cos 2u°$ on the same coordinate system for the interval $0° \leq u° < 360°$. Use these graphs to determine the number of solutions each of the following equations has in the interval $0° \leq u° < 360°$.

a. $\sin 3u° = 2 \cos 2u°$

b. $2 \cos 2u° = 1$

c. $\sin 3u° = \dfrac{-1}{2}$

VOCABULARY

Use each of the following correctly in a sentence to demonstrate that you understand its meaning. If you are not sure of the meaning of any word, refer back to the chapter.

amplitude
circular sector
complementary angles relation
co-named function
cosecant
cosine
cotangent
coterminal angles
first quadrant angle
first quadrant number
generated angle

period
phase number
quadrantal angle
quadrantal number
radian
reciprocal identity
reduction identity
standard position
tangent
terminal side
trigonometric function

REVIEW EXERCISES

1. Convert each radian measure to its equivalent degree measure.

a. $\dfrac{5\pi}{6}$

b. $\dfrac{4\pi}{3}$

c. $\dfrac{7\pi}{4}$

d. $-\pi$

e. $\dfrac{-2\pi}{3}$

f. $\dfrac{-3\pi}{2}$

g. $\dfrac{7\pi}{3}$

h. -2π

i. $\dfrac{7\pi}{12}$

j. $\dfrac{9\pi}{10}$

k. $\dfrac{11\pi}{15}$

l. $\dfrac{14\pi}{9}$

2. Convert each degree measure to its equivalent radian measure.

a. $120°$

b. $135°$

c. $-150°$

d. $-270°$

e. $240°$

f. $-210°$

g. $225°$

h. $20°$

i. $75°$

3. Determine the measures of all angles coterminal with an angle of 50°.

4. A circle of radius r has a central angle of θ radians or m degrees which intercepts an arc s units long. Determine r, θ, m and s for each of the following.

  a. $r = 2$, $s = 6$ **c.** $r = 10$, $m = 72°$ **e.** $s = 1.5$, $m = 150°$

  b. $r = 8$, $\theta = \dfrac{\pi}{4}$ **d.** $s = 9$, $\theta = \dfrac{3\pi}{7}$

5. Determine the area of a circular sector with radius 3 determined by a central angle of $\dfrac{2\pi}{3}$ radians.

6. Given the point $P(-\sqrt{11}, 5)$ on the terminal side of an angle of $u°$, determine the six trigonometric functions of $u°$.

7. Which trigonometric functions are not defined at 90°?

8. Given $\cos u° = \dfrac{-2}{5}$ and $180° < u° < 270°$, determine the other five trigonometric functions of $u°$.

9. Tell which trigonometric functions of $u°$ are positive in the interval $270° < u° < 360°$.

10. Determine the values of the trigonometric functions which are defined for 180°.

11. Determine the values of the six trigonometric functions for each of the following angle measures.

  a. 150°   **c.** 300°   **e.** $\dfrac{\pi}{6}$

  b. 225°   **d.** $-240°$ **f.** $\dfrac{-\pi}{4}$

12. Express each of the following in terms of the same trigonometric function of $u°$, where $0° < u° < 90°$.

  a. $\cos 110°$ **c.** $\tan 200°$ **e.** $\csc 320°$ **g.** $\cos(-70°)$

  b. $\sin 130°$ **d.** $\sec 200°$ **f.** $\sin(-40°)$ **h.** $\tan(-140°)$

13. Express each of the following in terms of its co-named function.

  a. $\tan 40°$ **c.** $\cos 140°$ **e.** $\cot 20°$

  b. $\sin(-20°)$ **d.** $\sec 80°$ **f.** $\csc(-10°)$

14. For each equation, determine two values of $u°$ between 0° and 360°.

  a. $\sin u° = \dfrac{-1}{2}$ **c.** $\tan u° = \sqrt{3}$ **e.** $\sec u° = -2$

  b. $\cos u° = \dfrac{\sqrt{3}}{2}$ **d.** $\csc u° = \dfrac{2}{\sqrt{3}}$ **f.** $\cot u° = -1$

15. Tell the period of each of the six trigonometric functions.

16. Use Table III and determine the following with accuracy to either four decimal places or four digits.

   a. sin 38°50′   **c.** tan 43°10′   **e.** sin 204°20′   **g.** cot 284°10′

   b. cos 72°20′   **d.** sec 80°40′   **f.** cos 146°40′   **h.** csc (−36°30′)

17. Interpolate to determine tan 42°16′ with accuracy to four digits.

18. Determine two values of $u°$, between 0° and 360°, for which cos $u° \doteq -0.8857$.

19. Interpolate and determine $u°$, between 0° and 90°, with accuracy to the nearest minute, so that tan $u° \doteq 0.7341$.

20. State the domain and range of each of the following.

   a. cosine   **b.** tangent   **c.** cosecant

21. Describe the variation in sin $u°$ as $u°$ increases from 180° to 270°.

22. State the complementary angles relation.

23. Determine the three pairs of reciprocal trigonometric functions.

24. Sketch the graphs of sine and cosecant for one period on one coordinate system.

25. Graph $y = \cos 3u°$ and determine the number of solutions for the equation $\cos 3u° = \dfrac{1}{2}$ in the interval 0° $\leq u° <$ 360°.

26. From the graph of cosine determine all values of $u°$ for which $\cos u° < \dfrac{1}{2}$.

27. Determine (1) the amplitude, (2) the period, and (3) the phase number of each of the following functions.

   a. $y = \dfrac{2}{3} \sin 3u°$ **b.** $y = -2 \cos \dfrac{1}{2}(u + 40)°$ **c.** $y = \sin (2u - 60)°$

28. Sketch the graph of $y = \dfrac{1}{2} \sin \dfrac{1}{2}(u - 120)°$ for one period.

CHAPTER TEST

1. Give the equivalent degree measure for $\dfrac{7\pi}{15}$ radians.

2. Give the equivalent radian measure for $-200°$.

3. Determine the radius of a circle, accurate to one decimal place, if a central angle of 135° intercepts an arc 3.3 units long.

4. What is the area of a circular sector with radius 4 determined by a central angle of $\frac{3\pi}{4}$ radians?

5. Given that the terminal side of an angle of $u°$ passes through the point $P(5, -2)$, determine the six trigonometric functions of $u°$.

6. Given $\sin u° = \frac{2}{3}$ and $90° < u° < 180°$, determine the other five trigonometric functions of $u°$.

7. Which trigonometric functions are not defined at $180°$?

8. Determine each of the following, if it exists.

a. $\sin 135°$ d. $\sec 120°$ g. $\tan 180°$ j. $\cos \frac{4\pi}{3}$

                                        h. $\sec 90°$

b. $\cos 210°$ e. $\csc 225°$ k. $\sin (-30°)$

                                        i. $\tan \frac{3\pi}{4}$

c. $\tan 300°$ f. $\cot 330°$ l. $\tan (-120°)$

9. Express each of the following in terms of the same trigonometric function of $u°$, where $0° < u° < 90°$.

a. $\cos 143°$ c. $\sin (-70°)$

b. $\tan 227°$ d. $\sec 340°$

10. Express each of the following in terms of its co-named function.

a. $\sec 40°$ b. $\cos 100°$

11. Determine two values of $u°$, between $0°$ and $360°$, for which $\cos u° = \frac{-1}{2}$.

12. State the period of tangent.

13. Given $\sin 16°20' \doteq .2812$ and $\sin 16°30' \doteq .2840$, determine $\sin 16°23'$ with accuracy to four decimal places.

14. State the domain and range of cotangent.

15. Describe the variation in $\cos u°$ as $u°$ increases from $90°$ to $180°$.

16. Sketch the graphs of cosine and secant for one period on one coordinate system.

17. Sketch the graph of $y = 3 \sin 2(u - 60)°$ for one period.

18. Determine the number of solutions for the equation $\sin 2u° = \frac{2}{3}$ in the interval $0° \le u° < 360°$.

CHAPTER 7

EQUATIONS AND IDENTITIES FOR ANGLE MEASURES

TRIGONOMETRIC IDENTITIES

Recall that an *identity* is defined as an equation which is true for all permissible values of the variables. Recall also that for any point $P(x, y)$ on the terminal side of an angle of $u°$ at a distance $r(r > 0)$ from the origin (see Figure 7–1) it is true that

$$x^2 + y^2 \equiv r^2$$

The definitions of the trigonometric functions of angle measures lead us to eight trigonometric identities. They are derived here for you.

From the identity $x^2 + y^2 \equiv r^2$ it follows that

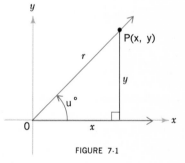

FIGURE 7-1

$$\frac{x^2}{r^2} + \frac{y^2}{r^2} \equiv 1 \qquad \text{Why?}$$

$$\left(\frac{x}{r}\right)^2 + \left(\frac{y}{r}\right)^2 \equiv 1 \qquad \text{Why?}$$

$$\cos^2 u° + \sin^2 u° \equiv 1 \qquad \text{Why?} \qquad [7.1]$$

Now consider the following derivation.

$$x^2 + y^2 \equiv r^2$$

$$\frac{x^2}{x^2} + \frac{y^2}{x^2} \equiv \frac{r^2}{x^2} \qquad \text{Why?}$$

$$1 + \tan^2 u° \equiv \sec^2 u° \qquad \text{Why?} \qquad [7.2]$$

185

And the following.

$$x^2 + y^2 \equiv r^2$$

$$\frac{x^2}{y^2} + \frac{y^2}{y^2} \equiv \frac{r^2}{y^2} \qquad \text{Why?}$$

$$\cot^2 u° + 1 \equiv \csc^2 u° \qquad \text{Why?}$$

$$1 + \cot^2 u° \equiv \csc^2 u° \qquad\qquad\qquad [7.3]$$

Identities [7.1], [7.2], and [7.3] are called the *squared identities*. Observe that, for identity [7.1], all real number degree measures are permissible values of $u°$. But for identity [7.2], the degree measures $(90 + 180k)°$ are not permissible values of $u°$. What values of $u°$ are not permissible for identity [7.3]?

The *reciprocal identities*

$$\csc u° \equiv \frac{1}{\sin u°} \qquad\qquad\qquad [7.4]$$

$$\sec u° \equiv \frac{1}{\cos u°} \qquad\qquad\qquad [7.5]$$

and

$$\cot u° \equiv \frac{1}{\tan u°} \qquad\qquad\qquad [7.6]$$

are easily derived. Identity [7.4] may be derived from the identity $\dfrac{r}{y} \equiv \dfrac{1}{\frac{y}{r}}$ and the definitions of csc and sin. The values of $u°$ which are not permissible for identity [7.4] are $180k°$.

The *ratio identities*

$$\tan u° \equiv \frac{\sin u°}{\cos u°} \qquad\qquad\qquad [7.7]$$

and

$$\cot u° \equiv \frac{\cos u°}{\sin u°} \qquad\qquad\qquad [7.8]$$

follow immediately from the definitions of the trigonometric functions involved.

These eight identities may be used to simplify trigonometric expressions and to prove other trigonometric identities. This is illustrated in the following examples.

Example 1   Simplify $\cos u° + \sin u° \cdot \tan u°$ and specify the permissible values of $u°$.

Solution $\cos u° + \sin u° \cdot \tan u° \equiv \cos u° + \sin u° \cdot \dfrac{\sin u°}{\cos u°} \qquad by\ 7.7$

$$\equiv \frac{\cos^2 u° + \sin^2 u°}{\cos u°}$$

$$\equiv \frac{1}{\cos u°} \qquad\qquad by\ 7.1$$

$$\equiv \sec u° \qquad\qquad by\ 7.5$$

The values of $u°$ which are not permissible are $(90 + 180k)°$ since $\tan u°$ (and $\sec u°$) is involved. Observe that the first step was to express all functions in terms of $\sin u°$ and $\cos u°$. This is often the best way to begin proving an identity if no other procedure suggests itself.

Example 2   Prove the identity csc $u° \cdot$ sec $u° -$ cot $u° \equiv$ tan $u°$.

Solution $$\text{csc } u° \cdot \text{sec } u° - \text{cot } u° \equiv \frac{1}{\sin u°} \cdot \frac{1}{\cos u°} - \frac{\cos u°}{\sin u°}$$
$$\text{by 7.4, 7.5, 7.8}$$

$$\equiv \frac{1 - \cos^2 u°}{\sin u° \cdot \cos u°}$$

$$\equiv \frac{\sin^2 u°}{\sin u° \cdot \cos u°} \qquad \text{by 7.1}$$

$$\equiv \frac{\sin u°}{\cos u°}$$

$$\equiv \text{tan } u° \qquad \text{by 7.7}$$

Example 3   Simplify tan $u°$ (cot $u° +$ tan $u°$) and specify the permissible values of $u°$.

Solution $$\text{tan } u° (\text{cot } u° + \text{tan } u°) \equiv \text{tan } u° \cdot \text{cot } u° + \text{tan}^2 u°$$
$$\equiv 1 + \text{tan}^2 u° \qquad \text{by 7.6}$$
$$\equiv \text{sec}^2 u° \qquad \text{by 7.2}$$

The values of $u°$ which are not permissible are $(90 + 180k)°$ and $180k°$ since tan $u°$ and cot $u°$, respectively, are involved. All the values of $u°$ which are not permissible may be expressed as $90k°$.

EXERCISES

1. Derive each of the following identities and in each case specify the values of $u°$ which are not permissible.

a. Identity [7.4], csc $u° \equiv \dfrac{1}{\sin u°}$

b. Identity [7.5], sec $u° \equiv \dfrac{1}{\cos u°}$

c. Identity [7.6], cot $u° \equiv \dfrac{1}{\tan u°}$

d. Identity [7.7], tan $u° \equiv \dfrac{\sin u°}{\cos u°}$

e. Identity [7.8], cot $u° \equiv \dfrac{\cos u°}{\sin u°}$

2. Simplify each expression and specify the values of $u°$ which are not permissible.

a. sin $u° \cdot$ cot $u°$

b. sec^2 $u° - 1$

c. $\dfrac{\sec u°}{\csc u°}$

d. cos $u° \cdot$ tan $u°$

e. cot $u°$ (tan $u° +$ cot $u°$)

f. $\dfrac{\sin u°}{\tan u°}$

g. $(1 - \cos u°)(1 + \cos u°)$

h. sin $u° +$ cos $u° \cdot$ cot $u°$

i. $\dfrac{\cos u° \cdot \tan u° + \sin u°}{\tan u°}$

j. $\sin u° (\csc u° - \sin u°)$

k. $\dfrac{\sin u° \cdot \tan u° \cdot \csc u°}{\sec u° \cdot \cot u° \cdot \cos u°}$

l. $\dfrac{\cot u°}{\cos u°}$

m. $\dfrac{1 + \cot^2 u°}{\csc u°}$

n. $\tan u° \left(\dfrac{1 + \cot u°}{1 + \tan u°}\right)$

o. $\dfrac{\tan u°}{\sin u°}$

p. $\cos u° + \cos u° \cdot \tan^2 u°$

q. $\cos u° (\sec u° - \cos u°)$

r. $\dfrac{1 + \tan^2 u°}{\tan^2 u°}$

s. $\dfrac{\sin u° + \cos u° \cdot \tan u°}{\cos u°}$

t. $\dfrac{1 + \tan^2 u°}{1 + \cot^2 u°}$

u. $\sec u° - \tan u° \cdot \sin u°$

v. $\dfrac{\cos u°}{\cot u°} + \dfrac{1}{\csc u°}$

w. $(1 - \sin^2 u°)(1 + \tan^2 u°)$

x. $\tan u° (\cos u° + \cot u° \cdot \sin u°)$

y. $\sin^2 u° (1 + \cot^2 u°)$

z. $\dfrac{\cos u°}{\tan u°} + \sin u°$

a'. $\sec^2 u° - \sec^2 u° \cdot \sin^2 u°$

b'. $\sin^2 u° \cdot \cot^2 u° + \cos^2 u° \cdot \tan^2 u°$

c'. $\cos^3 u° + \sin^2 u° \cdot \cos u°$

d'. $\dfrac{1 + \cot^2 u°}{\sec^2 u°}$

e'. $\dfrac{\sec^2 u° - 1}{\sin^2 u°}$

3. Prove each of the following identities.

a. $\tan u° + \cot u° \equiv \csc u° \cdot \sec u°$

b. $\dfrac{\sin u°}{1 - \cos u°} - \cot u° \equiv \csc u°$

c. $(\tan u° + \cot u°)^2 \equiv \sec^2 u° + \csc^2 u°$

d. $\sec^2 u° + \csc^2 u° \equiv \sec^2 u° \cdot \csc^2 u°$

e. $\dfrac{\cos u°}{1 + \sin u°} + \dfrac{\cos u°}{1 - \sin u°} \equiv 2 \sec u°$

f. $\sec^2 u° - \csc^2 u° \equiv \tan^2 u° - \cot^2 u°$

g. $\dfrac{\cos^4 u° - \sin^4 u°}{1 - \tan^4 u°} \equiv \cos^4 u°$

h. $1 + \cot^2 u° - \cos^2 u° - \cos^2 u° \cdot \cot^2 u° \equiv 1$

i. $(\tan u° + \cot u°)(\tan u° - \cot u°) \equiv \sec^2 u° - \csc^2 u°$

j. $\csc^4 u° - \cot^4 u° \equiv \csc^2 u° + \cot^2 u°$

k. $\dfrac{\sec u°}{\tan u° + \cot u°} \equiv \sin u°$

l. $\dfrac{1 + \cos u°}{\sin u°} + \dfrac{\sin u°}{1 + \cos u°} \equiv 2 \csc u°$

m. $\dfrac{2 \sin u° \cos u°}{\cos^2 u° - \sin^2 u°} \equiv \dfrac{2 \tan u°}{1 - \tan^2 u°}$

n. $1 - 2 \sin^2 u° + \sin^4 u° \equiv \cos^4 u°$

o. $\dfrac{\sin u°}{\csc u° - \cot u°} \equiv 1 + \cos u°$

IDENTITIES INVOLVING SUMS AND DIFFERENCES

In Chapter 6 we redefined the trigonometric functions as follows:

$$\cos \theta = \cos u° \qquad \sin \theta = \sin u° \qquad \tan \theta = \tan u°$$

where $u = \dfrac{180}{\pi} \cdot \theta$ for all permissible real numbers θ.

In Chapter 4 we derived the *Fundamental Identity*

$$\cos (\theta - \alpha) \equiv \cos \theta \cdot \cos \alpha + \sin \theta \cdot \sin \alpha$$

for all real numbers θ and α. From the Fundamental Identity, seven other identities were derived for all real numbers θ and α. As a consequence of redefining the trigonometric functions for angle measures, we have the *Fundamental Identity*

$$\cos (u - v)° \equiv \cos u° \cdot \cos v° + \sin u° \cdot \sin v° \qquad [7.9]$$

for real number angle measures $u°$ and $v°$. From this identity we may derive the following seven identities.

$$\cos (-v°) \equiv \cos v° \qquad\qquad\qquad\qquad\qquad [7.10]$$
$$\cos (90 - v)° \equiv \sin v° \qquad\qquad\qquad\qquad\quad [7.11]$$
$$\sin (90 - u)° \equiv \cos u° \qquad\qquad\qquad\qquad\quad [7.12]$$
$$\sin (-u°) \equiv -\sin u° \qquad\qquad\qquad\qquad\quad [7.13]$$
$$\cos (u + v)° \equiv \cos u° \cdot \cos v° - \sin u° \cdot \sin v° \qquad [7.14]$$
$$\sin (u + v)° \equiv \sin u° \cdot \cos v° + \cos u° \cdot \sin v° \qquad [7.15]$$
$$\sin (u - v)° \equiv \sin u° \cdot \cos v° - \cos u° \cdot \sin v° \qquad [7.16]$$

You should memorize the Fundamental Identity since it is essential in the derivations of other identities.

Study the following proofs of identities [7.10], [7.13], and [7.15]. You will be asked to prove the others as an exercise.

Proof of identity [7.10]

$$\cos (u - v)° \equiv \cos u° \cdot \cos v° + \sin u° \cdot \sin v° \quad by\ 7.9$$

Let $u° = 0°$; then, $\cos (0 - v)° \equiv \cos 0° \cdot \cos v° + \sin 0° \cdot \sin v°$

$$\cos (-v°) \equiv 1 \cdot \cos v° + 0 \cdot \sin v°$$

Hence, $\qquad\qquad \cos (-v°) \equiv \cos v°$

Proof of identity [7.13]

$$\sin v° \equiv \cos (90 - v)° \qquad\qquad\qquad by\ 7.11$$

Let $v° = -u°$; then, $\sin (-u°) \equiv \cos [90 - (-u)]°$

$$\equiv \cos (90 + u)°$$
$$\equiv \cos (-90 - u)° \qquad\qquad by\ 7.10$$
$$\equiv \cos (-90°) \cdot \cos u° +$$
$$\qquad\qquad \sin (-90°) \cdot \sin u° \quad by\ 7.9$$
$$\equiv 0 \cdot \cos u° + (-1) \sin u°$$

Hence, $\qquad \sin (-u°) \equiv -\sin u°$

Proof of identity [7.15]

$$\sin w° \equiv \cos (90 - w)° \qquad\qquad\qquad by\ 7.11$$

Let $w° = (u + v)°$; then, $\sin (u + v)° \equiv \cos [90 - (u + v)]°$

$$\equiv \cos [(90 - u) - v]°$$
$$\equiv \cos (90 - u)° \cdot \cos v° +$$
$$\qquad\qquad \sin (90 - u)° \cdot \sin v° \quad by\ 7.9$$

Hence, $\qquad \sin (u + v)° \equiv \sin u° \cdot \cos v° +$
$$\qquad\qquad\qquad\qquad \cos u° \cdot \sin v° \quad by\ 7.11,\ 7.12$$

The identities derived thus far may be used to derive the following identities.

$$\tan (u + v)^\circ \equiv \frac{\tan u^\circ + \tan v^\circ}{1 - \tan u^\circ \cdot \tan v^\circ} \qquad [7.17]$$

$$\tan (u - v)^\circ \equiv \frac{\tan u^\circ - \tan v^\circ}{1 + \tan u^\circ \cdot \tan v^\circ} \qquad [7.18]$$

$$\tan (-u^\circ) \equiv -\tan u^\circ \qquad [7.19]$$
$$\tan (90 - v)^\circ \equiv \cot v^\circ \qquad [7.20]$$

We shall begin the proof of identity [7.17] and then leave its completion as well as the proofs of [7.18], [7.19], and [7.20] as exercises.

Proof of identity [7.17]

$$\tan (u + v)^\circ \equiv \frac{\sin (u + v)^\circ}{\cos (u + v)^\circ} \qquad \textit{by 7.7}$$

$$\equiv \frac{\sin u^\circ \cdot \cos v^\circ + \cos u^\circ \cdot \sin v^\circ}{\cos u^\circ \cdot \cos v^\circ - \sin u^\circ \cdot \sin v^\circ} \qquad \textit{by 7.14, 7.15}$$

$$\equiv \frac{\dfrac{\sin u^\circ \cdot \cos v^\circ}{\cos u^\circ \cdot \cos v^\circ} + \dfrac{\cos u^\circ \cdot \sin v^\circ}{\cos u^\circ \cdot \cos v^\circ}}{\dfrac{\cos u^\circ \cdot \cos v^\circ}{\cos u^\circ \cdot \cos v^\circ} - \dfrac{\sin u^\circ \cdot \sin v^\circ}{\cos u^\circ \cdot \cos v^\circ}}$$

You will be asked to complete this proof in the exercises.

EXERCISES

1. Study the proof of identity [7.10], $\cos (-v^\circ) \equiv \cos v^\circ$. Then prove the following identities.

    a. Identity [7.11], $\cos (90 - v)^\circ \equiv \sin v^\circ$

    b. Identity [7.12], $\sin (90 - u)^\circ \equiv \cos u^\circ$
    Hint: Begin with [7.11], $\sin v^\circ \equiv \cos (90 - v)^\circ$, and let $v^\circ = (90 - u)^\circ$.

2. Prove identity [7.14], $\cos (u + v)^\circ \equiv \cos u^\circ \cdot \cos v^\circ - \sin u^\circ \cdot \sin v^\circ$.
    Hint: Begin with identity [7.9], $\cos (u - w)^\circ \equiv \cos u^\circ \cdot \cos w^\circ + \sin u^\circ \cdot \sin w^\circ$, and let $w^\circ = -v^\circ$.

3. Prove identity [7.16], $\sin (u - v)^\circ \equiv \sin u^\circ \cdot \cos v^\circ - \cos u^\circ \cdot \sin v^\circ$.

4. Prove identity [7.17], $\tan (u + v)^\circ \equiv \dfrac{\tan u^\circ + \tan v^\circ}{1 - \tan u^\circ \cdot \tan v^\circ}$. Refer to the beginning of the proof as shown above.

5. Prove each of the following identities.

    a. Identity [7.18], $\tan (u - v)^\circ \equiv \dfrac{\tan u^\circ - \tan v^\circ}{1 + \tan u^\circ \cdot \tan v^\circ}$

    b. Identity [7.19], $\tan (-v^\circ) \equiv -\tan v^\circ$

c. Identity [7.20], $\tan (90 - v)° \equiv \cot v°$ *Hint:* Begin with identity [7.7].

d. $\cot (-u°) \equiv -\cot u°$

e. $\cot (90 - v)° \equiv \tan v°$

6. Reduction identities were presented in Chapter 6 for certain values of the variable. Prove that these identities, as stated below, are true for all values of $v°$.

a. $\cos (180 - v)° \equiv -\cos v°$
  Hint: Begin with identity [7.9] and
     let $u° = 180°$.

b. $\sin (180 - v)° \equiv \sin v°$

c. $\cos (180 + v)° \equiv -\cos v°$

d. $\sin (180 + v)° \equiv -\sin v°$

e. $\cos (360 - v)° \equiv \cos v°$

f. $\sin (360 - v)° \equiv -\sin v°$

g. $\cos (v - 180)° \equiv -\cos v°$

h. $\sin (v - 180)° \equiv -\sin v°$

7. Prove that $180°$ is a period of tangent by proving the identity $\tan u° \equiv \tan (u + 180)°$.

8. Use the period identity $\tan u° \equiv \tan (u + 180k)°$ and the identity $\tan (-u°) \equiv -\tan u°$ to prove each of the following.

a. $\tan (180 - u)° \equiv -\tan u°$

b. $\tan (u - 180)° \equiv \tan u°$

c. $\tan (360 - u)° \equiv -\tan u°$

d. $\tan (u + 180)° \equiv \tan u°$

9. Given $\sin u° = \dfrac{-1}{3}$, $180° < u° < 270°$, $\cos v° = \dfrac{1}{4}$ and $270° < v° < 360°$. Determine each of the following. Use [7.1] for part **a.**

a. $\cos u°$

b. $\sin v°$

c. $\tan u°$

d. $\tan v°$

e. $\cos (u - v)°$

f. $\cos (-v°)$

g. $\sin (u + v)°$

h. $\sin (-u°)$

i. $\tan (u + v)°$

j. $\tan (-u°)$

k. $\cos (90 - u)°$

10. Simplify each expression.

a. $\cos^2 3w° + \sin^2 3w°$

b. $\sin (90 - 4w)°$

c. $\cos (90 - 5w)°$

d. $\sin (90 + 3w)°$

e. $\dfrac{\sin (-u°)}{-\cos u°}$

f. $\dfrac{\cos (-u°)}{-\sin u°}$

g. $\cos 4u° \cdot \cos 3v° + \sin 4u° \cdot \sin 3v°$

h. $\sin 5u° \cdot \cos 2v° + \cos 5u° \cdot \sin 2v°$

i. $\cos 7u° \cdot \cos 2u° - \sin 7u° \cdot \sin 2u°$

j. $\sin 3v° \cdot \cos 2v° - \cos 3v° \cdot \sin 2v°$

k. $\dfrac{\tan 3u° + \tan 5u°}{1 - \tan 3u° \cdot \tan 5u°}$

l. $\dfrac{\tan 5u° - \tan 2u°}{1 + \tan 5u° \cdot \tan 2u°}$

m. $\tan (90 - 3v)°$

n. $\tan (90 + 4u)°$

o. $\cos (u - 90)°$

p. $\sin (u - 90)°$

q. $\cos (90 + v)°$

r. $\sin (90 + v)°$

s. $\sin (u + v)° + \sin (u - v)°$

t. $\cos (u + v)° + \cos (u - v)°$

u. $\sin (u + v)° - \sin (u - v)°$

v. $\cos (u - v)° - \cos (u + v)°$

w. $1 - \cos 5u° \cdot \cos 2u° + \sin 5u° \cdot \sin 2u°$

x. $1 - \sin 5u° \cdot \cos 2u° - \cos 5u° \cdot \sin 2u°$

y. $\dfrac{\tan (u - v)° + \tan v°}{1 - \tan (u - v)° \cdot \tan v°}$

11. Compute each of the following using the technique illustrated in the example.

Example   Compute sin 15°.

Solution   Since 15° = (60 − 45)°, we use identity [7.16] as follows.

$$\sin 15° = \sin (60 - 45)°$$
$$= \sin 60° \cdot \cos 45° - \cos 60° \cdot \sin 45°$$
$$= \frac{\sqrt{3}}{2} \cdot \frac{\sqrt{2}}{2} - \frac{1}{2} \cdot \frac{\sqrt{2}}{2}$$
$$= \frac{\sqrt{6} - \sqrt{2}}{4}$$

a. cos 15°

b. tan 15°

c. sin 75°

d. tan 75°

e. cos 105°

f. tan 105°

12. Use identity [7.15] to determine $\sin (u + v)°$ for each set of conditions.

a. $\sin u° = \dfrac{3}{4}$, $90° < u° < 180°$, $\cos v° = \dfrac{-2}{3}$, and $180° < v° < 270°$

b. $\cos u° = 0.8$, $270° < u° < 360°$, $\cos v° = -0.8$, and $90° < v° < 180°$

13. Given $\tan u° = \dfrac{5}{3}$ and $\tan v° = \dfrac{-4}{3}$, determine each of the following.

a. $\tan (u + v)°$

b. $\tan (u - v)°$

14. What values of $u°$ are not permissible for the expression $\dfrac{4}{\tan u°} + \dfrac{5}{1 - \tan^2 u°}$?

15. Express $\sin 2u°$ in terms of $\sin u°$ and $\cos u°$.   *Hint:* $\sin 2u° \equiv \sin (u + u)°$.

16. Express $\cos 2u°$ in terms of $\sin u°$ and $\cos u°$.

17. Express $\tan 2u°$ in terms of $\tan u°$.

18. Expressions of the form $A \cos u° + B \sin u°$ occur frequently in the sciences. They are dealt with more readily in the equivalent form $C \sin (u + v)°$, where $C = \sqrt{A^2 + B^2}$, $\sin v° = \dfrac{A}{\sqrt{A^2 + B^2}}$, and $\cos v° = \dfrac{B}{\sqrt{A^2 + B^2}}$. That these are equivalent expressions may be shown as follows. Justify each step.

$$A \cos u° + B \sin u° \equiv \sqrt{A^2 + B^2} \left(\frac{A}{\sqrt{A^2 + B^2}} \cos u° + \frac{B}{\sqrt{A^2 + B^2}} \sin u° \right)$$

$$\equiv \sqrt{A^2 + B^2} (\sin v° \cdot \cos u° + \cos v° \cdot \sin u°)$$

$$\equiv \sqrt{A^2 + B^2} \sin (u + v)°$$

19. Use the results of Exercise 18 to express each of the following in the form $C \sin (u + v)°$ where C and v are real numbers.

Example $\cos u° - 2 \sin u°$

Since $A = 1$ and $B = -2$, we have $C = \sqrt{5} \doteq 2.2361$, $\sin v° = \frac{1}{\sqrt{5}} = \frac{\sqrt{5}}{5} \doteq .4472$, and $\cos v° = \frac{-2}{\sqrt{5}} = \frac{-2\sqrt{5}}{5} \doteq -.8944$.

It follows that $v° \doteq 153°30'$. Hence, $\cos u° - 2 \sin u°$ is equivalent to $2.24 \sin (u° + 153°30')$, accurate to 3 significant digits.

a. $3 \cos u° + \sqrt{3} \sin u°$

b. $6 \cos u° - 2\sqrt{3} \sin u°$

c. $2 \cos u° + 2 \sin u°$

d. $\cos u° - \sin u°$

e. $4 \cos u° + 3 \sin u°$

f. $2 \cos u° - 2 \sin u°$

IDENTITIES INVOLVING $2u°$ AND $\frac{u°}{2}$

Identities which express sin, cos, or tan of either $2u°$ or $\frac{u°}{2}$ in terms of sin, cos, and tan of $u°$ may be derived from identities proved earlier. These identities are listed below.

$$\sin 2u° \equiv 2 \sin u° \cdot \cos u° \tag{7.21}$$

$$\cos 2u° \equiv \cos^2 u° - \sin^2 u° \tag{7.22}$$

$$\cos 2u° \equiv 1 - 2 \sin^2 u° \tag{7.23}$$

$$\cos 2u° \equiv 2 \cos^2 u° - 1 \tag{7.24}$$

$$\tan 2u° \equiv \frac{2 \tan u°}{1 - \tan^2 u°} \tag{7.25}$$

$$\cos \frac{u°}{2} \equiv \pm \sqrt{\frac{1 + \cos u°}{2}} \tag{7.26}$$

$$\sin \frac{u°}{2} \equiv \pm \sqrt{\frac{1 - \cos u°}{2}} \tag{7.27}$$

$$\tan \frac{u°}{2} \equiv \frac{1 - \cos u°}{\sin u°} \tag{7.28}$$

$$\tan \frac{u°}{2} \equiv \frac{\sin u°}{1 + \cos u°} \tag{7.29}$$

In identities [7.26] and [7.27], the value of the right-hand member is chosen to be positive, negative or zero to agree with the left-hand member. This is indicated by the symbol $\pm$, which means that a choice is to be made.

Proof of identity [7.21]

$$\sin 2u^\circ \equiv \sin (u + u)^\circ$$
$$\equiv \sin u^\circ \cdot \cos u^\circ + \cos u^\circ \cdot \sin u^\circ \qquad by\ 7.15$$
$$\equiv 2 \sin u^\circ \cdot \cos u^\circ$$

Proof of identity [7.23]

$$\cos 2u^\circ \equiv \cos^2 u^\circ - \sin^2 u^\circ \qquad by\ 7.22$$
$$\equiv (1 - \sin^2 u^\circ) - \sin^2 u^\circ$$
$$\equiv 1 - 2 \sin^2 u^\circ$$

Proof of identity [7.26]

$$\cos 2v^\circ \equiv 2 \cos^2 v^\circ - 1 \qquad by\ 7.24$$
$$1 + \cos 2v^\circ \equiv 2 \cos^2 v^\circ$$
$$\cos^2 v^\circ \equiv \frac{1 + \cos 2v^\circ}{2}$$

Let $v^\circ = \dfrac{u^\circ}{2}$; then $\cos^2 \dfrac{u^\circ}{2} \equiv \dfrac{1 + \cos u^\circ}{2}$

$$\cos \frac{u^\circ}{2} \equiv \sqrt{\frac{1 + \cos u^\circ}{2}}, \text{ for } \cos \frac{u^\circ}{2} \geq 0$$

and $\cos \dfrac{u^\circ}{2} \equiv -\sqrt{\dfrac{1 + \cos u^\circ}{2}}$, for $\cos \dfrac{u^\circ}{2} < 0$

Proof of identity [7.28]

$$\tan v^\circ \equiv \frac{\sin v^\circ}{\cos v^\circ} \qquad by\ 7.7$$

$$\equiv \frac{\sin v^\circ}{\cos v^\circ} \cdot \frac{2 \sin v^\circ}{2 \sin v^\circ}$$

$$\equiv \frac{2 \sin^2 v^\circ}{2 \sin v^\circ \cdot \cos v^\circ}$$

$$\equiv \frac{1 - \cos 2v^\circ}{\sin 2v^\circ} \qquad by\ 7.23,\ 7.21$$

Let $v^\circ = \dfrac{u^\circ}{2}$. Then $\tan \dfrac{u^\circ}{2} \equiv \dfrac{1 - \cos u^\circ}{\sin u^\circ}$

This group of nine identities (7.21 through 7.29) may be used to prove other identities and to determine the trigonometric functions of certain angle measures. This is illustrated by the following examples.

Example 1   Prove the identity $\dfrac{1 - \cos 2u^\circ}{\sin 2u^\circ} \equiv \tan u^\circ$.

Solution $\dfrac{1 - \cos 2u^\circ}{\sin 2u^\circ} \equiv \dfrac{1 - (1 - 2 \sin^2 u^\circ)}{2 \sin u^\circ \cdot \cos u^\circ} \qquad by\ 7.23,\ 7.21$

$$\equiv \frac{2 \sin^2 u^\circ}{2 \sin u^\circ \cdot \cos u^\circ} \equiv \frac{\sin u^\circ}{\cos u^\circ} \equiv \tan u^\circ \qquad by\ 7.7$$

Example 2   Prove the identity $\dfrac{\tan u° + \sin u°}{2 \tan u°} \equiv \cos^2 \dfrac{u°}{2}$.

Solution

$$\frac{\tan u° + \sin u°}{2 \tan u°} \equiv \cos^2 \frac{u°}{2}$$

$$\frac{\dfrac{\sin u°}{\cos u°} + \sin u°}{\dfrac{2 \sin u°}{\cos u°}} \equiv \frac{1 + \cos u°}{2} \qquad\qquad \text{by 7.7, 7.26}$$

$$\frac{\cos u°}{\cos u°} \cdot \frac{\dfrac{\sin u°}{\cos u°} + \sin u°}{\dfrac{2 \sin u°}{\cos u°}} \equiv \frac{1 + \cos u°}{2}$$

$$\frac{\sin u° + \sin u° \cdot \cos u°}{2 \sin u°} \equiv \frac{1 + \cos u°}{2}$$

$$\frac{\sin u°(1 + \cos u°)}{2 \sin u°} \equiv \frac{1 + \cos u°}{2}$$

$$\frac{1 + \cos u°}{2} \equiv \frac{1 + \cos u°}{2}$$

Example 3   Given that $\sin u° = \dfrac{-1}{4}$ and $180° < u° < 270°$, determine (1) $\sin 2u°$, (2) $\cos 2u°$, and (3) $\tan 2u°$.

Solution   From identity [7.1], it follows that

$$\cos^2 u° + \left(\frac{-1}{4}\right)^2 = 1$$

$$\cos^2 u° = \frac{15}{16}$$

$$\cos u° = \frac{\sqrt{15}}{4} \text{ or } \cos u° = \frac{-\sqrt{15}}{4}$$

Thus, $\cos u° = \dfrac{-\sqrt{15}}{4}$ since $180° < u° < 270°$.

(1) $\sin 2u° \equiv 2 \sin u° \cdot \cos u°$ by 7.21

$$\sin 2u° = 2\left(\frac{-1}{4}\right)\left(\frac{-\sqrt{15}}{4}\right)$$

$$= \frac{\sqrt{15}}{8}$$

(2) $\cos 2u° \equiv 1 - 2 \sin^2 u°$ by 7.23

$$\cos 2u° = 1 - 2\left(\frac{-1}{4}\right)^2$$

$$= 1 - \frac{2}{16} = \frac{7}{8}$$

(3) $\tan u° \equiv \dfrac{\sin u°}{\cos u°}$ *by 7.7*

$\tan u° = \dfrac{-1}{4} \div \dfrac{-\sqrt{15}}{4} = \dfrac{1}{\sqrt{15}} = \dfrac{\sqrt{15}}{15}$

$\tan 2u° \equiv \dfrac{2 \tan u°}{1 - \tan^2 u°}$ *by 7.25*

$\tan 2u° = \dfrac{2\left(\dfrac{\sqrt{15}}{15}\right)}{1 - \left(\dfrac{1}{\sqrt{15}}\right)^2} = \dfrac{\dfrac{2\sqrt{15}}{15}}{1 - \dfrac{1}{15}}$

$\qquad\quad = \dfrac{2\sqrt{15}}{15} \cdot \dfrac{15}{14} = \dfrac{\sqrt{15}}{7}$

Example 4   Given $\sin u° = \dfrac{-3}{5}$, $\cos u° = \dfrac{4}{5}$, and $270° < u° < 360°$, determine

(1) $\sin \dfrac{u°}{2}$, (2) $\cos \dfrac{u°}{2}$, and (3) $\tan \dfrac{u°}{2}$.

Solution   (1) $\sin \dfrac{u°}{2} \equiv \pm\sqrt{\dfrac{1 - \cos u°}{2}}$ *by 7.27*

The positive sign is to be chosen since $135° < \dfrac{u°}{2} < 180°$

and thus, $\sin \dfrac{u°}{2} > 0$.

$\sin \dfrac{u°}{2} = \sqrt{\dfrac{1 - \dfrac{4}{5}}{2}} = \sqrt{\dfrac{1}{10}} = \dfrac{\sqrt{10}}{10}$

(2) $\cos \dfrac{u°}{2} \equiv \pm\sqrt{\dfrac{1 + \cos u°}{2}}$ *by 7.26*

The negative sign is to be chosen since $135° < \dfrac{u°}{2} < 180°$

and thus $\cos \dfrac{u°}{2} < 0$.

$\cos \dfrac{u°}{2} = -\sqrt{\dfrac{1 + \dfrac{4}{5}}{2}} = -\sqrt{\dfrac{9}{10}} = \dfrac{-3}{\sqrt{10}} = \dfrac{-3\sqrt{10}}{10}$

(3) $\tan \dfrac{u°}{2} \equiv \dfrac{1 - \cos u°}{\sin u°}$ *by 7.28*

$\tan \dfrac{u°}{2} \equiv \dfrac{1 - \dfrac{4}{5}}{\dfrac{-3}{5}} = \dfrac{-1}{3}$

EXERCISES

1. Study the proof of identity [7.21]. Then prove identity [7.22]:
$$\cos 2u° \equiv \cos^2 u° - \sin^2 u°.$$

2. Study the proof of identity [7.23]. Then prove identity [7.24]:
$$\cos 2u° \equiv 2\cos^2 u° - 1.$$

3. Prove identity [7.25]: $\tan 2u° \equiv \dfrac{2\tan u°}{1 - \tan^2 u°}.$

4. Study the proof of identity [7.26]. Then prove identity [7.27]:
$$\sin \frac{u°}{2} \equiv \pm\sqrt{\frac{1 - \cos u°}{2}}. \quad \textit{Hint: Begin with identity [7.23], } \cos 2v° \equiv 1 - 2\sin^2 v°,$$
and solve it for $\sin^2 v°$.

5. Study the proof of identity [7.28]. Then prove identity [7.29]:
$$\tan \frac{u°}{2} \equiv \frac{\sin u°}{1 + \cos u°}. \quad \textit{Hint: Begin the proof with identity [7.7].}$$

6. For each set of conditions, determine (1) $\sin 2u°$, (2) $\cos 2u°$, and (3) $\tan 2u°$.

   a. $\sin u° = \dfrac{2}{3}$ and $90° < u° < 180°$

   d. $\sin u° = \dfrac{-1}{3}$ and $270° < u° < 360°$

   b. $\cos u° = \dfrac{-3}{4}$ and $90° < u° < 180°$

   e. $\cos u° = \dfrac{2}{5}$ and $270° < u° < 360°$

   c. $\tan u° = \dfrac{5}{3}$ and $180° < u° < 270°$

7. For each interval given below, determine whether (1) $\sin \dfrac{u°}{2}$ and (2) $\cos \dfrac{u°}{2}$ are positive or negative.

   a. $90° < u° < 180°$ **b.** $180° < u° < 270°$ **c.** $270° < u° < 360°$

8. For each set of conditions, determine (1) $\sin \dfrac{u°}{2}$, (2) $\cos \dfrac{u°}{2}$, and (3) $\tan \dfrac{u°}{2}$.

   a. $\sin u° = \dfrac{-1}{4}$ and $270° < u° < 360°$

   c. $\sin u° = \dfrac{2}{3}$ and $360° < u° < 450°$

   b. $\cos u° = \dfrac{1}{3}$ and $270° < u° < 360°$

   d. $\cos u° = \dfrac{-3}{4}$ and $180° < u° < 270°$

9. Simplify each of the following.

   a. $\cos^2 \dfrac{u°}{2} - \sin^2 \dfrac{u°}{2}$ **d.** $2\cos^2 \dfrac{u°}{2}$ **g.** $1 - 2\sin^2 \dfrac{u°}{2}$

   b. $\dfrac{2\tan 3u°}{1 - \tan^2 3u°}$ **e.** $2\sin 3u° \cdot \cos 3u°$ **h.** $\dfrac{1 - \cos 2u°}{\sin u°}$

   c. $\dfrac{\sin 2u°}{2\sin u°}$ **f.** $\dfrac{1 + \cos 2u°}{\sin 2u°}$ **i.** $\dfrac{\cos 2u°}{\cos u° - \sin u°}$

10. Use identities involving $\dfrac{u^\circ}{2}$ to compute each of the following.

Example $\cos 105^\circ = -\sqrt{\dfrac{1 + \cos 210^\circ}{2}} = -\sqrt{\dfrac{1 + \dfrac{-\sqrt{3}}{2}}{2}} = \dfrac{-\sqrt{2 - \sqrt{3}}}{2}$

a. $\sin 22\dfrac{1}{2}^\circ$

b. $\tan 22\dfrac{1}{2}^\circ$

c. $\sin 15^\circ \cdot \cos 15^\circ$

d. $\tan 75^\circ \cdot \sin 75^\circ$

e. $\sin 67\dfrac{1}{2}^\circ$

f. $\dfrac{\tan 105^\circ}{\cos 105^\circ}$

g. $\tan 112\dfrac{1}{2}^\circ \cdot \sin 112\dfrac{1}{2}^\circ$

h. $\tan 157\dfrac{1}{2}^\circ$

i. $\cos 112\dfrac{1}{2}^\circ$

11. Prove each of the following identities.

a. $\dfrac{\sin 2u^\circ}{1 + \cos 2u^\circ} \equiv \tan u^\circ$

b. $(\sin u^\circ + \cos u^\circ)^2 - 1 \equiv \sin 2u^\circ$

c. $2 \sin u^\circ \cdot \cos^3 u^\circ + 2 \sin^3 u^\circ \cdot \cos u^\circ \equiv \sin 2u^\circ$

d. $2 \csc 2u^\circ \equiv \sec u^\circ \cdot \csc u^\circ$

e. $1 - \dfrac{1}{\sec 2u^\circ} \equiv \dfrac{2}{\csc^2 u^\circ}$

f. $\tan u^\circ \cdot \sin 2u^\circ \equiv 2 \sin^2 u^\circ$

g. $(\sin u^\circ - \cos u^\circ)^2 - \sin 2u^\circ \equiv 1$

h. $1 - \cos 2u^\circ \equiv 2 \sin^2 u^\circ$

i. $2 \cos^2 \dfrac{u^\circ}{2} - 1 \equiv \cos u^\circ$

j. $4 \sin^2 u^\circ \cdot \cos^2 u^\circ \equiv 1 - \cos^2 2u^\circ$

k. $\sin 2u^\circ \cdot \csc u^\circ - \cos 2u^\circ \cdot \sec u^\circ \equiv \sec u^\circ$

l. $\cos 4u^\circ \equiv 8 \cos^4 u^\circ - 8 \cos^2 u^\circ + 1$

m. $2 \cos \left(u + \dfrac{v}{2} \right)^\circ \cdot \sin \dfrac{v^\circ}{2} \equiv \sin (u + v)^\circ - \sin u^\circ$

n. $\sin 4u^\circ \equiv 4 \sin u^\circ \cdot \cos u^\circ \cdot \cos 2u^\circ$

o. $\dfrac{\sin 2u^\circ}{1 + \cos 2u^\circ} \equiv \dfrac{1 - \cos 2u^\circ}{\sin 2u^\circ}$

p. $\cos 2u^\circ \cdot \cos u^\circ + \sin 2u^\circ \cdot \sin u^\circ \equiv \cos u^\circ$

q. $\cos^4 u^\circ - \sin^4 u^\circ \equiv \cos 2u^\circ$

r. $\dfrac{\tan u^\circ + \sin u^\circ}{2 \tan u^\circ} \equiv \cos^2 \dfrac{u^\circ}{2}$

s. $\dfrac{2 \tan u^\circ}{1 + \tan^2 u^\circ} \equiv \sin 2u^\circ$

t. $\dfrac{\sin 2u^\circ}{\sin u^\circ} - \dfrac{\cos 2u^\circ}{\cos u^\circ} \equiv \sec u^\circ$

u. $\sin (u + v)^\circ + \sin (u - v)^\circ \equiv 2 \sin u^\circ \cdot \cos v^\circ$

v. $\left(\dfrac{1 + \tan u^\circ}{1 - \tan u^\circ} \right)^2 \equiv \dfrac{1 + \sin 2u^\circ}{1 - \sin 2u^\circ}$

w. $\tan \dfrac{u^\circ}{2} (1 + \cos u^\circ) \equiv \sin u^\circ$

x. $\dfrac{\cos 2u^\circ}{\sin u^\circ \cdot \cos u^\circ} \equiv \cot u^\circ - \tan u^\circ$

12. Express $\sin 3u^\circ$ in terms of $\sin u^\circ$.   *Hint:* $\sin 3u^\circ \equiv \sin (2u + u)^\circ$.

13. Express $\cos 3u^\circ$ in terms of $\cos u^\circ$.

14. Express $\tan 3u^\circ$ in terms of $\tan u^\circ$.

TRIGONOMETRIC EQUATIONS

In Chapter 4 we solved trigonometric equations, such as $2 \sin \theta + 1 = 0$, for real number values of θ. Now, we shall solve *trigonometric equations*, such as $2 \sin u° + 1 = 0$, for real number degree measures. To *solve a trigonometric equation*, such as the preceding one, means to find all real number degree measures $u°$ which satisfy the equation. Study the following examples which illustrate various techniques for solving trigonometric equations for degree measures.

Example 1   Solve $2 \sin u° + 1 = 0$ for all values of $u°$.

Solution $2 \sin u° + 1 = 0$

$$\sin u° = \frac{-1}{2}$$

From your work with the sine function, you know that there are two values of $u°$ in the interval $0° \leq u° < 360°$ for which $\sin u° = \frac{-1}{2}$. These values are $210°$ and $330°$. Since sine is a periodic function, there are infinitely many values of $u°$ for which $\sin u° = \frac{-1}{2}$. The complete solution set for $\sin u° = \frac{-1}{2}$ is $\{(210 + 360k)°, (330 + 360k)°\}$. What are the solutions in the interval $0° \leq u° < 720°$?

Example 2   Solve $3 \tan^2 u° = 1$ for all values of $u°$ in the interval $0° \leq u° < 360°$.

Solution $3 \tan^2 u° = 1$

$$\tan^2 u° = \frac{1}{3}$$

$$\tan u° = \frac{1}{\sqrt{3}} \text{ or } \tan u° = \frac{-1}{\sqrt{3}}$$

There are two values of $u°$, namely $30°$ and $210°$, for which $\tan u° = \frac{1}{\sqrt{3}}$ in the interval $0° \leq u° < 360°$. Also, there are two values of $u°$, namely $150°$ and $330°$, in this interval for which $\tan u° = \frac{-1}{\sqrt{3}}$. Hence, the solution set for $3 \tan^2 u° = 1$, where $0° \leq u° < 360°$, is $\{30°, 150°, 210°, 330°\}$.

Example 3   Solve $\sin u° + \sin u° \cdot \tan u° = 0$ for $0° \leq u° < 360°$.

Solution
$$\sin u° + \sin u° \cdot \tan u° = 0$$
Factoring, $\sin u° (1 + \tan u°) = 0$
$$(\sin u° = 0) \text{ or } (\tan u° = -1)$$
$$(u° = 0° \text{ or } u° = 180°) \text{ or } (u° = 135° \text{ or } u° = 315°)$$
The solution set is $\{0°, 135°, 180°, 315°\}$.

Example 4   Solve $2 \cos^2 u° - \cos u° = 1$ for $0° \leq u° < 360°$.

Solution   Since the equation is quadratic, we try to solve by factoring.
$$2 \cos^2 u° - \cos u° = 1$$
$$2 \cos^2 u° - \cos u° - 1 = 0$$
$$(2 \cos u° + 1)(\cos u° - 1) = 0$$
$$(2 \cos u° + 1 = 0) \text{ or } (\cos u° - 1 = 0)$$
$$\left(\cos u° = \frac{-1}{2}\right) \text{ or } (\cos u° = 1)$$
$$(u° = 120° \text{ or } u° = 240°) \text{ or } (u° = 0°)$$
Hence, the solution set for the specified interval is $\{0°, 120°, 240°\}$.

Example 5   Determine the solutions of $\tan^2 u° + \tan u° - 3 = 0$ to the nearest ten minutes for $0° \leq u° < 360°$.

Solution   The equation is quadratic and not factorable with respect to the set of rational numbers. Hence, we use the quadratic formula.
$$\tan^2 u° + \tan u° - 3 = 0$$
$$\tan u° = \frac{-1 \pm \sqrt{1 - 4(1)(-3)}}{2} = \frac{-1 \pm \sqrt{13}}{2}$$
$$\doteq \frac{-1 \pm 3.6056}{2}$$
Hence, $(\tan u° \doteq 1.3028)$ or $(\tan u° \doteq -2.3028)$.
Thus, $(u° \doteq 52°30'$ or $u° \doteq 180° + 52°30' = 232°30')$ or $(u° \doteq 180° - 66°30' = 113°30'$ or $u° \doteq 360° - 66°30' = 293°30')$. The solution set is $\{52°30', 113°30', 232°30', 293°30'\}$, each solution accurate to the nearest ten minutes.

Example 6   Solve $2 \cos 2u° = 1$ for $0° \leq u° < 360°$.

Solution   Since $u°$ is in the interval $0° \leq u° < 360°$, we determine $2u°$ in the interval $0° \leq 2u° < 720°$.
$$2 \cos 2u° = 1$$
$$\cos 2u° = \frac{1}{2}$$
The values of $2u°$ are $60°$, $300°$, $(60 + 360)°$ and $(300 + 360)°$ in the interval $0 \leq u° < 720°$. Hence, the values of $u°$ are $30°$, $150°$, $210°$ and $330°$. Verify that $210°$ is a solution of $\cos 2u° = \frac{1}{2}$.

Example 7   Solve $3 \cos u° - 4 \sin u° = 1$ for $0° \leq u° < 360°$.

Solution $3 \cos u° - 4 \sin u° = 1$
$$3 \cos u° = 4 \sin u° + 1$$
Squaring both members, $9 \cos^2 u° = 16 \sin^2 u° + 8 \sin u° + 1$
Substituting $1 - \sin^2 u°$ for $\cos^2 u°$,
$$9(1 - \sin^2 u°) = 16 \sin^2 u° + 8 \sin u° + 1$$
$$25 \sin^2 u° + 8 \sin u° - 8 = 0$$

By the quadratic formula,

$$\sin u° = \frac{-8 \pm \sqrt{64 - 4(25)(-8)}}{50} = \frac{-8 \pm \sqrt{864}}{50}$$

$$= \frac{-8 \pm 12\sqrt{6}}{50} = \frac{-4 \pm 6\sqrt{6}}{25}$$

Hence, $(\sin u° \doteq .4278)$ or $(\sin u° \doteq -.7478)$.
Thus, $(u° \doteq 25°20'$ or $u° = 154°40')$ or $(u° \doteq 228°20'$ or $u° \doteq 311°40')$.
In squaring both members, we obtain another equation which may have more solutions than the given equation. Checking each of these four values of $u°$ in the original equation shows that the only solutions are $25°20'$ and $228°20'$, each accurate to the nearest 10 minutes. Exercise 7 on page 203 shows an alternate method for solving equations of this form.

EXERCISES

1. For each equation, determine the number of solutions in the interval $0° \le u° < 360°$.

a. $\tan u° = 1$

b. $\cos u° = -2$

c. $4 \sin^2 u° = 1$

d. $2 \sin 2u° = 1$

e. $2 \cos 3u° = 1$

f. $(\tan u° + 1)(2 \sin u° - 1) = 0$

g. $\tan u° + \tan u° \cdot \cos u° = 0$

h. $2 \sin^2 u° - 3 \sin u° - 2 = 0$

i. $2 \cos 3u° = \sqrt{3}$

j. $\sin^2 u° - 2 \sin u° - 2 = 0$

2. For each equation, determine all solutions in the interval $0° \le u° < 360°$.

a. $\csc u° = 1$

b. $4 \cos^2 u° = 3$

c. $\sin^2 u° + \sin u° = 0$

d. $5 \cos u° + 4 = 3 \cos u° + 3$

e. $\sec u° = -\sqrt{2}$

f. $\dfrac{8 \sin u°}{3} = \dfrac{2}{\sin u°}$

g. $2 \sin^2 u° = 1$

h. $2 \sin 2u° = 1$

i. $3 \tan^2 u° = 1$

j. $2 \sin u° \cdot \cos u° - \sin u° = 0$

k. $2 \cos 3u° = \sqrt{3}$

l. $2 \sin u° \cos u° + \cos u° - 2 \sin u° - 1 = 0$

m. $\tan^2 u° + \tan u° = 0$

n. $2 \sin^2 u° - 5 \sin u° + 2 = 0$

o. $\tan^3 u° - 3 \tan u° = 0$

p. $\sin u° = \csc u°$

q. $\tan u° \cdot \cos u° - \cos u° = 0$

r. $\tan 2u° = 1$

s. $\cot u° \cdot \sin u° = 0$

t. $2 \sin u° \cdot \tan u° - \tan u° = 0$

u. $\sqrt{3} \tan^2 u° + 2 \tan u° - \sqrt{3} = 0$

v. $\cos^2 u° = \sin^2 u°$

w. $\tan u° = \cot u°$

x. $\tan^3 u° - \tan u° = 0$

3. Determine the solutions of each equation to the nearest ten minutes in the interval $0° \le u° < 360°$.

a. $3 \cos u° = 1$

b. $5 \csc u° = 9$

c. $3 \tan u° = 5$

d. $\sin^2 u° + \sin u° - 1 = 0$

e. $2 \cos u° + 2 \sin u° = \sqrt{2}$

f. $\cos u° + \sin u° = 1$

g. $5 \sin u° + 2 = 0$

h. $3 \sec u° - 4 = 0$

i. $2 \cot u° = 3$

j. $\cos^2 u° + 2 \cos u° - 2 = 0$

k. $2 \cos u° - \sin u° = 1$

l. $2 \cos u° + 5 \sin u° = 3$

4. The adjoining figure pictures a *pencil of light* passing through air and into a glass block at *C*. At *C*, the pencil of light is *refracted* (bent). The pencil of light passing through air forms an *angle of incidence* of $u°_{air}$ with the perpendicular to the glass surface at *C*. The refracted pencil of light passing through glass forms an *angle* of *refraction* of $u°_{glass}$ with this perpendicular. In 1621, W. Snell discovered that as light passes from air into glass

$$\frac{\sin u°_{air}}{\sin u°_{glass}} = n_{glass}$$

where n_{glass} is a constant called the *index of refraction* of glass. Each medium has such an index. For example,

$$n_{water} \doteq 1.33 \qquad n_{glycerin} \doteq 1.47$$
$$n_{diamond} \doteq 2.42 \qquad n_{quartz\ crystal} \doteq 1.54$$

a. Determine the measure of the angle of refraction as a pencil of light passes from air with a 30° angle of incidence into a diamond.

b. Determine the measure of the angle of refraction as a pencil of light passes from air with a 45° angle of incidence into glycerin.

c. Determine the measure of the angle of incidence for a pencil of light which passes from air into water with a 20° angle of refraction.

5. Given a medium such as water with an index n_{water} of refraction and a second medium, such as diamond, with an index $n_{diamond}$ of refraction,

$$\frac{\sin u°_{water}}{\sin u°_{diamond}} = \frac{n_{diamond}}{n_{water}} \qquad \text{[Snell's Law]}$$

for a pencil of light passing from the first medium (water) into the second medium (diamond). In general, for mediums 1 and 2, with indices of refraction, n_1 and n_2,

$$\frac{\sin u_1°}{\sin u_2°} = \frac{n_2}{n_1}$$

a. Determine the measure of the angle of refraction as a pencil of light passes from water with a 50° angle of incidence into a diamond.

b. Determine the measure of the angle of incidence as a pencil of light passes from glycerin into quartz crystal with a 20° angle of refraction.

6. For each of the following equations, use a trigonometric identity to obtain an equivalent equation which is more readily solved. Solve each equation for $0° \leq u° < 360°$.

Example   Solve $\sin 2u° - \cos u° = 0$ for $0° \leq u° < 360°$.

Solution
$$\sin 2u° - \cos u° = 0$$
$$2 \sin u° \cdot \cos u° - \cos u° = 0$$
$$\cos u° (2 \sin u° - 1) = 0$$
$$(\cos u° = 0) \text{ or } \left(\sin u° = \frac{1}{2}\right)$$
$$(u° = 90° \text{ or } u° = 270°) \text{ or } (u° = 30° \text{ or } u° = 150°)$$

Hence, the solution set is $\{30°, 90°, 150°, 270°\}$.

a. $\sin 2u° \cdot \sin u° - \cos u° = 0$

b. $\cos 2u° + \sin u° = 1$

c. $\sin^2 u° + \cos u° + 1 = 0$

d. $2 \cos^2 u° + 3 \sin u° - 3 = 0$

e. $\sin 2u° \cdot \cos u° -$
$$\cos 2u° \cdot \sin u° = 1$$

f. $\cos 2u° + 2 \cos^2 \frac{u°}{2} = 1$

g. $\cos 2u° \cdot \cos u° -$
$$\sin 2u° \cdot \sin u° = 1$$

h. $\sin 2u° = 2 \sin u°$

i. $\tan u° = \sin 2u°$

j. $4 \tan^2 u° - 3 \sec^2 u° = 0$

7. It can be shown that an equation of the form $A \cos u° + B \sin u° = C$ is equivalent to an equation of the form

$$\sin (u + v)° = \frac{C}{\sqrt{A^2 + B^2}} \quad \text{where} \quad \sin v° = \frac{A}{\sqrt{A^2 + B^2}} \quad \text{and } \cos v° = \frac{B}{\sqrt{A^2 + B^2}}$$

Use this theorem to solve each of the following equations for $u°$ to the nearest ten minutes in the interval $0° \leq u° < 360°$. *Note:* refer to Chapter 4, page 120.

Example   Solve: $2 \cos u° + 4 \sin u° = 3$ for $0° \leq u° < 360°$.

Solution $2 \cos u° + 4 \sin u° = 3$ is in the form $A \cos u° + B \sin u° = C$, where $A = 2$, $B = 4$ and $C = 3$.

Hence $\sin v° = \dfrac{A}{\sqrt{A^2 + B^2}} = \dfrac{2}{\sqrt{20}} = \dfrac{\sqrt{5}}{5} \doteq 0.4472$

and $\cos v° = \dfrac{B}{\sqrt{A^2 + B^2}} = \dfrac{4}{\sqrt{20}} = \dfrac{2\sqrt{5}}{5} \doteq 0.8944$

It follows that $v° \doteq 26°30'$

Then, $\sin (u° + 26°30') = \dfrac{C}{\sqrt{A^2 + B^2}} = \dfrac{3}{\sqrt{20}} = \dfrac{3\sqrt{5}}{10} \doteq 0.6708.$

Consequently, $u° + 26°30' \doteq 42°10'$ or $u° + 26°30' = 137°50'$

and $u° \doteq 15°40'$ or $u° \doteq 111°20'$

Thus, the solution set is $\{15°40', 111°20'\}$, with accuracy to the nearest 10 minutes.

a. $2 \cos u° + 2 \sin u° = \sqrt{2}$

b. $2 \cos u° - 2 \sin u° = \sqrt{6}$

c. $\sqrt{2} \cos u° + \sqrt{2} \sin u° = 2$

d. $3 \cos u° + 3 \sin u° = 2$

e. $\cos u° - 3 \sin u° = 2$

f. $3 \cos u° + 4 \sin u° = 3$

CIRCULAR MOTION

Consider the motion of the point P along the circle of radius 4 beginning at point $A(4, 0)$ (see Figure 7–2). The origin and the point P determine ray $\overrightarrow{OP}$. As point P moves along the circle at a constant speed, the ray $\overrightarrow{OP}$ rotates around the origin with constant *angular speed*. Suppose that $\overrightarrow{OP}$ rotates at a speed of $\dfrac{\pi}{12}$ radians per second. At the end of 8 seconds, $\overrightarrow{OP}$ has generated an angle of $\left(\dfrac{\pi}{12}\right) \cdot 8$ or $\dfrac{2\pi}{3}$ radians as shown in Figure 7–2 as shown at the right.

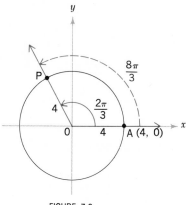

FIGURE 7·2

Furthermore, in each second P moves $4\left(\dfrac{\pi}{12}\right)$ or $\dfrac{\pi}{3}$ linear units along the circle.

After 8 seconds P has traveled $\left(\dfrac{\pi}{3}\right) \cdot 8$ or $\dfrac{8\pi}{3}$ linear units along the circle.

In general, as shown in Figure 7–3, if a point P moves along a circle of radius r with an angular speed of ω radians per second for t seconds, then ray $\overrightarrow{OP}$ has generated an angle of α radians, where

$$\alpha = \omega t$$

Furthermore, P has a *linear speed* along the circle of s linear units per second, where

$$s = r\omega.$$

At the end of t seconds P has traveled d units along the circle, where

$$d = r\omega t$$

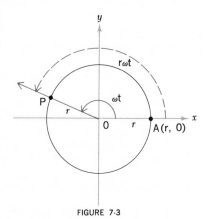

FIGURE 7·3

Example   A wheel with a diameter of 3 feet rotates on its axle with an angular speed of 10 revolutions per minute. Determine (1) the angular speed ω and (2) the linear speed s of a point on the rim in units per second. Also, determine (3) the measure α of the angle generated by a spoke of the wheel and (4) the distance d traveled by a point on the rim at the end of 36 seconds.

Solution

(1) ω = 10 revolutions per minute

$\quad$ = $10(2\pi)$ radians per minute

$\quad$ = $\dfrac{20\pi}{60}$ radians per second

$\quad$ = $\dfrac{\pi}{3}$ radians per second

(2) $s = r\omega$

$\quad$ = $\dfrac{3}{2} \cdot \dfrac{\pi}{3}$ feet per second

$\quad$ = $\dfrac{\pi}{2}$ feet per second

(3) $\alpha = \omega t$

$\quad$ = $\dfrac{\pi}{3} \cdot 36$ radians

$\quad$ = 12π radians

(4) $d = r\omega t$

$\quad$ = $\dfrac{3}{2} \cdot \dfrac{\pi}{3} \cdot 36$ feet

$\quad$ = 18π feet

EXERCISES

1. Determine the angular speed of each of the following in radians per minute.

   a. The minute hand of a clock.

   b. The hour hand of a clock.

   c. The spoke of a wheel which revolves with angular speed of 5 revolutions per second.

   d. An airplane propeller which makes 50 revolutions per second.

2. The minute hand of a clock is 3 inches long. How far does the tip move in 2 hours and 40 minutes?

3. The hour hand of a clock is 2 inches long. What is the linear speed of the tip?

4. Find the linear speed, in feet per second, of the tip of an 8-foot propeller which rotates at 3000 revolutions per minute.

5. The rotor of a gyroscope in an airplane spins at 36,000 revolutions per minute. The outer diameter is 2 inches. Find the linear speed, in miles per hour, of a point on the rotor's rim.

6. In 1933 the ocean liner *Conte Di Savoia* installed three gyroscope rotors. Each was 13 feet across, weighed 110 tons, and whirled 800 times a minute. Determine the linear speed of a point on the rim of such a rotor.

7. An automobile's tires have an outer diameter of 36 inches and revolve at 371 revolutions per minute. Find the speed of the car in miles per hour. Use $\pi \doteq \dfrac{22}{7}$.

8. A railroad track is laid on an arc of a circle of radius 1200 feet and is intercepted by a central angle of 30°. How many seconds will it take the engineer to round the curve at 40 miles per hour?

9. Two wheels 3 feet in diameter are connected by a belt. Each wheel revolves at 90 revolutions per minute. What is the linear speed of the belt in feet per second and the angular speed of each wheel in radians per second?

10. Two wheels 15 inches and 45 inches in diameter, respectively, are connected by a belt. The larger wheel revolves at 75 revolutions per minute. What is the linear speed of the belt in feet per second and the angular speed of the smaller wheel in radians per second?

11. Two meshed gears have centers 21 inches apart. The smaller rotates through 8 radians while the larger rotates through 6 radians. Determine the radius of each gear.

HARMONIC MOTION

Consider circular motion of a constant speed discussed in the previous section. Imagine that this motion is projected on a line. We then obtain *simple harmonic motion* along this line.

In Figure 7–4, the point P moves along the circle of radius r with angular speed of ω radians per second. The point P' moves up and down the vertical segment so as to be directly across from P. The vertical displacement of P from the x-axis, which is also the displacement of P' from A', is given by

$$y = r \sin \omega t$$

Examples of simple harmonic motion are the oscillations or vibrations of

a weight on a spring   an atom in a crystal
a piston in a cylinder   a simple pendulum

In each case, back and forth or up and down motion is repeated at regular time intervals. Does an object in simple harmonic motion have constant linear speed?

Example   Suppose P moves along a circle of radius 5 with an angular speed of $\frac{\pi}{3}$ radians per second. At the end of 4 seconds, P has generated an angle of $\frac{4\pi}{3}$ radians. Consequently, the displacement of P from the x-axis and the displacement of P' from A' is $5 \sin \frac{4\pi}{3}$ or $\frac{-5\sqrt{3}}{2}$. For this example, the displacement of P' from A' at the end of t seconds is given by $y = 5 \sin \frac{\pi}{3}t$.

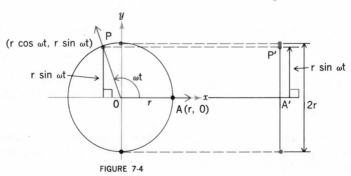

FIGURE 7-4

The example given is a simple harmonic motion with a period of 6 seconds, since P requires 6 seconds to make one revolution at the rate of $\frac{\pi}{3}$ radians per second. Likewise, P' requires 6 seconds to oscillate through one *cycle* along the segment which is 10 units long. In one second, P' has completed $\frac{1}{6}$ cycle and we say that P' vibrates at a *frequency* of $\frac{1}{6}$ cycle per second or 10 cycles per minute. The *amplitude*, or maximum displacement of P' from A', is 5 units. Maximum displacement above and below A' occurs at each $1\frac{1}{2} + 6n$ seconds and at each $4\frac{1}{2} + 6n$ seconds, where n is any natural number. That is, $5 \sin \frac{\pi}{3}t$ has its greatest absolute value for $t = 1\frac{1}{2} + 3n$ seconds. What is the displacement of P' from A' in this example at the end of $2\frac{1}{2}$ seconds? of 9 seconds? of $\frac{1}{3}$ period? of $2\frac{1}{12}$ periods?

In general, the equation
$$y = a \sin \omega t$$
describes a simple harmonic motion with amplitude equal to $|a|$, period of $\frac{2\pi}{\omega}$ seconds and frequency of $\frac{\omega}{2\pi}$ cycles per second, where ω is in radians per second and t is in seconds. Give the amplitude, period and frequency of the motion described by $y = 6 \sin \frac{\pi}{4}t$.

EXERCISES

1. Point A is the midpoint of a vertical segment which is 12 cm long. A point traverses this segment with a simple harmonic motion that has a 4-second period. When $t = 0$ seconds, the displacement from A is zero. Determine the displacement (negative below A and positive above A) from A at the end of the following time intervals.

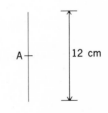

   a. $\frac{1}{2}$ period

   b. $1\frac{1}{3}$ seconds

   c. $\frac{3}{4}$ period

   d. 2 seconds

   e. $2\frac{1}{3}$ periods

   f. $1\frac{1}{2}$ seconds

   g. $\frac{7}{6}$ periods

   h. $3\frac{2}{3}$ seconds

   i. $1\frac{7}{8}$ periods

   j. $3\frac{1}{3}$ seconds

   k. 3 periods

2. Write an equation for the harmonic motion of Exercise 1.

3. For the harmonic motion of Exercise 1, when does maximum displacement occur? When does zero displacement occur?

4. A wheel revolves with angular speed of 8 revolutions, or cycles, per second. What is the period of this circular motion?

5. A wheel revolves with a period of $\dfrac{1}{10}$ second. What is its *frequency* in revolutions (or cycles) per second?

6. If T is the period in seconds and f is the frequency in cycles per second for a simple harmonic motion, express T in terms of f and express f in terms of T.

7. A simple harmonic motion is described by the equation $y = 10 \sin \dfrac{3\pi}{4} t$. Determine the period and the frequency, where t is in seconds.

8. Write an equation of the simple harmonic motion whose *amplitude*, or maximum displacement, is 8, whose period is 10 seconds, and whose displacement is 0 at 0 seconds.

9. Draw the graph of the harmonic motion specified by $y = 3 \sin \dfrac{\pi}{2} t$.

VOCABULARY

Use each of the following correctly in a sentence to demonstrate that you understand its meaning. If you are not sure of the meaning of any word refer back to the Chapter.

angular speed	ratio identity
Fundamental Identity	reciprocal identity
linear speed	simple harmonic motion
permissible value	squared identity

TWO IMPORTANT FACTS

1. $A \cos u^\circ + B \sin u^\circ = C$ is equivalent to $\sin (u + v)^\circ = \dfrac{\text{C}}{\sqrt{A^2 + B^2}}$ where $\sin v^\circ = \dfrac{A}{\sqrt{A^2 + B^2}}$ and $\cos v^\circ = \dfrac{B}{\sqrt{A^2 + B^2}}$.

2. $A \cos u^\circ + B \sin u^\circ$ is equivalent to $\sqrt{A^2 + B^2} \sin (u + v)^\circ$ where $\sin v^\circ = \dfrac{A}{\sqrt{A^2 + B^2}}$ and $\cos v^\circ = \dfrac{B}{\sqrt{A^2 + B^2}}$.

REVIEW EXERCISES

1. Given $\sin u^\circ = \dfrac{2}{5}$, $90^\circ < u^\circ < 180^\circ$, $\cos v^\circ = \dfrac{-2}{3}$ and $180^\circ < v^\circ < 270^\circ$, determine each of the following.

a. $\cos u^\circ$	**c.** $\sin v^\circ$	**e.** $\sin (u + v)^\circ$	**g.** $\tan (u + v)^\circ$
b. $\tan u^\circ$	**d.** $\tan v^\circ$	**f.** $\cos (u - v)^\circ$	**h.** $\tan (-u^\circ)$

i. $\cos\left(-u^\circ\right)$ **k.** $\cos 2u^\circ$ **m.** $\sin\dfrac{u^\circ}{2}$ **o.** $\tan\dfrac{u^\circ}{2}$

j. $\sin 2u^\circ$ **l.** $\tan 2u^\circ$ **n.** $\cos\dfrac{u^\circ}{2}$

2. Simplify.

a. $\dfrac{\sin\left(-u^\circ\right)}{-\cos u^\circ}$

b. $\dfrac{\tan u^\circ}{\sin u^\circ}$

c. $\sin 6u^\circ \cdot \cos 2u^\circ - \cos 6u^\circ \cdot \sin 2u^\circ$

d. $\dfrac{2\tan 3u^\circ}{1 - \tan^2 3u^\circ}$

e. $\cos u^\circ \cdot \csc u^\circ$

f. $\sin^2 u^\circ \left(1 + \tan^2 u^\circ\right)$

g. $\cos u^\circ \left(\sec u^\circ - \cos u^\circ\right)$

h. $\cot u^\circ \cdot \sin u^\circ$

i. $\dfrac{\sin 2u^\circ}{2\sin u^\circ}$

j. $\dfrac{1 + \cos 2u^\circ}{\cos u^\circ}$

k. $2\tan u^\circ \cdot \cos^2 u^\circ$

l. $2\sin 5u^\circ \cdot \cos 5u^\circ$

3. Compute each of the following.

a. $\cos 22\dfrac{1}{2}^\circ$ **b.** $\sin 75^\circ$ **c.** $\tan 67\dfrac{1}{2}^\circ$ **d.** $\cos 105^\circ$

4. Prove each of the following identities.

a. $\cos^4 u^\circ - \sin^4 u^\circ \equiv 1 - 2\sin^2 u^\circ$

b. $\cos u^\circ \cdot \cot u^\circ + \sin u^\circ \equiv \csc u^\circ$

c. $1 - \left(\cos u^\circ - \sin u^\circ\right)^2 \equiv \sin 2u^\circ$

d. $\dfrac{\sin 2u^\circ}{1 + \cos 2u^\circ} \equiv \tan u^\circ$

e. $2\sin^2 \dfrac{u^\circ}{2} + \cos u^\circ \equiv 1$

f. $\tan u^\circ + \cot u^\circ \equiv \csc u^\circ \cdot \sec u^\circ$

5. Solve each equation for u° in the interval $0^\circ \le u^\circ < 360^\circ$.

a. $2\cos u^\circ - 5 = 4\cos u^\circ - 4$

b. $4\sin^2 u^\circ = 3$

c. $2\sin 3u^\circ = 1$

d. $2\cos^2 u^\circ + \cos u^\circ = 0$

e. $\cos^2 u^\circ - 3\sin^2 u^\circ = 0$

f. $\cos 2u^\circ = \cos u^\circ$

g. $\sin 2u^\circ = \sin u^\circ$

h. $\tan^2 u^\circ = 3$

i. $2\sin u^\circ \cdot \tan u^\circ - \tan u^\circ = 0$

j. $\tan 2u^\circ = 1$

6. Determine the solutions of each equation to the nearest ten minutes in the interval $0^\circ \le u^\circ < 360^\circ$.

a. $5\sin u^\circ = 3$

b. $3\cos u^\circ + 2 = 0$

c. $5\tan u^\circ = 2$

d. $2\cos u^\circ + \sin u^\circ = 1$

7. Express each of the following in the form $a\sin\left(u + v\right)^\circ$ where a and v are real numbers.

a. $3\cos u^\circ + 3\sin u^\circ$ **b.** $2\cos u^\circ - 2\sin u^\circ$ **c.** $2\cos u^\circ + 3\sin u^\circ$

8. Determine the measure of the angle of refraction as a pencil of light passes from water with a 60° angle of incidence into quartz crystal.

9. For the harmonic motion described by $y = 5 \sin \frac{3\pi}{8} t$, give its amplitude, period and frequency, where t is in seconds.

CHAPTER TEST

1. Given $\cos u° = \frac{-2}{5}$, $90° < u° < 180°$, $\sin v° = \frac{-3}{5}$ and $270° < v° < 360°$, determine each of the following.

   a. $\cos (u + v)°$ **c.** $\tan (u + v)°$ **e.** $\cos 2u°$

   b. $\sin (u + v)°$ **d.** $\sin 2u°$ **f.** $\tan 2u°$

2. Simplify as much as possible.

   a. $\dfrac{-\cos u°}{\sin (-u°)}$ **e.** $\dfrac{\sin u°}{\tan u°}$

   b. $\cos (90 - v)°$ **f.** $\tan u° \cdot \csc u°$

   c. $\sin 3u° \cdot \cos 2u° + \cos 3u° \cdot \sin 2u°$ **g.** $(1 + \cot^2 u°)(1 - \sin^2 u°)$

   d. $\dfrac{\cos 2u° - 1}{2 \sin u°}$ **h.** $2 \sin 3v° \cdot \cos 3v°$

         i. $\tan u° (\cot u° - \cos u°)$

3. Given $\cos \dfrac{u°}{2} \equiv \pm\sqrt{\dfrac{1 + \cos u°}{2}}$ and $\sin \dfrac{u°}{2} \equiv \pm\sqrt{\dfrac{1 - \cos u°}{2}}$, determine each of the following.

   a. $\cos 112\dfrac{1}{2}°$ **b.** $\sin 15°$ **c.** $\tan 22\dfrac{1}{2}°$

4. Prove each identity.

   a. $\csc u° - \sin u° \equiv \cos u° \cdot \cot u°$ **c.** $(1 + \tan^2 u°) \cot u° \equiv \csc u° \cdot \sec u°$

   b. $\dfrac{\sec u°}{\cos u°} - 1 \equiv \tan^2 u°$ **d.** $\dfrac{2 \sin \dfrac{u°}{2} \cdot \cos \dfrac{u°}{2}}{\tan u°} \equiv \cos u°$

5. State the values of $u°$ which are not permissible for the expression $\dfrac{3}{\tan u°}$.

6. Solve each equation for the interval $0° \le u° < 360°$.

   a. $6 \sin u° + 3 = 0$ **d.** $2 \sin^2 u° + 3 \sin u° - 2 = 0$

   b. $3 \tan^2 u° = 1$ **e.** $2 \sin 2u° = \sqrt{3}$

   c. $2 \cos^2 u° = \cos u°$ **f.** $2 \cos u° \cdot \tan u° + \tan u° = 0$

7. Given that $A \cos u° + B \cos u° = C$ is equivalent to $\sin (u + v)° = \dfrac{C}{\sqrt{A^2 + B^2}}$,

where $\sin v° = \dfrac{A}{\sqrt{A^2 + B^2}}$ and $\cos v° = \dfrac{B}{\sqrt{A^2 + B^2}}$,

Solve: $3 \cos u° - 3 \sin u° = \dfrac{3\sqrt{2}}{2}$ for $0° \le u° < 360°$.

CUMULATIVE REVIEW
CHAPTERS 5–7

1. State the domain and range of each of the six trigonometric functions.

2. Determine the values of the six trigonometric functions for each of the following angle measures.

   a. 120°   **b.** $\dfrac{3\pi}{4}$ **c.** $\dfrac{4\pi}{3}$ **d.** 210°   **e.** 315°   **f.** $\dfrac{5\pi}{6}$

3. Convert each radian measure to its equivalent degree measure.

   a. $\dfrac{7\pi}{6}$ **c.** $\dfrac{-2\pi}{3}$ **e.** $\dfrac{5\pi}{4}$ **g.** $\dfrac{-3\pi}{10}$

   b. $\dfrac{3\pi}{2}$ **d.** -3π **f.** $\dfrac{7\pi}{12}$ **h.** $\dfrac{17\pi}{9}$

4. Convert each degree measure to its equivalent radian measure.

   a. 150°   **c.** −90°   **e.** 315°   **g.** −126°

   b. 240°   **d.** −720°   **f.** 75°   **h.** 100°

5. Determine the length of arc intercepted by a central angle of 3 radians on a circle of radius 5.

6. Determine the radius of a circle on which a central angle of $\dfrac{3\pi}{4}$ radians intercepts an arc of length 15.

7. Determine the area of a circular sector with radius 4 on the interior of a central angle of $\dfrac{5\pi}{8}$ radians.

8. Given a second quadrant number θ for which $\tan \theta = \dfrac{-5}{2}$, determine $\cos \theta$ and $\sin \theta$.

9. Determine the measures of all angles coterminal with a 40° angle.

10. Given the point $P(-5, 12)$ on the terminal side of an angle of $u°$, determine the six trigonometric functions of $u°$.

11. Given $\sin u° = \dfrac{-3}{4}$ and $180° < u° < 270°$, determine the other five trigonometric functions of $u°$.

12. Which trigonometric functions have positive values for third quadrant angle measures?

13. Draw the graph of tangent for the interval $-\pi < \theta < \pi$.

14. Sketch the graphs of cosine and secant for one period on one coordinate system.

15. Give the period, in radians and in degrees, for each trigonometric function.

16. Express each of the following in terms of the same trigonometric function of a first quadrant angle measure.

a. $\tan \dfrac{5\pi}{9}$ **c.** $\cot \dfrac{13\pi}{10}$ **e.** $\tan 2.5$ **g.** $\cot \dfrac{-3\pi}{7}$

b. $\cos 130°$ **d.** $\csc (-50°)$ **f.** $\sec 310°$ **h.** $\sin 190°$

17. Express $\sec 20°$ in terms of csc.

18. Express $\cot \dfrac{3\pi}{5}$ in terms of tan.

19. Describe the variation of $\sec \theta$ as θ increases from 0 to $\dfrac{\pi}{2}$.

20. Which of the following equations are identities?

a. $\tan \theta = \dfrac{\cos \theta}{\sin \theta}$ **d.** $\dfrac{\tan 3\theta + \tan \theta}{1 - \tan 3\theta \cdot \tan \theta} = \tan 4\theta$

b. $\tan \theta = \tan (\theta + k\pi)$,
for any integer k **e.** $\tan 2\theta = 2 \tan \theta$

c. $\tan (-5\theta) = \tan 5\theta$ **f.** $\tan (\theta - \pi) = \tan \theta$

21. Simplify.

a. $\dfrac{\sin (-\theta)}{\cos \theta}$ **e.** $\dfrac{\sin \theta}{\tan \theta}$ **i.** $\cos^2 \dfrac{5\pi}{12} - \sin^2 \dfrac{5\pi}{12}$

b. $\dfrac{\tan 5\theta - \tan 2\theta}{1 + \tan 5\theta \cdot \tan 2\theta}$ **f.** $2 \sin 15° \cos 15°$ **j.** $\cos^2 3\theta - \sin^2 3\theta$

g. $2 \cos^2 75° - 1$ **k.** $\cos^2 3\theta + \sin^2 3\theta$

c. $\tan (5\pi - \theta)$ **l.** $\sin 10° - \cos 80°$

d. $\tan (\theta - 3\pi)$ **h.** $1 - 2 \sin^2 \dfrac{3\pi}{8}$ **m.** $\cos 200° + \sin 110°$

22. Prove the following identities.

a. $\sin \theta \tan \theta + \cos \theta \equiv \sec \theta$ **b.** $\dfrac{\sin 2u°}{\tan u°} \equiv \dfrac{2}{1 + \tan^2 u°}$

23. Determine each of the following, accurate to four decimal places.

a. $\tan 2.76$ **b.** $\tan 0.814$

24. Interpolate to determine $\tan 48°23'$, accurate to four digits.

25. State the complementary angles relation.

26. State the three pairs of reciprocal trigonometric functions.

27. State (1) the amplitude, (2) the period, and (3) the phase number of each of the following functions.

a. $y = \dfrac{3}{4} \cos 2u°$ **b.** $y = -3 \sin \dfrac{1}{3}(u - 60)°$ **c.** $y = \cos (3u - 120)°$

28. Sketch the graph of $y = 2 \sin 3(u - 30)°$ for one period.

29. Given $\tan \theta = 3$ and $\tan \alpha = \dfrac{-1}{2}$, determine $\tan (\theta + \alpha)$ and $\tan 2\theta$.

30. Determine $\tan \dfrac{5\pi}{12}$.

31. Given a second quadrant number θ for which $\tan \theta = -2$, determine $\tan \dfrac{\theta}{2}$.

32. Solve each equation for $u°$ in the interval $0° \le u° < 360°$.

a. $\tan^2 u° = 3$

b. $\tan u° = \dfrac{\sqrt{3}}{3}$

c. $\cot u° = \tan u°$

d. $4 \cos^2 u° \cdot \tan^2 u° - 3 \tan^2 u° - 4 \cos^2 u° + 3 = 0$

e. $2 \cos u° \cdot \tan u° = \tan u°$

f. $2 \sin^2 u° - \sin u° = 1$

g. $2 \cos 2u° = -1$

33. Which values of θ are not permissible for the expression $\dfrac{2}{\tan \theta}$?

34. Describe the variation of $\tan \theta$ as θ increases from $\dfrac{\pi}{2}$ to π.

35. How many times will the graphs of sine and cosine intersect in the interval $0° \le u° < 360°$?

36. Which of the following is equivalent to $\cos (45 + u)°$?

a. $\dfrac{1}{2}(\cos u° + \sin u°)$ **c.** $\dfrac{\sqrt{2}}{2}(\cos u° + \sin u°)$

b. $\dfrac{1}{2}(\cos u° - \sin u°)$ **d.** $\dfrac{\sqrt{2}}{2}(\cos u° - \sin u°)$

37. Determine the smallest positive solution of each of the following equations.

a. $\cos (4u - 30)° = 0$ **c.** $\tan (2u - 25)° = 1$

b. $2 \sin (3u - 15)° = 0$ **d.** $\sin (120 - 3u)° = 1$

CHAPTER 8

INVERSE TRIGONOMETRIC FUNCTIONS

PRINCIPAL VALUES

Consider the following questions and the answers to them.

What is the square of 5?	answer: 25
What is the square of -5?	answer: 25

The following question is the *inverse* of the questions above.

What is *a* square root of 25?

There are two correct answers (5 and -5) to this inverse question. It is customary to designate the positive square root of a positive number x as being the *principal* square root of x. Accordingly, there is exactly one answer to each question of the form

What is the principal square root of x?

for a given value of x, where $x > 0$. What is the principal square root of 49? of 5?

Now consider the following questions and the answers to them.

What is sin 210° equal to?	answer: $\dfrac{-1}{2}$
What is sin 330° equal to?	answer: $\dfrac{-1}{2}$

The inverse of the questions above is

What is *an* angle measure whose sine value is $\dfrac{-1}{2}$?

There are infinitely many answers to this inverse question, since each of the angle measures $(210 + 360k)°$ and $(330 + 360k)°$ has a sine value of $\dfrac{-1}{2}$. In

214

this chapter we shall designate one angle measure, called *the principal angle measure*, which has a given sine, cosine or tangent value. Thus, there will be exactly one answer to each question of the form

What is the principal angle measure whose sine value is k
for a given value of k, where $-1 \leq k \leq 1$?

INVERSE OF A FUNCTION

Recall that any function may be thought of as a set of ordered pairs, no two of which have the same first component. Consider the function

$$m = \{(1, 3), (2, 6), (3, 9), (4, 12), \ldots\}$$

Verify that the following statements concerning the function m are true.

1. The *domain* of m is the set of all natural numbers, $\{1, 2, 3, 4, \ldots\}$.
2. The *range* of m is the set of all natural number multiples of 3, $\{3, 6, 9, 12, \ldots\}$.
3. The function m may be specified by the equation $m(x) = 3x$ with the condition that x is a natural number.
4. The function m is a *one-to-one function;* that is, each element in the range of m is paired with only one element in the domain of m.
5. The function m may be called *multiplying by 3*.

Consider the function q which contains only the ordered pairs (b, a) formed from the ordered pairs (a, b) belonging to m. Then

$$q = \{(3, 1), (6, 2), (9, 3), (12, 4), \ldots\}$$

Verify that the following statements concerning q and m are true.

1. The domain of q is the range of m.
2. The range of q is the domain of m.
3. The function q may be specified by the equation $q(x) = x \div 3$ with the condition that x is a natural number multiple of 3.
4. The function q is a one-to-one function.
5. The function q may be called *dividing by 3*.

We say that the function q, dividing by 3, is the *inverse* of the function m, multiplying by 3. Observe that $m(2) = 6$ and $q(6) = 2$, $m(7) = 21$, and $q(21) = 7$; and, in general, if $m(a) = b$, then $q(b) = a$.

DEFINITION OF INVERSE FUNCTION   Given two functions f and g such that $f(a) = b$ if and only if $g(b) = a$ for all a in the domain of f and for all b in the domain of g, then f is called the *inverse function* of g and g is the inverse function of f.

The notation f^{-1} (pronounced as *the inverse of f*) is used to name the inverse function of f, if f has an inverse function. That is, if f has an inverse function, f^{-1}, then

$$f(a) = b \text{ implies } f^{-1}(b) = a \qquad \text{and} \qquad f^{-1}(m) = n \text{ implies } f(n) = m.$$

Pronounce $f^{-1}(b)$ as *the inverse of f at b.* You are cautioned not to consider the -1 in the symbol f^{-1} as an exponent; it only denotes the inverse function of f. For the two functions m and q, discussed above, we have that

$$\text{if } m(a) = b, \text{ then } m^{-1}(b) = q(b) = a$$

Verify that

$$m(2) = 6 \text{ and } m^{-1}(6) = 2 \qquad\qquad m^{-1}(69) = 23$$
$$q(12) = 4 \text{ and } q^{-1}(4) = 12 \qquad\qquad q^{-1}(7) = 21$$

$m^{-1}(5)$ is undefined since 5 is not in the domain of m^{-1} (the domain of q)

Sometimes we are interested in determining the value of *a function of a function* at some number. For the two functions, m and q above, verify that

$$m(m(4)) = m(12) = 36 \qquad\qquad m^{-1}(m(9)) = m^{-1}(27) = 9$$
$$q(q(18)) = q(6) = 2 \qquad\qquad m(m^{-1}(369)) = m(123) = 369$$

What is $m^{-1}(m(5))$ equal to? $q(q^{-1}(15))$? $m^{-1}(q(45))$? $q(m^{-1}(12))$? Prove that for each x in the domain of m, $m^{-1}(m(x)) = x$.

The graphs of m and q are pictured in Figure 8-1. Verify that the graph of q (which is m^{-1}) is symmetric to the graph of m with respect to the graph of $y = x$; that is, the graph of m^{-1} is the "reflection" of the graph of m in the graph of $y = x$. In general, this is true for any two functions f and g such that $g = f^{-1}$.

Consider the function

$$h = \{(4, 3), (5, 3), (6, 2), (7, 2)\}$$

Observe that h does *not* have an inverse function since the *inverse set* of ordered pairs

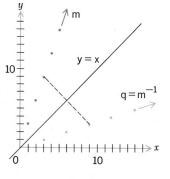

FIGURE 8-1

$$j = \{(3, 4), (3, 5), (2, 6), (2, 7)\}$$

is not a function. Why is this inverse set not a function? Prove that h is not a one-to-one function. In general, if a function f is not a one-to-one function, then f does not have an inverse function.

Let us consider the squaring function t for which

$$t(x) = x^2 \text{ and } x \text{ is a real number.}$$

We are interested in the following characteristics of t.

1. The domain of t is the set of all real numbers.
2. The range of t is the set of all non-negative real numbers. Why is -4 not in the range of t?
3. The function t is not a one-to-one function. For example, t pairs 4 in its range with both 2 and -2 in its domain. That is, $t(2) = 4$ and $t(-2) = 4$.
4. The function t does not have an inverse function, since (2, 4) and $(-2, 4)$ belong to t; and, consequently, both (4, 2) and (4, -2) belong to the inverse set which is not a function. Why not? Recall

that a function must be one-to-one to have an inverse function.

Though the squaring function t does not have an inverse function, we may define a function T (pronounced as *cap-t*), which is a portion of the squaring function t, so that

1. T has an inverse function, T^{-1}.   2. T has the same range as t.

To do so, we define T so that

$$T(x) = x^2 \text{ and } x \geq 0$$

Note: T is a one-to-one function. For example, $T(5) = 25$ but $T(-5)$ is undefined. Why?

T^{-1} (pronounced as *the inverse of cap-t*), the inverse function of T, is defined so that

$$T^{-1}(a^2) = a \text{ if and only if } T(a) = a^2 \text{ for } a \geq 0$$

or, more simply,

$$T^{-1}(x) = \sqrt{x} \text{ and } x \geq 0$$

Verify that

$$T(6) = 36 \text{ and } T^{-1}(36) = 6$$
$$T(\sqrt{7}) = 7 \text{ and } T^{-1}(7) = \sqrt{7}$$
$$T^{-1}(-4) \text{ is undefined. Why?}$$

In general, $T^{-1}(x)$ is the non-negative number whose square is x, provided that $x \geq 0$. What is $T^{-1}(16)$ equal to? $T^{-1}(121)$? $T^{-1}(3)$? $T^{-1}(0)$? $T^{-1}(-9)$?
Verify that

$$T^{-1}(T(7)) = T^{-1}(49) = 7$$
$$T(T^{-1}(15)) = T(\sqrt{15}) = 15$$

In general, for each $x \geq 0$, $T^{-1}(T(x)) = x$ and $T(T^{-1}(x)) = x$. Prove that this generalization is true.

The graphs of T and T^{-1} are pictured as solid portions of the graphs of t and t^{-1}. In Figures 8–2 and 8–3 notice the restrictions we have made in drawing the solid portions.

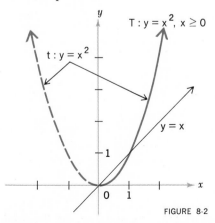

FIGURE 8-2

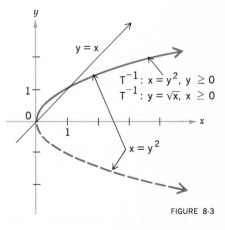

FIGURE 8-3

Verify each of the following true statements by referring to the appropriate figure.

1. T is a one-to-one function.
2. The range of T is the same as the range of t.
3. The domain of T^{-1} is the range of T and the range of T^{-1} is the domain of T.
4. The graphs of T and T^{-1} are symmetric to one another with respect to the graph of $y = x$.

The trigonometric functions are not one-to-one functions since each is a periodic function. For example, the sine function is not one-to-one, since

$$\sin 90° = \sin 450° = \sin (90 + 360k)° = 1$$

Does any trigonometric function have an inverse function? The answer is "*no*", since a function must be one-to-one to have an inverse function.

We shall seek to specify portions of the sin, cos, and tan functions so that each portion has an inverse function. In each case, we must (1) specify a one-to-one function and (2) maintain the range of the original function. The portions which we specify are the *Sine*, *Cosine*, and *Tangent* functions. They are called the *cap-trigonometric functions* because the first letter of each name is capitalized. Pronounce Sin as *cap-sine*.

DEFINITION OF CAP-SINE $\text{Sin } u° = \sin u°$ for $-90° \leq u° \leq 90°$

DEFINITION OF CAP-COSINE $\text{Cos } u° = \cos u°$ for $0° \leq u° \leq 180°$

DEFINITION OF CAP-TANGENT $\text{Tan } u° = \tan u°$ for $-90° < u° < 90°$

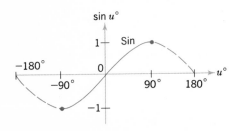

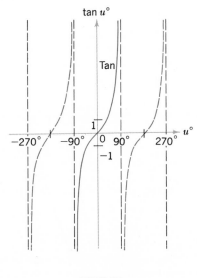

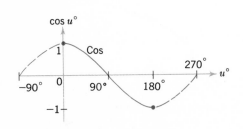

FIGURE 8-4

The graphs of cap-trigonometric functions, Sin, Cos, and Tan, are the solid portions of the curves in Figure 8–4.

Verify in the figure that
> 1. the domain of each cap-trigonometric function is the same as given by the definitions above;
> 2. each cap-trigonometric function is a one-to-one function; and
> 3. the range of Sin, Cos, and Tan is the same as the range of sin, cos, and tan, respectively.

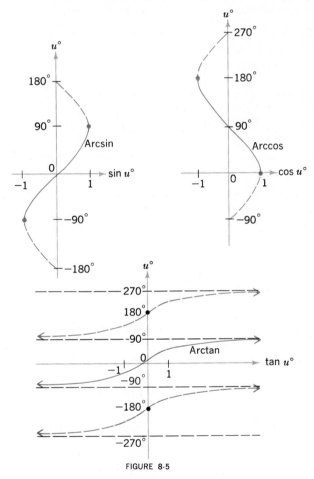

FIGURE 8-5

According to the definitions of the cap-trigonometric functions, we have that $\text{Sin } 45° = \dfrac{\sqrt{2}}{2}$, $\text{Cos } 150° = \dfrac{-\sqrt{3}}{2}$, and $\text{Tan } (-60°) = -\sqrt{3}$, while each of Sin 135°, Cos (−30°), and Tan 120° is undefined. Why? What is *the* solution of $\text{Sin } u° = \dfrac{-1}{2}$? of $\text{Cos } u° = \dfrac{-\sqrt{2}}{2}$? of $\text{Tan } u° = -1$?

We shall now define the inverse function of each of the cap-trigonometric functions. There are two kinds of notation in common use to denote the inverse function of a cap-trigonometric function. For example, the inverse of Sin is denoted by Sin^{-1} (pronounced as *inverse cap-sine*) and by Arcsin (pronounced as *cap-arcsine*).

> DEFINITION OF INVERSE CAP-SINE   *Given* Sin $u° = z$,
> Sin^{-1} $z = u°$ and Arcsin $z = u°$ for $-90° \le u° \le 90°$
>
> DEFINITION OF INVERSE CAP-COSINE   *Given* Cos $u° = z$,
> Cos^{-1} $z = u°$ and Arccos $z = u°$ for $0° \le u° \le 180°$
>
> DEFINITION OF INVERSE CAP-TANGENT   *Given* Tan $u° = z$,
> Tan^{-1} $z = u°$ and Arctan $z = u°$ for $-90° < u° < 90°$
>
> According to the definitions above,

$$\text{Sin}^{-1}\left(\frac{-1}{2}\right) = \text{Arcsin}\left(\frac{-1}{2}\right) = -30° \text{ and does not equal } 210°. \text{ Why not?}$$

$$\text{Cos}^{-1}\frac{\sqrt{2}}{2} = \text{Arccos}\frac{\sqrt{2}}{2} = 45° \text{ and does not equal } -45°. \text{ Why not?}$$

$$\text{Tan}^{-1}(-\sqrt{3}) = \text{Arctan}(-\sqrt{3}) = -60° \text{ and does not equal } 120°. \text{ Why not?}$$

Figure 8–5 shows the graphs of Arcsin, Arccos, and Arctan functions. Verify in the figure that the range of each function is as given in the definitions.

The following examples illustrate how one determines values involving inverse trigonometric functions. Study each example carefully.

Examples

1   Write an equation involving Sin $u°$ which is equivalent to the equation Sin$^{-1}\left(\frac{-1}{2}\right) = u°$ and solve it.

   Sin$^{-1}\left(\frac{-1}{2}\right) = u°$ is equivalent to Sin $u° = \left(\frac{-1}{2}\right)$. The solution of both equations is $-30°$. Thus, Sin$^{-1}\left(\frac{-1}{2}\right) = 30°$.

2   Arcsin $\left(\frac{\sqrt{3}}{2}\right) = $ Sin$^{-1}\left(\frac{\sqrt{3}}{2}\right) = 60°$. It is helpful to think of Arcsin $\frac{\sqrt{3}}{2}$ as the angle measure whose Sin is $\frac{\sqrt{3}}{2}$.

3   Arccos $(-1) = $ Cos$^{-1}(-1) = 180°$.

4   Arctan $(-\sqrt{3}) = $ Tan$^{-1}(-\sqrt{3}) = -60°$.

5   Arcsin $(\sin 45°) = $ Arcsin $\frac{\sqrt{2}}{2} = 45°$.

6   Sin$^{-1}(\sin 150°) = $ Sin$^{-1}\frac{1}{2} = 30°$.

7   Arccos $(\sin 210°) = $ Arccos $\frac{-1}{2} = 120°$.

8   Sin$^{-1}\left(\frac{1}{2}\right) + $ Sin$^{-1}\left(\frac{-\sqrt{3}}{2}\right) = 30° + (-60°) = -30°$.

Example   9   Determine $\tan\left(\text{Arccos }\dfrac{-2}{3}\right)$.

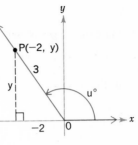

FIGURE 8-6

By definition, Arccos z must be in the interval $0° \le$ Arccos $z \le 180°$. It follows that $90° <$ Arccos $\dfrac{-2}{3} < 180°$. Figure 8–6 pictures the angle of $u°$ for which Cos $u° = \dfrac{-2}{3}$. From $x^2 + y^2 = r^2$, it follows that $y = \sqrt{5}$. Hence,

$$\tan\left(\text{Arccos }\frac{-2}{3}\right) = \frac{y}{x} = \frac{\sqrt{5}}{-2}.$$

If we wish to discuss *all* solutions of the equation $\sin u° = \dfrac{-\sqrt{2}}{2}$, we express them as arcsin $\dfrac{-\sqrt{2}}{2}$, without a capital letter. Note that, in this case, the solutions are *not* restricted to the unique solution of Sin $u° = \dfrac{-\sqrt{2}}{2}$. The notation arcsin $\dfrac{-\sqrt{2}}{2}$ names the set $\{.\,.\,.,\ -45°,\ -135°,\ -45° \pm 360°,\ -135°$ $\pm\ 360°,\ \dots\}$ or, more simply, $\{(-45 + 360k)°,\ (-135 + 360k)°\}$, for all integers k.

Thus,   arccos $\dfrac{1}{2}$ has the values $(60 + 360k)°$ and $(300 + 360k)°$

and   arctan $\dfrac{\sqrt{3}}{3}$ has the values $(30 + 180k)°$

while   Arccos $\dfrac{1}{2}$ is $60°$ only

and   Arctan $\dfrac{\sqrt{3}}{3}$ is $30°$ only.

The values in the range of Arcsin (Arccos, Arctan) are called the *principal values* of arcsin (arccos, arctan).

Examples

1   the principal value of arcsin $\dfrac{1}{2}$ is Arcsin $\dfrac{1}{2}$ or $30°$

2   the principal value of arccos $\dfrac{-\sqrt{2}}{2}$ is Arccos $\dfrac{-\sqrt{2}}{2}$ or $135°$

3   the principal value of arctan $(-\sqrt{3})$ is Arctan $(-\sqrt{3})$ or $-60°$

EXERCISES

1. State the ranges of Sin^{-1}, Cos^{-1}, and Tan^{-1}.

2. Solve each equation.

a. Sin $u° = \dfrac{1}{2}$

b. Cos $u° = \dfrac{-\sqrt{2}}{2}$

c. Tan $u° = -1$

d. Sin $u° = \dfrac{-\sqrt{3}}{2}$

e. Cos $u° = \dfrac{1}{2}$

f. Tan $u° = -\sqrt{3}$

g. Sin $u° = -1$

h. Cos $u° = \dfrac{-\sqrt{3}}{2}$

i. Tan $u° = \dfrac{\sqrt{3}}{3}$

3. Determine the value of each of the following.

a. Sin^{-1} (1)

b. Arccos (-1)

c. Tan^{-1} $\left(\dfrac{1}{\sqrt{3}}\right)$

d. Arcsin 0

e. Cos^{-1} $\dfrac{1}{2}$

f. Arctan $\dfrac{-\sqrt{3}}{3}$

g. Sin^{-1} $\dfrac{-1}{2}$

h. Arccos 0

i. Tan^{-1} (-1)

j. Arcsin $\dfrac{\sqrt{2}}{2}$

k. Cos^{-1} 1

l. Arctan 0

m. Sin^{-1} $\left(\dfrac{-\sqrt{3}}{2}\right)$

n. Arccos $\left(\dfrac{-1}{\sqrt{2}}\right)$

o. Tan^{-1} $\sqrt{3}$

p. Arcsin $\dfrac{1}{2}$

q. Cos^{-1} $\dfrac{-1}{2}$

r. Arctan $(-\sqrt{3})$

s. Sin^{-1} $\dfrac{\sqrt{3}}{2}$

t. Arccos $\left(\dfrac{-\sqrt{3}}{2}\right)$

u. Tan^{-1} 1

v. Arcsin (-1)

w. Cos^{-1} $\left(\dfrac{\sqrt{2}}{2}\right)$

x. Arcsin 2

4. Determine the value of each of the following.

a. sin $\left(\text{Sin}^{-1} \dfrac{\sqrt{3}}{2}\right)$

b. cos $\left(\text{Arccos} \dfrac{-1}{2}\right)$

c. tan (Tan^{-1} $\sqrt{3}$)

d. cot $\left(\text{Arcsin} \dfrac{1}{2}\right)$

e. csc $\left(\text{Cos}^{-1} \dfrac{-\sqrt{3}}{2}\right)$

f. sec (Arctan (-1))

g. sin $\left(\text{Arccos} \dfrac{\sqrt{2}}{2}\right)$

h. cos (Tan^{-1} 0)

i. tan $\left(\text{Sin}^{-1} \dfrac{-\sqrt{2}}{2}\right)$

j. sin $\left(\text{Arctan} \dfrac{-1}{\sqrt{3}}\right)$

k. cos (Arcsin 1)

l. tan (Cos^{-1} 1)

m. sin (Arccos 0)

n. cos (Tan^{-1} $(-\sqrt{3})$)

o. tan $\left(\text{Sin}^{-1} \dfrac{-\sqrt{3}}{2}\right)$

p. sin $\left(\text{Arccos} \dfrac{3}{5}\right)$

q. $\cos\left(Tan^{-1}\dfrac{-4}{3}\right)$

u. $\sec(Sin^{-1} 0.8)$

r. $\tan\left(Arcsin\dfrac{1}{4}\right)$

v. $\sin(Tan^{-1} 2)$

s. $\cot\left(Cos^{-1}\dfrac{-5}{6}\right)$

w. $\cos\left(Arcsin\dfrac{-5}{13}\right)$

t. $\csc\left(Arctan\dfrac{12}{5}\right)$

x. $\tan\left(Arccos\dfrac{12}{13}\right)$

5. Why could the domain of Sin not be specified as $0° \le u° \le 90°$?

6. Why could the domain of Cos not be specified as $0° \le u° \le 270°$?

7. Sketch the graph of $y = \cos u°$ for $-270° \le u° \le 270°$. On the same coordinate system, sketch the graph of $u° = \arccos y$ for $-270° \le u° \le 270°$. Indicate the graphs of Cos and Arccos with a darker marking.

8. Determine all values of each of the following.

a. $\arcsin\dfrac{\sqrt{3}}{2}$

d. $\arcsin 1$

g. $\arctan(-1)$

b. $\arccos\dfrac{-1}{2}$

e. $\arccos\dfrac{1}{\sqrt{2}}$

h. $\arccos(-1)$

c. $\arctan\sqrt{3}$

f. $\arcsin\dfrac{-\sqrt{2}}{2}$

i. $\arctan\dfrac{\sqrt{3}}{3}$

j. $\arcsin 0$

9. Solve each equation for $u°$ and express the solutions by using inverse notation.

Example $5 \sin u° = 2$

Solution $5 \sin u° = 2$

$\sin u° = \dfrac{2}{5}$

The solutions of this equation may be expressed as $\arcsin\dfrac{2}{5}$.

Note that $u° = \arcsin\dfrac{2}{5}$ has the same solutions as $5 \sin u° = 2$.

a. $5 \cos^2 u° = 3$

e. $\cos(3u - 24)° = 0.4426$

b. $\tan^2 u° = 4$

f. $\tan(2u + 18)° = 2.176$

c. $9 \sin^2 u° - 3 \sin u° - 2 = 0$

g. $2 \tan^2 u° + \tan u° - 4 = 0$

d. $2 \sin u° - 3 \sin^2 u° = 0$

h. $3 \sin^2 u° - 7 \sin u° + 2 = 0$

10. Define Cot, the cap-cotangent function.

11. Define Arccot, the inverse of the cap-cotangent function.

12. Determine each of the following.

a. Arcsin (sin 120°)

b. Cos⁻¹ (cos 120°)

c. Arctan (tan 120°)

d. Sin⁻¹ (cos 30°)

e. Arccos (tan 315°)

f. Tan⁻¹ (sin 90°)

g. Arcsin (tan 180°)

h. Cos⁻¹ (sin 300°)

i. Arctan (tan 210°)

j. Sin⁻¹ (cos (−60°))

k. Arccos (cos 210°)

l. Tan⁻¹ (tan (−10°))

m. $\mathrm{Cos}^{-1} \dfrac{\sqrt{3}}{2} + \mathrm{Cos}^{-1} \dfrac{-\sqrt{3}}{2}$

n. $\mathrm{Sin}^{-1} \dfrac{\sqrt{2}}{2} + \mathrm{Sin}^{-1} \dfrac{-\sqrt{2}}{2}$

INVERSE TRIGONOMETRIC EXPRESSIONS

Expressions involving inverse trigonometric functions may often be expressed in simpler terms. The following examples will show several ways of doing this.

Example 1   Compute the value of $\cos\left(2 \text{ Arctan } \dfrac{-5}{2}\right)$.

Solution   Let Arctan $\dfrac{-5}{2} = u°$ as shown in Figure 8–7.

Note that $-90° < \text{Arctan } \dfrac{-5}{2} < 0°$ (why?). It follows that

$$\cos u° = \frac{2}{\sqrt{29}} \text{ and } \sin u° = \frac{-5}{\sqrt{29}}$$

From the identity, $\cos 2u° \equiv \cos^2 u° - \sin^2 u°$, it follows that

$$\cos\left(2 \text{ Arctan } \frac{-5}{2}\right) = \cos 2u° = \frac{4}{29} - \frac{25}{29} = \frac{-21}{29}$$

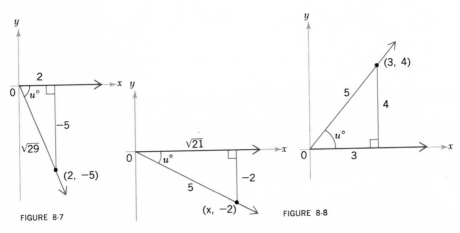

FIGURE 8-7   FIGURE 8-8

Example 2   Compute the value of $\cos\left(\text{Sin}^{-1} \dfrac{-2}{5} + \text{Tan}^{-1} \dfrac{4}{3}\right)$.

Solution   Let Sin⁻¹ $\dfrac{-2}{5} = u°$ and Tan⁻¹ $\dfrac{4}{3} = v°$ as shown in the diagrams of Figure 8–8.

Why are $u°$ and $v°$ fourth and first quadrant numbers, respectively? It follows that

$$\cos u° = \frac{\sqrt{21}}{5} \text{ and } \sin u° = \frac{-2}{5}$$

$$\cos v° = \frac{3}{5} \text{ and } \sin v° = \frac{4}{5}$$

From the identity, $\cos (u + v)° \equiv \cos u° \cos v° - \sin u° \sin v°$, it follows that

$$\cos \left(\mathrm{Sin}^{-1} \frac{-2}{5} + \mathrm{Tan}^{-1} \frac{4}{3} \right) = \cos (u + v)°$$

$$= \frac{\sqrt{21}}{5} \cdot \frac{3}{5} - \frac{-2}{5} \cdot \frac{4}{5} = \frac{3\sqrt{21} + 8}{25}$$

Example 3   Express $\cos (\mathrm{Tan}^{-1} 2z)$, for $z < 0$, in terms of z.

Solution   Let $\mathrm{Tan}^{-1} 2z = u°$ as shown in Figure 8–9 and then determine $\cos u°$. Note that $-90° < u° < 0°$ (why?). It follows that

$$\cos (\mathrm{Tan}^{-1} 2z) = \cos u° = \frac{1}{\sqrt{1 + 4z^2}} = \frac{\sqrt{1 + 4z^2}}{1 + 4z^2}$$

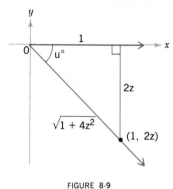

FIGURE 8-9

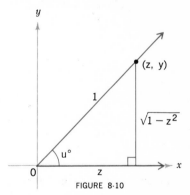

FIGURE 8-10

Example 4   Express $\tan (2 \, \mathrm{Cos}^{-1} z)$, for $z > 0$, in terms of z.

Solution   Let $\mathrm{Cos}^{-1} z = u°$ as shown in Figure 8–10 above at the right and then determine $\tan 2u°$. It follows that

$$\tan u° = \frac{\sqrt{1 - z^2}}{z}$$

From the identity, $\tan 2u° \equiv \frac{2 \tan u°}{1 - \tan^2 u°}$, it follows that

$\tan (2 \, \mathrm{Cos}^{-1} z) = \tan 2u°$

$$= \frac{2 \cdot \dfrac{\sqrt{1 - z^2}}{z}}{1 - \dfrac{1 - z^2}{z^2}} = \frac{\dfrac{2\sqrt{1 - z^2}}{z}}{\dfrac{2z^2 - 1}{z^2}} \cdot \frac{z^2}{z^2} = \frac{2z\sqrt{1 - z^2}}{2z^2 - 1}$$

Example 5   Express $\sin(\text{Tan}^{-1} 2z - \text{Cos}^{-1} z)$, for $-1 < z < 0$, in terms of z.

Solution   Let $\text{Tan}^{-1} 2z = u°$ and $\text{Cos}^{-1} z = v°$ as shown in Figure 8–11 and then determine $\sin(u - v)°$. From the drawings, it follows that

$$\sin u° = \frac{2z}{\sqrt{1 + 4z^2}} \text{ and } \cos u° = \frac{1}{\sqrt{1 + 4z^2}}$$

$$\sin v° = \sqrt{1 - z^2} \text{ and } \cos v° = z$$

Using the identity, $\sin(u - v)° \equiv \sin u° \cos v° - \cos u° \sin v°$, we obtain

$$\sin(\text{Tan}^{-1} 2z - \text{Cos}^{-1} z) = \sin(u - v)°$$

$$= \frac{2z}{\sqrt{1 + 4z^2}} \cdot z - \frac{1}{\sqrt{1 + 4z^2}} \cdot \sqrt{1 - z^2}$$

$$= \frac{2z^2 - \sqrt{1 - z^2}}{\sqrt{1 + 4z^2}}$$

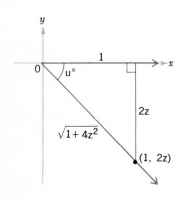

FIGURE 8·11

EXERCISES

1. Compute each of the following.

a. $\sin\left(2 \text{ Arctan } \dfrac{5}{3}\right)$

d. $\cos\left(\text{Arcsin } \dfrac{-2}{5} - \text{Arctan } 3\right)$

b. $\tan\left(2 \text{ Cos}^{-1} \dfrac{-3}{4}\right)$

e. $\tan\left(\text{Sin}^{-1} \dfrac{3}{4} - \text{Cos}^{-1} \dfrac{2}{3}\right)$

c. $\sin\left(\text{Tan}^{-1} \dfrac{-2}{5} + \text{Cos}^{-1} \dfrac{3}{5}\right)$

f. $\cos\left(\text{Arcsin } \dfrac{-3}{7}\right)$

2. Express each of the following in terms of z, for the stated restriction on z.

a. $\cos(\text{Sin}^{-1} z)$, $z > 0$

e. $\cos(2 \text{ Arctan } z)$, $z > 0$

b. $\sin(\text{Arctan } z)$, $z < 0$

f. $\sin(2 \text{ Cos}^{-1} z)$, $z < 0$

c. $\tan(\text{Cos}^{-1} z)$, $z > 0$

g. $\tan(\text{Sin}^{-1} 2z)$, $z > 0$

d. $\cos(\text{Tan}^{-1} z)$, $z < 0$

h. $\sin(\text{Arctan } 2z)$, $z < 0$

i. $\sin (\text{Cos}^{-1} z + \text{Tan}^{-1} z), 0 < z < 1$

j. $\cos (\text{Arctan } 2z + \text{Arcsin } 2z),$
$\qquad -1 < 2z < 0$

k. $\tan (\text{Sin}^{-1} z + \text{Cos}^{-1} 2z), z > 0$

l. $\sin (\text{Arcsin } z - \text{Arccos } z), z < 0$

m. $\cos (\text{Tan}^{-1} z - \text{Tan}^{-1} 2z), z > 0$

n. $\tan (\text{Arccos } 2z - \text{Arcsin } 2z), z < 0$

o. $\sin [(\text{Tan}^{-1} z) + 180°], z > 0$

p. $\cos [(\text{Arcsin } z) + 180°], z < 0$

VOCABULARY

Use each of the following correctly in a sentence to demonstrate that you understand its meaning. If you are not sure of the meaning of any word, refer back to the chapter.

arccos
arcsin
arctan
cap-arccosine, Arccos
cap-arcsine, Arcsin
cap-arctangent, Arctan
cap-cosine, Cos
cap-cotangent, Cot
cap-sine, Sin

$f^{-1} \qquad f^{-1}(x)$
function of a function
inverse of cap-cosine, Cos^{-1}
inverse of cap-sine, Sin^{-1}
inverse of cap-tangent, Tan^{-1}
inverse function
inverse of a function
one-to-one function
principal value

REVIEW EXERCISES

1. State the domain of Sin.

2. State the range of Arccos.

3. Solve each of the following equations.

a. $\text{Sin } u° = \dfrac{\sqrt{3}}{2}$

b. $\text{Cos } u° = \dfrac{\sqrt{2}}{2}$

c. $\text{Tan } u° = 1$

d. $\text{Sin } u° = \dfrac{-1}{2}$

e. $\text{Cos } u° = \dfrac{-\sqrt{3}}{2}$

f. $\text{Tan } u° = \dfrac{-\sqrt{3}}{3}$

4. Determine the value of each of the following.

a. $\text{Tan}^{-1} (-\sqrt{3})$

b. $\text{Arccos } \dfrac{1}{2}$

c. $\text{Sin}^{-1} \dfrac{-\sqrt{2}}{2}$

d. $\text{Arctan } 1$

e. $\text{Cos}^{-1} \dfrac{-\sqrt{3}}{2}$

f. $\text{Arcsin } \dfrac{\sqrt{3}}{2}$

g. $\sin \left(\text{Arccos } \dfrac{-5}{13} \right)$

h. $\cos (\text{Tan}^{-1} 4)$

i. $\tan \left(\text{Arcsin } \dfrac{2}{5} \right)$

j. $\sin \left(\text{Arctan } \dfrac{-4}{3} \right)$

k. $\cos (\text{Sin}^{-1} (-1))$

l. $\tan \left(\text{Arccos } \dfrac{\sqrt{2}}{3} \right)$

5. Determine all values of each of the following.

a. $\arcsin \dfrac{1}{2}$

b. $\arccos \dfrac{-\sqrt{3}}{2}$

c. $\arctan \sqrt{3}$

d. $\arcsin \dfrac{-1}{2}$

6. Determine the value of each of the following.

   a. Arcsin (cos 225°)   **c.** Arctan (tan 210°)   **e.** Cos⁻¹ (sin (−60°))

   b. Arccos (sin 150°)   **d.** Sin⁻¹ (cos 300°)   **f.** Tan⁻¹ (tan 120°)

7. Compute the value of each of the following.

   a. $\cos\left(2 \text{ Arcsin } \dfrac{3}{5}\right)$ **c.** $\tan\left(\text{Sin}^{-1} \dfrac{-1}{3} - \text{Cos}^{-1} \dfrac{2}{3}\right)$

   b. $\sin (2 \text{ Tan}^{-1} (-3))$ **d.** $\cos\left(\text{Arctan } (-2) + \text{Arcsin } \dfrac{4}{5}\right)$

8. Express each of the following in terms of z.

   a. sin (Cos⁻¹ z) for z > 0   **d.** tan (Arccos z − Arcsin z) for z < 0

   b. tan (Arcsin 2z) for z < 0   **e.** sin (2 Tan⁻¹ z) for z > 0

   c. cos (Tan⁻¹ z + Sin⁻¹ z) for 0 < z < 1   **f.** cos (Sin⁻¹ z) for z > 0

9. Solve each equation and express the solutions by using inverse notation.

   a. 12 sin u° cos u° + 9 sin u° − 4 cos u° − 3 = 0

   b. sin (5u − 75)° = 0.2317

CHAPTER TEST

1. State the domain of Cos, the cap-cosine function.

2. State the range of Arctan, the cap-arctangent function.

3. Each of the following equations involves a cap-trigonometric function. Solve each equation.

   a. Sin u° = −1   **b.** Cos u° = $\dfrac{-1}{2}$ **c.** Tan u° = $\dfrac{\sqrt{3}}{3}$ **d.** Sin u° = $\dfrac{-1}{2}$

4. Compute.

   a. Tan⁻¹ (−1)

   b. Sin⁻¹ $\dfrac{\sqrt{2}}{2}$

   c. Arccos $\dfrac{-\sqrt{3}}{2}$

   d. Arcsin $\dfrac{1}{2}$

   e. $\sin\left(\text{Sin}^{-1} \dfrac{3}{7}\right)$

   f. cos (Arctan 5)

   g. $\tan\left(\text{Cos}^{-1} \dfrac{-2}{5}\right)$

   h. $\sin\left(2 \text{ Tan}^{-1} \dfrac{-3}{4}\right)$

   i. Arccos (sin 120°)

5. Determine all values of arcsin $\dfrac{-1}{\sqrt{2}}$.

6. Express each of the following in terms of z.

   a. tan (Cos⁻¹ z) for z > 0   **c.** cos (2 Sin⁻¹ z) for z > 0

   b. sin (Arctan 2z) for z < 0   **d.** sin (Arccos z + Arctan z) for −1 < z < 0

CHAPTER 9

POLAR FORM OF A COMPLEX NUMBER

RECTANGULAR FORM OF A COMPLEX NUMBER

In this section we shall study complex numbers using *rectangular notation*. For the remainder of the chapter, complex numbers will be examined in *polar notation* which involves trigonometric functions.

> **DEFINITION OF COMPLEX NUMBER**   For all real numbers x and y, $x + yi$ is a *complex number z*; and for each complex number z, there exist real numbers x and y such that $z = x + yi$; in each case, i has the property that $i^2 = -1$.

The notation $x + yi$ is called the *rectangular form* of the complex number z.

Eight complex numbers are listed below using rectangular form.

$$2 + 3i \qquad\qquad 7 \qquad\qquad 0 \qquad\qquad -i$$

$$\sqrt{5} - \frac{1}{2}i \qquad\qquad 3i \qquad\qquad -\frac{2}{3}i \qquad\qquad -4$$

For each example of a complex number z above, determine real numbers x and y so that

$$z = x + yi$$

In the complex number system, the sum of the complex numbers $a + bi$ and $c + di$ is defined as follows:

$$(a + bi) + (c + di) = (a + c) + (b + d)i$$

For example,

1. $(5 - 3i) + (2 + 7i) = 7 + 4i$
2. $(\sqrt{3} + \sqrt{2}i) + (-3\sqrt{3} - 2\sqrt{2}i) = -2\sqrt{3} - \sqrt{2}i$

229

In the complex number system, the product of the complex numbers $a + bi$ and $c + di$ is defined as:

$$(a + bi) \cdot (c + di) = (ac - bd) + (ad + bc)i$$

For example,

1. $(3 + 4i) \cdot (2 - 3i) = 6 - 12i^2 - 9i + 8i = 18 - i$
2. $(5 - 3i) \cdot (5 + 3i) = 25 - 9i^2 = 34$

It can also be shown that the difference of $a + bi$ and $c + di$ is

$$(a + bi) - (c + di) = (a - c) + (b - d)i$$

For example,

1. $(2 + 3i) - (5 - 2i) = -3 + 5i$
2. $(-4 + 6i) - (3 + 2i) = -7 + 4i$

The quotient may be computed as follows:

$$
\begin{aligned}
(a + bi) \div (c + di) &= \frac{a + bi}{c + di} \\
&= \frac{a + bi}{c + di} \cdot \frac{c - di}{c - di} \\
&= \frac{ac - bdi^2 - adi + bci}{c^2 - d^2 i^2} \\
&= \frac{ac + bd}{c^2 + d^2} + \frac{(bc - ad)}{c^2 + d^2}i, \ [c^2 + d^2 \neq 0]
\end{aligned}
$$

For example,

1. $(2 - 3i) \div (3 + 4i) = \dfrac{2 - 3i}{3 + 4i} \cdot \dfrac{3 - 4i}{3 - 4i} = \dfrac{6 + 12i^2 - 8i - 9i}{9 - 16i^2}$

$$= \frac{-6}{25} + \frac{-17}{25}i$$

$$= \frac{-6}{25} - \frac{17}{25}i$$

2. $\dfrac{1 + 2i}{2 - 3i} = \dfrac{1 + 2i}{2 - 3i} \cdot \dfrac{2 + 3i}{2 + 3i} = \dfrac{2 + 6i^2 + 3i + 4i}{4 - 9i^2}$

$$= \frac{-4}{13} + \frac{7}{13}i$$

The definition of a complex number suggests that there is a one-to-one correspondence between the set of all complex numbers and the set of all ordered pairs of real numbers (x, y). A one-to-one correspondence can also be established between the set of all points in a plane and the set of all ordered pairs of real numbers (x, y). Consequently, the *graph* of the complex number z is the point $P(x, y)$ where $z = x + yi$. Figure 9–1 shows the graphs of the four complex numbers

$$z_1 = 2 + 3i \qquad\qquad z_3 = 2i = 0 + 2i$$
$$z_2 = -2 - 2i \qquad\qquad z_4 = -1 = -1 + 0i$$

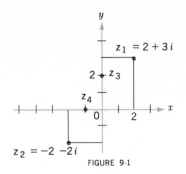

FIGURE 9·1

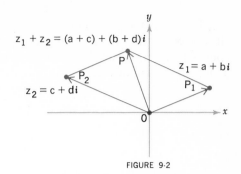

FIGURE 9·2

The sum of two complex numbers may be constructed geometrically by the *parallelogram method*, as shown in Figure 9–2. The graph of $z_1 + z_2$ is the point $P(a + c, b + d)$ where the graphs of z_1 and z_2 are the points $P_1(a, b)$ and $P_2(c, d)$, respectively. It can be shown that P is a vertex of parallelogram P_1OP_2P. In the next section we shall give a geometric interpretation of the product of two complex numbers.

In your study of real numbers, you defined the absolute value of a real number x as follows:

$$|x| = x \text{ for } x \geq 0 \qquad\qquad |x| = -x \text{ for } x < 0$$

In defining the absolute value of a complex number, we resort to the distance between the origin and the graph of a complex number. For example, for the four complex numbers shown in Figure 9–1 these distances can be computed as follows:

$$z_1 = 2 + 3i; \text{ distance: } \sqrt{2^2 + 3^2} = \sqrt{13}$$
$$z_2 = -2 - 2i; \text{ distance: } \sqrt{(-2)^2 + (-2)^2} = 2\sqrt{2}$$
$$z_3 = 2i = 0 + 2i; \text{ distance: } \sqrt{0^2 + 2^2} = 2$$
$$z_4 = -1 = -1 + 0i; \text{ distance: } \sqrt{(-1)^2 + 0^2} = 1$$

We define the *absolute value* of the complex number $x + yi$ to be the following:

$$|z| = |x + yi| = \sqrt{x^2 + y^2}$$

It can be shown that, for any two complex numbers z_1 and z_2,

$$|z_1| \cdot |z_2| = |z_1 \cdot z_2|$$

That is, the product of the absolute values of z_1 and z_2 is the absolute value of the product of z_1 and z_2. You will be asked to prove this as an exercise. This theorem tells us that the graph of $z_1 \cdot z_2$ is located on a circle of radius $|z_1 \cdot z_2|$ where the graphs of z_1 and z_2 are located on circles of radii $|z_1|$ and $|z_2|$, respectively. The circles with centers at the origin are shown in Figure 9–3.

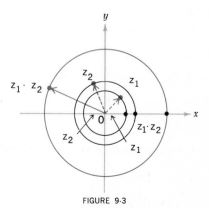

FIGURE 9·3

Recall that the symbol $\sqrt{-4}$ was undefined in the real number system since there is no real number whose square is -4. However, there are two complex numbers, namely $2i$ and $-2i$, each of whose squares is -4, as can be seen from the following:

$$(2i)^2 = (2i)(2i) = 4i^2 = -4$$
$$(-2i)^2 = (-2i)(-2i) = 4i^2 = -4$$

Hence, we say that

$$\sqrt{-4} = 2i \qquad \text{also,} \qquad -\sqrt{-4} = -2i$$

We are led to make the following definition.

DEFINITION OF $\sqrt{-x}$ FOR $x > 0$ For each real number $x > 0$,
$$\sqrt{-x} = i\sqrt{x} \qquad \text{and} \qquad -\sqrt{-x} = -i\sqrt{x}$$

The following examples involve $\sqrt{-x}$ for some $x > 0$.

Examples

$$\sqrt{-7} = i\sqrt{7}$$
$$-\sqrt{-8} = -i\sqrt{8} = -2i\sqrt{2}$$
$$\sqrt{-8} + \sqrt{-18} = 2i\sqrt{2} + 3i\sqrt{2} = 5i\sqrt{2}$$
$$\sqrt{-6} \cdot \sqrt{5} = (i\sqrt{6})(\sqrt{5}) = i\sqrt{30}$$
$$\sqrt{-4} \cdot \sqrt{-9} = (2i)(3i) = 6i^2 = -6$$

Note that $\sqrt{-4} \cdot \sqrt{-9} \neq \sqrt{(-4)(-9)}$ since $\sqrt{(-4)(-9)} = \sqrt{36} = 6$.

The *conjugate* of the complex number $a + bi$ is defined to be $a - bi$. In what way did we make use of the conjugate of a complex number in computing the quotient of complex numbers? The conjugate of $5 - 2i$ is $5 + 2i$. What is the conjugate of $-4 + 3i$? Of 7? Of $-4i$?

EXERCISES

1. Compute each sum or difference and express the result in rectangular form, that is, in the form $x + yi$.

   a. $(7 + 4i) + (5 + 2i)$

   b. $(-3 + 5i) + (8 - 2i)$

   c. $(9 - 4i) + (-2 - 6i)$

   d. $(\sqrt{5} + 2\sqrt{3}i) + (-3\sqrt{5} + \sqrt{3}i)$

   e. $5 + (-3 + 4i)$

   f. $(7 - 2i) + (3i)$

   g. $(6 + 2i) - (4 + 5i)$

   h. $(-2 + 4i) - (7 - 3i)$

   i. $(8 - 3i) - (-4 - 5i)$

   j. $(2\sqrt{2} + \sqrt{6}i) - (-\sqrt{2} + 3\sqrt{6}i)$

   k. $7 - (-2 - 5i)$

   l. $-5i - (6 - 2i)$

2. Compute each product or quotient and express the result in rectangular form, $x + yi$.

   a. $(3 + 2i)(4 + 5i)$

   b. $(2 - 3i)(5 + 4i)$

   c. $(4 - 2i)\left(2 - \frac{1}{2}i\right)$

   d. $(3i)(5i)$

e. $(2i)(-4i)$

f. $(\sqrt{3} + \sqrt{2}i)(2\sqrt{3} - 5\sqrt{2}i)$

g. $(4 - 3i)(4 + 3i)$

h. $(5 + \sqrt{2}i)(5 - \sqrt{2}i)$

i. $(4 + 3i)\left(\dfrac{4}{25} - \dfrac{3}{25}i\right)$

j. $(-2 - 5i)\left(\dfrac{-2}{29} + \dfrac{5}{29}i\right)$

k. $3(2 - 5i)$

l. $-4(-1 + 3i)$

m. $2i(3 - 6i)$

n. $-3i(5 + 2i)$

o. $(5 + 2i) \div (3 - 4i)$

p. $(-3 - 3i) \div (2 + 3i)$

q. $5 \div (3 - 5i)$

r. $(6 + 4i) \div 2$

s. $2i \div (1 + i)$

t. $(3 - i) \div (-4i)$

u. $(8 + 2i) \div i$

3. Solve the equation $z^4 = 16$ to determine the four fourth roots of 16 in the complex number system. *Hint:* $z^4 = 16$ is equivalent to $z^4 - 16 = 0$.

4. Show that each of -2, $1 + i\sqrt{3}$ and $1 - i\sqrt{3}$ is a cube root of -8 by computing the third power of each number.

5. Plot all of the following complex numbers on one coordinate plane.

a. $z_1 = 5 + 3i$

b. $z_2 = -6 + 4i$

c. $z_3 = -4 - 5i$

d. $z_4 = 6 - 3i$

e. $z_5 = i$

f. $z_6 = -i$

g. $z_7 = 4$

h. $z_8 = -3$

i. $z_9 = 5i$

j. $z_{10} = -6i$

k. $z_{11} = (2i)^2$

l. $z_{12} = -3i^2$

6. Plot each of the following pairs of complex numbers z_1 and z_2 on a separate coordinate system. Then construct the sum $z_1 + z_2$ of each pair by the parallelogram method.

a. $z_1 = 4 + 6i$; $z_2 = 7 + 4i$

b. $z_1 = 8 - 3i$; $z_2 = -5 - 6i$

c. $z_1 = 5i$; $z_2 = 3 + 6i$

d. $z_1 = -7 + 5i$; $z_2 = -4$

7. Prove that P_1OP_2P is a parallelogram given $P(a + c, b + d)$, $P_1(a, b)$, $P_2(c, d)$, and O, the origin, all points being on one coordinate plane.

8. For each complex number z of Exercise 5, determine $|z|$.

9. Given any pair of complex numbers z_1 and z_2 for which $z_1 = a + bi$ and $z_2 = c + di$, prove that $|z_1| \cdot |z_2| = |z_1 \cdot z_2|$.

10. For each pair of complex numbers z_1 and z_2 given in Exercise 6, determine the absolute value of their product, $|z_1 \cdot z_2|$.

11. Simplify each of the following.

a. $\sqrt{-9}$

b. $-\sqrt{-25}$

c. $\sqrt{-12}$

d. $-\sqrt{-50}$

e. $\sqrt{-27} + \sqrt{-3}$

f. $\sqrt{-75} - \sqrt{-48}$

g. $\sqrt{-8} \cdot \sqrt{-8}$

i. $\sqrt{-5} \cdot \sqrt{-3}$

k. $\dfrac{-6 + \sqrt{-12}}{4}$

h. $\sqrt{-9} \cdot \sqrt{-25}$

j. $\sqrt{-3} \cdot \sqrt{-6}$

12. The quadratic formula states that for all real numbers a, b and c ($a \neq 0$), the solution set of $az^2 + bz + c = 0$ is

$$\left\{ \frac{-b + \sqrt{b^2 - 4ac}}{2a}, \frac{-b - \sqrt{b^2 - 4ac}}{2a} \right\}$$

Solve each of the following equations for its complex number solutions. Simplify each answer.

a. $z^2 + 2z + 3 = 0$

f. $169z^2 + 625 = 0$

b. $2z^2 + z + 1 = 0$

g. $z^3 - 27 = 0$

c. $z^2 - 2z + 2 = 0$

[*Hint:* $z^3 - 27 \equiv (z - 3)(z^2 + 3z + 9)$]

d. $z^2 + 9 = 0$

h. $z^3 + 64 = 0$

e. $4z^2 + 3 = 0$

13. Express each of the following in rectangular form, $x + yi$.

a. $(1 + i)^2$

d. $(2 - \sqrt{3}i)^3$

f. $\left(\dfrac{3 - i\sqrt{3}}{2} \right)^3$

b. $(1 + i)^3$

e. $\left(\dfrac{3 + i\sqrt{3}}{2} \right)^3$

c. $(2 - \sqrt{3}i)^2$

14. Simplify each of the following. In **m-o**, n is any natural number.

a. i^2

d. i^5

g. i^8

j. i^{42}

m. i^{4n}

b. i^3

e. i^6

h. i^9

k. i^{63}

n. i^{4n+1}

c. i^4

f. i^7

i. i^{21}

l. i^{84}

o. i^{4n+2}

15. Compute and express each of the following products in the form $r(\cos u° + i \sin u°)$.

Example $5(\cos 70° + i \sin 70°) \cdot 3(\cos 40° + i \sin 40°)$
$= 15(\cos 70° \cos 40° + i^2 \sin 70° \sin 40° + i \sin 70° \cos 40° + i \cos 70° \sin 40°)$
$= 15[(\cos 70° \cos 40° - \sin 70° \sin 40°) + i(\sin 70° \cos 40° + \cos 70° \sin 40°)]$
$= 15[\cos (70 + 40)° + i \sin (70 + 40)°] =$
$15(\cos 110° + i \sin 110°)$

a. $3(\cos 50° + i \sin 50°) \cdot 7(\cos 20° + i \sin 20°)$

b. $\sqrt{5}(\cos 43° + i \sin 43°) \cdot \sqrt{3}(\cos 31° + i \sin 31°)$

c. $10(\cos 112° + i \sin 112°) \cdot 2(\cos 53° + i \sin 53°)$

d. $r_1(\cos v° + i \sin v°) \cdot r_2(\cos w° + i \sin w°)$, for $r_1 > 0$ and $r_2 > 0$

e. $[3(\cos 20° + i \sin 20°)]^2$

f. $[3(\cos 20° + i \sin 20°)]^3$

g. $[3(\cos 20° + i \sin 20°)]^4$

h. $[a(\cos v° + i \sin v°)]^n$, for $a > 0$ and n a natural number

16. Evaluate the polynomial $x^4 - 4x^3 + 6x^2 - 4x + 1$ for $x = \dfrac{1}{2} - \dfrac{\sqrt{3}}{2}i$.

17. What is the conjugate of each of the following complex numbers?

    a. $2 - 3i$ **b.** $5i$ **c.** $\dfrac{\sqrt{3}}{2} + 3i$ **d.** -4

18. Multiply each complex number of Exercise 17 by its conjugate. What do these results suggest about the product of a complex number and its conjugate?

19. Prove that the product of each complex number $x + yi$ and its conjugate is a real number.

POLAR FORM OF A COMPLEX NUMBER

Given two complex numbers, $z_1 = -2\sqrt{2} + 2\sqrt{2}\,i$ and $z_2 = -3\sqrt{3} - 3i$, plotted as shown in Figures 9–4 and 9–5, respectively.

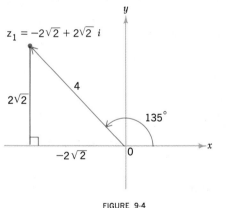

FIGURE 9-4

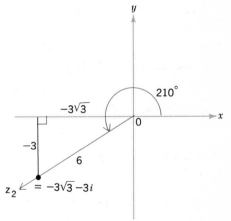

FIGURE 9-5

Verify that

$$|z_1| = \sqrt{(-2\sqrt{2})^2 + (2\sqrt{2})^2} = 4$$

$$|z_2| = \sqrt{(-3\sqrt{3})^2 + (-3)^2} = 6$$

and

$$z_1 = 4\left(\dfrac{-\sqrt{2}}{2} + \dfrac{\sqrt{2}}{2}i\right) = 4(\cos 135° + i \sin 135°)$$

$$z_2 = 6\left(\dfrac{-\sqrt{3}}{2} + \dfrac{-1}{2}i\right) = 6(\cos 210° + i \sin 210°)$$

In general, given any complex number z for which

$$z = x + yi$$

in rectangular form as shown in Figure 9–6,

$$|z| = r = \sqrt{x^2 + y^2}$$

and

$$x = r \cos u° \text{ and } y = r \sin u°$$

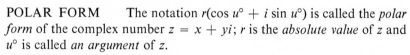

FIGURE 9-6 $z = x + yi$

Hence,

$$x + yi = r \cos u° + i r \sin u° = r(\cos u° + i \sin u°)$$

POLAR FORM   The notation $r(\cos u° + i \sin u°)$ is called the *polar form* of the complex number $z = x + yi$; r is the *absolute value* of z and $u°$ is called *an argument* of z.

We say that $u°$ is *an* argument of z since any one of $(u + 360k)°$, k any integer, is an argument of z; that is,

$$r(\cos u° + i \sin u°) \equiv r[\cos (u + 360k)° + i \sin (u + 360k)°]$$

If a complex number z has rectangular form $x + yi$ and polar form $r(\cos u° + i \sin u°)$,

then $$x + yi = r(\cos u° + i \sin u°)$$

The absolute value of z is given by

$$|z| = \sqrt{x^2 + y^2} = r$$

The argument $u°$ of z is given by

$$\cos u° = \frac{x}{r} \text{ and } \sin u° = \frac{y}{r}$$

One can easily change from one form to another as shown by the following examples.

Example 1   Express $-5 + 5i$ in polar form.

Solution   For $z = -5 + 5i$, we have
$$|z| = r = \sqrt{(-5)^2 + 5^2} = \sqrt{50} = 5\sqrt{2}$$
An argument of z is 135° since 135° is a solution of
$$\cos u° = \frac{-5}{5\sqrt{2}} \text{ and } \sin u° = \frac{5}{5\sqrt{2}}$$
The polar form of z is thus given by
$$r(\cos u° + i \sin u°) = 5\sqrt{2} (\cos 135° + i \sin 135°)$$
Since, for any integer k, $(135 + 360k)°$ is an argument of z, some other polar forms of z are
$$5\sqrt{2} (\cos 495° + i \sin 495°)$$
$$5\sqrt{2} [\cos (-225°) + i \sin (-225°)]$$

and in general, for each integer k,

$$5\sqrt{2}\,[\cos (135 + 360k)° + i \sin (135 + 360k)°]$$

is a polar form of $-5 + 5i$.

Example 2   Express $7(\cos 120° + i \sin 120°)$ in rectangular form.

Solution $7(\cos 120° + i \sin 120°) = 7\left(\dfrac{-1}{2} + \dfrac{\sqrt{3}}{2}i\right) = \dfrac{-7}{2} + \dfrac{7\sqrt{3}}{2}i$

The polar form of a complex number has a great advantage over the rectangular form when determining products and powers.

Given z_1 and z_2 such that

$$z_1 = r_1(\cos u° + i \sin u°)$$
$$z_2 = r_2(\cos v° + i \sin v°)$$

it follows that

$$\begin{aligned} z_1 \cdot z_2 &= [r_1(\cos u° + i \sin u°)] \cdot [r_2(\cos v° + i \sin v°)] \\ &= r_1 r_2[\cos u° \cos v° + i^2 \sin u° \sin v° + \\ &\qquad\qquad i \sin u° \cos v° + i \cos u° \sin v°] \\ &= r_1 r_2[(\cos u° \cos v° - \sin u° \sin v°) + \\ &\qquad\qquad i(\sin u° \cos v° + \cos u° \sin v°)] \\ &= r_1 r_2[\cos (u + v)° + i \sin (u + v)°] \end{aligned}$$

This tells us that

1. the absolute value of $z_1 \cdot z_2$ is the *product* of the absolute values of z_1 and z_2;
2. the argument of $z_1 \cdot z_2$ is the *sum* of the chosen arguments of z_1 and z_2.

For example,

$$5(\cos 20° + i \sin 20°) \cdot \sqrt{3}(\cos 50° + i \sin 50°) = 5\sqrt{3}\,(\cos 70° + i \sin 70°).$$

What is the polar form of the product of $3\sqrt{2}\,(\cos 34° + i \sin 34°)$ and $2\sqrt{5}$ $(\cos 114° + i \sin 114°)$?

Given complex numbers $z_1 = \dfrac{3}{2} + \dfrac{\sqrt{3}}{2}i = \sqrt{3}(\cos 30° + i \sin 30°)$

and $z_2 = -2 + 2\sqrt{3}i = 4(\cos 120° + i \sin 120°)$,

we may compute the product $z_1 z_2$ using either rectangular notation or polar notation.

$$\begin{aligned} z_1 z_2 &= \left(\dfrac{3}{2} + \dfrac{\sqrt{3}}{2}i\right)(-2 + 2\sqrt{3}i) \\ &= -3 + 3i^2 + 3\sqrt{3}i - \sqrt{3}i \\ &= -6 + 2\sqrt{3}i \\ z_1 z_2 &= \sqrt{3}(\cos 30° + i \sin 30°) \cdot 4(\cos 120° + i \sin 120°) \\ &= 4\sqrt{3}(\cos 150° + i \sin 150°) \end{aligned}$$

Is it easier to compute products in rectangular form or in polar form? You should verify that $4\sqrt{3}(\cos 150° + i \sin 150°)$ is equal to $-6 + 2\sqrt{3}i$.

We now have a means for constructing the product of z_1 and z_2. This is illustrated in Figure 9-7.

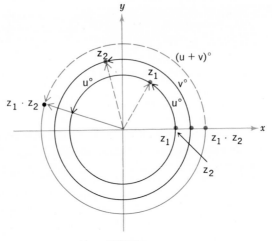

FIGURE 9-7

How is $|z_1 \cdot z_2|$ determined? How is an argument of $z_1 \cdot z_2$ determined?

To express the conjugate of $r(\cos u° + i \sin u°)$ in polar form, observe that

If $x + yi = r(\cos u° + i \sin u°)$ where $\cos u° = \dfrac{x}{r}$ and $\sin u° = \dfrac{y}{r}$,

it follows that the conjugate of $x + yi$ is

$$x - yi = r(\cos u° - i \sin u°) = r[\cos (-u°) + i \sin (-u°)]$$

What is the polar form of the conjugate of $\sqrt{3}(\cos 60° + i \sin 60°)$? of $2[\cos (-20°) + i \sin (-20°)]$? of $\cos 140° - i \sin 140°$?

The quotient of $z_1 = r_1(\cos u° + i \sin u°)$ and $z_2 = r_2(\cos v° + i \sin v°) \neq 0$ is also readily determined in polar form, since

$$\frac{z_1}{z_2} = \frac{r_1(\cos u° + i \sin u°)}{r_2(\cos v° + i \sin v°)}$$

$$= \frac{r_1(\cos u° + i \sin u°)}{r_2(\cos v° + i \sin v°)} \cdot \frac{r_2[\cos (-v°) + i \sin (-v°)]}{r_2[\cos (-v°) + i \sin (-v°)]}$$

$$= \frac{r_1 r_2[\cos (u - v)° + i \sin (u - v)°]}{r_2 r_2(\cos 0° + i \sin 0°)}$$

$$= \frac{r_1}{r_2}[\cos (u - v)° + i \sin (u - v)°]$$

For example,

$$9(\cos 80° + i \sin 80°) \div 1.5(\cos 25° + i \sin 25°) = 6(\cos 55° + i \sin 55°)$$

What is the polar form of the quotient of $6(\cos 125° + i \sin 125°)$ and $4(\cos 73° + i \sin 73°)$? Compute $z_1 \div z_2$ in both rectangular and polar forms, where $z_1 = 3 + 3\sqrt{3}i = 6(\cos 60° + i \sin 60°)$ and $z_2 = 2\sqrt{3} + 2i = 4(\cos 30° + i \sin 30°)$. In which form is it easier to compute the quotient of two complex numbers?

Natural number powers of complex numbers can be determined as special cases of multiplication.

Example 1 $[3(\cos 25° + i \sin 25°)]^2 = 9(\cos 50° + i \sin 50°)$

Example 2 $[3(\cos 25° + i \sin 25°)]^3 = 27(\cos 75° + i \sin 75°)$

Example 3 $[3(\cos 25° + i \sin 25°)]^4 = 81(\cos 100° + i \sin 100°)$

In general, for each complex number $z = r(\cos u° + i \sin u°)$ and for each natural number n,

$$z^n = [r(\cos u° + i \sin u°)]^n = r^n(\cos nu° + i \sin nu°)$$

This statement is also true for each *real number n* and is known as *de Moivre's Theorem*. What is $[2\sqrt{3} (\cos 55° + i \sin 55°)]^4$ equal to? Given $z = -2\sqrt{2} + 2\sqrt{2}i = 4(\cos 135° + i \sin 135°)$, compute z^4 in both rectangular and polar forms. In which form is it easier to compute powers of complex numbers?

EXERCISES

1. Express each of the following complex numbers in polar form. For Exercises **i-l**, determine arguments to the nearest 10 minutes.

   a. $3 + 3\sqrt{3}i$ **f.** $3i$ **k.** $-3 + 2i$

   b. $-4\sqrt{2} + 4\sqrt{2}i$ **g.** -4 **l.** $-5 - 4i$

   c. $-4 - 4\sqrt{3}i$ **h.** $-2i$ **m.** $\cos 70° - i \sin 70°$

   d. $\sqrt{6} - \sqrt{2}i$ **i.** $3 + 4i$ **n.** $3(\cos 125° - i \sin 125°)$

   e. 5   **j.** $2 - 5i$

2. Express each of the following complex numbers in rectangular form.

   a. $4(\cos 225° + i \sin 225°)$ **e.** $3(\cos 90° + i \sin 90°)$

   b. $5(\cos 30° + i \sin 30°)$ **f.** $6.2(\cos 180° + i \sin 180°)$

   c. $10(\cos 120° + i \sin 120°)$ **g.** $\frac{1}{2}(\cos 0° + i \sin 0°)$

   d. $4\sqrt{2} (\cos 300° + i \sin 300°)$ **h.** $7.8(\cos 270° + i \sin 270°)$

3. Express the conjugate of each of the following complex numbers in polar form.

   a. $\cos 80° + i \sin 80°$ **d.** $3(\cos 70° + i \sin 70°)$

   b. $\cos (-40°) + i \sin (-40°)$ **e.** $\sqrt{2}[\cos (-130°) + i \sin (-130°)]$

   c. $\cos 110° - i \sin 110°$ **f.** $4(\cos 20° - i \sin 20°)$

4. Express each of the following complex numbers in two other polar forms by using different arguments.

   a. $4(\cos 20° + i \sin 20°)$ **c.** $5[\cos (-10°) + i \sin (-10°)]$

   b. $3(\cos 200° + i \sin 200°)$ **d.** $2(\cos 110° + i \sin 110°)$

5. Express each product in polar form.

   a. $2(\cos 40° + i \sin 40°) \cdot 7(\cos 130° + i \sin 130°)$

   b. $\frac{1}{3}(\cos 100° + i \sin 100°) \cdot 12(\cos 160° + i \sin 160°)$

   c. $2\sqrt{3}[\cos(-20°) + i \sin(-20°)] \cdot 3\sqrt{5}(\cos 100° + i \sin 100°)$

   d. $1.2[\cos(-110°) + i \sin(-110°)] \cdot 12(\cos 105° + i \sin 105°)$

6. Express each quotient in polar form.

   a. $\dfrac{8(\cos 140° + i \sin 140°)}{2(\cos 40° + i \sin 40°)}$

   c. $\dfrac{6[\cos(-20°) + i \sin(-20°)]}{\sqrt{3}[\cos(-220°) + i \sin(-220°)]}$

   b. $\dfrac{3(\cos 75° + i \sin 75°)}{6(\cos 287° + i \sin 287°)}$

   d. $\dfrac{10}{4(\cos 53° + i \sin 53°)}$

7. Express each power in polar form.

   a. $[4(\cos 23° + i \sin 23°)]^3$

   b. $[\sqrt{5}(\cos 110° + i \sin 110°)]^4$

   c. $\left[\dfrac{1}{2}\left(\cos(-20°) + i \sin(-20°)\right)\right]^5$

   d. $[2\sqrt{3}(\cos 300° + i \sin 300°)]^6$

8. Repeat Exercise 16 on page 235, but this time use polar form in raising x to the various powers.

9. Construct the complex number $z_1 = 2(\cos 35° + i \sin 35°)$ by constructing an angle of 35° in standard position and plotting z_1 on the terminal side so that $|z_1| = 2$. In a similar manner, construct $z_2 = \frac{7}{2}(\cos 75° + i \sin 75°)$. Then construct $z_1 \cdot z_2$ by the technique shown in Figure 9–7.

10. Prove that $[r(\cos u° + i \sin u°)]^2 \equiv r^2(\cos 2u° + i \sin 2u°)$, thereby verifying de Moivre's Theorem for the case $n = 2$.

11. Prove $[r(\cos u° + i \sin u°)]^{-1} \equiv \frac{1}{r}[\cos(-u°) + i \sin(-u°)] \equiv \frac{1}{r}(\cos u° - i \sin u°)$,

   $r \neq 0$.   Hint: $[r(\cos u° + i \sin u°)]^{-1} \equiv \dfrac{1}{r(\cos u° + i \sin u°)}$.

12. Use the theorem of Exercise 11 to express each of the following in polar form.

   a. $[2(\cos 40° + i \sin 40°)]^{-1}$

   b. $\left[\dfrac{1}{4}(\cos 15° + i \sin 15°)\right]^{-3}$

   c. $[r(\cos u° + i \sin u°)]^{-n}$, for any natural number n.

   d. $\dfrac{1}{\cos 3u° - i \sin 3u°}$

   e. $\dfrac{\cos 2u° + i \sin 2u°}{\cos 5u° - i \sin 5u°}$

13. Given $z = \cos \theta + i \sin \theta$, it follows by de Moivre's Theorem that

$$z^3 \equiv \cos 3\theta + i \sin 3\theta$$

Using rectangular notation and multiplying, we find also that

$$
\begin{aligned}
z^3 &\equiv (\cos \theta + i \sin \theta)^2(\cos \theta + i \sin \theta) \\
&\equiv (\cos^2 \theta - \sin^2 \theta + 2i \cos \theta \sin \theta)(\cos \theta + i \sin \theta) \\
&\equiv \cos^3 \theta - 3 \cos \theta \sin^2 \theta + i\,(3 \cos^2 \theta \sin \theta - \sin^3 \theta)
\end{aligned}
$$

Since $a + bi = c + di$ if and only if $a = c$ and $b = d$, it follows that

$$\cos 3\theta \equiv \cos^3 \theta - 3 \cos \theta \sin^2 \theta$$
$$\sin 3\theta \equiv 3 \cos^2 \theta \sin \theta - \sin^3 \theta$$

In a similar manner, derive identities which express $\cos 4\theta$ and $\sin 4\theta$ in terms of $\cos \theta$ and $\sin \theta$.

ROOTS OF A COMPLEX NUMBER

Recall that an argument of a complex number is not unique. For example, the complex number $4\sqrt{2} + 4\sqrt{2}i$ has other polar forms, some of which are

$$8(\cos 45° + i \sin 45°) \qquad\qquad 8(\cos 765° + i \sin 765°)$$
$$8(\cos 405° + i \sin 405°) \qquad\qquad 8(\cos 1125° + i \sin 1125°)$$

We shall now use the above polar forms of $4\sqrt{2} + 4\sqrt{2}i$ to determine z_1, z_2 and z_3, the three distinct cube roots of $4\sqrt{2} + 4\sqrt{2}i$. Let $r(\cos u° + i \sin u°)$ be a cube root of $4\sqrt{2} + 4\sqrt{2}i$. Then, by de Moivre's Theorem,

$$
\begin{aligned}
z_1{}^3 &= [r_1(\cos u_1° + i \sin u_1°)]^3 = 8(\cos 45° + i \sin 45°) \\
z_2{}^3 &= [r_2(\cos u_2° + i \sin u_2°)]^3 = 8(\cos 405° + i \sin 405°) \\
z_3{}^3 &= [r_3(\cos u_3° + i \sin u_3°)]^3 = 8(\cos 765° + i \sin 765°)
\end{aligned}
$$

It follows that three distinct cube roots of $4\sqrt{2} + 4\sqrt{2}i$ are

$$
\begin{aligned}
z_1 &= r_1(\cos u_1° + i \sin u_1°) = 2(\cos 15° + i \sin 15°) \\
z_2 &= r_2(\cos u_2° + i \sin u_2°) = 2(\cos 135° + i \sin 135°) \\
z_3 &= r_3(\cos u_3° + i \sin u_3°) = 2(\cos 255° + i \sin 255°)
\end{aligned}
$$

Observe that these three cube roots of $4\sqrt{2} + 4\sqrt{2}i$ are distinct, since no two have arguments differing by an integral multiple of $360°$.

You might suspect that there is a fourth cube root, z_4, of $4\sqrt{2} + 4\sqrt{2}i$. If we let

$$z_4{}^3 = [r_4(\cos u_4° + i \sin u_4°)]^3 = 8(\cos 1125° + i \sin 1125°),$$

it follows that

$$z_4 = r_4(\cos u_4° + i \sin u_4°) = 2(\cos 375° + i \sin 375°).$$

But

$$z_4 = z_1 \text{ since } 2(\cos 375° + i \sin 375°) = 2(\cos 15° + i \sin 15°).$$

It can be shown that each non-zero complex number z has n distinct nth roots, where n is any natural number greater than 1.

The graphs of the three cube roots of $4\sqrt{2} + 4\sqrt{2}i$ are related geometrically to the graph of $4\sqrt{2} + 4\sqrt{2}i$. Observe in Figure 9–8 that

1. $|4\sqrt{2} + 4\sqrt{2}i| = 8$ and the graphs of the cube roots are located on a circle of radius $\sqrt[3]{8}$ with center at the origin.
2. The graphs of the three cube roots separate the circle into three congruent arcs, each of 120°.
3. An argument of $4\sqrt{2} + 4\sqrt{2}i$ is 45° and, hence, an argument of one cube root is 45° ÷ 3, or 15°. Thus, arguments of the other cube roots are 15° + 120° and 15° + 2 · 120°.

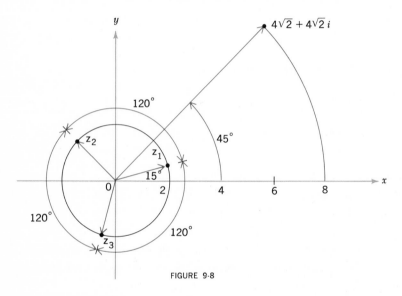

FIGURE 9-8

Verify that, in general,

$$\left(\sqrt[n]{r} \left[\cos \left(\frac{u + 360k}{n} \right)^{\circ} + i \sin \left(\frac{u + 360k}{n} \right)^{\circ} \right] \right)^{n}$$
$$= r[\cos (u + 360k)^{\circ} + i \sin (u + 360k)^{\circ}]$$
$$= r(\cos u^{\circ} + i \sin u^{\circ})$$

Hence, the numbers

$$\sqrt[n]{r} \left[\cos \left(\frac{u + 360k}{n} \right)^{\circ} + i \sin \left(\frac{u + 360k}{n} \right)^{\circ} \right]$$

are the n distinct nth roots of $r(\cos u^{\circ} + i \sin u^{\circ})$ where k is any integer and n is a natural number ($n > 1$). For example, the four distinct fourth roots of $r(\cos u^{\circ} + i \sin u^{\circ})$ are given by

$$\sqrt[4]{r} \left[\cos \left(\frac{u + 360k}{4} \right)^{\circ} + i \sin \left(\frac{u + 360k}{4} \right)^{\circ} \right]$$

where k assumes the values 0, 1, 2, and 3.

In summary these four distinct fourth roots are

$$\sqrt[4]{r}\left(\cos\frac{u°}{4} + i\sin\frac{u°}{4}\right) \qquad (k = 0)$$

$$\sqrt[4]{r}\left[\cos\left(\frac{u}{4} + 90\right)° + i\sin\left(\frac{u}{4} + 90\right)°\right] \qquad (k = 1)$$

$$\sqrt[4]{r}\left[\cos\left(\frac{u}{4} + 180\right)° + i\sin\left(\frac{u}{4} + 180\right)°\right] \qquad (k = 2)$$

$$\sqrt[4]{r}\left[\cos\left(\frac{u}{4} + 270\right)° + i\sin\left(\frac{u}{4} + 270\right)°\right] \qquad (k = 3)$$

Observe that

$$\sqrt[4]{r}\left[\cos\left(\frac{u}{4} + 360\right)° + i\sin\left(\frac{u}{4} + 360\right)°\right] \qquad (k = 4)$$

is equal to the first fourth root found above. In general, by letting k assume the values 0, 1, 2, ..., $n - 1$, we determine the n distinct nth roots of $r(\cos u° + i\sin u°)$. The following example illustrates the solution of a typical problem.

Example   Determine the 5 fifth roots of $-2 + 2\sqrt{3}i$.

First, we determine a polar form of $-2 + 2\sqrt{3}i$.
$$-2 + 2\sqrt{3}i = 4(\cos 120° + i\sin 120°)$$
The 5 fifth roots of $4(\cos 120° + i\sin 120°)$ are given by
$$\sqrt[5]{4}\left[\cos\left(\frac{120 + 360k}{5}\right)° + i\sin\left(\frac{120 + 360k}{5}\right)°\right]$$
where k assumes the values 0, 1, 2, 3, and 4. Hence, the 5 fifth roots of $-2 + 2\sqrt{3}i$ are

$\sqrt[5]{4}\ (\cos 24° + i\sin 24°)$ $\sqrt[5]{4}\ (\cos 240° + i\sin 240°)$

$\sqrt[5]{4}\ (\cos 96° + i\sin 96°)$ $\sqrt[5]{4}\ (\cos 312° + i\sin 312°)$

$\sqrt[5]{4}\ (\cos 168° + i\sin 168°)$

Alternate Solution   First we determine a polar form of $-2 + 2\sqrt{3}i$.
$$-2 + 2\sqrt{3}i = 4(\cos 120° + i\sin 120°)$$
Then we seek a complex number $r(\cos u° + i\sin u°)$ for which
$$[r(\cos u° + i\sin u°)]^5 = 4(\cos 120° + i\sin 120°)$$
By de Moivre's Theorem, it is obvious that $\sqrt[5]{4}\ (\cos 24° + i\sin 24°)$ is one fifth root of $-2 + 2\sqrt{3}i$. Since the 5 fifth roots are distributed uniformly on a circle, we know that consecutive arguments differ by 360° ÷ 5 or 72°. Hence, the remaining arguments are $(24 + 72)°$, $(24 + 2 \cdot 72)°$, $(24 + 3 \cdot 72)°$ and $(24 + 4 \cdot 72)°$. Thus the four other fifth roots are

$\sqrt[5]{4}\ (\cos 96° + i\sin 96°)$ $\sqrt[5]{4}\ (\cos 240° + i\sin 240°)$

$\sqrt[5]{4}\ (\cos 168° + i\sin 168°)$ $\sqrt[5]{4}\ (\cos 312° + i\sin 312°)$

EXERCISES

1. Find the four fourth roots of each of the following. Express all roots in both polar and rectangular forms.

   a. $16(\cos 120° + i \sin 120°)$ **c.** -16

   b. $-3 - 3\sqrt{3}i$ **d.** $81i$

2. Find the five fifth roots of each of the following. Express each root in polar form.

   a. $32(\cos 135° + i \sin 135°)$ **c.** i

   b. $-4\sqrt{3} + 4i$ **d.** -32

3. Determine the three cube roots of each of the following. Express each root in both polar and rectangular forms.

   a. 27 **c.** $2(\cos 100° + i \sin 100°)$

   b. $-8i$ **d.** -1

4. Determine all complex number solutions of each equation.

   a. $z^3 = 8$

   b. $z^3 - 1 = 0$ **f.** $z^2 + 16 = 0$

   c. $z^4 = i$ **g.** $z^2 = -3\sqrt{3} + 3i$

   d. $z^4 - 16 = 0$ **h.** $z^3 + 4i = 4\sqrt{3}$

   e. $z^5 + i = 0$ **i.** $z^4 + 8 + 8\sqrt{3}i = 0$

5. Verify that $\dfrac{-1 + i\sqrt{3}}{2}$ is a cube root of 1 by computing the third power of $\dfrac{-1 + i\sqrt{3}}{2}$. What are the other two cube roots of 1?

6. Study Figure 9–8. Then construct each of the following.

   a. $\dfrac{81}{16}(\cos 120° + i \sin 120°)$ and each of its fourth roots

   b. $8i$ and each of its cube roots

VOCABULARY

Use each of the following correctly in a sentence to demonstrate that you understand its meaning. If you are not sure of the meaning of any word, refer back to the chapter.

absolute value of complex number   de Moivre's Theorem
argument of complex number   graph of complex number
complex number   polar form of complex number
conjugate of a complex number   rectangular form of complex number

REVIEW EXERCISES

1. Compute and express the results in rectangular form.

   a. $(3 - 5i) + (2 + 6i)$

   b. $\left(-2\frac{1}{2} - 3i\right) + \left(\frac{2}{3} - 3i\right)$

   c. $(2\sqrt{3} - \sqrt{5}i) - (-7\sqrt{3} - 2\sqrt{5}i)$

   d. $-6i - (4 + 2i)$

   e. $(3 - 2i)(-4 + 3i)$

   f. $7i(2 - 3i)$

   g. $\dfrac{3 + 2i}{4 - 2i}$

   h. $\dfrac{5 - 4i}{2i}$

   i. i^{27}

   j. $(4 - 3i)^2$

   k. $(\sqrt{5} - 3i)(\sqrt{5} + 3i)$

2. Plot $z_1 = 5 + 4i$ and $z_2 = 6 - 3i$ on a coordinate plane and construct the sum of z_1 and z_2 by the parallelogram method.

3. For each of the following complex numbers, determine (1) the absolute value, (2) an argument, and (3) the conjugate of the number.

   a. $-6\sqrt{3} - 6i$

   b. $-4i$

   c. $-5\sqrt{2} + 5\sqrt{2}i$

   d. $3 - 4i$

   e. $3(\cos 60° + i \sin 60°)$

   f. $2(\cos 45° - i \sin 45°)$

4. Simplify.

   a. $\sqrt{-16}$

   b. $\sqrt{-8} - \sqrt{-18}$

   c. $\sqrt{-3} \cdot \sqrt{-12}$

   d. $\dfrac{-10 - \sqrt{-50}}{15}$

5. Solve each equation for its complex number solutions.

   a. $z^2 + 7 = 0$

   b. $z^2 + z + 1 = 0$

   c. $z^3 = 64$

   d. $z^4 = -16$

6. Express each of the following in polar form.

   a. $-7 + 7i$

   b. $-9 - 9\sqrt{3}i$

   c. $-5i$

   d. 6

   e. $\cos 35° - i \sin 35°$

   f. $2(\cos 40° - i \sin 40°)$

7. Express each of the following in rectangular form.

   a. $4\sqrt{2}(\cos 315° + i \sin 315°)$

   b. $6.4(\cos 150° + i \sin 150°)$

   c. $\frac{1}{8}(\cos 90° + i \sin 90°)$

   d. $\sqrt{5}(\cos 180° + i \sin 180°)$

8. List three polar forms of the complex number $\dfrac{-\sqrt{2}}{2} - \dfrac{\sqrt{6}}{2}i$.

9. Express each product in polar form.

   a. $5\sqrt{2}(\cos 140° + i \sin 140°) \cdot 3\sqrt{2}(\cos 80° + i \sin 80°)$

   b. $\frac{1}{8}[\cos (-50°) + i \sin (-50°)] \cdot 1.6(\cos 40° + i \sin 40°)$

10. Express each quotient in polar form.

   a. $\dfrac{4(\cos 12° + i \sin 12°)}{6(\cos 36° + i \sin 36°)}$

   b. $\dfrac{2.4[\cos (-37°) + i \sin (-37°)]}{1.8(\cos 59° + i \sin 59°)}$

   c. $\dfrac{\cos 2u° + i \sin 2u°}{(\cos 3u° + i \sin 3u°)(\cos 4u° - i \sin 4u°)}$

   d. $\dfrac{2}{\cos 20° + i \sin 20°}$

11. Express each power in polar form.

   a. $[\sqrt{5}(\cos 14° + i \sin 14°)]^4$

   b. $[3\sqrt{7}(\cos 22° + i \sin 22°)]^3$

   c. $[\sqrt{2}(\cos 10° + i \sin 10°)]^{-4}$

   d. $[2(\cos 120° + i \sin 120°)]^3$

12. Determine the five fifth roots of each of the following complex numbers.

   a. $-16 + 16\sqrt{3}i$

   b. $5(\cos 225° + i \sin 225°)$

   c. $3i$

   d. -1

13. Express the three cube roots of $-8i$ in rectangular form.

14. Express the sixth power of $1 - i\sqrt{3}$ in polar form.

15. In which quadrant is the graph of the conjugate of $2 - 3i$?

16. In which quadrant is the graph of the conjugate of $3(\cos 140° + i \sin 140°)$?

17. Use de Moivre's Theorem to derive identities which express $\cos 2\theta$ and $\sin 2\theta$ in terms of $\sin \theta$ and $\cos \theta$.

CHAPTER TEST

1. Determine (1) the absolute value, (2) an argument, and (3) the conjugate of each of the following complex numbers.

   a. $\sqrt{2} - \sqrt{2}i$

   b. -7

   c. $3i$

   d. $4(\cos 30° - i \sin 30°)$

2. Compute each of the following and express the result in polar form.

   a. $6(\cos 39° + i \sin 39°) \cdot \frac{1}{2}(\cos 72° + i \sin 72°)$

   b. $\dfrac{8(\cos 27° + i \sin 27°)}{4(\cos 63° + i \sin 63°)}$

   c. $[2\sqrt{3}(\cos 11° + i \sin 11°)]^3$

   d. $[\sqrt{3}(\cos 25° + i \sin 25°)]^{-2}$

3. Compute each of the following and express the result in rectangular form.

   a. $(5 - 4i) + (-2 + i)$

   b. $(-2\sqrt{3} + 4i) - (3\sqrt{3} - 2i)$

   c. $(5 - 3i)(3 + 4i)$

   d. $\dfrac{2 + 3i}{3 - 4i}$

   e. $(4 - 2i)^2$

4. Simplify.

   a. i^{18}

   b. $\sqrt{-25}$

   c. $\sqrt{-40} + \sqrt{-90}$

   d. $\sqrt{-8} \cdot \sqrt{-2}$

   e. $\dfrac{-9 - \sqrt{-45}}{6}$

5. Solve each equation for its complex number solutions.

   a. $z^2 + 5 = 0$

   b. $z^2 + 3z + 3 = 0$

   c. $z^3 = -8$

   d. $z^4 = -16$

6. Determine a polar form of $\dfrac{3}{2} - \dfrac{\sqrt{3}}{2}i$.

7. What is the rectangular form of $4\sqrt{2}(\cos 300° + i \sin 300°)$?

8. Determine the three cube roots of $3(\cos 27° + i \sin 27°)$.

9. Determine the four fourth roots of $-2 + 2\sqrt{3}i$.

10. Express the fourth power of $2\sqrt{2} + 2\sqrt{2}i$ in polar form.

CHAPTER 10

TRIANGLES AND VECTORS

RIGHT TRIANGLES

The subject of trigonometry began over two thousand years ago. It was invented for the purpose of *solving triangles*. In fact, the word "trigonometry" is derived from Greek words which mean "triangle measurement." To solve a triangle means to determine the measures of all of its angles and sides.

We shall first learn to solve *right triangles*. When discussing right triangle *ABC*, ∠*C* is the right angle unless stated otherwise (see Figure 10–1). We now review some vocabulary concerning right triangle *ABC*.

1. $\overline{AB}$, the longest side, is called the *hypotenuse*.

2. $\overline{BC}$ is the leg *adjacent* to *B* and *opposite* to *A*.

3. $\overline{AC}$ is the leg adjacent to *A* and opposite to *B*.

4. The measures of the sides opposite the vertices *A*, *B*, and *C* are given by *a*, *b*, and *c*, respectively.

5. Angles *A* and *B* are *complementary;* that is, $m\angle A + m\angle B = 90°$. Why?

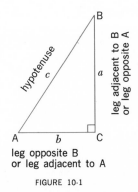

FIGURE 10-1

For the purpose of solving right triangles, the trigonometric functions of acute angle measures are defined as follows. Given right triangle *ABC* as shown in Figure 10–2 with ∠*A* *in standard position,*

$$\sin m \angle A = \frac{a}{c} \qquad \csc m \angle A = \frac{c}{a}$$

$$\cos m \angle A = \frac{b}{c} \qquad \sec m \angle A = \frac{c}{b}$$

$$\tan m \angle A = \frac{a}{b} \qquad \cot m \angle A = \frac{b}{a}$$

FIGURE 10-2

These definitions are more easily recalled and applied in the following form.

$$\sin m \angle A = \frac{\text{length of opposite leg}}{\text{length of hypotenuse}}$$

$$\cos m \angle A = \frac{\text{length of adjacent leg}}{\text{length of hypotenuse}}$$

$$\tan m \angle A = \frac{\text{length of opposite leg}}{\text{length of adjacent leg}}$$

Observe that, for $\angle B$ of right triangle ABC, the following are true.

$$\sin m \angle B = \frac{b}{c} \qquad\qquad \csc m \angle B = \frac{c}{b}$$

$$\cos m \angle B = \frac{a}{c} \qquad\qquad \sec m \angle B = \frac{c}{a}$$

$$\tan m \angle B = \frac{b}{a} \qquad\qquad \cot m \angle B = \frac{a}{b}$$

Hence, for right triangle ABC,

$$\sin m \angle A = \cos m \angle B \qquad \sec m \angle A = \csc m \angle B \qquad \tan m \angle A = \cot m \angle B$$

You should recall the above as a special case of the complementary angles relation derived in Chapter 6.

EXERCISES

1. For the triangle KLM pictured at the right, determine the following values.

   a. $\sin m \angle K$ **e.** $\sec m \angle K$

   b. $\cos m \angle K$ **f.** $\cot m \angle K$

   c. $\tan m \angle K$ **g.** $\sin m \angle L$

   d. $\csc m \angle K$ **h.** $\cos m \angle L$

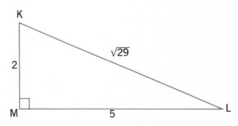

2. For the triangle XYZ pictured at the right, determine the following values.

   a. $\sin m \angle X$ **e.** $\sin m \angle Y$

   b. $\cos m \angle X$ **f.** $\cos m \angle Y$

   c. $\tan m \angle X$ **g.** $\tan m \angle Y$

   d. $\cot m \angle X$ **h.** $\cot m \angle Y$

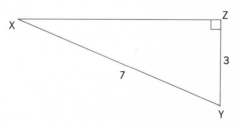

3. Construct a right triangle ABC with $m \angle A = 45°$ and $AC = 4$. Determine the following.

   a. sin 45°   **b.** csc 45°   **c.** cos 45°   **d.** sec 45°   **e.** tan 45°   **f.** cot 45°

4. Construct a right triangle ABC with $m \angle A = 30°$ and $BC = 4$. Determine the following.

   a. sin 30°   **c.** tan 30°   **e.** sec 30°   **g.** sin 60°   **i.** tan 60°   **k.** sec 60°

   b. cos 30°   **d.** csc 30°   **f.** cot 30°   **h.** cos 60°   **j.** csc 60°   **l.** cot 60°

5. For the two right triangles ABC and $AB'C'$, shown at the right, prove that (1) $m \angle B = m \angle B'$ and (2) sin $m \angle B =$ sin $m \angle B'$. Does this show that the value of the sine function depends upon the measure of the angle and not upon the lengths of the sides of the right triangle?

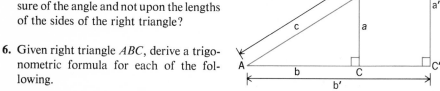

6. Given right triangle ABC, derive a trigonometric formula for each of the following.

   Example Find b in terms of tan $m \angle A$ and a.

   Solution By definition, tan $m \angle A = \dfrac{a}{b}$. Hence, $b = \dfrac{a}{\tan m \angle A}$.

   a. a in terms of sin $m \angle A$ and c **b.** c in terms of cos $m \angle A$ and b

SOLVING RIGHT TRIANGLES

A right triangle is uniquely determined if the measures of either (1) two sides or (2) an acute angle and one side are given. In either case, the remaining parts of the triangle may be determined by using an appropriate trigonometric function and Table III.

     The computed measure of a side or angle of a triangle should be no more accurate than the least accurate given measurement (see Appendix A, pages 290–292). If sin $u°$ is given as .352, accurate to three significant digits, we know that $.3515 <$ sin $u° < .3525$. Hence, we can only tell that $u°$ is in the interval $20°35' < u° < 20°39'$ (see Table III). In this case, we say that $u°$ is $20°40'$, accurate to the nearest 10 minutes. In a similar manner, it can be shown that (except for $u°$ near 0° or 90°) the accuracy of $u°$ is determined by the accuracy of the measured sides of a triangle. This relation is given by the following table.

measures of angles are accurate to the	if measures of sides are accurate to
nearest degree	2 digits
nearest 10 minutes	3 digits
nearest minute	4 digits

Study the following examples which illustrate the solution of right triangles to the degree of accuracy justified by the given data.

Example 1   Solve the triangle shown at the right. Data are given to three significant digits.

Solution   (1) Solving for a, $\tan 68°20' \doteq \dfrac{a}{3.42}$

$a \doteq 3.42 \times \tan 68°21' \doteq 3.42 \times 2.517$
$\doteq 8.61$, accurate to three digits

(2) Solving for c, $\cos 68°20' \doteq \dfrac{3.42}{c}$

$c \doteq \dfrac{3.42}{\cos 68°20'} \doteq \dfrac{3.42}{.3692} \doteq 9.26$

(3) Solving for $m \angle B$,
$m \angle B \doteq 90° - 68°20' = 21°40'$, accurate to the nearest 10 minutes

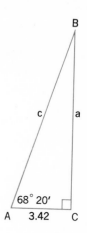

Example 2   Solve the triangle shown at the right. Data are given to two significant digits.

Solution   (1) Solving for $m \angle A$,

$\cos m \angle A \doteq \dfrac{27}{32} \doteq .84$

$m \angle A \doteq 33°$, accurate to the nearest degree

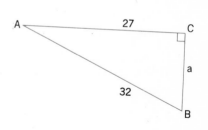

(2) Solving for $m \angle B$,
$m \angle B \doteq 90° - 33° = 57°$, accurate to the nearest degree

(3) Solving for a, $\sin 33° \doteq \dfrac{a}{32}$

$a \doteq 32 \times \sin 33° \doteq 32 \times .545 \doteq 17$, accurate to two digits
Determine a using the Pythagorean Relation. Compare the result with the above.

Example 3   Solve the triangle shown at the right.

Solution   (1) Solving for a, $\cos 39°10' \doteq \dfrac{a}{54.3}$

$a \doteq 54.3 \times \cos 39°10'$
$\doteq 54.3 \times .7753 \doteq 42.1$

(2) Solving for b, $\sin 39°10' \doteq \dfrac{b}{54.3}$

$b \doteq 54.3 \times \sin 39°10'$
$\doteq 54.3 \times .6316 \doteq 34.3$

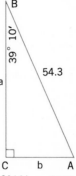

(3) Solving for $m \angle A$, $m \angle A \doteq 90° - 39°10' = 50°50'$

EXERCISES

1. Solve each equation for the specified variable.

   a. $\cos m\angle A = \dfrac{b}{c}$; for b; for c **b.** $\tan m\angle A = \dfrac{a}{b}$; for a; for b

2. For each right triangle ABC, tell the accuracy of the measures of the sides and angles which would be justified by the given data.

   a. $a = 4.26$, $m\angle B = 53°20'$ **c.** $m\angle A = 39°24'$, $b = 1724$

   b. $a = 27.9$, $b = 43.62$ **d.** $a = 2.73$, $m\angle B = 14°17'$

3. Solve each right triangle below to the degree of accuracy warranted by the given data.

a.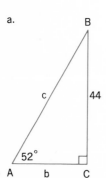

b.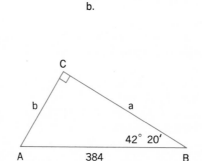

c.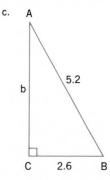

4. For the rectangular solid shown at the right below determine the measures of the following angles to the nearest 10 minutes.

   a. $\angle BGC$

   b. $\angle CHG$

   c. $\angle BDC$

   d. $\angle BHD$

   e. $\angle AGD$

   f. $\angle AGE$

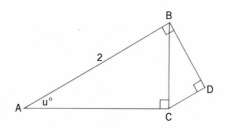

5. For right triangle ABC, it is known that $AB = 1$ and that $30° \le m\angle A \le 60°$. What are the possible values of BC?

6. For the accompanying figure,

   $\overline{AB} \parallel \overline{CD}$
   $\overline{BC} \perp \overline{AC}$
   $\overline{BD} \perp \overline{CD}$
   $AB = 2$
   $m\angle BAC = u°$

   Prove that $CD = 2 \sin^2 u°$

SOLVING RIGHT TRIANGLES BY LOGARITHMS

The computing of products and quotients while solving triangles may be accomplished by using logarithms. Appendix C is a review of computation using logarithms and should be studied before proceeding further in this section. We use Table IV to determine log x for x accurate to either three or four significant digits and Table V to determine the logarithm of a trigonometric function of $u°$, where $u°$ is accurate to either the nearest 10 minutes or nearest minute.

A portion of Table V is reproduced in Figure 10–3. In Table V, as in Table III, degree measures from 0° to 45° in multiples of 10′ are given in the left-hand column and used with headings at the top of the other columns. The right-hand column of degree measures from 45° to 90° is read *from bottom to top* and used with headings *at the bottom* of the other columns.

degrees	log sin	log cos	log tan	log cot	
32°0′	9.7242	9.9284	9.7958	10.2042	58°0′
10′	.7262	.9276	.7986	.2014	50′
20′	.7282	.9268	.8014	.1986	40′
30′	.7302	.9260	.8042	.1958	30′
40′	.7322	.9252	.8070	.1930	20′
50′	.7342	.9244	.8097	.1903	10′
33°0′	9.7361	9.9236	9.8125	10.1875	57°0′
10′	.7380	.9228	.8153	.1847	50′
	log cos	log sin	log cot	log tan	degrees

Figure 10–3

Observe that 10 is to be subtracted from each entry for a logarithm. Why? Thus,

$$\log \sin 32°0′ \doteq 9.7242 - 10 = -1 + .7242$$
$$\log \cos 32°20′ \doteq 9.9268 - 10 = -1 + .9268$$
$$\log \sin 57°20′ \doteq 9.9252 - 10 = -1 + .9252$$
$$\log \tan 57°40′ \doteq 10.1986 - 10 = 0 + .1986$$

Check each of the above readings in Figure 10–3.

The following examples illustrate the use of Tables IV and V in solving right triangles for specified parts.

Example 1   If $\tan 68°20′ \doteq \dfrac{43.9}{b}$ determine b, accurate to three digits.

Solution
$$b \doteq \frac{43.9}{\tan 68°20′}$$
$$\log b \doteq \log 43.9 - \log \tan 68°20′$$
$$\doteq (1 + .6425) - (10.4009 - 10) \qquad \text{[Tables IV, V]}$$
$$\doteq (1 + .6425) - (0 + .4009)$$
$$= 1 + .2416$$
$$b \doteq 17.4 \qquad\qquad\qquad\qquad\qquad \text{[Table IV]}$$

Example 2   If $\sin m \angle A \doteq \dfrac{32.46}{37.19}$ determine $m \angle A$, accurate to the nearest minute.

Solution $\log \sin m \angle A \doteq \log 32.46 - \log 37.19$

$\qquad\qquad \doteq (1 + .5113) - (1 + .5704)$ [Interpolating in Table IV]

$\qquad\qquad = (0 + 1.5113) -$ [The first expression is
$\qquad\qquad\qquad (1 + .5704)$ regrouped so that the
$\qquad\qquad = -1 + .9409$ mantissa will be positive
$\qquad\qquad = 9.9409 - 10$ after subtracting.]
$\qquad m \angle A \doteq 60°47'$ [Interpolating in Table V]

EXERCISES

1. Use Table V to determine the logarithm of each of the following.

   a. $\sin 39°40'$ c. $\tan 41°50'$ e. $\sin 72°50'$ g. $\tan 58°40'$

   b. $\cos 24°10'$ d. $\cot 17°30'$ f. $\cos 63°20'$ h. $\cot 77°20'$

2. Tell the characteristic of each logarithm in Exercise 1.

3. Determine $u°$ in the interval $0° < u° < 90°$, accurate to the nearest ten minutes, for the following equations.

   a. $\log \sin u° \doteq 9.6644 - 10$ e. $\log \sin u° \doteq 9.9512 - 10$

   b. $\log \cos u° \doteq 9.9361 - 10$ f. $\log \cos u° \doteq 9.7282 - 10$

   c. $\log \tan u° \doteq 9.9341 - 10$ g. $\log \tan u° \doteq 10.1046 - 10$

   d. $\log \cot u° \doteq 10.5473 - 10$ h. $\log \cot u° \doteq 9.7902 - 10$

4. Use Table V and interpolate to determine the following, accurate to four decimal places.

   a. $\log \sin 32°27'$ b. $\log \cos 18°43'$ c. $\log \tan 43°12'$ d. $\log \cot 20°38'$

5. Use Table V and interpolate to determine $u°$ in the interval $0° < u° < 90°$, accurate to the nearest minute, for the following equations.

   a. $\log \sin u° \doteq 9.7426 - 10$ c. $\log \tan u° \doteq 9.8659 - 10$

   b. $\log \cos u° \doteq 9.8825 - 10$ d. $\log \cot u° \doteq 10.4260 - 10$

6. Use logarithms to solve each right triangle ABC for the part indicated and to the degree of accuracy justified by the given data. Sketch a triangle for each exercise.

   a. $m \angle A = 28°40'$, $a = .574$; determine b, determine c

   b. $m \angle B = 56°20'$, $c = 43.8$; determine a, determine b

   c. $a = 1236$, $c = 1822$; determine $m \angle B$, determine b

APPLICATIONS

The solving of triangles is a simple but important application of the trigono-metric functions. It provides a means for the *indirect measurement* of segments or angles. In this section we consider some typical problems involving indirect measurement.

Consider the problem of determining the height above ground of a spout on a railroad company's water tower (see Figure 10–4). Supposing that it is not convenient to climb the tower, we measure along the level ground from D to E and find that $DE \doteq 84.5$ feet. Using a *sextant* to measure $\angle CAB$, the *angle of elevation* to the spout, we determine that $m \angle CAB \doteq 37°20'$. Solving right triangle ABC for BC, we compute that $BC \doteq 64.4$ feet. Knowing that our eye level (at A) is 5 feet above the ground, we conclude that the spout is approximately 69.4 feet above the ground.

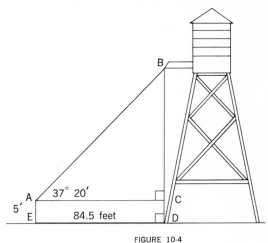

FIGURE 10-4

Observe that in solving the above problem, we selected and sketched a right triangle that suited the conditions of the problem. The triangle was then solved for the desired part by techniques shown in the preceding sections. In solving such problems it is best to begin by drawing a figure.

When using a sextant to measure an angle at B in a vertical plane (see Figure 10–5a) by sighting upward to A, the angle KBA is called the *angle of elevation*. If you are at A and sighting downward to B, as in Figure 10–5b, the angle JAB is called the *angle of depression*. Note that in both cases the angle is acute and is formed by a horizontal ray and the *line of sight* from the observer's eye to the sighted object.

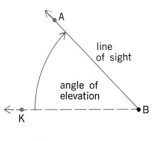

FIGURE 10-5 a

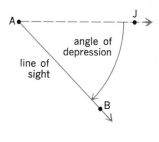

FIGURE 10-5b

In navigation at sea, the direction or *bearing* of a ray along which a ship sails is given by stating the measure of the acute angle which this ray forms with a north-south line. Bearings of N 30° E, N 50° W, S 40° E and S 70° W are shown in the figure below.

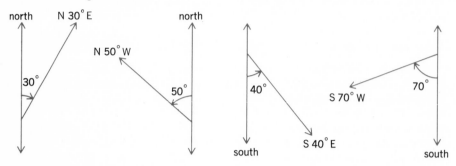

In aerial navigation, the bearing or *course* of a ray along which a plane flies is given by stating the non-negative measure of the angle which this ray forms with a ray due north. Such angles are measured in a clockwise direction. Courses of 40°, 130°, 230°, and 320° are shown in the figure below.

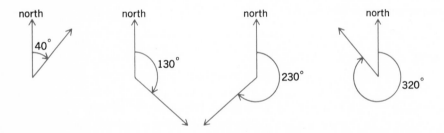

Example   A plane flew a course of 325° for three hours at a speed of 220 mph. How far to the west has it flown?

Solution   The plane has flown a distance of 3 × 220 or 660 miles. We sketch the figure shown at the right and solve for *x*.

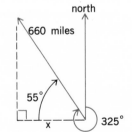

$$\cos 55° = \frac{x}{660}$$
$$x = 660 \cos 55°$$
$$\doteq 379 \text{ miles}$$

EXERCISES

1. A 45-foot ladder must not form an angle greater than 68° with the ground to be considered safe. What is the maximum height such a ladder will safely reach on a wall?

2. In Exercise 1, how far from the wall is a person when he stands at the foot of the ladder?

3. At a point 324 feet from the base of a building, the angle of elevation to the top of the building is 27°40'. Assume that the sextant was held 5 feet above the ground. What is the height of the building?

4. From an airplane flying 2700 feet above sea level the angles of depression to two ships due west are 27° and 19°. Find the distance between the ships.

5. A regular octagon, 6.8 cm. on an edge, is inscribed in a circle. Determine the radius.

6. Two towers are 74 feet apart. From the top of one tower, the angle of depression to the base of the other tower is 42° and the angle of elevation to its top is 23°. What is the height of the taller tower?

7. A tower stands on a horizontal plane. The angle of elevation at a certain point on the plane is 32°. At a point 100 feet nearer the tower the angle of elevation is 47°. How high is the tower?

8. Determine the area of a regular octagon inscribed in a circle of radius 12.

9. Determine the measures of the following angles to the nearest 10 minutes for the pyramid shown at the right with rectangular base *ABCD*.

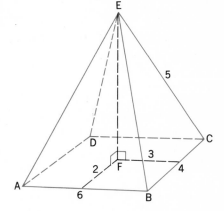

a. ∠*ADB*	**d.** ∠*BEC*
b. ∠*BEF*	**e.** ∠*ABE*
c. ∠*CBE*	**f.** ∠*AEB*

10. From *A*, a pilot is to fly a course at 90° for 400 miles to *B*. From *B*, he is to fly to *C* which is 600 miles north of *A*. Determine the direction of his course from *B* to *C*.

11. From *A*, a pilot flew a course at 65° for 340 miles to *B*. From *B*, he flew a course at 155° for 610 miles to *C*. What is the direction and distance of a flight from *C* to *A*?

12. From *A*, a ship sailed S 50° E for 42 nautical miles. At this point it sailed S 40° W for 76 nautical miles. At this point what is its distance and its bearing from *A*?

13. For the figure determine *BC* in each case.

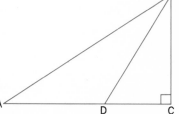

a. $m∠A = 30°$, $AD = 10$, $m∠BDC = 45°$

b. $m∠A = 45°$, $AD = 20$, $m∠BDC = 60°$

c. $m∠A = 30°$, $AD = 10$, $m∠BDC = 60°$

d. $m∠A = u°$, $AD = n$,
  $m∠BDC = v°$ $(u < v)$

14. Given obtuse triangle *ABC* with $AB = BC$ and $m∠C = u°$. Prove $AC = 2(AB) \cos u°$.

OBLIQUE TRIANGLES AND THE LAW OF SINES

In this section we shall discuss the solution of *oblique triangles*, that is, triangles which are not right triangles. Recall from plane geometry that a triangle is uniquely determined if data are given for any of the following cases.

CASE 1   Two angles and one side (*ASA* or *AAS*).

CASE 2   Two sides and the included angle (*SAS*).

CASE 3   Three sides (*SSS*).

CASE 4   Two sides and the angle opposite one of them (*SSA*).

Note: CASE 4 is called the *ambiguous case* since this information may determine no triangle, exactly one triangle, or two triangles.

Our goal is to develop techniques for solving triangles in each of the four cases. To accomplish this, we use two theorems, the *Law of Sines* and the *Law of Cosines*.

LAW OF SINES   For each oblique triangle *ABC*,

$$\frac{a}{\sin m \angle A} = \frac{b}{\sin m \angle B} = \frac{c}{\sin m \angle C}$$

In other words, the measures of sides are proportional to the sines of measures of angles opposite the sides.

PROOF OF LAW OF SINES

Given oblique triangle *ABC*, let *h* be the altitude from *C*. Angle *A* is either acute or obtuse as shown in Figure 10–6. In each case, for right triangle *BCD*, we have

$$\sin m \angle B = \frac{h}{a}$$

and for right triangle *ACD*, we have

$$\sin m \angle A = \frac{h}{b}$$

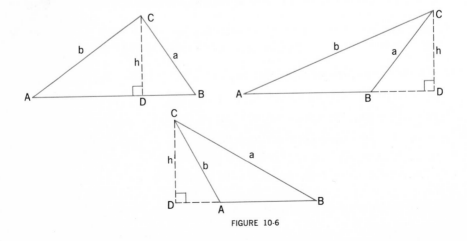

FIGURE 10-6

Hence,

$$h = a \sin m\angle B = b \sin m\angle A.$$

Dividing by $\sin m\angle A \cdot \sin m\angle B$ yields

$$\frac{a}{\sin m\angle A} = \frac{b}{\sin m\angle B}$$

If h were the altitude from B, we would have obtained

$$\frac{a}{\sin m\angle A} = \frac{c}{\sin m\angle C}$$

The last two equations may be written as

$$\frac{a}{\sin m\angle A} = \frac{b}{\sin m\angle B} = \frac{c}{\sin m\angle C}$$

which is the Law of Sines.

The Law of Sines is used to solve triangles for CASE 1 (*ASA* or *AAS*), as illustrated by the following example.

Example   Solve triangle ABC, given $m\angle A = 43°$, $m\angle B = 32°$, and $b = 14$.
(1) To solve for a, we select the appropriate equation from the Law of Sines.

$$\frac{a}{\sin m\angle A} = \frac{b}{\sin m\angle B}$$

$$\frac{a}{\sin 43°} = \frac{14}{\sin 32°}$$

$$a = \frac{14 \sin 43°}{\sin 32°} \doteq \frac{14 \times .684}{.530} \doteq 18$$

(2) solving for $m\angle C$,

$$m\angle C = 180° - (m\angle A + m\angle B)$$
$$\doteq 180° - (43° + 32°) \doteq 105°$$

(3) To solve for c, we select the appropriate equation from the Law of Sines.

$$\frac{c}{\sin m\angle C} = \frac{b}{\sin m\angle B}$$

$$\frac{c}{\sin 105°} = \frac{14}{\sin 32°}$$

$$c = \frac{14 \sin 105°}{\sin 32°} = \frac{14 \sin 75°}{\sin 32°}$$

$$\doteq \frac{14 \times .966}{.530} \doteq 26$$

The Law of Sines is also used to solve triangles for CASE 4 (*SSA*). Given a, b, and $m\angle A$, there may be none, one, or two triangles determined as shown in Figure 10-7. Hence CASE 4 is called the *ambiguous case*.

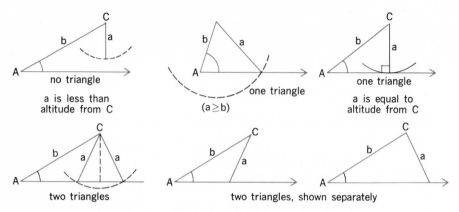

two triangles, shown separately

a is greater than altitude from C but is less than b

FIGURE 10-7

The following examples illustrate the use of the Law of Sines in solving triangles for CASE 4.

Example 1   Solve triangle ABC, given $a = 15$, $b = 24$, and $m \angle A = 43°$

Solution   To solve for $m \angle B$:

$$\frac{15}{\sin 43°} = \frac{24}{\sin m \angle B}$$

$$\sin m \angle B = \frac{24 \sin 43°}{15} \doteq \frac{24 \times .682}{15} \doteq 1.091$$

There is no $\angle B$ for which $\sin m \angle B > 1$. Hence, no triangle is determined by the given data. Which picture in Figure 10–7 illustrates this example?

Example 2   Draw pictures of two triangles, AB_1C_1 and AB_2C_2, for which $m \angle A = 34°$, $a = 17$, and $b = 26$. Then solve both triangles.

Solution

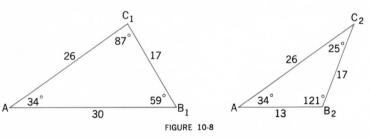

FIGURE 10-8

(1) To solve for $m \angle B$:

$$\frac{17}{\sin 34°} = \frac{26}{\sin m \angle B}$$

$$\sin m \angle B = \frac{26 \sin 34°}{17} \doteq \frac{26 \times .559}{17} \doteq .855$$

There is a first quadrant $\angle B_1$ and a second quadrant $\angle B_2$ for which sin $m \angle B \doteq .855$. Hence,

$$m \angle B_1 \doteq 59° \text{ and } m \angle B_2 \doteq 180° - 59° = 121°$$

and two triangles may possibly be determined.

(2) Solving for $m \angle C$:

$$m \angle C_1 = 180° - (m \angle A + m \angle B_1) \doteq 87°$$
$$m \angle C_2 = 180° - (m \angle A + m \angle B_2) \doteq 25°$$

(3) To solve for c:

$$\frac{17}{\sin 34°} = \frac{c_1}{\sin 87°} \qquad\qquad \frac{17}{\sin 34°} = \frac{c_2}{\sin 25°}$$

$$c_1 = \frac{17 \sin 87°}{\sin 34°} \qquad\qquad c_2 = \frac{17 \sin 25°}{\sin 34°}$$

$$\doteq 30 \qquad\qquad\qquad\qquad \doteq 13$$

The given data determined two triangles, AB_1C_1 and AB_2C_2, which were solved above. Which picture in Figure 10-7 illustrates this example?

Example 3   Solve triangle ABC, given $a = 1.8$, $b = 1.2$, and $m \angle A = 47°$.

Solution   (1) To solve for $m \angle B$:

$$\frac{1.8}{\sin 47°} = \frac{1.2}{\sin m \angle B}$$

$$\sin m \angle B = \frac{1.2 \sin 47°}{1.8} \doteq \frac{1.2 \times .731}{1.8} \doteq .487$$

$$m \angle B_1 \doteq 29° \text{ and } m \angle B_2 \doteq 180° - 29° = 151°$$

(2) To solve for $m \angle C_1$ and $m \angle C_2$:

$$m \angle C_1 = 180° - (m \angle A + m \angle B_1)$$
$$\doteq 180° - (47° + 29°)$$
$$= 104°$$
$$m \angle C_2 = 180° - (m \angle A + m \angle B_2)$$
$$\doteq 180° - (47° + 151°)$$
$$= 180° - 198°$$

There is no $\angle C_2$. Why not? Hence, only one triangle is determined by the given data. Which picture in Figure 10-7 illustrates this example?

(3) To solve for c:

$$\frac{1.8}{\sin 47°} = \frac{c}{\sin 104°}$$

$$c = \frac{1.8 \sin 104°}{\sin 47°} = \frac{1.8 \sin 76°}{\sin 47°} \doteq 2.4$$

EXERCISES

1. Given oblique triangle ABC with h the altitude from B to $\overline{AC}$, prove that

$$\frac{a}{\sin m \angle A} = \frac{c}{\sin m \angle C}.$$

2. Show that the Law of Sines is also true for each right triangle.

3. Solve triangle ABC, given the following data for Case 1 (*ASA* or *AAS*).

   a. $m \angle A = 135°, b = 16, m \angle B = 30°$

   b. $m \angle B = 120°, a = 14, m \angle C = 30°$

   c. $m \angle B = 40°, b = 24, m \angle C = 20°$

   d. $m \angle A = 125°, b = 8.2, m \angle C = 32°$

   e. $m \angle A = 72°20', c = 22.4, m \angle C = 43°40'$

   f. $m \angle B = 122°10', b = 38.4, m \angle C = 48°20'$

4. Use logarithms to solve triangle ABC with $m \angle A = 34°10', m \angle B = 71°30', b = 232$.

5. Prove that the area of oblique triangle ABC is given by $\frac{1}{2}bc \sin m \angle A$.

6. Use the formula of Exercise 5 to determine the area of triangle ABC, given the following data.

   a. $m \angle A = 30°, b = 12, c = 15$ **d.** $m \angle A = 90°, b = 17, c = 16$

   b. $m \angle A = 70°, b = 10, c = 15$ **e.** $m \angle C = 42°, a = 18, b = 14$

   c. $m \angle A = 140°, b = 15, c = 10$ **f.** $m \angle B = 110°, a = 4.3, c = 8.2$

7. For triangle ABC, $a = 6, b = 8$ and the area of ABC is 15. Determine $m \angle C$.

8. For the figure at the right, determine the area of the shaded region for the following data.

   a. $r = 5, u° = 120°$ **c.** $r = 4, u° = 150°$

   b. $r = 2, u° = 45°$ **d.** $r = r_1, u° = u_1°$

9. You are given the values of $m \angle A$, a and b, satisfying the conditions given below. In each case, determine whether none, one or two triangles are determined. The altitude from C is h.

   a. $m \angle A < 90°, a = b$ **e.** $m \angle A < 90°, a = h$

   b. $m \angle A > 90°, a = b$ **f.** $m \angle A < 90°, a < h$

   c. $m \angle A < 90°, a > b$ **g.** $m \angle A > 90°, a > b$

   d. $m \angle A < 90°, h < a < b$ **h.** $m \angle A > 90°, a < b$

10. Determine $\sin m \angle A$, $\sin m \angle B$, and $\sin m \angle C$ for each triangle ABC, given the following data.

   a. $m \angle A = 100°$, $m \angle B = 55°$ **b.** $m \angle A = 50°$, $m \angle B = 20°$

11. Determine two values of $m \angle A$, $0° < m \angle A < 180°$, for which each of the following equations is true.

   a. $\sin m \angle A \doteq 0.6604$ **b.** $\sin m \angle A \doteq 0.8371$

12. For each of the following sets of conditions, sketch two triangles AB_1C_1 and AB_2C_2.

   a. $m \angle A = 45°$, $b = 6.0$, $a = 4.9$ **b.** $m \angle A = 30°$, $b = 8.0$, $a = 5.2$

13. Solve triangles AB_1C_1 and AB_2C_2 in Exercises 12a and 12b.

14. Solve triangle ABC, given the following data for Case 4 (*SSA*).

   a. $m \angle A = 34°$, $a = 22$, $b = 32$

   b. $m \angle C = 42°$, $c = 15$, $b = 24$

   c. $m \angle A = 127°20'$, $a = 18.3$, $c = 12.4$

   d. $m \angle A = 46°40'$, $a = 29.1$, $b = 17.2$

   e. $m \angle C = 62°50'$, $c = 21.4$, $b = 23.1$

15. The longer diagonal of a parallelogram is 26 inches long and forms angles of 41° and 28° with the sides. Determine the lengths of the sides.

16. Determine all values of a such that for each value of a there exist two triangles, AB_1C_1 and AB_2C_2, each with $m \angle A = 30°$ and with $AC = 10$. See the figure at the right.

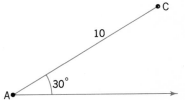

17. For triangle ABC, $b = 6$, $c = 8$, and $m \angle B = 30°$. Determine $\sin m \angle C$.

18. The side of an embankment is inclined 35° from the horizontal. A vertical pole is anchored on the slope by a wire from the top of the pole to a point 92 feet down the embankment from the foot of the pole. The wire is inclined 52° from the horizontal. Find the height of the pole.

19. A triangular plot of ground has frontages of 87 feet and 94 feet on two streets which intersect at an angle of 79°. Find the area of the plot.

20. Cities A, B, and C are joined by straight highways. The direction of C from A is N 40° E. The highway from A to B is 180 miles long in the direction N 70° E. The highway from C to B is in the direction N 60° W. Al drives a truck at an average speed of 45 mph from A to B by way of C. Bill drives a car at an average speed of 60 mph directly from A to B. If Bill left A two hours after Al did, who will arrive at B first and how much earlier than the other boy?

THE LAW OF COSINES

To solve triangles for CASE 2 (*SAS*) or CASE 3 (*SSS*), we use the Law of Cosines.

LAW OF COSINES

For any triangle ABC, $a^2 = b^2 + c^2 - 2bc \cos m \angle A$

$b^2 = a^2 + c^2 - 2ac \cos m \angle B$, and $c^2 = a^2 + b^2 - 2ab \cos m \angle C$

PROOF OF LAW OF COSINES

Let triangle ABC be on a coordinate plane with $\angle A$ in standard position and B at $(c, 0)$ as shown in Figure 10–9. Let the coordinates of C be (x, y). Then

$$\cos m \angle A = \frac{x}{b} \text{ and } \sin m \angle A = \frac{y}{b}$$

Hence, $x = b \cos m \angle A$ and $y = b \sin m \angle A$

and the coordinates of C are $(b \cos m \angle A, b \sin m \angle A)$.

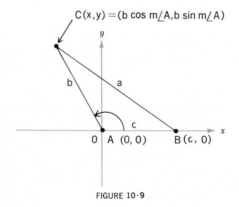

FIGURE 10-9

By the Distance Formula,

$$CB = a = \sqrt{(b \cos m \angle A - c)^2 + (b \sin m \angle A - 0)^2}$$

Thus, $a^2 = b^2 \cos^2 m \angle A - 2bc \cos m \angle A + c^2 + b^2 \sin^2 m \angle A$

$a^2 = b^2 (\cos^2 m \angle A + \sin^2 m \angle A) + c^2 - 2bc \cos m \angle A$

$a^2 = b^2 + c^2 - 2bc \cos m \angle A$

And we have derived the first equation of the Law of Cosines. The last two equations of the Law of Cosines may be derived in a similar manner by placing $\angle B$ and then $\angle C$ in standard position.

The following examples illustrate the use of the Law of Cosines in solving triangles for CASE 2 (*SAS*) and CASE 3 (*SSS*).

Example 1   Solve triangle ABC, given $a = 23$, $c = 31$, and $m \angle B = 112°$.

Solution   (1) Solving for b, we select the appropriate equation from the Law of Cosines.

$$b^2 = a^2 + c^2 - 2ac \cos m \angle B$$
$$b^2 = 23^2 + 31^2 - 2(23)(31) \cos 112°$$
$$\doteq 23^2 + 31^2 + 2(23)(31) \cos 68° \quad [\cos 112° = -\cos 68°]$$
$$\doteq 529 + 961 + 1426(.3746) \doteq 2024 \qquad \text{[Tables II, III]}$$

Hence, $b \doteq 45$ [Table II]

(2) To solve for $m \angle A$, we use the Law of Sines:

$$\frac{45}{\sin 112°} = \frac{23}{\sin m \angle A}$$

$$\sin m \angle A = \frac{23 \sin 68°}{45} \doteq .474$$

Hence, $m \angle A \doteq 28°$

Why is $m \angle A \neq 180° - 28° = 152°$?

(3) Solving for $m \angle C$: $m \angle C = 180° - (m \angle A + m \angle B) \doteq 40°$

Example 2   Solve triangle ABC, given $a = 43$, $b = 29$, and $m \angle C = 28°$.

Solution   (1) Solving for c:

$$c^2 = a^2 + b^2 - 2ab \cos m \angle C$$
$$= 43^2 + 29^2 - 2(43)(29) \cos 28°$$
$$\doteq 1849 + 841 - 2494(.8829) \doteq 488 \quad \text{[Tables II, III]}$$
$$c \doteq 22$$

(2) Solving for $m \angle A$:

$$\cos m \angle A = \frac{b^2 + c^2 - a^2}{2bc}$$

$$= \frac{29^2 + 22^2 - 43^2}{2(29)(22)} \doteq -.411$$

$$m \angle A \doteq 180° - 66° = 114°$$

Angle A is a second quadrant angle since $\cos m \angle A < 0$.

(3) Solving for $m \angle B$: $m \angle B = 180° - (m \angle A + m \angle C) \doteq 38°$.

Example 3   Solve triangle ABC, given $a = 25$, $b = 18$, and $c = 12$.

Solution   (1) To solve for $m \angle A$, we select the equation which involves $m \angle A$,
$$a^2 = b^2 + c^2 - 2bc \cos m \angle A$$

and solve it for $\cos m \angle A$.

$$\cos m \angle A = \frac{b^2 + c^2 - a^2}{2bc}$$

Substituting the values of a, b, and c, we obtain

$$\cos m \angle A = \frac{18^2 + 12^2 - 25^2}{2(18)(12)} \doteq -.363$$

$$m \angle A \doteq 180° - 69° = 111°$$

Observe that $\angle A$ is a second quadrant angle since $\cos m \angle A < 0$.

(2) In a similar manner, $m \angle B$ and $m \angle C$ can be determined.

EXERCISES

1. Establish a coordinate system on a plane containing oblique triangle ABC with $\angle B$ in standard position. Derive the second equation of the Law of Cosines.

2. Show that the Pythagorean Theorem is a special case of the Law of Cosines.

3. Prove the converse of the Pythagorean Theorem; that is, prove that if $a^2 + b^2 = c^2$, then triangle ABC is a right triangle with right angle at C.

4. Tell why the Law of Cosines does not lend itself well to the use of logarithms.

5. Solve each triangle ABC, given the following data for Case 2 (*SAS*).

   a. $m \angle A = 60°, b = 12, c = 15$ **d.** $m \angle A = 135°, b = 15, c = 10$

   b. $m \angle B = 120°, a = 14, c = 22$ **e.** $m \angle B = 117°, a = 3.2, c = 2.4$

   c. $m \angle C = 30°, a = 24, b = 12$ **f.** $m \angle C = 27°, a = 16, b = 20$

6. Given the Law of Cosines, express (1) $\cos m \angle A$, (2) $\cos m \angle B$, and (3) $\cos m \angle C$ in terms of a, b, and c.

7. Determine the angle measures for each triangle ABC, given the following data.

   a. $a = 14, b = 16, c = 20$ **d.** $a = 17, b = 20, c = 32$

   b. $a = 20, b = 20, c = 36$ **e.** $a = 2.0, b = 4.2, c = 2.5$

   c. $a = 3.2, b = 2.8, c = 2.6$ **f.** $a = 5, b = 10, c = 5\sqrt{3}$

8. Determine the measure of the largest angle of a triangle with sides 12, 14, 18.

9. Two sides and the included angle of a parallelogram measure 24 inches, 20 inches and 110°, respectively. Determine the length of each diagonal.

10. Two sides and the longer diagonal of a parallelogram measure 25, 30, and 40 units, respectively. Determine the length of the shorter diagonal.

11. Given a parallelogram with adjacent sides of a units and b units, with acute angle of $u°$, and with longer diagonal of d units, prove that $d^2 = a^2 + b^2 + 2ab \cos u°$.

12. Given $A(0, 0)$, $B(a, b)$, and $C(c, d)$ on a coordinate plane with $m \angle BAC = u°$. Use the Law of Cosines and express $AB \cdot AC \cdot \cos u°$ in terms of a, b, c, and d.

13. Point A is inaccessible from B. At point C, $\angle ACB$ is measured as 72°. C is measured as being 52 yards and 64 yards from A and B, respectively. Determine the distance between A and B.

14. A ship leaves its harbor traveling at a speed of 42 knots in the direction N 52° E. Two hours later it changes direction and travels N 32° E at the same speed. Determine the ship's distance and direction from harbor 3.5 hours after leaving. (1 knot is a speed of 1 nautical mile per hour.)

15. Two ships leave harbor at the same time. The first one heads N 16° W at a speed of 38 knots. The other heads N 34° E at a speed of 32 knots. Determine the distance between the ships at the end of 2.0 hours and the direction from the second ship to the first.

16. Given any oblique triangle *ABC* with *h*, the altitude from *C*, as shown at the right. Use the equation

$$\cos m \angle C = \frac{a^2 + b^2 - c^2}{2ab}$$

from the Law of Cosines to prove that

$$\cos (u + v)° = \cos u° \cos v° - \sin u° \sin v°$$

17. A ship sailed from its harbor in the direction N 42° E for 23 nautical miles. A second ship sailed from this harbor with a bearing of N 38° W for 72 nautical miles. After both ships are anchored, how far apart are they and what is the direction of the second ship from the first?

18. A plane took off from an airport and flew a course of 140° at a speed of 260 mph for three hours. It then changed to a course of 220° and a speed of 230 mph. Five hours after takeoff, what is the plane's distance and direction from the airport?

19. A ship sailed from harbor with a speed of 22 knots in the direction S 52° W. At the end of $1\frac{1}{2}$ hours it changed to a bearing of N 22° W and a speed of 18 knots. After two hours on the second course, what is the distance of the ship from harbor and what is its direction?

VECTORS

In this section we shall be concerned with *vectors* and their applications to the study of those phenomena which possess both *magnitude* and *direction*. Three such phenomena are *displacement, force,* and *velocity*. Examples of these are given below. For each example, observe that a picture of a *directed line segment* indicates the magnitude and direction of the phenomenon. Directed line segments are called *vectors* when used in this way.

      1. *Displacement* results when an object is moved from one place to another. The *displacement vector* results from a move of 3 miles (magnitude) to the northeast (direction).

      2. *Force* is the abstraction which the physicist uses to describe

"pushes" and "pulls" and to account for the effects produced by these pushes and pulls. The *force vector* represents the force exerted by a 30-gram weight (magnitude) suspended on a coil spring stretching it downward (direction).

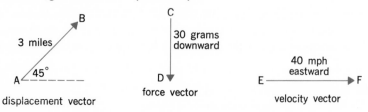

displacement vector   force vector   velocity vector

3. *Velocity* is the speed of a moving object in a stated direction. The *velocity vector* shown represents the velocity of a car which is traveling at a speed of 40 mph (magnitude) to the east (direction). Observe that the term "speed" designates only how fast an object moves and does not indicate the direction; the term "velocity" indicates both the speed and the direction.

In each figure above, the length of the segment was determined by an appropriate scale.

We now introduce some definitions and symbols which are needed for our study of vectors. The *directed line segment* shown in Figure 10–10 is a *vector*. We use a half-arrow and write $\overrightarrow{PQ}$ as a name for the vector. P is called the *origin* or *initial point* of the vector. The *terminal point* Q is indicated by the arrowhead in the figure. Frequently we use one letter in naming a vector. For example, $\overrightarrow{A}$ is shown in Figure 10–11.

FIGURE 10-10   FIGURE 10-11

The *magnitude* of $\overrightarrow{PQ}$ is indicated by the symbol $|\overrightarrow{PQ}|$ and is equal to PQ, the length of $\overline{PQ}$. Thus, the magnitude of a vector is a non-negative real number. For the vectors of Figures 10–10 and 10–11, $|\overrightarrow{PQ}| = 5$ and $|\overrightarrow{A}| = 4$.

The direction of $\overrightarrow{PQ}$ is the same as the direction of the terminal side of the generated angle which has its vertex at the origin of the vector; its initial side is in the positive horizontal direction and its terminal side contains the vector. For the vectors of Figures 10–10 and 10–11, generated angles of 135° and −210°, respectively, determine the directions of the vectors.

Consider a velocity vector $\overrightarrow{V}$ representing a speed of 40 mph to the northeast. Its magnitude is $|\overrightarrow{V}| = 40$ mph and its direction is the same as that of the terminal side of a generated angle of 45°. For the three examples of vectors given at the beginning of this section, state (1) the magnitude and (2) an angle measure which determines the direction for each vector.

Figure 10–12 shows three vectors, $\overrightarrow{A}$, $\overrightarrow{B}$, and $\overrightarrow{C}$, on a coordinate plane. Observe that $|\overrightarrow{A}| = |\overrightarrow{B}| = |\overrightarrow{C}| = 5$ and that all three vectors have the same direction. In such a case we say that the vectors are *equivalent* and write $\overrightarrow{A} \overset{e}{=} \overrightarrow{B} \overset{e}{=} \overrightarrow{C}$. In general,

> two vectors are called equivalent if and only if they have the same magnitude and direction.

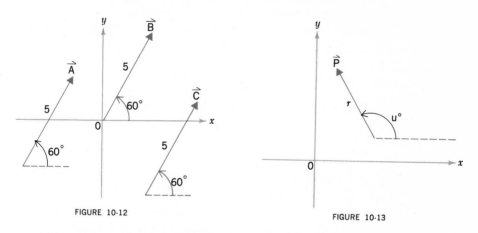

FIGURE 10-12   FIGURE 10-13

It is easy to conclude that there are infinitely many vectors in the plane which are equivalent to $\overrightarrow{A}$. Among them there is only one vector with initial point at the origin of the coordinate plane. This vector is $\overrightarrow{B}$. We say that $\overrightarrow{B}$ is in *standard position*. In general,

> a vector is in standard position if and only if its origin is the origin of the chosen coordinate system.

It follows from the definition of equivalent vectors that, given $\overrightarrow{P}$ in a coordinate plane with magnitude r and direction determined by $u°$ as shown in Figure 10–13, each vector equivalent to $\overrightarrow{P}$ has the same magnitude and direction as $\overrightarrow{P}$. To specify the set of all vectors equivalent to $\overrightarrow{P}$, we write $\{[r, u°]\}$. The notation $[r, u°]$ is called the *polar form* of $\overrightarrow{P}$ (and of any vector equivalent to $\overrightarrow{P}$). Three of the vectors specified by the polar form $[5, 60°]$ were shown in Figure 10–12.

Suppose $M(-4, 1)$ is taken as the initial point of a vector (see Figure 10–14). A displacement of 3 units to the right, (3), followed by a displacement of 2 units downward, (-2), would put us at $N(-1, -1)$. We say that $\overrightarrow{MN}$ has x-component

3 and y-component -2. The notation $[3, -2]$ is called the rectangular form of $\overrightarrow{MN}$ (and of any vector equivalent to $\overrightarrow{MN}$).

Three of the vectors specified by the rectangular form $[3, -2]$ are shown in Figure 10–14. Verify that the x- and y-components of $\overrightarrow{C}$ and $\overrightarrow{E}$ are 3 and -2, respectively. Note that $\overrightarrow{C}$ is in standard position and its terminal point is $(3, -2)$. In general, the vector in standard position which belongs to the set of vectors $\{[m, n]\}$ has (m, n) for its terminal point. Sketch the vector $\overrightarrow{AB}$ which has initial point $A(2, -3)$ and rectangular form $[-5, 4]$.

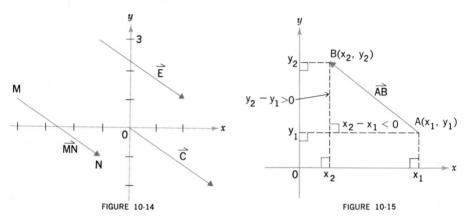

FIGURE 10-14   FIGURE 10-15

In general, given $\overrightarrow{AB}$ in a coordinate plane with $A(x_1, y_1)$ and $B(x_2, y_2)$ as shown in Figure 10–15, the numbers $x_2 - x_1$ and $y_2 - y_1$ are called the *x-component* and the *y-component*, respectively, of $\overrightarrow{AB}$. In most discussions of vectors, the initial and terminal points of vectors are not as important as their x- and y-components. It can be shown that equivalent vectors have the same x-component and the same y-component. To specify the set of all vectors equivalent to $\overrightarrow{AB}$, we can use the notation $\{[x_2 - x_1, y_2 - y_1]\}$. The notation $[x_2 - x_1, y_2 - y_1]$ is called the *rectangular form* of $\overrightarrow{AB}$.

If any vector $\overrightarrow{X}$ is specified in rectangular form by $[a, b]$ (see Figure 10–16), its magnitude is given by

$$|\overrightarrow{X}| = \sqrt{a^2 + b^2}$$

Furthermore, if $\overrightarrow{Y}$ is specified by $[c, d]$, then

$$\overrightarrow{X} \stackrel{e}{=} \overrightarrow{Y} \text{ if and only if } a = c \text{ and } b = d$$

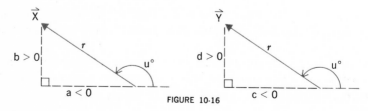

FIGURE 10-16

Given either the polar form $[r, u°]$ or the rectangular form $[a, b]$ of a vector, the other form is readily obtained by trigonometry.

Example 1   Suppose $\vec{A}$ is specified in polar form by $[4, -30°]$ as shown in Figure 10–17. We determine the rectangular form $[x, y]$ of $\vec{A}$ as follows.

$$\cos(-30°) = \frac{x}{4} \text{ and } \sin(-30°) = \frac{y}{4} \text{ (why?)}$$
$$x = 4\cos(-30°) \text{ and } y = 4\sin(-30°)$$
$$x = 2\sqrt{3} \text{ and } y = -2$$

Hence, the rectangular form of $\vec{A}$ is $[2\sqrt{3}, -2]$.

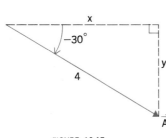

FIGURE 10-17

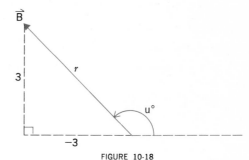

FIGURE 10-18

Example 2   Suppose $\vec{B}$ is specified in rectangular form by $[-3, 3]$ as shown in Figure 10–18. We determine $[r, u°]$, the polar form of $\vec{B}$, as follows.

$$|\vec{B}| = r = \sqrt{(-3)^2 + 3^2} = \sqrt{18} = 3\sqrt{2}$$
$$\cos u° = \frac{-3}{3\sqrt{2}} = \frac{-1}{\sqrt{2}} \text{ and } \sin u° = \frac{3}{3\sqrt{2}} = \frac{1}{\sqrt{2}}$$

Hence, $u° = 135°$.

Thus, the polar form of $\vec{B}$ is $[3\sqrt{2}, 135°]$.

In general, given $\vec{X}$ with polar form $[r, u°]$ and with rectangular form $[x, y]$ as shown in Figure 10–19,

$$[x, y] = [r, u°]$$

if and only if

$$r = \sqrt{x^2 + y^2} \text{ and } \cos u° = \frac{x}{r} \text{ and } \sin u° = \frac{y}{r}.$$

Observe that the polar form $[r, u°]$ is equivalent to the rectangular form $[r \cos u°, r \sin u°]$. Express $[-8, -8]$ in polar form. Express $[10, -30°]$ in rectangular form.

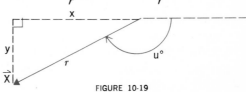

FIGURE 10-19

EXERCISES

1. For each of the following vectors,

    (1) draw a picture of the vector

    (2) state its magnitude and an angle measure which determines its direction

    (3) express it in polar and rectangular forms

    a. $\overrightarrow{D}$, a displacement vector representing a move of 25 miles in the southwesterly direction.

    b. $\overrightarrow{F}$, a force vector with a magnitude of 50 pounds in the upward direction.

    c. $\overrightarrow{V}$, a velocity vector of 30 knots N 20° E.

2. Given that $\overrightarrow{AB}$ is specified by [4, 150°], draw pictures of the following vectors.

    a. $\overrightarrow{AB}$, with A at $(2, -4)$.

    b. Three other vectors equivalent to $\overrightarrow{AB}$.

    c. $\overrightarrow{C}$, in standard position with $\overrightarrow{C} \overset{e}{=} \overrightarrow{AB}$.

3. Sketch a vector specified by each of the following and express it in rectangular form.

    a. [4, 135°]   **c.** [5, 0°]   **e.** [2, −30°]   **g.** [3, −90°]

    b. [6, 210°]   **d.** [8, −120°]   **f.** [7, 180°]   **h.** [1.2, 40°]

4. Sketch a vector specified by each of the following and express it in polar form.

    a. [6, 6]   **c.** [0, 3]   **e.** $[5\sqrt{3}, -5]$ **g.** [2, 5]

    b. $[-4, 4\sqrt{3}]$ **d.** [3, −3]   **f.** [−4, 0]   **h.** [−5, −4]

5. Express $\overrightarrow{AB}$ in rectangular form given the following coordinates of A and B.

    a. $A(3, -5)$, $B(1, 2)$ **c.** $A(-2.9, 4)$, $B(4.1, -2.6)$ **e.** $A(0, 0)$, $B(a, b)$

    b. $A(4, 2)$, $B(6, -3)$ **d.** $A(\sqrt{2}, \sqrt{5})$, $B(3\sqrt{2}, 4\sqrt{5})$ **f.** $A(m, n)$, $B(f, g)$

6. Given that $\overrightarrow{X}$ is specified by [3, 5] and $\overrightarrow{Y}$ is specified by $[6a, 4 - b]$. Determine a and b so that $\overrightarrow{X} \overset{e}{=} \overrightarrow{Y}$.

7. Determine the magnitude of each vector specified by $[c + 2, c - 3]$.

8. Determine the magnitude of each vector specified by [0, 0].

ADDITION OF VECTORS

We now turn our attention to the addition of vectors and show how this operation can be defined in terms of the components of vectors. The definition of addition for vectors is suggested by the result of two successive displacements (see Figure 10–20). A displacement from O to P, followed by a displacement from P to Q, is equivalent to a displacement from O to Q. Hence it is logical to conclude that $\overrightarrow{OP} + \overrightarrow{PQ} = \overrightarrow{OQ}$.

DEFINITION OF VECTOR ADDITION If $\vec{A}$ and $\vec{B}$ are specified by $[a, b]$ and $[c, d]$, respectively, then $\vec{A} + \vec{B}$ is specified by $[a + c, b + d]$. That is, $[a, b] + [c, d] = [a + c, b + d]$.

Observe in Figure 10–21 that, according to the above definition, $\vec{OA} + \vec{OB} = \vec{OC}$ where $OACB$ is a parallelogram. In physics it is shown that any set of given forces acting simultaneously on an object is equivalent to a single force, called their *resultant*. The resultant force vector is the sum of the given force vectors.

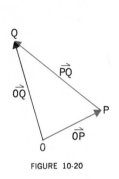

FIGURE 10-20

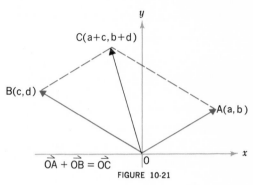

$\vec{OA} + \vec{OB} = \vec{OC}$ FIGURE 10-21

Hence, a resultant may be constructed by either the "*triangle*" *method* of Figure 10–20 or the "*parallelogram*" *method* of Figure 10–21.

Conversely, given any vector $\vec{A}$, $\vec{A}$ can be *resolved* into horizontal and vertical *vector components*, $\vec{X}$ and $\vec{Y}$. That is, for each vector $\vec{A}$, there is a horizontal vector $\vec{X}$ and a vertical vector $\vec{Y}$ such that $\vec{X} + \vec{Y} = \vec{A}$. This is illustrated in Figure 10–22.

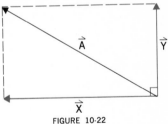

FIGURE 10-22

Example 1   Given velocity vectors $\vec{CA}$ and $\vec{CB}$ as shown below, construct their resultant by the triangle method.

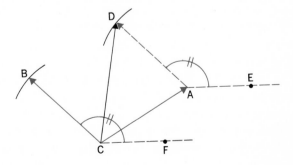

First construct $\overrightarrow{AD}$ as shown so that $\overrightarrow{AD} \stackrel{c}{=} \overrightarrow{CB}$ $(m \angle EAD = m \angle FCB)$. Then $\overrightarrow{CA} + \overrightarrow{CB} = \overrightarrow{CA} + \overrightarrow{AD} = \overrightarrow{CD}$. Thus $\overrightarrow{CD}$ is the resultant of $\overrightarrow{CA}$ and $\overrightarrow{CB}$.

Example 2   Given force vectors $\overrightarrow{AB}$ and $\overrightarrow{AC}$ as shown below, construct their resultant by the parallelogram method.

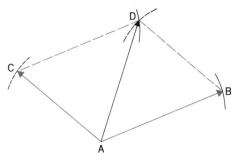

First construct D, so that $ABDC$ is a parallelogram (see picture). Then $\overrightarrow{AD}$ is the resultant of $\overrightarrow{AB}$ and $\overrightarrow{AC}$.

Example 3   Given a force vector $\overrightarrow{F}$ specified by [40, 30°] as shown at the right, resolve $\overrightarrow{F}$ into its horizontal and vertical vector components and determine their magnitudes. First, let $\overrightarrow{X}$ and $\overrightarrow{Y}$ be horizontal and vertical vector components of $\overrightarrow{F}$ as shown at the right. Then

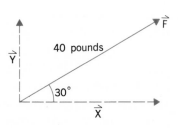

$$\cos 30° = \frac{|\overrightarrow{X}|}{40} \text{ and } \sin 30° = \frac{|\overrightarrow{Y}|}{40}$$

$$|\overrightarrow{X}| = 40 \cos 30° \doteq 40 \times .866 \doteq 35$$
$$|\overrightarrow{Y}| = 40 \sin 30° = 40 \times .500 = 20$$

The picture for this example can be drawn to scale and the answers obtained without doing any computations. Explain.

Is there a vector of magnitude zero? To answer this question, recall that the sum of any two vectors is a vector. Compute the sum of vectors determined by [4, −2] and [−4, 2]. You should have obtained [0, 0]. {[0, 0]} is the set of all *zero vectors*. What is the magnitude of each zero vector?

If the result of several forces, $\overrightarrow{F_1}, \overrightarrow{F_2}, \overrightarrow{F_3}, \ldots$, acting on a stationary object leaves the object at rest, then the object is said to be in *equilibrium* and the resultant of $\overrightarrow{F_1}, \overrightarrow{F_2}, \overrightarrow{F_3}, \ldots$ is a zero vector. Figure 10–23 shows $\overrightarrow{F_1}, \overrightarrow{F_2},$ and $\overrightarrow{F_3}$ acting on an object at A resulting in $\overrightarrow{F_r}$. Thus, the object at A is not in equilibrium. Figure 10–24 shows $\overrightarrow{F_4}$, $\overrightarrow{F_5}$, and $\overrightarrow{F_6}$ acting on an object at B which is in equilibrium. Hence, $\overrightarrow{F_4} + \overrightarrow{F_5} + \overrightarrow{F_6}$ is a zero vector, $\overrightarrow{BB}$.

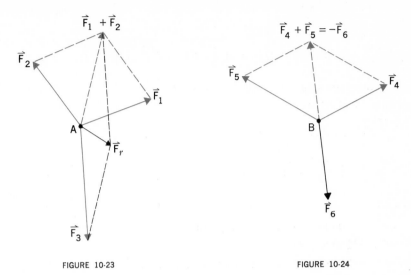

FIGURE 10-23   FIGURE 10-24

The preceding discussion may be applied to the problem of determining the force exerted at a point on a rope from which a weight is suspended. Figure 10–25 shows a 500-pound weight suspended from C by a cord. It is held in equilibrium by cords from C to A and from C to B forming angles of 45° and 30° with the horizontals as is shown in the picture. It is important to know that the forces exerted on C by the cords from A and B are along the cords and away from C. The force exerted on C by the vertical cord has a magnitude of 500 pounds and is directed downward. Our problem is to determine the force exerted on C by each of the other two ropes.

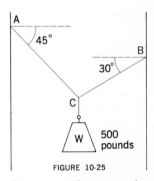

FIGURE 10-25

To solve this problem, we construct a *vector diagram* as shown on the next page. Force vectors $\overrightarrow{P}$ and $\overrightarrow{Q}$ represent the forces exerted on C by the cords from B and A, respectively. Their direction is along the cords and away from C. Force vector $\overrightarrow{T}$ represents the force exerted on C by the cord attached to the 500-pound weight. Its direction is downward. Since the weight is in equilibrium, the resultant of $\overrightarrow{P}$, $\overrightarrow{Q}$, and $\overrightarrow{T}$ is a zero vector specified by [0, 0]. Observe that $\overrightarrow{P} + \overrightarrow{Q} = -\overrightarrow{T}$ and $\overrightarrow{T} + (-\overrightarrow{T})$ is a zero vector. The vectors $\overrightarrow{P}$, $\overrightarrow{Q}$, and $\overrightarrow{T}$ are specified in rectangular form as follows.

$$\overrightarrow{P}: [\,|\overrightarrow{P}|\cos 30°,\ |\overrightarrow{P}|\sin 30°] = \left[\frac{\sqrt{3}}{2}\,|\overrightarrow{P}|,\ \frac{1}{2}\,|\overrightarrow{P}|\right]$$

$\vec{Q}$: $[\,|\vec{Q}|\cos 135°,\ |\vec{Q}|\sin 135°] = \left[\dfrac{-\sqrt{2}}{2}\,|\vec{Q}|,\ \dfrac{\sqrt{2}}{2}\,|\vec{Q}|\right]$

$\vec{T}$: $[0,\ -500]$

Now, $\vec{P} + \vec{Q} + \vec{T} = [0,\ 0]$ Why?

Hence, $\left[\dfrac{\sqrt{3}}{2}\,|\vec{P}| + \dfrac{-\sqrt{2}}{2}\,|\vec{Q}| + 0,\ \dfrac{1}{2}\,|\vec{P}| + \dfrac{\sqrt{2}}{2}\,|\vec{Q}| - 500\right] = [0,\ 0].$

Equating corresponding components yields a system of two linear equations.

$$\dfrac{\sqrt{3}}{2}\,|\vec{P}| - \dfrac{\sqrt{2}}{2}\,|\vec{Q}| = 0$$

$$\dfrac{1}{2}\,|\vec{P}| + \dfrac{\sqrt{2}}{2}\,|\vec{Q}| = 500$$

Solving the system for $|\vec{P}|$ and $|\vec{Q}|$, we find that

$|\vec{P}| = 500\,(\sqrt{3} - 1) \doteq 366$ pounds

$|\vec{Q}| = 250\,\sqrt{2}\,(3 - \sqrt{3})$

$\quad = 250\,(3\,\sqrt{2} - \sqrt{6}) \doteq 449$ pounds

Of course, we know that $|\vec{T}| = 500$ pounds. Supposing that all three cords are about equally strong, which cord is most likely to break? least likely to break?

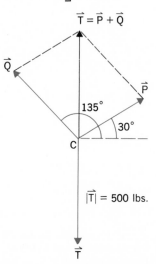

Consider now the problem of determining the force exerted on a point C from which a 400-pound weight is suspended (see Figure 10–26). The weight is held in equilibrium by the forces exerted on C by a cord from A and a brace hinged at B as shown in the figure. This problem is similar to the previous one except that the force exerted by the brace is in line with the brace and in the direction of C from B. A vector diagram in Figure 10–27 shows the three force vectors acting on C.

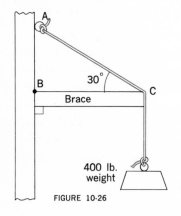

FIGURE 10-26

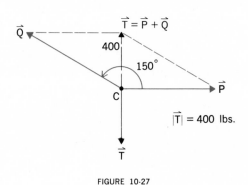

FIGURE 10-27

EXERCISES

1. Express each sum in rectangular form.

   a. $[6, 2] + [-3, 4]$ **c.** $[2, 30°] + [4, 60°]$ **e.** $[3, 5] + [-4, -2] + [1, -3]$

   b. $[-4, 2] + [-3, 3]$ **d.** $[6, 120°] + [8, -45°]$ **f.** $[7, -5] + [-7, 5] + [2, 3]$

2. For each vector which is specified below, (1) construct the vector, (2) construct $\overrightarrow{X}$ and $\overrightarrow{Y}$, a pair of horizontal and vertical vector components of the vector and (3) determine the magnitudes of $\overrightarrow{X}$ and $\overrightarrow{Y}$.

   a. $[4, -2]$ **b.** $[2, 30°]$ **c.** $[-3, 4]$ **d.** $[3, -45°]$ **e.** $[-5, -3]$

   f. A displacement vector of 4 miles to the northwest.

   g. A force vector of 50 pounds directed up a plane inclined 30° to the horizontal.

   h. A velocity vector of 500 mph N 30° E.

   i. $[r, u°]$

3. Given $\overrightarrow{A}$ and $\overrightarrow{B}$ specified by $[4, 4]$ and $[-6, 8]$ with initial points $(1, 2)$ and $(-2, -2)$, respectively, construct each of the following.

   a. $\overrightarrow{A}$ and $\overrightarrow{B}$ **b.** $\overrightarrow{A} + \overrightarrow{B}$ by the *parallelogram* method.

4. Given any two vectors specified by $[-5, -6]$ and $[8, -4]$, construct their sum by the *triangle* method.

5. Given force vectors $\overrightarrow{A}$, $\overrightarrow{B}$, and $\overrightarrow{C}$ specified by $[-4, -5]$, $[-5, 10]$ and $[9, -5]$, each with initial point $P(3, -2)$. Construct $\overrightarrow{A}$, $\overrightarrow{B}$, $\overrightarrow{C}$, and their resultant.

6. Determine the magnitude in pounds of the resultant of two forces of 5 and 8 pounds, respectively, which act on the same point and form an angle of 120° with each other.

7. Given forces F and G acting simultaneously on an object, specify $\overrightarrow{G}$ so that the object is in equilibrium where $\overrightarrow{F}$ is specified as follows.

   a. $[7, 3]$ **b.** $[-4, 2]$ **c.** $[6, 30°]$ **d.** $[5, 135°]$

8. Determine the magnitude of the resultant of forces $\overrightarrow{F}$ and $\overrightarrow{G}$ which act on the same point, where $\overrightarrow{F}$ and $\overrightarrow{G}$ are specified as follows.

   a. $\overrightarrow{F}$: $[4, 30°]$; $\overrightarrow{G}$: $[3, 90°]$ **c.** $\overrightarrow{F}$: $[16, 0°]$; $\overrightarrow{G}$: $[10, 120°]$

   b. $\overrightarrow{F}$: $[5, 45°]$; $\overrightarrow{G}$: $[2, 135°]$ **d.** $\overrightarrow{F}$: $[3, 90°]$; $\overrightarrow{G}$: $[10, 210°]$

9. Given three forces A, B, and C acting simultaneously on an object, specify $\overrightarrow{C}$ in rectangular form so that the object is in equilibrium where $\overrightarrow{A}$ and $\overrightarrow{B}$ are specified as follows.

   a. $[4, 3]$ and $[2, -5]$ **c.** $[4, 30°]$ and $[8, 120°]$

   b. $[-7, 2]$ and $[3, -6]$ **d.** $[2, 60°]$ and $[6, -45°]$

10. Three vectors specified by [5, −2], [−4, 2] and [a, b], respectively, have the same origin. Their resultant is a zero vector. Determine [a, b].

11. Three forces A, B, and C operate away from an object at P, leaving it in equilibrium. The direction of $\overrightarrow{C}$ is downward and $|\overrightarrow{C}| = 5$. The directions of $\overrightarrow{A}$ and $\overrightarrow{B}$ are given by 30° and 120°, respectively. Draw a vector diagram which shows that $\overrightarrow{A} + \overrightarrow{B} + \overrightarrow{C}$ is a zero vector. *Hint:* Sketch $\overrightarrow{C}$ first and then $-\overrightarrow{C}$.

12. Three vectors specified by [2, 30°], [3, 120°], and [r, u°], respectively, have the same origin. Their sum is a zero vector. Determine r, the magnitude of [r, u°].

13. Solve each system of linear equations for $|\overrightarrow{X}|$ and $|\overrightarrow{Y}|$.

a.
$$2|\overrightarrow{X}| + 3|\overrightarrow{Y}| = 7$$
$$4|\overrightarrow{X}| + 5|\overrightarrow{Y}| = 12$$

b.
$$\frac{1}{2}|\overrightarrow{X}| - \frac{\sqrt{3}}{2}|\overrightarrow{Y}| = 0$$
$$\frac{\sqrt{3}}{2}|\overrightarrow{X}| + \frac{1}{2}|\overrightarrow{Y}| = 50$$

c.
$$\frac{\sqrt{3}}{2}|\overrightarrow{X}| + \frac{1}{2}|\overrightarrow{Y}| = 1000$$
$$\frac{-1}{2}|\overrightarrow{X}| + \frac{\sqrt{3}}{2}|\overrightarrow{Y}| = 0$$

14. For each of the following schemes, a weight is suspended from C by a cord. The weight is held in equilibrium by cords from C to A and B which form angles as shown. In each problem, determine (1) the force exerted on C by each of the three cords, (2) which of the three cords is most likely to break, and (3) which is least likely to break, assuming the cords are equally strong.

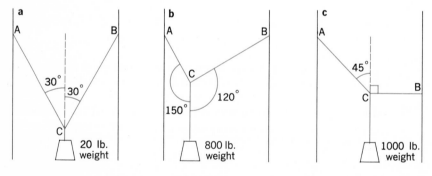

15. For the data given in Figures 10–26 and 10–27, determine the forces exerted on C by the two cords and the brace.

16. A 100-pound mass is held stationary at C on "a rigid and frictionless" inclined plane $\overline{AB}$ by forces represented by $\overrightarrow{CD}$ and $\overrightarrow{CE}$, parallel to the plane and perpendicular to the plane, respectively (see the diagram at the right). The plane makes a 30° angle with the horizontal. Determine the magnitudes of $\overrightarrow{CD}$ and $\overrightarrow{CE}$.

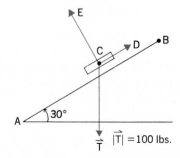

INNER PRODUCT OF VECTORS

There are several kinds of products which involve vectors. One useful kind is called the *inner* or *dot product*.

> **DEFINITION OF INNER (DOT) PRODUCT**   The *inner product*, $\vec{X} \cdot \vec{Y}$ (pronounce $\vec{X} \cdot \vec{Y}$ as $\vec{X}$ *dot* $\vec{Y}$), of two non-zero vectors $\vec{X}$ and $\vec{Y}$ is the real number $|\vec{X}| \times |\vec{Y}| \times \cos u°$, where $u°$ is the measure of the angle between $\vec{X}$ and $\vec{Y}$. If $\vec{X}$ or $\vec{Y}$ is a zero vector, then $\vec{X} \cdot \vec{Y} = 0$.

Observe that, even though $\vec{X}$ and $\vec{Y}$ are vectors, the inner product $\vec{X} \cdot \vec{Y}$ is not a vector. It is a real number. Whenever the inner product is indicated, one must be careful to use a dot for multiplication. The multiplication cross ($\times$) is used to indicate the *cross product* of vectors, another kind of multiplication. Recall that $|\vec{X}|$ is not the vector but its magnitude.

In order for this definition to be clear, we must define the measure of the angle between two vectors.

> **DEFINITION OF MEASURE OF ANGLE BETWEEN TWO VECTORS**   If $\vec{M}$ and $\vec{N}$ are any two non-zero vectors so that $\vec{M} \stackrel{e}{=} \vec{OA}$ and $\vec{N} \stackrel{e}{=} \vec{OB}$, then the measure of the angle between $\vec{M}$ and $\vec{N}$ is equal to the measure of angle AOB.

Figure 10–28 illustrates this definition. The measure of the angle between $\vec{M}$ and $\vec{N}$ is $u°$, the measure of $\angle AOB$, where $\vec{OA} \stackrel{e}{=} \vec{M}$ and $\vec{OB} \stackrel{e}{=} \vec{N}$.

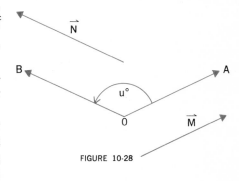

FIGURE 10-28

The inner product has many applications. One of them is a test for perpendicularity. Recall that cos 90° = 0. Since two vectors are perpendicular if the angle between them is a right angle, we state a theorem concerning perpendicularity of vectors as follows:

Theorem 1   Two non-zero vectors $\vec{X}$ and $\vec{Y}$ are perpendicular if and only if $\vec{X} \cdot \vec{Y} = 0$.

Proof $\vec{X} \cdot \vec{Y} = |\vec{X}| \times |\vec{Y}| \times \cos u°$ by definition of inner product. The product $|\vec{X}| \times |\vec{Y}| \times \cos u°$ is 0 if and only if at least one of its factors is 0. But $|\vec{X}| \neq 0$ and $|\vec{Y}| \neq 0$ (why?). Therefore, $\cos u° = 0$. Thus, $\vec{X} \cdot \vec{Y} = 0$ if and only if $\cos u° = 0$. It follows then that $\vec{X}$ and $\vec{Y}$ are perpendicular if and only if $\vec{X} \cdot \vec{Y} = 0$.

Study the following examples which involve inner products.

Example 1   Compute $\vec{X} \cdot \vec{Y}$ if $|\vec{X}| = 3$, $|\vec{Y}| = 8$ and the angle between $\vec{X}$ and $\vec{Y}$ is a 60° angle.

$$\vec{X} \cdot \vec{Y} = |\vec{X}| \times |\vec{Y}| \times \cos u°$$
$$= 3 \times 8 \times \cos 60° = 12$$

Example 2   Compute $\vec{X} \cdot \vec{Y}$ where $\vec{X}$ and $\vec{Y}$ are specified by [4, 30°] and [5, 150°].

The angle between $\vec{X}$ and $\vec{Y}$ measures 150° − 30° or 120°.
Hence $\vec{X} \cdot \vec{Y} = 4 \times 5 \times \cos 120° = -10$

Example 3   Determine the measure of the angle between $\vec{X}$ and $\vec{Y}$ if $|\vec{X}| = 3$, $|\vec{Y}| = 4$ and $\vec{X} \cdot \vec{Y} = -2$.

$$\vec{X} \cdot \vec{Y} = |\vec{X}| \times |\vec{Y}| \times \cos u°$$
$$-2 = 3 \times 4 \times \cos u°$$
$$\cos u° = \frac{-1}{6} \doteq -.1667$$
$$u° \doteq 180° - 80° = 100°$$
$$[\cos 80° \doteq .1667; \cos u° \equiv -\cos u° (180 - u)°]$$

The following theorem supplies a useful formula for the inner product of vectors.

Theorem 2   If $\vec{X}$ and $\vec{Y}$ are any two vectors specified by [a, b] and [c, d], respectively, then $\vec{X} \cdot \vec{Y} = ac + bd$.

Proof

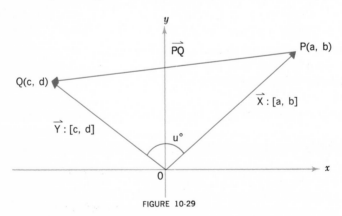

FIGURE 10-29

According to the Law of Cosines (see Figure 10–29),

$$|\vec{PQ}| = |\vec{X}|^2 + |\vec{Y}|^2 - 2|\vec{X}| \times |\vec{Y}| \times \cos u°$$

Hence, by the Distance Formula and the definition of magnitude of a vector,

$$(a - c)^2 + (b - d)^2 = (a^2 + b^2) + (c^2 + d^2) - 2|\vec{X}| \times |\vec{Y}| \times \cos u°$$
$$|\vec{X}| \times |\vec{Y}| \times \cos u° = \frac{a^2 + b^2 + c^2 + d^2 - (a - c)^2 - (b - d)^2}{2}$$

But the left member is equal to $\vec{X} \cdot \vec{Y}$ by the definition of inner product, and the right member may be simplified to $ac + bd$. Thus, $\vec{X} \cdot \vec{Y} = ac + bd$.

Example 1 Compute $\vec{X} \cdot \vec{Y}$ if $\vec{X}$ and $\vec{Y}$ are specified by [3, 7] and [−2, 3], respectively.
By Theorem 2,
$$\vec{X} \cdot \vec{Y} = 3(-2) + 7(3) = 15.$$

Example 2 Show that $\vec{X}$ and $\vec{Y}$ are perpendicular if $\vec{X}$ and $\vec{Y}$ are specified by [8, −5] and [5, 8].
By Theorem 2,
$$\vec{X} \cdot \vec{Y} = 8(5) + (-5)(8) = 0.$$
Hence, $\vec{X}$ is perpendicular to $\vec{Y}$ by Theorem 1.

Example 3 Determine a so that $\vec{X}$ is perpendicular to $\vec{Y}$ where $\vec{X}$ and $\vec{Y}$ are specified by [2, 3] and [a, −4], respectively.
By Theorem 2,
$$\vec{X} \cdot \vec{Y} = 2a + (-12).$$
$\vec{X}$ is perpendicular to $\vec{Y}$ if and only if $\vec{X} \cdot \vec{Y} = 0$, by Theorem 1. Hence, $\vec{X} \cdot \vec{Y} = 0$ if and only if $a = 6$.

The term "work," as used in physics, provides another concept which can be discussed in terms of vectors and illustrates another use of inner product. If a three-pound object is moved through a five-foot displacement by a force with *the same direction* as the displacement, then the amount of work done is 15 *foot-pounds*.

Suppose, as shown in Figure 10–30, an object is moved through a displacement $\vec{D}$ by a force $\vec{F}$ with the same direction as that of $\vec{D}$. Then the amount of work done is $|\vec{F}| \times |\vec{D}|$ foot-pounds, where the magnitudes of $\vec{F}$ and $\vec{D}$ are given in pounds and feet, respectively.

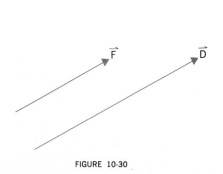

FIGURE 10-30

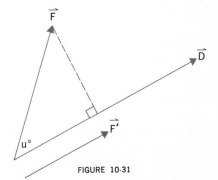

FIGURE 10-31

Suppose, as shown in Figure 10–31, an object is moved through a displacement $\vec{D}$ by a force $\vec{F}$ acting at an angle of $u°$ to $\vec{D}$. Let $\vec{F'}$ be the vector component of $\vec{F}$ in the direction of $\vec{D}$. That is, $|\vec{F'}| = |\vec{F}| \cos u°$ and $\vec{F'}$ has the same direction as $\vec{D}$. Then the amount of work done is

$$|\vec{F'}| \times |\vec{D}| = (|\vec{F}| \cos u°)\, |\vec{D}|$$
$$= |\vec{F}| \times |\vec{D}| \times \cos u°$$
$$= \vec{F} \cdot \vec{D}$$

In both cases (Figures 10–30 and 10–31), the amount of work done is $\vec{F} \cdot \vec{D}$. Show that this is true for the case where $\vec{F}$ and $\vec{D}$ have the same direction.

Consider the work done when a truck tows a boxcar along a railroad track by a cable so that the cable maintains an angle of $u°$ to the track (see Figure 10–32).

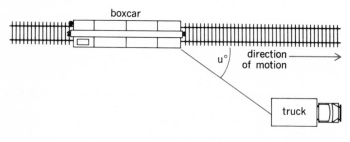

FIGURE 10-32

The direction of a force transmitted by a cable is along the line of the cable. Suppose the truck exerts a force $\vec{F}$ of 1000 pounds at an angle of 45° to the track. How much work does the truck do in moving a string of boxcars through a displacement $\vec{D}$ of 1500 feet down the track? Notice that $\vec{F}$ is specified by [1000, 45°]. $\vec{D}$ is specified by [1500, 0°]. The work done is given by the following equation:

$$\vec{F} \cdot \vec{D} = |\vec{F}| \times |\vec{D}| \times \cos 45°$$
$$\doteq 1000 \times 1500 \times .707$$
$$\doteq 1.5 \times 10^6 \times 7.07 \times 10^{-1}$$
$$\doteq 10.6 \times 10^5$$

Thus, approximately 1,060,000 foot-pounds of work is done.

Suppose a 10-pound weight is to be moved 20 feet up a plane inclined 25° from the horizontal as shown in Figure 10–33. The weight is exerting a force $\vec{F}$ of 10 pounds downward. To move the object vertically upward, we would have to exert an upward force slightly greater in magnitude than 10 pounds. What would happen if the force exerted upward was equal to $-\vec{F}$? To move the object up the plane, we would have to exert a force slightly greater in magnitude than $\vec{F'}$, where $\vec{F'}$ is the vector component of $-\vec{F}$ in the direction of $\vec{D}$. The number of foot-pounds of work done in moving the weight 20 feet up the plane is slightly greater than $-\vec{F} \cdot \vec{D}$, which can be computed as follows:

$$|\vec{F'}| \times |\vec{D}| = (|-\vec{F}| \cos 65°)\, |\vec{D}|$$
$$= |-\vec{F}| \times |\vec{D}| \times \cos 65°$$
$$= -\vec{F} \cdot \vec{D}$$

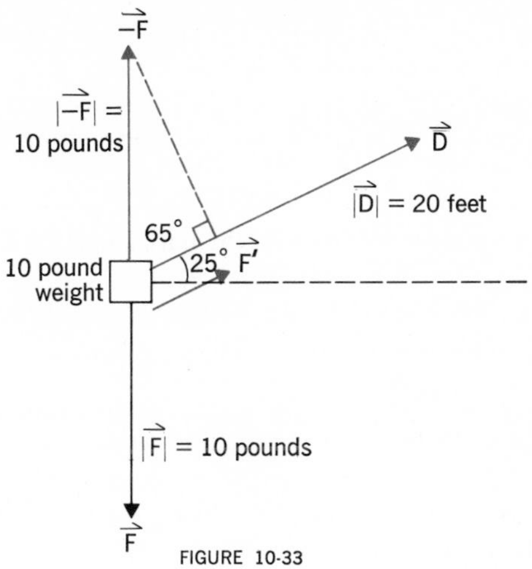

FIGURE 10-33

Verify that 85 foot-pounds of work is done while moving the 10-pound weight 20 feet up the incline.

EXERCISES

1. Determine the measure of the angle between the pairs of vectors specified below.

   a. [4, 60°] and [2, 150°]   c. [3, 3] and [−4, 4]   e. [4, 3] and [0, 5]

   b. [5, 120°] and [3, −135°]   d. [−5, 5$\sqrt{3}$] and [2, 2]   f. [2, 3] and [4, 1]

2. Compute the inner product of each pair of vectors specified below.

   a. [3, 60°] and [8, 105°]   g. [5, 40°] and [2, 105°]

   b. [5, −20°] and [2, 40°]   h. [3, 4] and [−2, 5]

   c. [4, 60°] and [5, 150°]   i. [−2, 3] and [4, 3]

   d. [7, 30°] and [2, 30°]   j. [100, 2] and [3, 50]

   e. [9, 110°] and [4, −70°]   k. [6, −9] and [3, 2]

   f. [r, u°] and [s, v°]   l. [m, n] and [−n, m]

3. Determine the measure of the angle between $\vec{X}$ and $\vec{Y}$ if $|\vec{X}| = 4$, $|\vec{Y}| = 3$ and $\vec{X} \cdot \vec{Y}$ has each of the following values.

   a. 0   b. 6   c. −6   d. 12   e. 3   f. 4

4. Prove that each vector specified by [a, b] is perpendicular to each vector specified by [−b, a], provided $a^2 + b^2 \neq 0$.

5. Determine x for each of the following so that the two vectors in each case are perpendicular.

a. [5, 3] and [x, 5]   **c.** [−6, 4] and [x, 1]

b. [4, 2] and [3, x]   **d.** [1.2, −1.6] and [−4, x]

6. If the truck of Figure 10–32 exerts a force of 1500 pounds at an angle of 30° to the track, how much work does the truck do in moving a string of cars 2000 feet?

7. You pull a small wagon a distance of 100 feet by a rope with a force of 15 pounds. The rope maintains an angle of 20° with the horizontal. Find the work that you do.

8. How much work is done while moving a 30-pound object 10 feet up an inclined plane which forms a 20° angle with the horizontal?

9. How much work is done by a 150-pound boy while climbing 40 feet up a ladder which forms an angle of 60° with the ground?

10. Determine the amount of work done in moving a 100-pound weight from the first floor of a building to the second floor, which is 10 feet above the first floor, under each of the following conditions.

a. Pulling the weight vertically upward by a rope.

b. Carrying the weight up a ladder inclined 60° to the horizontal.

c. Pushing the weight up a plane inclined 30° to the horizontal.

11. Show that the force needed to move a mass of w pounds up a "rigid and frictionless" plane inclined at an angle of α radians to the horizontal has a magnitude of w sin α pounds.

VOCABULARY

Use each of the following correctly in a sentence to demonstrate that you understand its meaning. If you are not sure of the meaning of any word, refer back to the chapter.

ambiguous case

angle between vectors

angle of depression

angle of elevation

direction of a vector

displacement

dot product of vectors

equivalent vectors

inner product of vectors

Law of Cosines

Law of Sines

logarithm

magnitude of a vector

origin of vector

parallelogram method

polar form of vector

rectangular form of vector

resolving a vector

resultant

sextant

solving triangles

standard position of vector

REVIEW EXERCISES

1. Given right triangle ABC with $a = 2$ and $c = 3$, determine the following.

   a. $\cos m \angle A$ **c.** $\csc m \angle A$

   b. $\tan m \angle B$ **d.** $\sin m \angle B$

2. Solve each right triangle ABC below to the degree of accuracy warranted by the given data.

   a. $a = 42, m \angle A = 36°$ **b.** $a = 53.9, c = 72.4$

3. Use logarithms to solve each right triangle ABC for the part indicated.

   a. $m \angle A = 32°40', b = 21.6$; determine c.

   b. $a = 4.36, b = 3.72$; determine $m \angle B$.

4. From the edge of a cliff, 173 feet above the water, the angle of depression to a ship at sea is $15°40'$. How far is the ship from the base of the cliff?

5. Determine the area of right triangle ABC if $AB = 16$ and $\tan m \angle A = \dfrac{4}{3}$.

6. Solve each oblique triangle ABC for the indicated part.

   a. $m \angle A = 52°, m \angle B = 37°, c = 4.3$; determine a.

   b. $m \angle A = 41°, m \angle B = 62°, b = 28$; determine c.

   c. $m \angle A = 33°, b = 25, c = 23$; determine a.

   d. $a = 12, b = 15, c = 20$; determine $m \angle B$.

7. Determine the area of triangle ABC, given $m \angle A = 52°, b = 14$, and $c = 22$.

8. Determine whether the given data for triangle ABC determine none, one, or two triangles.

   a. $m \angle A = 32°, a = 14, b = 22$ **c.** $m \angle A = 43°, a = 28, b = 42$

   b. $m \angle A = 69°, a = 43, b = 37$

9. Solve triangle ABC, given $m \angle A = 33°, a = 15$, and $b = 23$.

10. Each of the following vectors is expressed in polar form. Give the equivalent rectangular form.

    a. $[4, 120°]$ **c.** $[2, 90°]$

    b. $[5, -135°]$ **d.** $[3, 50°]$

11. Each of the following vectors is expressed in rectangular form. Give the equivalent polar form.

    a. $[5, -5]$ **b.** $[0, 4]$ **c.** $[-3, 3\sqrt{3}]$ **d.** $[2, 4]$

12. Express each sum in rectangular form.

    a. $[8, -3] + [2, 7]$ **c.** $[2, 150°] + [4, -60°]$

    b. $[-5, 6] + [-2, -3]$ **d.** $[3, 120°] + [5, 90°]$

13. Given $\overrightarrow{A}$, specified by $[4, -30°]$, with initial point $(5, 3)$.

    a. Construct $\overrightarrow{A}$.

    b. Construct horizontal and vertical vector components of $\overrightarrow{A}$.

    c. Determine the magnitudes of the horizontal and vertical vector components of $\overrightarrow{A}$.

14. Given $\overrightarrow{AB}$ with $A(-2, 5)$ and $B(3, -4)$, determine the x- and y-components of $\overrightarrow{AB}$.

15. Given force vectors $\overrightarrow{A}$, $\overrightarrow{B}$, and $\overrightarrow{C}$ specified by $[10, 4]$, $[-6, 8]$ and $[4, -6]$, respectively, construct their resultant.

16. A 200-pound block is held stationary on a plane inclined at 30° to the horizontal by a force A operating parallel to and up the plane and a force B perpendicular to the plane. Determine the magnitudes of $\overrightarrow{A}$ and $\overrightarrow{B}$.

17. Compute the inner product of each pair of vectors specified below.

    a. $[4, 42°]$ and $[3, 72°]$ **c.** $[-3, 4]$ and $[2, 5]$

    b. $[2, 40°]$ and $[5, 175°]$ **d.** $[8, 6]$ and $[3, -4]$

18. Determine x for each of the following so that the two vectors in each case are perpendicular.

    a. $[4, 6]$ and $[x, 2]$ **b.** $[1.2, 0.6]$ and $[x, 6]$

19. How much work is done while moving a 50-pound object 30 feet up a plane inclined at 20° to the horizontal?

20. How much work is done by a force of 30 pounds acting at an angle of 60° to a displacement of 20 feet?

CHAPTER TEST

1. Given right triangle ABC with $b = 4$ and $c = 6$, determine the following.
    a. $\sin m \angle A$ **b.** $\cot m \angle B$

2. Given right triangle ABC with $a = 23$ and $m \angle B = 37°$, determine c.

3. A boy 4 feet 6 inches tall casts a shadow 3 feet 8 inches long. Determine the angle of elevation of the sun at that time.

4. Given triangle ABC with $m \angle A = 43°$, $m \angle B = 26°$ and $c = 22$, determine a.

5. Given triangle ABC with $m \angle A = 42°$, $b = 12$, and $c = 15$, determine a.

6. Given triangle ABC with $a = 5$, $b = 7$, and $c = 10$, determine $m \angle A$ to the nearest degree.

7. Express the following polar forms of vectors in their equivalent rectangular form.
   a. [6, 150°]   b. [4, −45°]

8. Given $\overrightarrow{AB}$ with $A(−3, 1)$ and $B(4, 2)$, determine the rectangular form of $\overrightarrow{AB}$.

9. Express the following rectangular forms of vectors in their equivalent polar forms.
   a. [−2, 2]   b. [4√3, −4]

10. Express each sum in rectangular form.
    a. [−5, 3] + [2, −6]   b. [4, 135°] + [2, −60°]

11. Forces A, B, and C act on an object leaving it in equilibrium. Vector $\overrightarrow{C}$ is specified by [20, −90°]. The directions of $\overrightarrow{A}$ and $\overrightarrow{B}$ are determined by 45° and 120°, respectively.
    a. Draw a vector diagram which shows that $\overrightarrow{A} + \overrightarrow{B} + \overrightarrow{C}$ is a zero vector.
    b. Write the system of two linear equations which you would solve to determine the magnitudes of $\overrightarrow{A}$ and $\overrightarrow{B}$.

12. Compute the inner product of each pair of vectors specified below.
    a. [3, 50°] and [5, 110°]   b. [2, 6] and [−3, 4]

13. Determine x so that the vectors [5, 10] and [4, x] are perpendicular.

14. How much work is done by a force of 100 pounds acting at an angle of 30° through a displacement of 10 feet?

15. Determine the area of triangle ABC if $b = 10$, $c = 20$ and $m \angle A = 30°$.

CUMULATIVE REVIEW
CHAPTERS 8–10

1. State the domain of Cos and the range of Arccos. [Caution: Cos is a cap-trigonometric function; Arccos is an inverse of a cap-trigonometric function.]

2. Determine the values of the following.

   a. $\text{Arcsin} \dfrac{-1}{2}$ c. $\text{Arctan} \sqrt{3}$ e. $\text{Arccos} \dfrac{1}{2}$ g. $\sin\left(\text{Arccos} \dfrac{2}{5}\right)$

   b. $\text{Cos}^{-1} \dfrac{-\sqrt{3}}{2}$ d. $\text{Sin}^{-1} \dfrac{\sqrt{2}}{2}$ f. $\text{Tan}^{-1} \dfrac{-\sqrt{3}}{3}$ h. $\cos(\text{Tan}^{-1} 3)$

3. What set of angle measures is equal to $\text{arcsin} \dfrac{1}{2}$?

4. Determine each of the following.
   a. $\text{Arcsin} (\cos 135°)$ c. $\text{Arctan} (\tan 120°)$

   b. $\text{Cos}^{-1}\left(\sin \dfrac{5\pi}{4}\right)$ d. $\text{Sin}^{-1}\left(\cos \dfrac{-5\pi}{6}\right)$

5. Compute each value.

   a. $\cos\left(2 \text{Arcsin} \dfrac{-3}{4}\right)$ b. $\tan\left(\text{Arctan} \dfrac{3}{4} + \text{Arcsin} \dfrac{5}{13}\right)$

6. Express the following in terms of z.

   a. $\cos (\mathrm{Tan}^{-1} z)$ for $z > 0$ **c.** $\sin (2\ \mathrm{Tan}^{-1} z)$ for $z > 0$

   b. $\tan (\mathrm{Arccos}\ 2z)$ for $z < 0$ **d.** $\cos (\mathrm{Arccos}\ z - \mathrm{Arcsin}\ z)$ for $z < 0$

7. Use inverse notation to express all the solutions of $6 \sin u° - 4 = 2 \sin u° - 3$.

8. Compute and express the results in rectangular form.

   a. $(7 - 2i) - (4 - 5i)$ **c.** $(2 + 3i) \div (3 - 4i)$

   b. $(3 - 3i)(-2 + 4i)$ **d.** $(\sqrt{6} + 2i)(\sqrt{6} - 2i)$

9. Express each of the following complex numbers in polar form.

   a. $4\sqrt{3} - 4i$ **b.** $-3i$ **c.** $-3\sqrt{2} + 3\sqrt{2}i$ **d.** $3(\cos 50° - i \sin 50°)$

10. Express each of the following in rectangular form.

   a. $5\sqrt{2}\ (\cos 225° + i \sin 225°)$ **b.** $3.2(\cos 90° + i \sin 90°)$

11. Simplify.

   a. $\sqrt{-75} + \sqrt{-12}$ **b.** $\sqrt{-2} \cdot \sqrt{-8}$

12. Determine the complex number solutions of each equation.

   a. $z^2 = -6$ **b.** $z^2 + 2z + 3 = 0$

13. Determine the four distinct fourth roots of $8 + 8\sqrt{3}i$.

14. Compute, expressing each result in polar form.

   a. $2\sqrt{3}(\cos 70° + i \sin 70°) \cdot \sqrt{3}(\cos 70° + i \sin 70°)$

   b. $\dfrac{15(\cos 40° + i \sin 40°)}{10(\cos 30° + i \sin 30°)}$

   c. $[\sqrt{3}(\cos 11° + i \sin 11°)]^6$

   d. $[2(\cos 21° + i \sin 21°)]^{-3}$

15. Given right triangle ABC with $a = 2$ and $c = 5$. Determine $\tan m \angle A$ and determine $m \angle B$.

16. Determine the area of oblique triangle ABC, given $m \angle A = 60°$, $b = 7$ and $c = 8$.

17. Determine the area of right triangle ABC, if $AB = 15$ and $\tan m \angle A = \dfrac{4}{3}$.

18. Determine $\sin m \angle A$ for triangle ABC, given $m \angle B = 30°$, $a = 5$ and $b = 4$.

19. Determine a for oblique triangle ABC, where $m \angle A = 43°$, $m \angle B = 57°$ and $c = 24$.

20. Determine $\cos m \angle A$ for triangle ABC, where $a = 10$, $b = 5$ and $c = 6$.

21. Determine a for triangle ABC, where $m \angle A = 60°$, $b = 4$ and $c = 6$.

22. The angle of depression from the top of a lighthouse to a ship at sea is $10°20'$. The lighthouse is 150 feet high. How far is the ship from the lighthouse?

23. Give the rectangular form of the vectors specified by $[10, 150°]$.

24. Give the polar form of the vectors specified by $[-6, 6\sqrt{3}]$.

25. Express each sum in rectangular form.

    a. $[5, -4] + [3, 7]$ **b.** $[3, 150°] + [5, -120°]$

26. Determine the magnitudes of the horizontal and vertical vector components of $\overrightarrow{A}$, where $\overrightarrow{A}$ is specified by $[5, 30°]$.

27. Specify the resultant of vectors $\overrightarrow{A}$, $\overrightarrow{B}$ and $\overrightarrow{C}$, where the vectors are specified by $[3, 9]$, $[-4, 2]$ and $[5, -6]$, respectively.

28. A 50-pound mass is held stationary on a plane inclined at $30°$ to the horizontal by a force A operating up the plane and a force B operating perpendicular to the plane. Determine the magnitudes of $\overrightarrow{A}$ and $\overrightarrow{B}$.

29. Compute the inner product of each pair of vectors specified below.

    a. $[2, 37°]$ and $[5, 97°]$ **b.** $[4, -2]$ and $[-3, -5]$

30. Determine x so that the vectors specified by $[5, 3]$ and $[x, 4]$ are perpendicular.

31. How many foot-pounds of work are done by a force of 20 pounds acting at an angle of $45°$ through a displacement of 30 feet?

32. How much work is done while moving a 40-pound mass 25 feet up a plane inclined at $30°$ to the horizontal?

33. A level road runs due north beside a cliff. From the top of the cliff, the angles of depression to two successive half-mile posts to the north are $42°$ and $68°$, respectively. Determine the height of the cliff above the road.

34. For each oblique triangle ABC specified below, determine the values of $\dfrac{\sin m \angle A}{\sin m \angle B}$ and $\dfrac{\sin m \angle C}{\sin m \angle A}$.

    a. $a = 7$, $b = 4$, $c = 9$ **b.** $a = 8$, $b = 20$, $c = 16$

35. Given triangle ABC with $b = 4$, $c = 15$, and $m \angle A = 30°$, determine the area of triangle ABC.

ACCURACY

Data which are obtained by measuring with an instrument are never exact. Suppose, for example, that an instrument, calibrated in units of 0.01 inch, were used to measure the inside of a cylinder. If the measurement is read as 3.42 inches, this tells us that the actual length is closer to 3.42 than to either 3.41 or 3.43 inches. Figure A–1 shows four segments, the length of each of which would be read as 3.42 inches on the ruler shown. Note that every segment whose terminal point is between A (3.415) and B (3.425) would be reported as being 3.42 inches long. Hence, a measurement of 3.42 inches means that the true length x is in the interval $3.415 < x < 3.425$ and has a *possible error* of 0.005 inch.

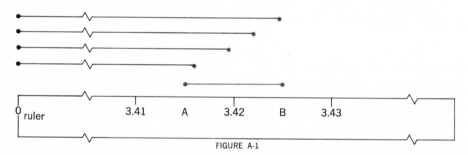

FIGURE A-1

The three digits, 3, 4, and 2, in 3.42, are considered to be significant. We say that this measurement is *accurate to three significant digits*, or, simply, *accurate to three digits*.

To tell the number of significant digits in the expression of a measurement, we may use *scientific notation*. You will recall that every positive number x may be expressed in scientific notation as $x = n(10^k)$ where $1 \leq n < 10$ and k is an integer. For example,

$$.00432 = 4.32 \times 10^{-3} \qquad 432 = 4.32 \times 10^2 \qquad 4.32 = 4.32 \times 10^0$$

Thus, a measurement of x units may be expressed in scientific notation as $n(10^k)$ units, where the numeral for n contains *only the significant digits*.

The following four measurements are each accurate to 3 significant digits.

> 23.7 mm. since it is equal to $2.37(10^1)$ mm.
> .00512 ft. since it is equal to $5.12(10^{-3})$ ft.
> 609 yd. since it is equal to $6.09(10^2)$ yd.
> .0406 cm. since it is equal to $4.06(10^{-2})$ cm.

Observe in the examples above that

> 1. zeros between non-zero digits, as in 609 yd., are always significant.
> 2. for numbers less than one, as in .00512 ft., zeros between the

decimal point and the first non-zero digit are never significant.

For a measurement such as 3200 feet, the zeros may or may not be significant. There are three possibilities for a measurement of 3200 feet.

1. If correct to the nearest 100 feet, it means 32 multiples of 100 feet and there are two significant digits. This is indicated as $3.2(10^3)$ ft. in scientific notation.
2. If correct to the nearest 10 feet, it means 320 multiples of 10 feet and there are three significant digits as indicated by $3.20(10^3)$ ft.
3. If correct to the nearest 1 foot, it means 3200 multiples of 1 foot and there are four significant digits as indicated by $3.200(10^3)$ ft.

For a measurement such as 6.20 cm., it is implied that the measuring instrument is calibrated to 0.01 cm. and that the length is closer to 6.20 than to 6.19 or 6.21 cm. It is accurate to three significant digits. A measurement recorded as 6.2 cm. implies a calibration of 0.1 cm.; it means that the length of the object is closer to 6.2 than to 6.1 or 6.3 cm. In scientific notation, 6.20 cm. and 6.2 cm. are expressed as $6.20(10^0)$ cm. and $6.2(10^0)$ cm., respectively.

The greatest *possible error* in a measurement of 43.12 cm. is .005 cm., since the true length x must be in the interval $43.115 < x < 43.125$. The accuracy of a measurement is determined by its *relative error*, the ratio of the possible error to the actual measurement. For example, a measurement of 43.12 cm. is more accurate than one of 7.94 cm., since the relative error of the first, .005/43.12, is less than that of the second, .005/7.94. Observe that 43.12 cm. is accurate to 4 digits while 7.94 cm. is accurate to 3 digits and, in general, a measurement to n digits is more accurate than one to $n - 1$ digits.

Whenever you are directed to *round* data, it is to either (1) a specified number of significant digits or (2) a specified number of decimal places. For example, to an accuracy of two digits,

4.37 cm. is rounded to 4.4 cm.   0.0632 mm. is rounded to 0.063 mm.
7380 ft. is rounded to 7400 ft.   6.02 gm. is rounded to 6.0 gm.

and to an accuracy of two decimal places,

7.218 cm. is rounded to 7.22 cm.   0.063 mm. is rounded to 0.06 mm.

Whenever the block of digits being dropped is 5, 50, 500, etc., it is common practice in scientific and statistical work to round so that the last remaining significant digit is even. For example,

73,500 is rounded to 74,000, accurate to 2 digits
6.250 is rounded to 6.2, accurate to 1 decimal place.

In computations involving measurement data, you must be careful not to obtain a greater degree of accuracy than is warranted. If the dimensions of a rectangle were measured as 4.3 in. and 6.72 in., then the true area of the rectangle would be between a minimum of

4.25×6.715 sq. in., which is equal to 28.53875 sq. in., and a maximum of

4.35 × 6.725 sq. in., which is equal to 29.25375 sq. in.

The best estimate of the true area is 29 sq. in., with accuracy to 2 significant digits. Observe that the product, 4.3 × 6.72 = 28.896, rounded to 2-digit accuracy, also gives 29. Hence, as a rule, a *product* or *quotient* involving measurement data should be rounded to the same degree of accuracy as the least accurate factor.

If four recorded measurements of 6.37 cm., 2.4 cm., 8.237 cm., and 5.68 cm. are to be added, then the true sum is between a minimum of 22.6265 cm. and a maximum of 22.7475 cm. as shown below. The best estimate of the sum is 22.7 cm., accurate to one decimal place. Observe that (1) adding the recorded data and rounding or (2) rounding the recorded data and adding also yield the best estimate of the sum where the rounding is to the same number of decimal places as the data with the fewest decimal places. Hence, a rule for the *addition* and *subtraction* of measurement data is that the result should contain no more decimal places than the data with the fewest decimal places.

Minimum	Recorded	Maximum	Rounded
6.365	6.37	6.375	6.4
2.35	2.4	2.45	2.4
8.2365	8.237	8.2375	8.2
5.675	5.68	5.685	5.7
22.6265	22.687	22.7475	22.7

EXERCISES

1. Tell the number of significant digits for each of the following measurements.

a. 47.02 mm.　　　c. 0.0032 gm.　　　e. 78.0 cm.

b. 1024 ft.　　　d. 43.20 cm.　　　f. 2800 miles, correct to the nearest ten miles

2. Round each of the following to an accuracy of two significant digits.

a. 0.7848　　　c. 71.50　　　e. 5.772

b. 58600　　　d. 0.625　　　f. 0.00684

3. Round each of the following to an accuracy of two decimal places.

a. 4.713　　　c. 3.2047　　　e. 1.665

b. 6.2887　　　d. 5.466　　　f. 3.7350

4. Compute the area of each triangle, where the base b and the altitude h were measured as given below.

a. $b = 12.4$ cm.; $h = 8.7$ cm.　　　*answer:* 54 sq. cm.

b. $b = 5.62$ in.; $h = 6.13$ in.

c. $b = 42.62$ ft.; $h = 30.4$ ft.

INTERPOLATION

Suppose you are given a number θ to three decimal places and you are to determine approximations of $\sin \theta$ and $\cos \theta$ by the use of Table I. This can be achieved by using the technique of *interpolation*. This technique will be illustrated for an increasing linear function f specified by $f(x) = 0.7x + 1$. The graph of f and a table of values for x and $f(x)$ are given in Figure B–1.

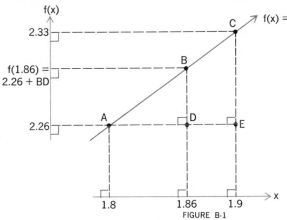

x	f(x)
1.1	1.77
1.2	1.84
1.3	1.91
1.4	1.98
1.5	2.05
1.6	2.12
1.7	2.19
1.8	2.26
1.9	2.33
2.0	2.40
2.1	2.47
2.2	2.54

FIGURE B-1

Observe in Figure B–1 that

    1. $f(1.8) = 2.26$ and $f(1.9) = 2.33$
    2. $f(1.86) = 2.26 + BD$
    3. $\triangle ABD$ is similar to $\triangle ACE$

Hence,
$$\frac{AD}{AE} = \frac{BD}{CE}$$
$$\frac{.06}{.1} = \frac{BD}{.07}$$
$$BD = \frac{.06 \times .07}{.1} = .042 \doteq .04$$

Thus, $f(1.86) = 2.26 + BD \doteq 2.30$.

To determine $f(1.53)$, with accuracy to two decimal places, it is convenient to arrange the work as shown below. Note that $1.5 < 1.53 < 1.6$ and, hence, $2.05 < f(1.53) < 2.12$; furthermore, $f(1.53) = 2.05 + n$.

$$.1 \left[\begin{array}{c} .03 \left[\begin{array}{cc} x & f(x) \\ 1.5 & 2.05 \\ 1.53 & ? \\ 1.6 & 2.12 \end{array} \right] n \end{array} \right] .07$$

The changes in x, (.03 and .1), are proportional to the changes in $f(x)$, (n and .07). Thus,

$$\frac{.03}{.1} = \frac{n}{.07}$$

$$\frac{3}{10} = \frac{n}{.07}$$

$$n = \frac{3(.07)}{10} = \frac{.21}{10} = .021 \doteq .02$$

Hence, $f(1.53) = 2.05 + n \doteq 2.05 + .02 = 2.07$.

To determine x to two decimal places so that $f(x) = 2.22$, we proceed as follows. Note that $2.19 < 2.22 < 2.26$ and $1.7 < x < 1.8$ and $x = 1.7 + n$.

$$.1 \begin{bmatrix} n \begin{bmatrix} \begin{array}{cc} x & f(x) \\ 1.7 & 2.19 \\ ? & 2.22 \\ 1.8 & 2.26 \end{array} \end{bmatrix} .03 \end{bmatrix} .07$$

The changes in x, (n and 0.1), are proportional to the changes in $f(x)$, (.03 and .07). Thus,

$$\frac{n}{.1} = \frac{.03}{.07}$$

$$n = .1\left(\frac{3}{7}\right) \doteq .04$$

Hence, $x = 1.7 + n \doteq 1.7 + .04 = 1.74$.

The graphs of sine and cosine are not straight lines; however, over a short interval they do not depart very much from a straight line. Hence, we shall use *linear* interpolation as in the preceding discussion whenever θ is given to three decimal places. Study the following examples to learn how this is done.

Example 1   Use Table I and interpolate to determine sin 1.213, with accuracy to four decimal places.

$$.01 \begin{bmatrix} .003 \begin{bmatrix} \begin{array}{cc} \theta & \sin\theta \\ 1.21 & .9356 \\ 1.213 & ? \\ 1.22 & .9391 \end{array} \end{bmatrix} n \end{bmatrix} .0035$$

$$\frac{.003}{.01} = \frac{n}{.0035}$$

$$\frac{3}{10} = \frac{n}{.0035}$$

$$n = \frac{3(.0035)}{10} = \frac{.0105}{10} = .00105$$

Thus, sin $1.213 \doteq 0.9356 + .00105 \doteq 0.9366$. Notice that we rounded 0.93665 to 0.9366. Read Appendix A, page 290, for a discussion of the rules for rounding data.

Example 2 Determine cos 1.223, with accuracy to four decimal places.

$$.01 \begin{bmatrix} .003 \begin{bmatrix} \begin{array}{cc} \theta & \cos \theta \\ 1.22 & 0.3436 \\ 1.223 & ? \end{array} \end{bmatrix} n \\ 1.23 \quad 0.3342 \end{bmatrix} -.0094$$

Observe that while θ is increasing, cos θ is decreasing. Thus, for a positive change in θ, the change in cos θ is negative. Thus,

$$\frac{.003}{.01} = \frac{n}{-.0094}$$

$$\frac{3}{10} = \frac{n}{-.0094}$$

$$n = \frac{3(-.0094)}{10} = \frac{-.0282}{10} = -.00282 \doteq -.0028$$

Hence, cos $1.223 \doteq 0.3436 + n \doteq 0.3436 + (-.0028) = 0.3408$.

Interpolation also permits us to express θ, with accuracy to *three* decimal places, for a given value of cos θ or sin θ. The next two examples show how this is done.

Example 3 Determine θ, with accuracy to three decimal places, if sin $\theta \doteq$ 0.9377 and $0 < \theta < \frac{\pi}{2}$.

$$.01 \begin{bmatrix} n \begin{bmatrix} \begin{array}{cc} \theta & \sin \theta \\ 1.21 & 0.9356 \\ ? & 0.9377 \end{array} \end{bmatrix} .0021 \\ 1.22 \quad 0.9391 \end{bmatrix} .0035$$

$$\frac{n}{.01} = \frac{.0021}{.0035}$$

$$n = \frac{21}{35} \times .01 = .006$$

Hence, $\theta = 1.21 + .006 = 1.216$.

Example 4 Determine θ to three decimal places if cos $\theta \doteq 0.3382$ and $0 < \theta < \frac{\pi}{2}$.

$$.01 \begin{bmatrix} n \begin{bmatrix} \begin{array}{cc} \theta & \cos \theta \\ 1.22 & 0.3436 \\ ? & 0.3382 \end{array} \end{bmatrix} -.0054 \\ 1.23 \quad 0.3342 \end{bmatrix} -.0094$$

$$\frac{n}{.01} = \frac{-.0054}{-.0094}$$

$$n = \frac{54}{94} \times .01 \doteq 0.006$$

Hence, $\theta = 1.22 + n \doteq 1.22 + 0.006 = 1.226$.

Suppose you are given a number x to four significant digits and you are to determine an approximation of $\log x$ by the use of Table IV. This can be achieved by the technique of linear interpolation, since the graph of log does not depart very much from a straight line over a short interval. Study the following example to learn how this is done.

Example Use Table IV and interpolate to determine $\log 2.574$, with accuracy to four decimal places.

$$.01 \left[.004 \left[\begin{array}{cc} x & \log x \\ 2.57 & .4099 \\ 2.574 & ? \end{array} \right] n \right] .0017$$
$$2.58 \qquad .4116$$

$$\frac{.004}{.01} = \frac{n}{.0017}$$

$$n = \frac{4(.0017)}{10} = \frac{.0068}{10} \doteq .0007$$

Thus, $\log 2.574 \doteq .4099 + n \doteq .4106$.

Conversely, interpolation also permits us to express x, with accuracy to four significant digits, for a given value of $\log x$. The next example shows how this is done.

Example Determine x, with accuracy to four significant digits, if $\log x \doteq .4241$.

$$.01 \left[n \left[\begin{array}{cc} x & \log x \\ 2.65 & .4232 \\ ? & .4241 \end{array} \right] .0009 \right] .0017$$
$$2.66 \qquad .4249$$

$$\frac{n}{.01} = \frac{.0009}{.0017}$$

$$n = \frac{9(.01)}{17} \doteq .005$$

Thus, $x = 2.65 + .005 \doteq 2.655$.

LOGARITHMS

In the solving of triangles, a solution may be expressed as a product or a quotient. In this appendix we review the computing of an approximation of a product or a quotient by the use of *logarithms*. First, we shall review how to determine $\log x$ for $x > 0$. Recall that $\log x$ $(x > 0)$ is defined so that

$$\log x = a \text{ if and only if } x = 10^a$$

For example,   if $x = 1000 = 10^3$, then $\log 1000 = 3$

if $x = .01 = 10^{-2}$, then $\log .01 = -2$

If x is not an integer power of 10, then $\log x$ may be approximated as follows.
1. For each real number x in the interval $1 \le x < 10$, $\log x$ is in the interval $0 \le \log x < 1$.
   a. If x is given to two decimal places, then $\log x$ is given to four decimal places by Table IV. Figure C–1 shows a portion of Table IV and indicates how to read this table to determine that $\log 4.21 \doteq .6243$ and that $\log 4.42 \doteq .6454$. In Table IV, all decimal points have been omitted but are to be assumed as shown in Figure C–1.

N	0	1	2	3
4.0	.6021			.6053
4.1	.6128			.6160
4.2		.6243		.6263
4.3	.6335	.6345		.6365
4.4			.6454	.6464

Figure C–1

   b. If x is given to three decimal places, then $\log x$ is determined to four decimal places by interpolating in Table IV, as shown in Appendix B on pages 293–296.
2. Each positive number x may be expressed in scientific notation as $x = n \cdot 10^k$, where $1 \le n < 10$ and k is an integer. For example,

    $.00279 = 2.79 \times 10^{-3}$ $279 = 2.79 \times 10^2$
        $2.79 = 2.79 \times 10^0$ $27900 = 2.79 \times 10^4$

3. For each positive number x *not* in the interval $1 \le x < 10$, let x be expressed in scientific notation as $x = n \cdot 10^k$. Then $\log x = \log (n \cdot 10^k) = k + \log n$. For example,

$\log 4420 = \log (4.42 \times 10^3) = 3 + \log 4.42 \doteq 3 + .6454$
$\log 44.2 = \log (4.42 \times 10^1) = 1 + \log 4.42 \doteq 1 + .6454$
$\log .442 = \log (4.42 \times 10^{-1}) = -1 + \log 4.42 \doteq -1 + .6454$
$\log .00442 = \log (4.42 \times 10^{-3}) = -3 + \log 4.42 \doteq -3 + .6454$

The integer k is called the *characteristic* of log x; log n is called the *mantissa* of log x. For log $4420 = 3 + \log 4.42 \doteq 3 + .6454$, the characteristic is 3 and the mantissa is .6454.

4. Given log $x = k + \log n$, where k is an integer and log n is in the interval $0 \leq \log n < 1$, x is given by $x = n \cdot 10^k$.

 a. Suppose log $x \doteq 3 + .6243$

 From Table IV we find that log $4.21 \doteq .6243$

 Hence, $x \doteq 4.21 \times 10^3 = 4210$.

 b. Suppose log $x \doteq -2 + .6454$

 From Table IV, log $4.42 \doteq .6454$

 Hence, $x \doteq 4.42 \times 10^{-2} = .0442$.

 c. Suppose log $x \doteq 2 + .3471$

 Log n is not found in Table IV, but n and x may be determined accurate to four digits by interpolating in Table IV as shown in Appendix B on pages 293–296.

The product of positive numbers may be approximated readily by logarithms. To achieve this, we use Table IV and the theorem which states that for all positive real numbers m and n,

$$\log (m \times n) = \log m + \log n.$$

Example 1   Compute 3.29×2.16 with accuracy to three significant digits.

$$\log (3.29 \times 2.16) = \log 3.29 + \log 2.16$$
$$\doteq .5172 + .3345 = .8517$$

In Table IV we find that .8517 is nearer log 7.11 than log 7.10. Therefore, $3.29 \times 2.16 \doteq 7.11$, accurate to three digits.

Example 2   Compute $3294 \times .04716$ with accuracy to four significant digits. Let $m = 3294$ and $n = .04716$. Interpolating in Table IV,

$$\log m \doteq 3 + .5177 \text{ and } \log n \doteq -2 + .6735.$$

Hence, $\log (m \times n) \doteq (3 + .5177) + (-2 + .6735)$

$$= 2 + .1912$$

Interpolating in Table IV, we find that log $1.553 \doteq .1912$. Hence, $3294 \times .04716 \doteq 155.3$, accurate to four digits.

The quotient of positive real numbers is approximated by using the theorem which states that for positive real numbers m and n,

$$\log \frac{m}{n} = \log m - \log n$$

Example 1   Compute $\dfrac{2.16}{3.29}$ with accuracy to three significant digits.

$$\log \frac{2.16}{3.29} = \log 2.16 - \log 3.29$$

$$\doteq .3345 - .5172 \qquad \text{[Table IV]}$$

$$= (-1 + 1.3345) - (.5172)$$

$$= -1 + .8173$$

Thus, $\frac{2.16}{3.29} \doteq .657$, accurate to three digits. [Table IV]

Observe that, since $.3345 - .5172 < 0$, we changed $.3345$ to $-1 + 1.3345$ so that $1.3345 - .5172$ would be positive.

Example 2   Compute $\frac{.05783}{43.62}$ with accuracy to four significant digits.

Let $m = .05783$ and $n = 43.62$. Interpolating in Table IV,

$$\log m \doteq -2 + .7621 \text{ and } \log n = 1 + .6397.$$

Hence, $\log \frac{m}{n} \doteq (-2 + .7621) - (1 + .6397)$

$$= -3 + .1224$$

Interpolating in Table IV, we find that $\log 1.325 \doteq .1224$.

Thus, $\frac{.05783}{43.62} \doteq .001325$, accurate to four digits.

To compute the value of expressions of either the form $\frac{ab}{c}$ or $\frac{a}{bc}$, we use one of the theorems which state that for all positive real numbers a, b, and c,

$$\log \frac{a \times b}{c} = \log a + \log b - \log c \qquad \log \frac{a}{b \times c} = \log a - (\log b + \log c)$$

Example 1   Compute $\frac{472 \times .0576}{.231}$ with accuracy to three significant digits.

$$\log \frac{472 \times .0576}{.231} = \log 472 + \log .0576 - \log .231$$

$$\doteq (2 + .6739) + (-2 + .7604) - (-1 + .3636)$$

$$= 2 + .0707$$

Thus, $\frac{472 \times .0576}{.231} \doteq 118$, accurate to three digits.

Example 2   Compute $\frac{27.2}{496 \times .0614}$ with accuracy to three significant digits.

$$\log \frac{27.2}{496 \times .0614} = \log 27.2 - [\log 496 + \log .0614]$$

$$\doteq (1 + .4346) - [(2 + .6955) + (-2 + .7882)]$$

$$= (0 + 1.4346) - (1 + .4837)$$

$$= -1 + .9509$$

Thus, $\frac{27.2}{496 \times .0614} \doteq .893$, accurate to three digits.

I   TRIGONOMETRIC FUNCTION VALUES (RADIANS)

x Rdn.	Degrees in x	sin x	cos x	tan x	x Rdn.	Degrees in x	sin x	cos x	tan x
.00	0°00'	.0000	1.0000	.0000	.40	22°55'	.3894	.9211	.4228
.01	0°34'	.0100	.9999	.0100	.41	23°30'	.3986	.9171	.4346
.02	1°09'	.0200	.9998	.0200	.42	24°04'	.4078	.9131	.4466
.03	1°43'	.0300	.9996	.0300	.43	24°38'	.4169	.9090	.4586
.04	2°18'	.0400	.9992	.0400	.44	25°13'	.4259	.9048	.4708
.05	2°52'	.0500	.9988	.0500	.45	25°47'	.4350	.9004	.4831
.06	3°26'	.0600	.9982	.0601	.46	26°21'	.4440	.8960	.4954
.07	4°01'	.0699	.9976	.0701	.47	26°56'	.4529	.8916	.5080
.08	4°35'	.0799	.9968	.0802	.48	27°30'	.4618	.8870	.5206
.09	5°09'	.0899	.9960	.0902	.49	28°04'	.4706	.8823	.5334
.10	5°44'	.0998	.9950	.1003	.50	28°39'	.4794	.8776	.5463
.11	6°18'	.1098	.9940	.1104	.51	29°13'	.4882	.8727	.5594
.12	6°52'	.1197	.9928	.1206	.52	29°48'	.4969	.8678	.5726
.13	7°27'	.1296	.9916	.1307	.53	30°22'	.5055	.8628	.5859
.14	8°01'	.1395	.9902	.1409	.54	30°56'	.5141	.8577	.5994
.15	8°36'	.1494	.9888	.1511	.55	31°31'	.5227	.8525	.6131
.16	9°10'	.1593	.9872	.1614	.56	32°05'	.5312	.8473	.6270
.17	9°44'	.1692	.9856	.1717	.57	32°40'	.5396	.8419	.6410
.18	10°19'	.1790	.9838	.1820	.58	33°14'	.5480	.8365	.6552
.19	10°53'	.1889	.9820	.1923	.59	33°48'	.5564	.8309	.6696
.20	11°28'	.1987	.9801	.2027	.60	34°23'	.5646	.8253	.6841
.21	12°02'	.2085	.9780	.2131	.61	34°57'	.5729	.8196	.6989
.22	12°36'	.2182	.9759	.2236	.62	35°31'	.5810	.8139	.7139
.23	13°11'	.2280	.9737	.2341	.63	36°06'	.5891	.8080	.7291
.24	13°45'	.2377	.9713	.2447	.64	36°40'	.5972	.8021	.7445
.25	14°19'	.2474	.9689	.2553	.65	37°14'	.6052	.7961	.7602
.26	14°54'	.2571	.9664	.2660	.66	37°49'	.6131	.7900	.7761
.27	15°28'	.2667	.9638	.2768	.67	38°23'	.6210	.7838	.7922
.28	16°03'	.2764	.9611	.2876	.68	38°58'	.6288	.7776	.8087
.29	16°37'	.2860	.9582	.2984	.69	39°32'	.6365	.7712	.8253
.30	17°11'	.2955	.9553	.3093	.70	40°06'	.6442	.7648	.8423
.31	17°46'	.3051	.9523	.3203	.71	40°41'	.6518	.7584	.8595
.32	18°20'	.3146	.9492	.3314	.72	41°15'	.6594	.7518	.8771
.33	18°54'	.3240	.9460	.3425	.73	41°50'	.6669	.7452	.8949
.34	19°29'	.3335	.9428	.3537	.74	42°24'	.6743	.7385	.9131
.35	20°03'	.3429	.9394	.3650	.75	42°58'	.6816	.7317	.9316
.36	20°38'	.3523	.9359	.3764	.76	43°33'	.6889	.7248	.9504
.37	21°12'	.3616	.9323	.3879	.77	44°07'	.6961	.7179	.9697
.38	21°46'	.3709	.9287	.3994	.78	44°41'	.7033	.7109	.9893
.39	22°21'	.3802	.9249	.4110	.79	45°16'	.7104	.7038	1.0092
x Rdn.	Degrees in x	sin x	cos x	tan x	x Rdn.	Degrees in x	sin x	cos x	tan x

I   TRIGONOMETRIC FUNCTION VALUES (RADIANS)

x Rdn.	Degrees in x	sin x	cos x	tan x	x Rdn.	Degrees in x	sin x	cos x	tan x
.80	45°50′	.7174	.6967	1.0296	1.20	68°45′	.9320	.3624	2.5722
.81	46°25′	.7243	.6895	1.0505	1.21	69°20′	.9356	.3530	2.6503
.82	46°59′	.7312	.6822	1.0717	1.22	69°54′	.9391	.3436	2.7328
.83	47°33′	.7379	.6749	1.0934	1.23	70°28′	.9425	.3342	2.8198
.84	48°08′	.7446	.6675	1.1156	1.24	71°03′	.9458	.3248	2.9119
.85	48°42′	.7513	.6600	1.1383	1.25	71°37′	.9490	.3153	3.0096
.86	49°16′	.7578	.6524	1.1616	1.26	72°12′	.9521	.3058	3.1133
.87	49°51′	.7643	.6448	1.1853	1.27	72°46′	.9551	.2963	3.2236
.88	50°25′	.7707	.6372	1.2097	1.28	73°20′	.9580	.2867	3.3413
.89	51°00′	.7771	.6294	1.2346	1.29	73°55′	.9608	.2771	3.4672
.90	51°34′	.7833	.6216	1.2602	1.30	74°29′	.9636	.2675	3.6021
.91	52°08′	.7895	.6138	1.2864	1.31	75°03′	.9662	.2578	3.7471
.92	52°43′	.7956	.6058	1.3133	1.32	75°38′	.9687	.2482	3.9033
.93	53°17′	.8016	.5978	1.3409	1.33	76°12′	.9712	.2385	4.0723
.94	53°52′	.8076	.5898	1.3692	1.34	76°47′	.9735	.2288	4.2556
.95	54°26′	.8134	.5817	1.3984	1.35	77°21′	.9757	.2190	4.4552
.96	55°00′	.8192	.5735	1.4284	1.36	77°55′	.9779	.2092	4.6734
.97	55°35′	.8249	.5653	1.4592	1.37	78°30′	.9799	.1994	4.9131
.98	56°09′	.8305	.5570	1.4910	1.38	79°04′	.9818	.1896	5.1774
.99	56°43′	.8360	.5487	1.5237	1.39	79°38′	.9837	.1798	5.4707
1.00	57°18′	.8415	.5403	1.5574	1.40	80°13′	.9854	.1700	5.7979
1.01	57°52′	.8468	.5319	1.5922	1.41	80°47′	.9871	.1601	6.1654
1.02	58°26′	.8521	.5234	1.6281	1.42	81°22′	.9886	.1502	6.5811
1.03	59°01′	.8573	.5148	1.6652	1.43	81°56′	.9901	.1403	7.0555
1.04	59°35′	.8624	.5062	1.7036	1.44	82°30′	.9915	.1304	7.6018
1.05	60°10′	.8674	.4976	1.7433	1.45	83°05′	.9927	.1205	8.2381
1.06	60°44′	.8724	.4889	1.7844	1.46	83°39′	.9939	.1106	8.9886
1.07	61°18′	.8772	.4801	1.8270	1.47	84°14′	.9949	.1006	9.8874
1.08	61°53′	.8820	.4713	1.8712	1.48	84°48′	.9959	.0907	10.983
1.09	62°27′	.8866	.4625	1.9171	1.49	85°22′	.9967	.0807	12.350
1.10	63°02′	.8912	.4536	1.9648	1.50	85°57′	.9975	.0707	14.101
1.11	63°36′	.8957	.4447	2.0143	1.51	86°31′	.9982	.0608	16.428
1.12	64°10′	.9001	.4357	2.0660	1.52	87°05′	.9987	.0508	19.670
1.13	64°45′	.9044	.4267	2.1198	1.53	87°40′	.9992	.0408	24.498
1.14	65°19′	.9086	.4176	2.1759	1.54	88°14′	.9995	.0308	32.461
1.15	65°53′	.9128	.4085	2.2345	1.55	88°48′	.9998	.0208	48.078
1.16	66°28′	.9168	.3993	2.2958	1.56	89°23′	.9999	.0108	92.620
1.17	67°02′	.9208	.3902	2.3600	1.57	89°57′	1.0000	.0008	1255.8
1.18	67°36′	.9246	.3809	2.4273	1.58	90°32′	1.0000	−.0092	−108.65
1.19	68°11′	.9284	.3717	2.4979	1.59	91°06′	.9998	−.0192	−52.067
x Rdn.	Degrees in x	sin x	cos x	tan x	x Rdn.	Degrees in x	sin x	cos x	tan x

II POWERS, ROOTS, AND RECIPROCALS 1-100

n	n^2	n^3	$\sqrt{n}$	$\sqrt[3]{n}$	$1/n$	n	n^2	n^3	$\sqrt{n}$	$\sqrt[3]{n}$	$1/n$
1	1	1	1.000	1.000	1.0000	51	2,601	132,651	7.141	3.708	.0196
2	4	8	1.414	1.260	.5000	52	2,704	140,608	7.211	3.733	.0192
3	9	27	1.732	1.442	.3333	53	2,809	148,877	7.280	3.756	.0189
4	16	64	2.000	1.587	.2500	54	2,916	157,464	7.348	3.780	.0185
5	25	125	2.236	1.710	.2000	55	3,025	166,375	7.416	3.803	.0182
6	36	216	2.449	1.817	.1667	56	3,136	175,616	7.483	3.826	.0179
7	49	343	2.646	1.913	.1429	57	3,249	185,193	7.550	3.849	.0175
8	64	512	2.828	2.000	.1250	58	3,364	195,112	7.616	3.871	.0172
9	81	729	3.000	2.080	.1111	59	3,481	205,379	7.681	3.893	.0169
10	100	1,000	3.162	2.154	.1000	60	3,600	216,000	7.746	3.915	.0167
11	121	1,331	3.317	2.224	.0909	61	3,721	226,981	7.810	3.936	.0164
12	144	1,728	3.464	2.289	.0833	62	3,844	238,328	7.874	3.958	.0161
13	169	2,197	3.606	2.351	.0769	63	3,969	250,047	7.937	3.979	.0159
14	196	2,744	3.742	2.410	.0714	64	4,096	262,144	8.000	4.000	.0156
15	225	3,375	3.873	2.466	.0667	65	4,225	274,625	8.062	4.021	.0154
16	256	4,096	4.000	2.520	.0625	66	4,356	287,496	8.124	4.041	.0152
17	289	4,913	4.123	2.571	.0588	67	4,489	300,763	8.185	4.062	.0149
18	324	5,832	4.243	2.621	.0556	68	4,624	314,432	8.246	4.082	.0147
19	361	6,859	4.359	2.668	.0526	69	4,761	328,509	8.307	4.102	.0145
20	400	8,000	4.472	2.714	.0500	70	4,900	343,000	8.367	4.121	.0143
21	441	9,261	4.583	2.759	.0476	71	5,041	357,911	8.426	4.141	.0141
22	484	10,648	4.690	2.802	.0455	72	5,184	373,248	8.485	4.160	.0139
23	529	12,167	4.796	2.844	.0435	73	5,329	389,017	8.544	4.179	.0137
24	576	13,824	4.899	2.884	.0417	74	5,476	405,224	8.602	4.198	.0135
25	625	15,625	5.000	2.924	.0400	75	5,625	421,875	8.660	4.217	.0133
26	676	17,576	5.099	2.962	.0385	76	5,776	438,976	8.718	4.236	.0132
27	729	19,683	5.196	3.000	.0370	77	5,929	456,533	8.775	4.254	.0130
28	784	21,952	5.292	3.037	.0357	78	6,084	474,552	8.832	4.273	.0128
29	841	24,389	5.385	3.072	.0345	79	6,241	493,039	8.888	4.291	.0127
30	900	27,000	5.477	3.107	.0333	80	6,400	512,000	8.944	4.309	.0125
31	961	29,791	5.568	3.141	.0323	81	6,561	531,441	9.000	4.327	.0123
32	1,024	32,768	5.657	3.175	.0312	82	6,724	551,368	9.055	4.344	.0122
33	1,089	35,937	5.745	3.208	.0303	83	6,889	571,787	9.110	4.362	.0120
34	1,156	39,304	5.831	3.240	.0294	84	7,056	592,704	9.165	4.380	.0119
35	1,225	42,875	5.916	3.271	.0286	85	7,225	614,125	9.220	4.397	.0118
36	1,296	46,656	6.000	3.302	.0278	86	7,396	636,056	9.274	4.414	.0116
37	1,369	50,653	6.083	3.332	.0270	87	7,569	658,503	9.327	4.431	.0115
38	1,444	54,872	6.164	3.362	.0263	88	7,744	681,472	9.381	4.448	.0114
39	1,521	59,319	6.245	3.391	.0256	89	7,921	704,969	9.434	4.465	.0112
40	1,600	64,000	6.325	3.420	.0250	90	8,100	729,000	9.487	4.481	.0111
41	1,681	68,921	6.403	3.448	.0244	91	8,281	753,571	9.539	4.498	.0110
42	1,764	74,088	6.481	3.476	.0238	92	8,464	778,688	9.592	4.514	.0109
43	1,849	79,507	6.557	3.503	.0233	93	8,649	804,357	9.644	4.531	.0108
44	1,936	85,184	6.633	3.530	.0227	94	8,836	830,584	9.695	4.547	.0106
45	2,025	91,125	6.708	3.557	.0222	95	9,025	857,375	9.747	4.563	.0105
46	2,116	97,336	6.782	3.583	.0217	96	9,216	884,736	9.798	4.579	.0104
47	2,209	103,823	6.856	3.609	.0213	97	9,409	912,673	9.849	4.595	.0103
48	2,304	110,592	6.928	3.634	.0208	98	9,604	941,192	9.899	4.610	.0102
49	2,401	117,649	7.000	3.659	.0204	99	9,801	970,299	9.950	4.626	.0101
50	2,500	125,000	7.071	3.684	.0200	100	10,000	1,000,000	10.000	4.642	.0100

III   TRIGONOMETRIC FUNCTION VALUES (DEGREES)

Degrees	Radians	Sin	Csc	Tan	Cot	Sec	Cos		
0° 0′	.0000	.0000	——	.0000	——	1.000	1.0000	1.5708	90° 0′
10′	029	029	343.8	029	343.8	000	000	679	50′
20′	058	058	171.9	058	171.9	000	000	650	40′
30′	.0087	.0087	114.6	.0087	114.6	1.000	1.0000	1.5621	30′
40′	116	116	85.95	116	85.94	000	.9999	592	20′
50′	145	145	68.76	145	68.75	000	999	563	10′
1° 0′	.0175	.0175	57.30	.0175	57.29	1.000	.9998	1.5533	89° 0′
10′	204	204	49.11	204	49.10	0c0	998	504	50′
20′	233	233	42.98	233	42.96	000	997	475	40′
30′	.0262	.0262	38.20	.0262	38.19	1.000	.9997	1.5446	30′
40′	291	291	34.38	291	34.37	000	996	417	20′
50′	320	320	31.26	320	31.24	001	995	388	10′
2° 0′	.0349	.0349	28.65	.0349	28.64	1.001	.9994	1.5359	88° 0′
10′	378	378	26.45	378	26.43	001	993	330	50′
20′	407	407	24.56	407	24.54	001	992	301	40′
30′	.0436	.0436	22.93	.0437	22.90	1.001	.9990	1.5272	30′
40′	465	465	21.49	466	21.47	001	989	243	20′
50′	495	494	20.23	495	20.21	001	988	213	10′
3° 0′	.0524	.0523	19.11	.0524	19.08	1.001	.9986	1.5184	87° 0′
10′	553	552	18.10	553	18.07	002	985	155	50′
20′	582	581	17.20	582	17.17	002	983	126	40′
30′	.0611	.0610	16.38	.0612	16.35	1.002	.9981	1.5097	30′
40′	640	640	15.64	641	15.60	002	980	068	20′
50′	669	669	14.96	670	14.92	002	978	039	10′
4° 0′	.0698	.0698	14.34	.0699	14.30	1.002	.9976	1.5010	86° 0′
10′	727	727	13.76	729	13.73	003	974	981	50′
20′	756	756	13.23	758	13.20	003	971	952	40′
30′	.0785	.0785	12.75	.0787	12.71	1.003	.9969	1.4923	30′
40′	814	814	12.29	816	12.25	003	967	893	20′
50′	844	843	11.87	846	11.83	004	964	864	10′
5° 0′	.0873	.0872	11.47	.0875	11.43	1.004	.9962	1.4835	85° 0′
10′	902	901	11.10	904	11.06	004	959	806	50′
20′	931	929	10.76	934	10.71	004	957	777	40′
30′	.0960	.0958	10.43	.0963	10.39	1.005	.9954	1.4748	30′
40′	989	987	10.13	992	10.08	005	951	719	20′
50′	.1018	.1016	9.839	.1022	9.788	005	948	690	10′
6° 0′	.1047	.1045	9.567	.1051	9.514	1.006	.9945	1.4661	84° 0′
10′	076	074	9.309	080	9.255	006	942	632	50′
20′	105	103	9.065	110	9.010	006	939	603	40′
30′	.1134	.1132	8.834	.1139	8.777	1.006	.9936	1.4573	30′
40′	164	161	8.614	169	8.556	007	932	544	20′
50′	193	190	8.405	198	8.345	007	929	515	10′
7° 0′	.1222	.1219	8.206	.1228	8.144	1.008	.9925	1.4486	83° 0′
10′	251	248	8.016	257	7.953	008	922	457	50′
20′	280	276	7.834	287	7.770	008	918	428	40′
30′	.1309	.1305	7.661	.1317	7.596	1.009	.9914	1.4399	30′
40′	338	334	7.496	346	7.429	009	911	370	20′
50′	367	363	7.337	376	7.269	009	907	341	10′
8° 0′	.1396	.1392	7.185	.1405	7.115	1.010	.9903	1.4312	82° 0′
10′	425	421	7.040	435	6.968	010	899	283	50′
20′	454	449	6.900	465	6.827	011	894	254	40′
30′	.1484	.1478	6.765	.1495	6.691	1.011	.9890	1.4224	30′
40′	513	507	6.636	524	6.561	012	886	195	20′
50′	542	536	6.512	554	6.435	012	881	166	10′
9° 0′	.1571	.1564	6.392	.1584	6.314	1.012	.9877	1.4137	81° 0′
		Cos	Sec	Cot	Tan	Csc	Sin	Radians	Degrees

III   TRIGONOMETRIC FUNCTION VALUES (DEGREES)

Degrees	Radians	Sin	Csc	Tan	Cot	Sec	Cos		
9° 0'	.1571	.1564	6.392	.1584	6.314	1.012	.9877	1.4137	81° 0'
10'	600	593	277	614	197	013	872	108	50'
20'	629	622	166	644	6.084	013	868	079	40'
30'	.1658	.1650	6.059	.1673	5.976	1.014	.9863	1.4050	30'
40'	687	679	5.955	703	871	014	858	1.4021	20'
50'	716	708	855	733	769	015	853	1.3992	10'
10° 0'	.1745	.1736	5.759	.1763	5.671	1.015	.9848	1.3963	80° 0'
10'	774	765	665	793	576	016	843	934	50'
20'	804	794	575	823	485	016	838	904	40'
30'	.1833	.1822	5.487	.1853	5.396	1.017	.9833	1.3875	30'
40'	862	851	403	883	309	018	827	846	20'
50'	891	880	320	914	226	018	822	817	10'
11° 0'	.1920	.1908	5.241	.1944	5.145	1.019	.9816	1.3788	79° 0'
10'	949	937	164	.1974	5.066	019	811	759	50'
20'	978	965	089	.2004	4.989	020	805	730	40'
30'	.2007	.1994	5.016	.2035	4.915	1.020	.9799	1.3701	30'
40'	036	.2022	4.945	065	843	021	793	672	20'
50'	065	051	876	095	773	022	787	643	10'
12° 0'	.2094	2079	4.810	.2126	4.705	1.022	.9781	1.3614	78° 0'
10'	123	108	745	156	638	023	775	584	50'
20'	153	136	682	186	574	024	769	555	40'
30'	.2182	.2164	4.620	.2217	4.511	1.024	.9763	1.3526	30'
40'	211	193	560	247	449	025	757	497	20'
50'	240	221	502	278	390	026	750	468	10'
13° 0'	.2269	.2250	4.445	.2309	4.331	1.026	.9744	1.3439	77° 0'
10'	298	278	390	339	275	027	737	410	50'
20'	327	306	336	370	219	028	730	381	40'
30'	.2356	.2334	4.284	.2401	4.165	1.028	.9724	1.3352	30'
40'	385	363	232	432	113	029	717	323	20'
50'	414	391	182	462	061	030	710	294	10'
14° 0'	.2443	.2419	4.134	.2493	4.011	1.031	.9703	1.3265	76° 0'
10'	473	447	086	524	3.962	031	696	235	50'
20'	502	476	4.039	555	914	032	689	206	40'
30'	.2531	.2504	3.994	.2586	3.867	1.033	.9681	1.3177	30'
40'	560	532	950	617	821	034	674	148	20'
50'	589	560	906	648	776	034	667	119	10'
15° 0'	.2618	.2588	3.864	.2679	3.732	1.035	.9659	1.3090	75° 0'
10'	647	616	822	711	689	036	652	061	50'
20'	676	644	782	742	647	037	644	032	40'
30'	.2705	.2672	3.742	.2773	3.606	1.038	.9636	1.3003	30'
40'	734	700	703	805	566	039	628	1.2974	20'
50'	763	728	665	836	526	039	621	945	10'
16° 0'	.2793	.2756	3.628	.2867	3.487	1.040	.9613	1.2915	74° 0'
10'	822	784	592	899	450	041	605	886	50'
20'	851	812	556	931	412	042	596	857	40'
30'	.2880	.2840	3.521	.2962	3.376	1.043	.9588	1.2828	30'
40'	909	868	487	.2994	340	044	580	799	20'
50'	938	896	453	.3026	305	045	572	770	10'
17° 0'	.2967	.2924	3.420	.3057	3.271	1.046	.9563	1.2741	73° 0'
10'	996	952	388	089	237	047	555	712	50'
20'	.3025	.2979	357	121	204	048	546	683	40'
30'	.3054	.3007	3.326	.3153	3.172	1.048	.9537	1.2654	30'
40'	083	035	295	185	140	049	528	625	20'
50'	113	062	265	217	108	050	520	595	10'
18° 0'	.3142	.3090	3.236	.3249	3.078	1.051	.9511	1.2566	72° 0'
	Cos	Sec	Cot	Tan	Csc	Sin	Radians	Degrees	

III TRIGONOMETRIC FUNCTION VALUES (DEGREES)

Degrees	Radians	Sin	Csc	Tan	Cot	Sec	Cos		
18° 0′	.3142	.3090	3.236	.3249	3.078	1.051	.9511	1.2566	72° 0′
10′	171	118	207	281	047	052	502	537	50′
20′	200	145	179	314	3.018	053	492	508	40′
30′	.3229	.3173	3.152	.3346	2.989	1.054	.9483	1.2479	30′
40′	258	201	124	378	960	056	474	450	20′
50′	287	228	098	411	932	057	465	421	10′
19° 0′	.3316	.3256	3.072	.3443	2.904	1.058	.9455	1.2392	71° 0′
10′	345	283	046	476	877	059	446	363	50′
20′	374	311	3.021	508	850	060	436	334	40′
30′	.3403	.3338	2.996	.3541	2.824	1.061	.9426	1.2305	30′
40′	432	365	971	574	798	062	417	275	20′
50′	462	393	947	607	773	063	407	246	10′
20° 0′	.3491	.3420	2.924	.3640	2.747	1.064	.9397	1.2217	70° 0′
10′	520	448	901	673	723	065	387	188	50′
20′	549	475	878	706	699	066	377	159	40′
30′	.3578	.3502	2.855	.3739	2.675	1.068	.9367	1.2130	30′
40′	607	529	833	772	651	069	356	101	20′
50′	636	557	812	805	628	070	346	072	10′
21° 0′	.3665	.3584	2.790	.3839	2.605	1.071	.9336	1.2043	69° 0′
10′	694	611	769	872	583	072	325	1.2014	50′
20′	723	638	749	906	560	074	315	1.1985	40′
30′	.3752	.3665	2.729	.3939	2.539	1.075	.9304	1.1956	30′
40′	782	692	709	.3973	517	076	293	926	20′
50′	811	719	689	.4006	496	077	283	897	10′
22° 0′	.3840	.3746	2.669	.4040	2.475	1.079	.9272	1.1868	68° 0′
10′	869	773	650	074	455	080	261	839	50′
20′	898	800	632	108	434	081	250	810	40′
30′	.3927	.3827	2.613	.4142	2.414	1.082	.9239	1.1781	30′
40′	956	854	595	176	394	084	228	752	20′
50′	985	881	577	210	375	085	216	723	10′
23° 0′	.4014	.3907	2.559	.4245	2.356	1.086	.9205	1.1694	67° 0′
10′	043	934	542	279	337	088	194	665	50′
20′	072	961	525	314	318	089	182	636	40′
30′	.4102	.3987	2.508	.4348	2.300	1.090	.9171	1.1606	30′
40′	131	.4014	491	383	282	092	159	577	20′
50′	160	041	475	417	264	093	147	548	10′
24° 0′	.4189	.4067	2.459	.4452	2.246	1.095	.9135	1.1519	66° 0′
10′	218	094	443	487	229	096	124	490	50′
20′	247	120	427	522	211	097	112	461	40′
30′	.4276	.4147	2.411	.4557	2.194	1.099	.9100	1.1432	30′
40′	305	173	396	592	177	100	088	403	20′
50′	334	200	381	628	161	102	075	374	10′
25° 0′	.4363	.4226	2.366	.4663	2.145	1.103	.9063	1.1345	65° 0′
10′	392	253	352	699	128	105	051	316	50′
20′	422	279	337	734	112	106	038	286	40′
30′	.4451	.4305	2.323	.4770	2.097	1.108	.9026	1.1257	30′
40′	480	331	309	806	081	109	013	228	20′
50′	509	358	295	841	066	111	.9001	199	10′
26° 0′	.4538	.4384	2.281	.4877	2.050	1.113	.8988	1.1170	64° 0′
10′	567	410	268	913	035	114	975	141	50′
20′	596	436	254	950	020	116	962	112	40′
30′	.4625	.4462	2.241	.4986	2.006	1.117	.8949	1.1083	30′
40′	654	488	228	.5022	1.991	119	936	054	20′
50′	683	514	215	059	977	121	923	1.1025	10′
27° 0′	.4712	.4540	2.203	.5095	1.963	1.122	.8910	1.0996	63° 0′
		Cos	Sec	Cot	Tan	Csc	Sin	Radians	Degrees

III TRIGONOMETRIC FUNCTION VALUES (DEGREES)

Degrees	Radians	Sin	Csc	Tan	Cot	Sec	Cos		Degrees
27° 0'	.4712	.4540	2.203	.5095	1.963	1.122	.8910	1.0996	63° 0'
10'	741	566	190	132	949	124	897	966	50'
20'	771	592	178	169	935	126	884	937	40'
30'	.4800	.4617	2.166	.5206	1.921	1.127	.8870	1.0908	30'
40'	829	643	154	243	907	129	857	879	20'
50'	858	669	142	280	894	131	843	850	10'
28° 0'	.4887	.4695	2.130	.5317	1.881	1.133	.8829	1.0821	62° 0'
10'	916	720	118	354	868	134	816	792	50'
20'	945	746	107	392	855	136	802	763	40'
30'	.4974	.4772	2.096	.5430	1.842	1.138	.8788	1.0734	30'
40'	.5003	797	085	467	829	140	774	705	20'
50'	032	823	074	505	816	142	760	676	10'
29° 0'	.5061	.4848	2.063	.5543	1.804	1.143	.8746	1.0647	61° 0'
10'	091	874	052	581	792	145	732	617	50'
20'	120	899	041	619	780	147	718	588	40'
30'	.5149	.4924	2.031	.5658	1.767	1.149	.8704	1.0559	30'
40'	178	950	020	696	756	151	689	530	20'
50'	207	.4975	010	735	744	153	675	501	10'
30° 0'	.5236	.5000	2.000	.5774	1.732	1.155	.8660	1.0472	60° 0'
10'	265	025	1.990	812	720	157	646	443	50'
20'	294	050	980	851	709	159	631	414	40'
30'	.5323	.5075	1.970	.5890	1.698	1.161	.8616	1.0385	30'
40'	352	100	961	930	686	163	601	356	20'
50'	381	125	951	.5969	675	ī65	587	327	10'
31° 0'	.5411	.5150	1.942	.6009	1.664	1.167	.8572	1.0297	59° 0'
10'	440	175	932	048	653	169	557	268	50'
20'	469	200	923	088	643	171	542	239	40'
30'	.5498	.5225	1.914	.6128	1.632	1.173	.8526	1.0210	30'
40'	527	250	905	168	621	175	511	181	20'
50'	556	275	896	208	611	177	496	152	10'
32° 0'	.5585	.5299	1.887	.6249	1.600	1.179	.8480	1.0123	58° 0'
10'	614	324	878	289	590	181	465	094	50'
20'	643	348	870	330	580	184	450	065	40'
30'	.5672	.5373	1.861	.6371	1.570	1.186	.8434	1.0036	30'
40'	701	398	853	412	560	188	418	1.0007	20'
50'	730	422	844	453	550	190	403	.9977	10'
33° 0'	.5760	.5446	1.836	.6494	1.540	1.192	.8387	.9948	57° 0'
10'	789	471	828	536	530	195	371	919	50'
20'	818	495	820	577	520	197	355	890	40'
30'	.5847	.5519	1.812	.6619	1.511	1.199	.8339	.9861	30'
40'	876	544	804	661	501	202	323	832	20'
50'	905	568	796	703	1.492	204	307	803	10'
34° 0'	.5934	.5592	1.788	.6745	1.483	1.206	.8290	.9774	56° 0'
10'	963	616	781	787	473	209	274	745	50'
20'	992	640	773	830	464	211	258	716	40'
30'	.6021	.5664	1.766	.6873	1.455	1.213	.8241	.9687	30'
40'	050	688	758	916	446	216	225	657	20'
50'	080	712	751	.6959	437	218	208	628	10'
35° 0'	.6109	.5736	1.743	.7002	1.428	1.221	.8192	.9599	55° 0'
10'	138	760	736	046	419	223	175	570	50'
20'	167	783	729	089	411	226	158	541	40'
30'	.6196	.5807	1.722	.7133	1.402	1.228	.8141	.9512	30'
40'	225	831	715	177	393	231	124	483	20'
50'	254	854	708	221	385	233	107	454	10'
36° 0'	.6283	.5878	1.701	.7265	1.376	1.236	.8090	.9425	54° 0'
		Cos	Sec	Cot	Tan	Csc	Sin	Radians	Degrees

III   TRIGONOMETRIC FUNCTION VALUES (DEGREES)

Degrees	Radians	Sin	Csc	Tan	Cot	Sec	Cos		
36° 0'	.6283	.5878	1.701	.7265	1.376	1.236	.8090	.9425	**54° 0'**
10'	312	901	695	310	368	239	073	396	50'
20'	341	925	688	355	360	241	056	367	40'
30'	.6370	.5948	1.681	.7400	1.351	1.244	.8039	.9338	30'
40'	400	972	675	445	343	247	021	308	20'
50'	429	.5995	668	490	335	249	.8004	279	10'
37° 0'	.6458	.6018	1.662	.7536	1.327	1.252	.7986	.9250	**53° 0'**
10'	487	041	655	581	319	255	969	221	50'
20'	516	065	649	627	311	258	951	192	40'
30'	.6545	.6088	1.643	.7673	1.303	1.260	.7934	.9163	30'
40'	574	111	636	720	295	263	916	134	20'
50'	603	134	630	766	288	266	898	105	10'
38° 0'	.6632	.6157	1.624	.7813	1.280	1.269	.7880	.9076	**52° 0'**
10'	661	180	618	860	272	272	862	047	50'
20'	690	202	612	907	265	275	844	.9018	40'
30'	.6720	.6225	1.606	.7954	1.257	1.278	.7826	.8988	30'
40'	749	248	601	.8002	250	281	808	959	20'
50'	778	271	595	050	242	284	790	930	10'
39° 0'	.6807	.6293	1.589	.8098	1.235	1.287	.7771	.8901	**51° 0'**
10'	836	316	583	146	228	290	753	872	50'
20'	865	338	578	195	220	293	735	843	40'
30'	.6894	.6361	1.572	.8243	1.213	1.296	.7716	.8814	30'
40'	923	383	567	292	206	299	698	785	20'
50'	952	406	561	342	199	302	679	756	10'
40° 0'	.6981	.6428	1.556	.8391	1.192	1.305	.7660	.8727	**50° 0'**
10'	.7010	450	550	441	185	309	642	698	50'
20'	039	472	545	491	178	312	623	668	40'
30'	.7069	.6494	1.540	.8541	1.171	1.315	.7604	.8639	30'
40'	098	517	535	591	164	318	585	610	20'
50'	127	539	529	642	157	322	566	581	10'
41° 0'	.7156	.6561	1.524	.8693	1.150	1.325	.7547	.8552	**49° 0'**
10'	185	583	519	744	144	328	528	523	50'
20'	214	604	514	796	137	332	509	494	40'
30'	.7243	.6626	1.509	.8847	1.130	1.335	.7490	.8465	30'
40'	272	648	504	899	124	339	470	436	20'
50'	301	670	499	.8952	117	342	451	407	10'
42° 0'	.7330	.6691	1.494	.9004	1.111	1.346	.7431	.8378	**48° 0'**
10'	359	713	490	057	104	349	412	348	50'
20'	389	734	485	110	098	353	392	319	40'
30'	.7418	.6756	1.480	.9163	1.091	1.356	.7373	.8290	30
40'	447	777	476	217	085	360	353	261	20'
50'	476	799	471	271	079	364	333	232	10'
43° 0'	.7505	.6820	1.466	.9325	1.072	1.367	.7314	.8203	**47° 0'**
10'	534	841	462	380	066	371	294	174	50'
20'	563	862	457	435	060	375	274	145	40'
30'	.7592	.6884	1.453	.9490	1.054	1.379	.7254	.8116	30'
40'	621	905	448	545	048	382	234	087	20'
50'	650	926	444	601	042	386	214	058	10'
44° 0'	.7679	.6947	1.440	.9657	1.036	1.390	.7193	.8029	**46° 0'**
10'	709	967	435	713	030	394	173	.7999	50'
20'	738	.6988	431	770	024	398	153	970	40'
30'	.7767	.7009	1.427	.9827	1.018	1.402	.7133	.7941	30'
40'	796	030	423	884	012	406	112	912	20'
50'	825	050	418	.9942	006	410	092	883	10'
45° 0'	.7854	.7071	1.414	1.000	1.000	1.414	.7071	.7854	**45° 0'**
		Cos	**Sec**	**Cot**	**Tan**	**Csc**	**Sin**	**Radians**	**Degrees**

IV   MANTISSAS

n	0	1	2	3	4	5	6	7	8	9
10	0000	0043	0086	0128	0170	0212	0253	0294	0334	0374
11	0414	0453	0492	0531	0569	0607	0645	0682	0719	0755
12	0792	0828	0864	0899	0934	0969	1004	1038	1072	1106
13	1139	1173	1206	1239	1271	1303	1335	1367	1399	1430
14	1461	1492	1523	1553	1584	1614	1644	1673	1703	1732
15	1761	1790	1818	1847	1875	1903	1931	1959	1987	2014
16	2041	2068	2095	2122	2148	2175	2201	2227	2253	2279
17	2304	2330	2355	2380	2405	2430	2455	2480	2504	2529
18	2553	2577	2601	2625	2648	2672	2695	2718	2742	2765
19	2788	2810	2833	2856	2878	2900	2923	2945	2967	2989
20	3010	3032	3054	3075	3096	3118	3139	3160	3181	3201
21	3222	3243	3263	3284	3304	3324	3345	3365	3385	3404
22	3424	3444	3464	3483	3502	3522	3541	3560	3579	3598
23	3617	3636	3655	3674	3692	3711	3729	3747	3766	3784
24	3802	3820	3838	3856	3874	3892	3909	3927	3945	3962
25	3979	3997	4014	4031	4048	4065	4082	4099	4116	4133
26	4150	4166	4183	4200	4216	4232	4249	4265	4281	4298
27	4314	4330	4346	4362	4378	4393	4409	4425	4440	4456
28	4472	4487	4502	4518	4533	4548	4564	4579	4594	4609
29	4624	4639	4654	4669	4683	4698	4713	4728	4742	4757
30	4771	4786	4800	4814	4829	4843	4857	4871	4886	4900
31	4914	4928	4942	4955	4969	4983	4997	5011	5024	5038
32	5051	5065	5079	5092	5105	5119	5132	5145	5159	5172
33	5185	5198	5211	5224	5237	5250	5263	5276	5289	5302
34	5315	5328	5340	5353	5366	5378	5391	5403	5416	5428
35	5441	5453	5465	5478	5490	5502	5514	5527	5539	5551
36	5563	5575	5587	5599	5611	5623	5635	5647	5658	5670
37	5682	5694	5705	5717	5729	5740	5752	5763	5775	5786
38	5798	5809	5821	5832	5843	5855	5866	5877	5888	5899
39	5911	5922	5933	5944	5955	5966	5977	5988	5999	6010
40	6021	6031	6042	6053	6064	6075	6085	6096	6107	6117
41	6128	6138	6149	6160	6170	6180	6191	6201	6212	6222
42	6232	6243	6253	6263	6274	6284	6294	6304	6314	6325
43	6335	6345	6355	6365	6375	6385	6395	6405	6415	6425
44	6435	6444	6454	6464	6474	6484	6493	6503	6513	6522
45	6532	6542	6551	6561	6571	6580	6590	6599	6609	6618
46	6628	6637	6646	6656	6665	6675	6684	6693	6702	6712
47	6721	6730	6739	6749	6758	6767	6776	6785	6794	6803
48	6812	6821	6830	6839	6848	6857	6866	6875	6884	6893
49	6902	6911	6920	6928	6937	6946	6955	6964	6972	6981
50	6990	6998	7007	7016	7024	7033	7042	7050	7059	7067
51	7076	7084	7093	7101	7110	7118	7126	7135	7143	7152
52	7160	7168	7177	7185	7193	7202	7210	7218	7226	7235
53	7243	7251	7259	7267	7275	7284	7292	7300	7308	7316
54	7324	7332	7340	7348	7356	7364	7372	7380	7388	7396

IV   MANTISSAS

n	0	1	2	3	4	5	6	7	8	9
55	7404	7412	7419	7427	7435	7443	7451	7459	7466	7474
56	7482	7490	7497	7505	7513	7520	7528	7536	7543	7551
57	7559	7566	7574	7582	7589	7597	7604	7612	7619	7627
58	7634	7642	7649	7657	7664	7672	7679	7686	7694	7701
59	7709	7716	7723	7731	7738	7745	7752	7760	7767	7774
60	7782	7789	7796	7803	7810	7818	7825	7832	7839	7846
61	7853	7860	7868	7875	7882	7889	7896	7903	7910	7917
62	7924	7931	7938	7945	7952	7959	7966	7973	7980	7987
63	7993	8000	8007	8014	8021	8028	8035	8041	8048	8055
64	8062	8069	8075	8082	8089	8096	8102	8109	8116	8122
65	8129	8136	8142	8149	8156	8162	8169	8176	8182	8189
66	8195	8202	8209	8215	8222	8228	8235	8241	8248	8254
67	8261	8267	8274	8280	8287	8293	8299	8306	8312	8319
68	8325	8331	8338	8344	8351	8357	8363	8370	8376	8382
69	8388	8395	8401	8407	8414	8420	8426	8432	8439	8445
70	8451	8457	8463	8470	8476	8482	8488	8494	8500	8506
71	8513	8519	8525	8531	8537	8543	8549	8555	8561	8567
72	8573	8579	8585	8591	8597	8603	8609	8615	8621	8627
73	8633	8639	8645	8651	8657	8663	8669	8675	8681	8686
74	8692	8698	8704	8710	8716	8722	8727	8733	8739	8745
75	8751	8756	8762	8768	8774	8779	8785	8791	8797	8802
76	8808	8814	8820	8825	8831	8837	8842	8848	8854	8859
77	8865	8871	8876	8882	8887	8893	8899	8904	8910	8915
78	8921	8927	8932	8938	8943	8949	8954	8960	8965	8971
79	8976	8982	8987	8993	8998	9004	9009	9015	9020	9025
80	9031	9036	9042	9047	9053	9058	9063	9069	9074	9079
81	9085	9090	9096	9101	9106	9112	9117	9122	9128	9133
82	9138	9143	9149	9154	9159	9165	9170	9175	9180	9186
83	9191	9196	9201	9206	9212	9217	9222	9227	9232	9238
84	9243	9248	9253	9258	9263	9269	9274	9279	9284	9289
85	9294	9299	9304	9309	9315	9320	9325	9330	9335	9340
86	9345	9350	9355	9360	9365	9370	9375	9380	9385	9390
87	9395	9400	9405	9410	9415	9420	9425	9430	9435	9440
88	9445	9450	9455	9460	9465	9469	9474	9479	9484	9489
89	9494	9499	9504	9509	9513	9518	9523	9528	9533	9538
90	9542	9547	9552	9557	9562	9566	9571	9576	9581	9586
91	9590	9595	9600	9605	9609	9614	9619	9624	9628	9633
92	9638	9643	9647	9652	9657	9661	9666	9671	9675	9680
93	9685	9689	9694	9699	9703	9708	9713	9717	9722	9727
94	9731	9736	9741	9745	9750	9754	9759	9763	9768	9773
95	9777	9782	9786	9791	9795	9800	9805	9809	9814	9818
96	9823	9827	9832	9836	9841	9845	9850	9854	9859	9863
97	9868	9872	9877	9881	9886	9890	9894	9899	9903	9908
98	9912	9917	9921	9926	9930	9934	9939	9943	9948	9952
99	9956	9961	9965	9969	9974	9978	9983	9987	9991	9996

V   LOGARITHMS OF TRIGONOMETRIC FUNCTION VALUES *

Angle	L Sin	d 1'	L Tan	cd 1'	L Cot	d 1'	L Cos	
0° 0'	—		—		—	.0	10.0000	90° 0'
10'	7.4637	301.1	7.4637	301.1	12.5363	.0	.0000	50'
20'	.7648	176.0	.7648	176.1	.2352	.0	.0000	40'
30'	7.9408	125.0	7.9409	124.9	12.0591	.0	.0000	30'
40'	8.0658	96.9	8.0658	96.9	11.9342	.0	.0000	20'
50'	.1627	79.2	.1627	79.2	.8373	.1	10.0000	10'
1° 0'	8.2419	66.9	8.2419	67.0	11.7581	.0	9.9999	89° 0'
10'	.3088	58.0	.3089	58.0	.6911	.0	.9999	50'
20'	.3668	51.1	.3669	51.2	.6331	.0	.9999	40'
30'	.4179	45.8	.4181	45.7	.5819	.1	.9999	30'
40'	.4637	41.3	.4638	41.5	.5362	.0	.9998	20'
50'	.5050	37.8	.5053	37.8	.4947	.1	.9998	10'
2° 0'	8.5428	34.8	8.5431	34.8	11.4569	.0	9.9997	88° 0'
10'	.5776	32.1	.5779	32.2	.4221	.1	.9997	50'
20'	.6097	30.0	.6101	30.0	.3899	.0	.9996	40'
30'	.6397	28.0	.6401	28.1	.3599	.1	.9996	30'
40'	.6677	26.3	.6682	26.3	.3318	.0	.9995	20'
50'	.6940	24.8	.6945	24.9	.3055	.1	.9995	10'
3° 0'	8.7188	23.5	8.7194	23.5	11.2806	.1	9.9994	87° 0'
10'	.7423	22.2	.7429	22.3	.2571	.0	.9993	50'
20'	.7645	21.2	.7652	21.3	.2348	.1	.9993	40'
30'	.7857	20.2	.7865	20.2	.2135	.1	.9992	30'
40'	.8059	19.2	.8067	19.4	.1933	.1	.9991	20'
50'	.8251	18.5	.8261	18.5	.1739	.1	.9990	10'
4° 0'	8.8436	17.7	8.8446	17.8	11.1554	.1	9.9989	86° 0'
10'	.8613	17.0	.8624	17.1	.1376	.0	.9989	50'
20'	.8783	16.3	.8795	16.5	.1205	.1	.9988	40'
30'	.8946	15.8	.8960	15.8	.1040	.1	.9987	30'
40'	.9104	15.2	.9118	15.4	.0882	.1	.9986	20'
50'	.9256	14.7	.9272	15.4	.0728	.1	.9985	10'
5° 0'	8.9403	14.2	8.9420	14.8	11.0580	.2	9.9983	85° 0'
10'	.9545	13.7	.9563	14.3	.0437	.1	.9982	50'
20'	.9682	13.4	.9701	13.8	.0299	.1	.9981	40'
30'	.9816	12.9	.9836	13.5	.0164	.1	.9980	30'
40'	8.9945	12.5	8.9966	13.0	11.0034	.1	.9979	20'
50'	9.0070	12.2	9.0093	12.7	10.9907	.2	.9977	10'
6° 0'	9.0192	11.9	9.0216	12.3	10.9784	.1	9.9976	84° 0'
10'	.0311	11.5	.0336	12.0	.9664	.1	.9975	50'
20'	.0426	11.3	.0453	11.7	.9547	.2	.9973	40'
30'	.0539	10.9	.0567	11.4	.9433	.1	.9972	30'
40'	.0648	10.7	.0678	11.1	.9322	.1	.9971	20'
50'	.0755	10.4	.0786	10.8	.9214	.2	.9969	10'
7° 0'	9.0859	10.2	9.0891	10.5	10.9109	.1	9.9968	83° 0'
10'	.0961	9.9	.0995	10.4	.9005	.2	.9966	50'
20'	.1060	9.7	.1096	10.1	.8904	.2	.9964	40'
30'	.1157	9.5	.1194	9.8	.8806	.1	.9963	30'
40'	.1252	9.3	.1291	9.7	.8709	.2	.9961	20'
50'	.1345	9.1	.1385	9.4	.8615	.2	.9959	10'
8° 0'	9.1436	8.9	9.1478	9.3	10.8522	.1	9.9958	82° 0'
10'	.1525	8.7	.1569	9.1	.8431	.2	.9956	50'
20'	.1612	8.5	.1658	8.9	.8342	.2	.9954	40'
30'	.1697	8.4	.1745	8.7	.8255	.2	.9952	30'
40'	.1781	8.2	.1831	8.6	.8169	.2	.9950	20'
50'	.1863	8.0	.1915	8.4	.8085	.2	.9948	10'
9° 0'	9.1943		9.1997	8.2	10.8003	.2	9.9946	81° 0'
	L Cos	d 1'	L Cot	cd 1'	L Tan	1 d'	L Sin	Angle

* Subtract 10 from each entry in this table to obtain the proper logarithm of the indicated trigonometric function.

V   LOGARITHMS OF TRIGONOMETRIC FUNCTION VALUES

Angle	L Sin	d 1'	L Tan	cd 1'	L Cot	d 1'	L Cos	Angle
9° 0'	9.1943		9.1997		10.8003		9.9946	81° 0'
		7.9		8.1		.2		
10'	.2022		.2078		.7922		.9944	50'
		7.8		8.0		.2		
20'	.2100		.2158		.7842		.9942	40'
		7.6		7.8		.2		
30'	.2176		.2236		.7764		.9940	30'
		7.5		7.7		.2		
40'	.2251		.2313		.7687		.9938	20'
		7.3		7.6		.2		
50'	.2324		.2389		.7611		.9936	10'
		7.3		7.4		.2		
10° 0'	9.2397		9.2463		10.7537		9.9934	80° 0'
		7.1		7.3		.3		
10'	.2468		.2536		.7464		.9931	50'
		7.0		7.3		.2		
20'	.2538		.2609		.7391		.9929	40'
		6.8		7.1		.2		
30'	.2606		.2680		.7320		.9927	30'
		6.8		7.0		.3		
40'	.2674		.2750		.7250		.9924	20'
		6.6		6.9		.2		
50'	.2740		.2819		.7181		.9922	10'
		6.6		6.8		.3		
11° 0'	9.2806		9.2887		10.7113		9.9919	79° 0'
		6.4		6.6		.2		
10'	.2870		.2953		.7047		.9917	50'
		6.4		6.7		.3		
20'	.2934		.3020		.6980		.9914	40'
		6.3		6.5		.2		
30'	.2997		.3085		.6915		.9912	30'
		6.1		6.4		.3		
40'	.3058		.3149		.6851		.9909	20'
		6.1		6.3		.2		
50'	.3119		.3212		.6788		.9907	10'
		6.0		6.3		.3		
12° 0'	9.3179		9.3275		10.6725		9.9904	78° 0'
		5.9		6.1		.3		
10'	.3238		.3336		.6664		.9901	50'
		5.8		6.1		.2		
20'	.3296		.3397		.6603		.9899	40'
		5.7		6.1		.3		
30'	.3353		.3458		.6542		.9896	30'
		5.7		5.9		.3		
40'	.3410		.3517		.6483		.9893	20'
		5.6		5.9		.3		
50'	.3466		.3576		.6424		.9890	10'
		5.5		5.8		.3		
13° 0'	9.3521		9.3634		10.6366		9.9887	77° 0'
		5.4		5.7		.3		
10'	.3575		.3691		.6309		.9884	50'
		5.4		5.7		.3		
20'	.3629		.3748		.6252		.9881	40'
		5.3		5.6		.3		
30'	.3682		.3804		.6196		.9878	30'
		5.2		5.5		.3		
40'	.3734		.3859		.6141		.9875	20'
		5.2		5.5		.3		
50'	.3786		.3914		.6086		.9872	10'
		5.1		5.4		.3		
14° 0'	9.3837		9.3968		10.6032		9.9869	76° 0'
		5.0		5.3		.3		
10'	.3887		.4021		.5979		.9866	50'
		5.0		5.3		.3		
20'	.3937		.4074		.5926		.9863	40'
		4.9		5.3		.4		
30'	.3986		.4127		.5873		.9859	30'
		4.9		5.1		.3		
40'	.4035		.4178		.5822		.9856	20'
		4.8		5.2		.3		
50'	.4083		.4230		.5770		.9853	10'
		4.7		5.1		.4		
15° 0'	9.4130		9.4281		10.5719		9.9849	75° 0'
		4.7		5.0		.3		
10'	.4177		.4331		.5669		.9846	50'
		4.6		5.0		.3		
20'	.4223		.4381		.5619		.9843	40'
		4.6		4.9		.4		
30'	.4269		.4430		.5570		.9839	30'
		4.5		4.9		.3		
40'	.4314		.4479		.5521		.9836	20'
		4.5		4.8		.4		
50'	.4359		.4527		.5473		.9832	10'
		4.4		4.8		.4		
16° 0'	9.4403		9.4575		10.5425		9.9828	74° 0'
		4.4		4.7		.4		
10'	.4447		.4622		.5378		.9825	50'
		4.4		4.7		.4		
20'	.4491		.4669		.5331		.9821	40'
		4.2		4.7		.4		
30'	.4533		.4716		.5284		.9817	30'
		4.3		4.6		.4		
40'	.4576		.4762		.5238		.9814	20'
		4.2		4.6		.3		
50'	.4618		.4808		.5192		.9810	10'
		4.1		4.5		.4		
17° 0'	9.4659		9.4853		10.5147		9.9806	73° 0'
		4.1		4.5		.4		
10'	.4700		.4898		.5102		.9802	50'
		4.1		4.5		.4		
20'	.4741		.4943		.5057		.9798	40'
		4.0		4 4		.4		
30'	.4781		.4987		.5013		.9794	30'
		4.0		4.4		.4		
40'	.4821		.5031		.4969		.9790	20'
		4.0		4.4		.4		
50'	.4861		.5075		.4925		.9786	10'
		3.9		4.3		.4		
18° 0'	9.4900		9.5118		10.4882		9.9782	72° 0'
	L Cos	d 1'	L Cot	cd 1'	L Tan	d 1'	L Sin	Angle

V   LOGARITHMS OF TRIGONOMETRIC FUNCTION VALUES

Angle	L Sin	d 1'	L Tan	cd 1'	L Cot	d 1'	L Cos	Angle
18° 0'	9.4900		9.5118		10.4882		9.9782	72° 0'
		3.9		4.3		.4		
10'	.4939		.5161		.4839		.9778	50'
		3.8		4.2		.4		
20'	.4977		.5203		.4797		.9774	40'
		3.8		4.2		.4		
30'	.5015		.5245		.4755		.9770	30'
		3.7		4.2		.5		
40'	.5052		.5287		.4713		.9765	20'
		3.8		4.2		.4		
50'	.5090		.5329		.4671		.9761	10'
		3.6		4.1		.4		
19° 0'	9.5126		9.5370		10.4630		9.9757	71° 0'
		3.7		4.1		.5		
10'	.5163		.5411		.4589		.9752	50'
		3.6		4.0		.4		
20'	.5199		.5451		.4549		.9748	40'
		3.6		4.0		.5		
30'	.5235		.5491		.4509		.9743	30'
		3.5		4.0		.4		
40'	.5270		.5531		.4469		.9739	20'
		3.6		4.0		.5		
50'	.5306		.5571		.4429		.9734	10'
		3.5		4.0		.4		
20° 0'	9.5341		9.5611		10.4389		9.9730	70° 0'
		3.4		3.9		.5		
10'	.5375		.5650		.4350		.9725	50'
		3.4		3.9		.4		
20'	.5409		.5689		.4311		.9721	40'
		3.4		3.8		.5		
30'	.5443		.5727		.4273		.9716	30'
		3.4		3.9		.5		
40'	.5477		.5766		.4234		.9711	20'
		3.3		3.8		.5		
50'	.5510		.5804		.4196		.9706	10'
		3.3		3.8		.4		
21° 0'	9.5543		9.5842		10.4158		9.9702	69° 0'
		3.3		3.7		.5		
10'	.5576		.5879		.4121		.9697	50'
		3.3		3.8		.5		
20'	.5609		.5917		.4083		.9692	40'
		3.2		3.7		.5		
30'	.5641		.5954		.4046		.9687	30'
		3.2		3.7		.5		
40'	.5673		.5991		.4009		.9682	20'
		3.1		3.7		.5		
50'	.5704		.6028		.3972		.9677	10'
		3.2		3.6		.5		
22° 0'	9.5736		9.6064		10.3936		9.9672	68° 0'
		3.1		3.6		.5		
10'	.5767		.6100		.3900		.9667	50'
		3.1		3.6		.6		
20'	.5798		.6136		.3864		.9661	40'
		3.0		3.6		.5		
30'	.5828		.6172		.3828		.9656	30'
		3.1		3.6		.5		
40'	.5859		.6208		.3792		.9651	20'
		3.0		3.5		.5		
50'	.5889		.6243		.3757		.9646	10'
		3.0		3.6		.6		
23° 0'	9.5919		9.6279		10.3721		9.9640	67° 0'
		2.9		3.5		.5		
10'	.5948		.6314		.3686		.9635	50'
		3.0		3.4		.6		
20'	.5978		.6348		.3652		.9629	40'
		2.9		3.5		.5		
30'	.6007		.6383		.3617		.9624	30'
		2.9		3.4		.6		
40'	.6036		.6417		.3583		.9618	20'
		2.9		3.5		.5		
50'	.6065		.6452		.3548		.9613	10'
		2.8		3.4		.6		
24° 0'	9.6093		9.6486		10.3514		9.9607	66° 0'
		2.8		3.4		.5		
10'	.6121		.6520		.3480		.9602	50'
		2.8		3.3		.6		
20'	.6149		.6553		.3447		.9596	40'
		2.8		3.4		.6		
30'	.6177		.6587		.3413		.9590	30'
		2.8		3.3		.6		
40'	.6205		.6620		.3380		.9584	20'
		2.7		3.4		.5		
50'	.6232		.6654		.3346		.9579	10'
		2.7		3.3		.6		
25° 0'	9.6259		9.6687		10.3313		9.9573	65° 0'
		2.7		3.3		.6		
10'	.6286		.6720		.3280		.9567	50'
		2.7		3.2		.6		
20'	.6313		.6752		.3248		.9561	40'
		2.7		3.3		.6		
30'	.6340		.6785		.3215		.9555	30'
		2.6		3.2		.6		
40'	.6366		.6817		.3183		.9549	20'
		2.6		3.3		.6		
50'	.6392		.6850		.3150		.9543	10'
		2.6		3.2		.6		
26° 0'	9.6418		9.6882		10.3118		9.9537	64° 0'
		2.6		3.2		.7		
10'	.6444		.6914		.3086		.9530	50'
		2.6		3.2		.6		
20'	.6470		.6946		.3054		.9524	40'
		2.5		3.2		.6		
30'	.6495		.6977		.3023		.9518	30'
		2.6		3.1		.6		
40'	.6521		.7009		.2991		.9512	20'
		2.5		3.2		.7		
50'	.6546		.7040		.2960		.9505	10'
		2.4		3.2		.6		
27° 0'	9.6570		9.7072		10.2928		9.9499	63° 0'
	L Cos	d 1'	L Cot	cd 1'	L Tan	d 1'	L Sin	Angle

V   LOGARITHMS OF TRIGONOMETRIC FUNCTION VALUES

Angle	L Sin	d 1′	L Tan	cd 1′	L Cot	d 1′	L Cos	Angle
27° 0′	9.6570		9.7072		10.2928		9.9499	**63° 0′**
10′	.6595	2.5	.7103	3.1	.2897	.7	.9492	50′
20′	.6620	2.5	.7134	3.1	.2866	.6	.9486	40′
30′	.6644	2.4	.7165	3.1	.2835	.7	.9479	30′
40′	.6668	2.4	.7196	3.1	.2804	.6	.9473	20′
50′	.6692	2.4	.7226	3.0	.2774	.7	.9466	10′
28° 0′	9.6716	2.4	9.7257	3.1	10.2743	.7	9.9459	**62° 0′**
10′	.6740	2.4	.7287	3.0	.2713	.6	.9453	50′
20′	.6763	2.3	.7317	3.0	.2683	.7	.9446	40′
30′	.6787	2.4	.7348	3.0	.2652	.7	.9439	30′
40′	.6810	2.3	.7378	3.1	.2622	.7	.9432	20′
50′	.6833	2.3	.7408	3.0	.2592	.7	.9425	10′
29° 0′	9.6856	2.3	9.7438	3.0	10.2562	.7	9.9418	**61° 0′**
10′	.6878	2.2	.7467	3.0	.2533	.7	.9411	50′
20′	.6901	2.3	.7497	2.9	.2503	.7	.9404	40′
30′	.6923	2.2	.7526	3.0	.2474	.7	.9397	30′
40′	.6946	2.3	.7556	2.9	.2444	.7	.9390	20′
50′	.6968	2.2	.7585	2.9	.2415	.7	.9383	10′
30° 0′	9.6990	2.2	9.7614	2.9	10.2386	.8	9.9375	**60° 0′**
10′	.7012	2.2	.7644	3.0	.2356	.7	.9368	50′
20′	.7033	2.1	.7673	2.9	.2327	.7	.9361	40′
30′	.7055	2.2	.7701	2.8	.2299	.8	.9353	30′
40′	.7076	2.1	.7730	2.9	.2270	.7	.9346	20′
50′	.7097	2.1	.7759	2.9	.2241	.8	.9338	10′
31° 0′	9.7118	2.1	9.7788	2.9	10.2212	.7	9.9331	**59° 0′**
10′	.7139	2.1	.7816	2.8	.2184	.8	.9323	50′
20′	.7160	2.1	.7845	2.9	.2155	.8	.9315	40′
30′	.7181	2.1	.7873	2.8	.2127	.7	.9308	30′
40′	.7201	2.0	.7902	2.9	.2098	.8	.9300	20′
50′	.7222	2.1	.7930	2.8	.2070	.8	.9292	10′
32° 0′	9.7242	2.0	9.7958	2.8	10.2042	.8	9.9284	**58° 0′**
10′	.7262	2.0	.7986	2.8	.2014	.8	.9276	50′
20′	.7282	2.0	.8014	2.8	.1986	.8	.9268	40′
30′	.7302	2.0	.8042	2.8	.1958	.8	.9260	30′
40′	.7322	2.0	.8070	2.8	.1930	.8	.9252	20′
50′	.7342	2.0	.8097	2.7	.1903	.8	.9244	10′
33° 0′	9.7361	1.9	9.8125	2.8	10.1875	.8	9.9236	**57° 0′**
10′	.7380	1.9	.8153	2.8	.1847	.8	.9228	50′
20′	.7400	2.0	.8180	2.7	.1820	.9	.9219	40′
30′	.7419	1.9	.8208	2.8	.1792	.8	.9211	30′
40′	.7438	1.9	.8235	2.7	.1765	.8	.9203	20′
50′	.7457	1.9	.8263	2.8	.1737	.9	.9194	10′
34° 0′	9.7476	1.9	9.8290	2.7	10.1710	.8	9.9186	**56° 0′**
10′	.7494	1.8	.8317	2.7	.1683	.9	.9177	50′
20′	.7513	1.9	.8344	2.7	.1656	.8	.9169	40′
30′	.7531	1.8	.8371	2.7	.1629	.9	.9160	30′
40′	.7550	1.9	.8398	2.7	.1602	.9	.9151	20′
50′	.7568	1.8	.8425	2.7	.1575	.9	.9142	10′
35° 0′	9.7586	1.8	9.8452	2.7	10.1548	.8	9.9134	**55° 0′**
10′	.7604	1.8	.8479	2.7	.1521	.9	.9125	50′
20′	.7622	1.8	.8506	2.7	.1494	.9	.9116	40′
30′	.7640	1.8	.8533	2.7	.1467	.9	.9107	30′
40′	.7657	1.7	.8559	2.6	.1441	.9	.9098	20′
50′	.7675	1.8	.8586	2.7	.1414	.9	.9089	10′
36° 0′	9.7692	1.7	9.8613	2.7	10.1387	.9	9.9080	**54° 0′**
	L Cos	d 1′	L Cot	cd 1′	L Tan	d 1′	L Sin	Angle

V   LOGARITHMS OF TRIGONOMETRIC FUNCTION VALUES

Angle	L Sin	d 1′	L Tan	cd 1′	L Cot	d 1′	L Cos	
36° 0′	9.7692		9.8613		10.1387		9.9080	**54° 0′**
10′	.7710	1.8	.8639	2.6	.1361	1.0	.9070	50′
20′	.7727	1.7	.8666	2.7	.1334	.9	.9061	40′
30′	.7744	1.7	.8692	2.6	.1308	.9	.9052	30′
40′	.7761	1.7	.8718	2.6	.1282	1.0	.9042	20′
50′	.7778	1.7	.8745	2.7	.1255	.9	.9033	10′
37° 0′	9.7795	1.7	9.8771	2.6	10.1229	1.0	9.9023	**53° 0′**
10′	.7811	1.6	.8797	2.6	.1203	.9	.9014	50′
20′	.7828	1.7	.8824	2.7	.1176	1.0	.9004	40′
30′	.7844	1.6	.8850	2.6	.1150	.9	.8995	30′
40′	.7861	1.7	.8876	2.6	.1124	1.0	.8985	20′
50′	.7877	1.6	.8902	2.6	.1098	1.0	.8975	10′
38° 0′	9.7893	1.6	9.8928	2.6	10.1072	1.0	9.8965	**52° 0′**
10′	.7910	1.7	.8954	2.6	.1046	1.0	.8955	50′
20′	.7926	1.6	.8980	2.6	.1020	1.0	.8945	40′
30′	.7941	1.5	.9006	2.6	.0994	1.0	.8935	30′
40′	.7957	1.6	.9032	2.6	.0968	1.0	.8925	20′
50′	.7973	1.6	.9058	2.6	.0942	1.0	.8915	10′
39° 0′	9.7989	1.6	9.9084	2.6	10.0916	1.0	9.8905	**51° 0′**
10′	.8004	1.5	.9110	2.6	.0890	1.0	.8895	50′
20′	.8020	1.6	.9135	2.5	.0865	1.1	.8884	40′
30′	.8035	1.5	.9161	2.6	.0839	1.0	.8874	30′
40′	.8050	1.5	.9187	2.6	.0813	1.0	.8864	20′
50′	.8066	1.6	.9212	2.5	.0788	1.1	.8853	10′
40° 0′	9.8081	1.5	9.9238	2.6	10.0762	1.0	9.8843	**50° 0′**
10′	.8096	1.5	.9264	2.6	.0736	1.1	.8832	50′
20′	.8111	1.5	.9289	2.5	.0711	1.1	.8821	40′
30′	.8125	1.4	.9315	2.6	.0685	1.1	.8810	30′
40′	.8140	1.5	.9341	2.6	.0659	1.0	.8800	20′
50′	.8155	1.5	.9366	2.5	.0634	1.1	.8789	10′
41° 0′	9.8169	1.4	9.9392	2.6	10.0608	1.1	9.8778	**49° 0′**
10′	.8184	1.5	.9417	2.5	.0583	1.1	.8767	50′
20′	.8198	1.4	.9443	2.6	.0557	1.1	.8756	40′
30′	.8213	1.5	.9468	2.5	.0532	1.1	.8745	30′
40′	.8227	1.4	.9494	2.6	.0506	1.1	.8733	20′
50′	.8241	1.4	.9519	2.5	.0481	1.1	.8722	10′
42° 0′	9.8255	1.4	9.9544	2.5	10.0456	1.1	9.8711	**48° 0′**
10′	.8269	1.4	.9570	2.6	.0430	1.2	.8699	50′
20′	.8283	1.4	.9595	2.5	.0405	1.1	.8688	40′
30′	.8297	1.4	.9621	2.6	.0379	1.2	.8676	30′
40′	.8311	1.4	.9646	2.5	.0354	1.1	.8665	20′
50′	.8324	1.3	.9671	2.5	.0329	1.2	.8653	10′
43° 0′	9.8338	1.4	9.9697	2.6	10.0303	1.2	9.8641	**47° 0′**
10′	.8351	1.3	.9722	2.5	.0278	1.2	.8629	50′
20′	.8365	1.4	.9747	2.5	.0253	1.1	.8618	40′
30′	.8378	1.3	.9772	2.5	.0228	1.2	.8606	30′
40′	.8391	1.3	.9798	2.6	.0202	1.2	.8594	20′
50′	.8405	1.4	.9823	2.5	.0177	1.2	.8582	10′
44° 0′	9.8418	1.3	9.9848	2.5	10.0152	1.3	9.8569	**46° 0′**
10′	.8431	1.3	.9874	2.6	.0126	1.2	.8557	50′
20′	.8444	1.3	.9899	2.5	.0101	1.2	.8545	40′
30′	.8457	1.3	.9924	2.5	.0076	1.3	.8532	30′
40′	.8469	1.2	.9949	2.5	.0051	1.2	.8520	20′
50′	.8482	1.3	9.9975	2.6	.0025	1.3	.8507	10′
45° 0′	9.8495	1.3	10.0000	2.5	10.0000	1.2	9.8495	**45° 0′**
	L Cos	d 1′	L Cot	cd 1′	L Tan	d 1′	L Sin	Angle

INDEX

ANSWERS

PAGE 5 **1.a.** $\{-4, -3, -2, -1, 0, 1, 2, 3, 4\}$ **b.** $\{1, 0, -1, -2, \ldots\}$ **c.** $\{\ldots, -8,$
$-4, 0, 4, \ldots\}$ **d.** $\{2, 3, 4, 5\}$ **e.** $\{(0, 0), (1, 0), (2, 0), (-1, 0), (-2, 0), (0, 1), (0, 2),$
$(0, -1), (0, -2), (1, 1), (-1, 1), (-1, -1), (1, -1)\}$ **f.** $\{(5, 0), (4, 3), (3, 4), (0, 5),$
$(-3, 4), (-4, 3), (-5, 0), (-4, -3), (-3, -4), (0, -5), (3, -4), (4, -3)\}$ **g.** $\{\ldots, -16,$
$-8, 0, 8, 16, 24, \ldots\}$ **h.** $\{\ldots, -8, -3, 2, 7, 12, \ldots\}$ **i.** $\{\ldots, -4\pi, -2\pi, 0, 2\pi,$
$4\pi, \ldots\}$ **j.** $\{\ldots, -3\pi, -\pi, \pi, 3\pi, \ldots\}$ **k.** $\{-4, 4\}$ **l.** $\{-2\sqrt{3}, 2\sqrt{3}\}$ **m.** ϕ
2.a. d, f, h are rational.   **4.a.** $(-2, -7), (0, -3), (2, 1),$ etc.   **b.** $(-2, 6), (0, 3), (2, 0),$ etc.
c. $(-2, 2), (0, 2), (2, 2),$ etc.   **d.** $(\frac{1}{6}, 6), (1, 1), (-5, -\frac{1}{5}),$ etc.   **5.a.** $(-2, 5), (0, 1), (2, 5),$ etc.
b. $(-5, 0), (0, -5), (0, 5),$ etc.   **c.** $(-1, 0), (1, 0), (0, -1),$ etc.   **d.** $(-1, 1), (-1, -1),$
$(1, -1),$ etc.   **6.a.** $\{\frac{3}{2}, -\frac{5}{4}\}$ **b.** $\{\frac{-9 + \sqrt{57}}{4}, \frac{-9 - \sqrt{57}}{4}\}$ **c.** $\{\frac{5 + \sqrt{37}}{6}, \frac{5 - \sqrt{37}}{6}\}$
d. $\{0\}$ **e.** ϕ **f.** $\{\frac{1}{\sqrt{2}}, -\frac{1}{\sqrt{2}}\}$ **g.** $\{\frac{\sqrt{3}}{2}, \frac{-\sqrt{3}}{2}\}$ **h.** $\{2\}$ **i.** $\{4\}$

PAGES 11–13   **1.a.** 1   **b.** 2   **c.** 1   **d.** 1   **e.** 2   **f.** 1   **g.** 1   **h.** 2   **i.** 2   **j.** 1   **k.** 1   **l.** 1
m. 2   **n.** 1   **o.** 1   **p.** 2   **q.** 1   **r.** 1   **s.** 1   **t.** 2   **2.a.** $\overrightarrow{AB}, \overrightarrow{AC}, \overrightarrow{AD}, \overrightarrow{BD}$ **b.** $\overrightarrow{AB}, \overrightarrow{AC}, \overrightarrow{AD},$
$\overrightarrow{BD}, \overrightarrow{DB}$ **c.** $\angle BAC$ **d.** $\angle CAD$ **e.** supplementary   **f.** Two angles have vertex A.
g. exterior   **3.** 19; 31°; 59°   **4.a.** a diameter   **b.** central angle   **c.** the diameter   **d.** chord
e. center   **f.** semicircle   **g.** the radius   **h.** circumference   **i.** a radius   **j.** major arc
k. the diameter   **l.** circumference   **5.a.** 72°; 288°   **b.** 72°; 288°   **c.** 2π **d.** 4π **e.** $\frac{2\pi}{5}$
f. $\frac{4\pi}{5}$ **g.** $\frac{8\pi}{5}$ **h.** $\frac{16\pi}{5}$ **6.** m minor arc $\overset{\frown}{AB} = m$ minor arc $\overset{\frown}{CD} = x°$; m major arc $\overset{\frown}{AB} = m$
major arc $\overset{\frown}{CD} = (360 - x)°$ **7.** minor arc $\overset{\frown}{AB} : \frac{\pi x}{180}$; minor arc $\overset{\frown}{CD} : \frac{r\pi x}{180}$; major arc
$\overset{\frown}{AB} : \frac{\pi(360 - x)}{180}$; major arc $\overset{\frown}{CD} : \frac{r\pi(360 - x)}{180}$ **8.a.** $\frac{\pi}{4}$ **b.** $\frac{\pi}{2}$ **c.** $\frac{3\pi}{4}$ **d.** π **e.** $\frac{5\pi}{4}$ **f.** $\frac{3\pi}{2}$
g. $\frac{7\pi}{4}$ **h.** $\frac{3\pi}{4}$ **i.** $\frac{5\pi}{4}$ **9.a.** $\frac{\pi}{6}$ **b.** $\frac{\pi}{3}$ **c.** $\frac{\pi}{2}$ **d.** $\frac{2\pi}{3}$ **e.** $\frac{5\pi}{6}$ **f.** π **g.** $\frac{7\pi}{6}$ **h.** $\frac{4\pi}{3}$ **i.** $\frac{3\pi}{2}$ **j.** $\frac{5\pi}{3}$
k. $\frac{11\pi}{6}$ **10. c, d, f, g** are False   **11.** $BC = \frac{40}{9}$; $DF = \frac{36}{5}; \frac{5}{9}$ **12.** 79°, $40\frac{2}{3}$°, $60\frac{1}{3}$°   **13.a.** 5
b. $\sqrt{29}$ **c.** $\sqrt{2}$ **d.** 13   **14.a.** $\sqrt{35}$ **b.** 6   **c.** $\sqrt{5}$ **d.** $\sqrt{3}$ **15.a.** $BC = 3$, $AC = 3\sqrt{3}$
b. $BC = 1$, $AB = 2$ **c.** $AB = 8$, $AC = 4\sqrt{3}$ **d.** $BC = \frac{7}{2}$, $AC = \frac{7\sqrt{3}}{2}$ **e.** $BC = \frac{5\sqrt{3}}{3}$,
$AB = \frac{10\sqrt{3}}{3}$ **f.** $AB = 4$, $AC = 2\sqrt{3}$ **g.** $BC = \frac{\sqrt{5}}{2}$, $AC = \frac{\sqrt{15}}{2}$ **h.** $BC = \frac{2\sqrt{3}}{3}$,
$AB = \frac{4\sqrt{3}}{3}$ **i.** $AB = 2\sqrt{2}$, $AC = \sqrt{6}$ **16.a.** $ST = 7$, $RT = 7\sqrt{2}$ **b.** $RS = 1$, $RT = \sqrt{2}$
c. $RS = ST = 5$ **d.** $RS = ST = \frac{\sqrt{2}}{3}$ **e.** $ST = \frac{1}{4}$, $RT = \frac{\sqrt{2}}{4}$ **f.** $RS = ST = \frac{3\sqrt{2}}{2}$

PAGES 17–18 **1.a.** $(3, -2)$ **b.** $(2, 3)$ **c.** $(-4, -3)$ **d.** $(-3, 0)$ **e.** $(4.5, 1.5)$ **f.** $(0, -1)$
g. $(-1.5, 3.5)$ **h.** $(1.5, -3)$ **i.** $(-.7, -1.3)$ **j.** $(4, 0)$ **k.** $(0, 2)$ **l.** $(-2.3, 2.7)$
4.a. $3\sqrt{10}$ **b.** 10 **c.** 10 **d.** 10 **e.** $7\sqrt{2}$ **f.** $\sqrt{41}$ **5.a.** 12 **b.** $\sqrt{7}$ **c.** $\sqrt{5}$
6.a. $x^2 + y^2 = 25$ **b.** $x^2 + y^2 = 9$ **c.** $x^2 + y^2 = 100$ **d.** $x^2 + y^2 = 100$
e.–h. $x^2 + y^2 = 1$ **7.a.** 10π **b.** 6π **c., d.** 20π **e.–h.** 2π **8.** $(\frac{1}{\sqrt{2}}, \frac{1}{\sqrt{2}})$, $(\frac{-1}{\sqrt{2}}, \frac{-1}{\sqrt{2}})$
9. $(\frac{-1}{\sqrt{2}}, \frac{1}{\sqrt{2}})$, $(\frac{1}{\sqrt{2}}, \frac{-1}{\sqrt{2}})$

PAGES 20–21 **1.a.** L, T, V **b.** H, U, S **c.** J, N, K **d.** M, Q, I **e.** R, E, R **f.** F, G, G
2.a. $(6, 2)$; $(-6, -2)$; $(6, -2)$ **b.** $(-3, 4)$; $(3, -4)$; $(-3, -4)$ **c.** $(-6, -3)$; $(6, 3)$;
$(-6, 3)$ **d.** $(4, -4)$; $(-4, 4)$; $(4, 4)$ **e.** $(6, 0)$; $(-6, 0)$; $(6, 0)$ **f.** $(0, 4)$; $(0, -4)$; $(0, -4)$
g. $(-m, n)$; $(m, -n)$; $(-m, -n)$ **h.** (c, d); $(-c, -d)$; $(c, -d)$ **i.** $(-t, -h)$; (t, h); $(-t, h)$
3.a. $C(-a, b), F(a, -b), D(-a, -b)$ **b.** $E(-m, n), A(m, -n), B(-m, -n)$ **4.a.** $(4, 7)$
b. $(2, -6)$ **c.** $(-5, 3)$ **d.** $(-8, -2)$ **e.** (b, a) **f.** $(-2n, m)$ **g.** $(2a, -3c)$ **h.** $(-d, -c)$
i. $(m - n, a + b)$ **5.a.** $(-7, 4)$; $(7, -4)$; $(-7, -4)$ **b.** $(6, 2)$; $(-6, -2)$; $(6, -2)$
c. $(-3, -5)$; $(3, 5)$; $(-3, 5)$ **d.** $(2, -8)$; $(-2, 8)$; $(2, 8)$ **e.** $(-a, b)$; $(a, -b)$; $(-a, -b)$
f. $(-m, -2n)$; $(m, 2n)$; $(-m, 2n)$ **g.** $(3c, 2a)$; $(-3c, -2a)$; $(3c, -2a)$ **h.** $(c, -d)$;
$(-c, d)$; (c, d) **i.** $(-a - b, m - n)$; $(a + b, n - m)$; $(-a - b, n - m)$

PAGES 23–24 **1.a.** $\{3, 2, 1, 5\}$; $\{2, 3, 4\}$ **b.** {odd integers}; $\{6k\}$, k is any integer.
c. R; $\{y \mid y \geq 1\}$ **d.** R; R **e.** $\{x \mid x \geq 0\}$; $\{y \mid y \geq 0\}$ **f.** R; $\{3\}$
g. R; $\{y \mid -2 \leq y \leq 2\}$ **2.a.** 50 **b.** 2.21 **c.** 4 **d.** $25a^2 + 1$ **e.** $c^2 + 6c + 10$ **f.** $\frac{3}{2}$
3. b, c, g, h, i, j are *functions*

PAGES 24–26 REVIEW EXERCISES **1.a.** $\{-\sqrt{17}, \sqrt{17}\}$ **b.** $\{0, 7\}$ **c.** ϕ
d. $\{\frac{-3 + \sqrt{17}}{4}, \frac{-3 - \sqrt{17}}{4}\}$ **e.** $\{3\}$ **f.** $\{\pi\}$ **2.a.** rational **b.** rational **c.** irrational
d. rational **e.** irrational **f.** irrational **4.a.** $(-3, -8), (-1, -3), (1, 2)$, etc. **b.** $(-2, 1)$,
$(2, -1), (1, 2)$, etc. **c.** $(-3, 0)$; $(-3, 5)$; $(-3, 7)$, etc. **d.** $(3, 1)$; $(-2, 1)$; $(6, 1)$, etc.
5. (x, y) such that $x < 0$ and $y > 0$. **6.a.** Two angles have vertex C. Two arcs have end
points A, B. **b.** $\angle AOB$, $\angle BOD$; $\angle OCD$, $\angle ODC$; $\angle AOB$, $\angle BOC$ **c.** $\overrightarrow{AD}$; $\overrightarrow{OA}$, $\overrightarrow{OB}$,
$\overrightarrow{OC}$, $\overrightarrow{CO}$, $\overrightarrow{OD}$, etc.; $\overrightarrow{OB}$, etc. **d.** $\overparen{ABC}$, $\overparen{BCD}$; $\overparen{BAD}$, $\overparen{CDA}$, etc. **e.** $\overleftrightarrow{CD}$ **f.** $\overparen{ACD}$
g. $\angle AOB$, $\angle COB$; $\angle BOD$; $\angle COD$, etc. **h.** $\overleftrightarrow{CO}$ and $\overleftrightarrow{CD}$, etc. **i.** B **7.a.** $36°$ **b.** $324°$
c. $324°$ **d.** 4π **e.** $\frac{2\pi}{5}$ **f.** $\frac{27\pi}{5}$ **g.** $36°$ **h.** 6π **8.** $\sqrt{29}$ **9.** 4; $4\sqrt{3}$ **10.** $5\sqrt{2}$
12. $x^2 + y^2 = 16$ **13.a.** 8 **b.** $\sqrt{85}$ **c.** 8 **d.** $5\sqrt{2}$ **14.a.** $P(3, 4)$ **b.** $P(-3, -4)$
c. $P(3, -4)$ **d.** $P(4, -3)$ **15.a.** yes **b.** yes **c.** yes **d.** no: $(6, 2)$, $(6, -2)$
e. no: $(3, 3)$, $(3, -3)$ **f.** yes **16.a.** $\{2, 4, 6, \ldots\}$, $\{7, 14, 21, \ldots\}$ **b.** R, $\{y \mid y \geq 3\}$
c. R, $\{y \mid y \geq 3\}$ **d.** $\{x \mid x \geq 2\}$, $\{y \mid y \geq 0\}$ **e.** R, R **17.a.** 97 **b.** $4a^2 - 3$ **c.** 2
d. $t^2 - 4t + 1$ **e.** $\pi^2 - 3$ **18.** $\{\ldots, -1, 2, 5, 8, \ldots\}$

PAGES 26–27 CHAPTER TEST **1.a.** $\{\sqrt{6}, -\sqrt{6}\}$ **b.** $\{\frac{-3 + \sqrt{65}}{4}, \frac{-3 - \sqrt{65}}{4}\}$ **c.** ϕ
d. $\{4\}$ **2.a.** irrational **b.** irrational **c.** rational **d.** irrational **4.a.** $10°$ **b.** $100°$
5. 3; $3\sqrt{3}$ **6.** 28 **7.a.** F **b.** F **c.** F **d.** T **e.** T **f.** F **g.** T **h.** T **i.** F **j.** F
9.a. $\sqrt{29}$ **b.** $\sqrt{t^2 - 6t + 4c^2 - 8c + 13}$ **10.a.** $(a, -b)$ **b.** $(-a, -b)$ **c.** $(-a, b)$
d. (b, a) **11.a.** $\{3, 6, 9, \ldots\}$, $\{1, 2, 3, \ldots\}$ **b.** R, $\{y \mid y \geq 4\}$ **c.** $\{x \mid x \geq 5\}$,
$\{y \mid y \geq 0\}$ **12.a.** -4 **b.** $-15c - 2$ **c.** $\pi - 2$ **d.** $6m - 5$ **13.a.** $120°$ **b.** $\frac{8\pi}{3}$
14. $x^2 + y^2 = 4$

PAGES 30–31 **1.a.** $P(-1, 0.6)$ **b.** $P(-1, -0.2)$ **c.** $P(1, -0.5)$ **d.** $P(-1, 0)$
e. $P(0.4, -1)$ **f.** $P(-0.7, -1)$ **g.** $P(-0.9, 1)$ **h.** $P(0.3, 1)$ **i.** $P(1, 1)$ **j.** $P(1, 1)$ **2.a.** F
b. T **c.** T **d.** T **e.** T **f.** F **g.** T **h.** F **i.** T **j.** T **k.** T **l.** T **m.** T **n.** T **o.** T
p. T **q.** T **r.** T **3.a.** R, the set of all real numbers **b.** The set of points on square
$TCRV$ with vertices at $(1, 1)$, $(-1, 1)$, $(-1, -1)$ and $(1, -1)$

PAGES 32–33 **1.** 2π **2.** $\frac{\pi}{4}$ **3.** See art below. **4.a.** $(A, \frac{11\pi}{4})$, $(A, \frac{19\pi}{4})$, $(A, \frac{27\pi}{4})$, $(A, \frac{-13\pi}{4})$, $(A, \frac{-5\pi}{4})$, etc. **b.** $(A, \frac{\pi}{4})$, $(A, \frac{9\pi}{4})$, $(A, \frac{17\pi}{4})$, $(A, \frac{-23\pi}{4})$, $(A, \frac{-15\pi}{4})$, etc. **5.a.** $\frac{\pi}{4}$ **b.** $\frac{3\pi}{2}$ **c.** $\frac{3\pi}{4}$ **d.** $\frac{5\pi}{4}$ **e.** $\frac{\pi}{2}$ **f.** $\frac{7\pi}{4}$ **6.** 2π **7.** $\frac{\pi}{6}$ **8.a.** $\frac{\pi}{6}$ **b.** $\frac{\pi}{3}$ **c.** $\frac{5\pi}{6}$ **d.** $\frac{5\pi}{3}$ **e.** $\frac{2\pi}{3}$ **f.** $\frac{3\pi}{2}$ **g.** $\frac{7\pi}{6}$ **h.** $\frac{4\pi}{3}$ **i.** $\frac{11\pi}{6}$ **j.** π

3a.

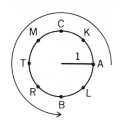

3b.

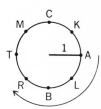

3c.

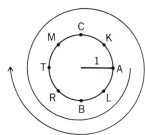

3d.

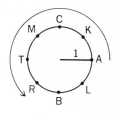

3e.

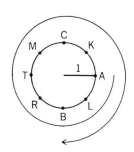

3f.

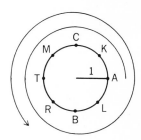

PAGES 34–35 **1.a.** C **b.** L **c.** L **d.** M **e.** A **f.** B **g.** R **h.** T **2.a.** C **b.** F **c.** R **d.** V **e.** L **f.** G **g.** T **h.** D

PAGES 38–39 **2.a.** T **b.** F **c.** T **d.** T **e.** T **f.** T **g.** T **h.** F **i.** T **j.** T **k.** T **3.** The set of all real numbers. **4.** The set of points on the unit circle. **8.a.** π **b.** $\frac{3\pi}{4}$ **c.** $\frac{5\pi}{3}$ **d.** $\frac{\pi}{6}$ **e.** π **f.** 0 **g.** $\frac{4\pi}{3}$ **h.** $\frac{\pi}{2}$ **i.** $\frac{7\pi}{4}$ **j.** $\frac{7\pi}{6}$ **k.** $\frac{5\pi}{6}$ **l.** 0 **m.** $7 - 2\pi$ **n.** $32 - 10\pi$ **o.** $-5 + 2\pi$ **9.a.** $7 + 2\pi, 7 + 4\pi, 7 + 6\pi$ **b.** $7 - 4\pi, 7 - 6\pi, 7 - 8\pi$

PAGES 42–43 **1.a.** $\frac{\pi}{4}, \frac{9\pi}{4}, \frac{-7\pi}{4}$, etc. **b.** $\frac{\pi}{2}, \frac{5\pi}{2}, \frac{-3\pi}{2}$, etc. **c.** $\frac{7\pi}{4}, \frac{15\pi}{4}, \frac{-\pi}{4}$, etc. **d.** $\pi, 3\pi, -\pi$, etc. **e.** $\frac{5\pi}{4}, \frac{13\pi}{4}, \frac{-3\pi}{4}$, etc. **f.** $\frac{3\pi}{4}, \frac{11\pi}{4}, \frac{-5\pi}{4}$, etc. **2.a.** $(\frac{1}{\sqrt{2}}, \frac{-1}{\sqrt{2}})$ **b.** $(0, 1)$

c. $(-1, 0)$ **d.** $(\frac{-1}{\sqrt{2}}, \frac{-1}{\sqrt{2}})$ **e.** $(\frac{1}{\sqrt{2}}, \frac{-1}{\sqrt{2}})$ **f.** $(1, 0)$ **g.** $(\frac{-1}{\sqrt{2}}, \frac{1}{\sqrt{2}})$ **h.** $(0, -1)$ **3.a.** A **b.** C
c. B **d.** N **e.** N **f.** C **4.a.** $\frac{\pi}{3}, \frac{7\pi}{3}, \frac{-5\pi}{3}$, etc. **b.** $\frac{\pi}{6}, \frac{13\pi}{6}, \frac{-11\pi}{6}$, etc. **c.** $\frac{4\pi}{3}, \frac{10\pi}{3}, \frac{-2\pi}{3}$, etc.
d. $\frac{11\pi}{6}, \frac{23\pi}{6}, \frac{-\pi}{6}$, etc. **e.** $\frac{7\pi}{6}, \frac{19\pi}{6}, \frac{-5\pi}{6}$, etc. **f.** $\frac{2\pi}{3}, \frac{8\pi}{3}, \frac{-4\pi}{3}$, etc. **g.** $\frac{3\pi}{2}, \frac{7\pi}{2}, \frac{-\pi}{2}$, etc.
h. $\frac{5\pi}{6}, \frac{17\pi}{6}, \frac{-7\pi}{6}$, etc. **5.a.** $(\frac{1}{2}, \frac{\sqrt{3}}{2})$ **b.** $(\frac{-\sqrt{3}}{2}, \frac{1}{2})$ **c.** $(\frac{\sqrt{3}}{2}, \frac{1}{2})$ **d.** $(\frac{-1}{2}, \frac{-\sqrt{3}}{2})$ **e.** $(\frac{\sqrt{3}}{2}, \frac{-1}{2})$
f. $(\frac{-1}{2}, \frac{\sqrt{3}}{2})$ **g.** $(\frac{1}{2}, \frac{-\sqrt{3}}{2})$ **h.** $(\frac{-\sqrt{3}}{2}, \frac{-1}{2})$ **6.a.** F **b.** Q **c.** A **d.** T **e.** Q **f.** B **7.a.** $(.7, .7)$
b. $(1, -.1)$ **c.** $(.5, .9)$ **d.** $(-.7, -.7)$ **e.** $(-.7, .7)$ **f.** $(-.4, -.9)$ **g.** $(-.7, .7)$
h. $(-.6, .8)$ **i.** $(.8, -.7)$

PAGES 45–46 **1.a.** $(1, 0)$ **b.** $(\frac{1}{\sqrt{2}}, \frac{1}{\sqrt{2}})$ **c.** $(\frac{\sqrt{3}}{2}, \frac{1}{2})$ **d.** $(0, 1)$ **e.** $(\frac{-1}{2}, \frac{\sqrt{3}}{2})$ **f.** $(\frac{-1}{\sqrt{2}}, \frac{-1}{\sqrt{2}})$
g. $(-1, 0)$ **h.** $(\frac{-1}{\sqrt{2}}, \frac{1}{\sqrt{2}})$ **i.** $(0, -1)$ **j.** $(\frac{1}{\sqrt{2}}, \frac{-1}{\sqrt{2}})$ **k.** $(\frac{1}{2}, \frac{\sqrt{3}}{2})$ **l.** $(\frac{-1}{2}, \frac{-\sqrt{3}}{2})$ **2.a.** $P(\frac{\sqrt{3}}{2}, \frac{1}{2})$
b. $P(\frac{-1}{\sqrt{2}}, \frac{1}{\sqrt{2}})$ **c.** $P(\frac{1}{2}, \frac{-\sqrt{3}}{2})$ **d.** $P(-1, 0)$ **e.** $P(1, 0)$ **f.** $P(\frac{-\sqrt{3}}{2}, \frac{1}{2})$ **g.** $P(1, 0)$
h. $P(\frac{1}{2}, \frac{-\sqrt{3}}{2})$ **i.** $P(\frac{-1}{2}, \frac{-\sqrt{3}}{2})$ **j.** $P(0, -1)$ **k.** $P(0, 1)$ **l.** $P(0, -1)$ **m.** $P(-1, 0)$
n. $P(\frac{-1}{\sqrt{2}}, \frac{-1}{\sqrt{2}})$ **o.** $P(\frac{-\sqrt{3}}{2}, \frac{-1}{2})$ **3.a.** T **b.** F **c.** T **d.** T **e.** T **f.** F **g.** T **h.** T **i.** F
j. T **k.** F **l.** T **m.** F **n.** T **o.** F **p.** T **q.** T **r.** T **s.** T **t.** T **u.** T **v.** T **w.** T
x. T **4.** R, the set of all real numbers. **5.** The set of all points on the unit circle in
standard position; that is, the set of all points $P(x, y)$ such that $x^2 + y^2 = 1$. **6.** There
is no real number y for which $2^2 + y^2 = 1$. **7.** $\frac{\sqrt{15}}{4}$ and $\frac{-\sqrt{15}}{4}$

PAGE 48 **1.a.** 1 **b.** 4 **c.** 0.2 **d.** 6 **e.** 4 **f.** 4 **g.** 3 **h.** 4 **2.a.** $f(3) = f(5) = f(7) = 3$
b. T **c.** T **d.** T **e.** There is none.

PAGE 51 **1.** 24 hrs. **2.** 1 yr. **3.** No change. **4.** Four times as long. **5.** $\frac{1}{4}$ cycle per sec.
6. 5 sec., $\frac{1}{5}$ cycle per sec. **7.** $f = \frac{1}{2}\pi\sqrt{\frac{g}{l}}$ **8.** 1 meter **9.** 0.8 ft. **10.** 2.3 sec. **11.** Elements
of medium move perpendicular to line of energy flow in transverse waves and parallel
to line of energy flow in longitudinal waves. **12.** There is no air to compress and expand.

PAGES 52–53 REVIEW EXERCISES **1.** $\theta = \frac{3\pi}{4}, \frac{11\pi}{4}, \frac{-5\pi}{4}, \frac{-13\pi}{4}$, etc. **2.a.** yes **b.** no
c. yes **3.a.** $(\frac{-1}{\sqrt{2}}, \frac{1}{\sqrt{2}})$ **b.** $(\frac{1}{2}, \frac{-\sqrt{3}}{2})$ **c.** $(\frac{-\sqrt{3}}{2}, \frac{1}{2})$ **d.** $(\frac{1}{2}, \frac{\sqrt{3}}{2})$ **e.** $(\frac{\sqrt{3}}{2}, \frac{1}{2})$ **f.** $(\frac{1}{\sqrt{2}}, \frac{1}{\sqrt{2}})$
g. $(-1, 0)$ **h.** $(\frac{\sqrt{3}}{2}, \frac{-1}{2})$ **i.** $(\frac{-1}{\sqrt{2}}, \frac{-1}{\sqrt{2}})$ **j.** $(0, -1)$ **k.** $(1, 0)$ **l.** $(0, 1)$ **4.a.** $\frac{3\pi}{2}$ **b.** $\frac{2\pi}{3}$
c. $\frac{7\pi}{4}$ **d.** $\frac{5\pi}{6}$ **5.a.** $-\pi$ **b.** $\frac{-5\pi}{4}$ **c.** $\frac{-5\pi}{6}$ **d.** $\frac{-5\pi}{3}$ **6.** R, the set of all real numbers.
7. Set of all points on unit circle in standard position; that is, all points $P(x, y)$ for which
$x^2 + y^2 = 1$. **8.** $x^2 + y^2 = 1$ **9.** $\frac{\sqrt{5}}{3}$ and $\frac{-\sqrt{5}}{3}$ **10.** 2π **12.** $\frac{2}{5}$ cycle per sec.
13. $\frac{5}{16}$ cycle per sec.

PAGES 53–54 CHAPTER TEST **1.** $\theta = \frac{5\pi}{6}, \frac{17\pi}{6}, \frac{-7\pi}{6}$, etc. **2.a.** $\frac{\pi}{2}$ **b.** $\frac{4\pi}{3}$ **c.** $\frac{\pi}{6}$ **d.** π
3.a. $(\frac{-1}{2}, \frac{\sqrt{3}}{2})$ **b.** $(\frac{1}{\sqrt{2}}, \frac{-1}{\sqrt{2}})$ **c.** $(\frac{-\sqrt{3}}{2}, \frac{-1}{2})$ **d.** $(0, 1)$ **e.** $(-1, 0)$ **f.** $(\frac{-1}{2}, \frac{\sqrt{3}}{2})$
4. $\frac{2\pi}{3}, \frac{8\pi}{3}, \frac{-4\pi}{3}, \frac{-10\pi}{3}$, etc. **5.** $\frac{\sqrt{7}}{4}, \frac{-\sqrt{7}}{4}$ **6.a.** F **b.** F **c.** T **d.** T **e.** T **f.** T **g.** F
h. F **i.** F **j.** F **7.a.** 6 **b.** $-6, 0, 12, 18, 24$, etc. **8.** $2\frac{1}{2}$ sec., $\frac{2}{5}$ cycle per sec.

PAGES 57–60 **1.a.** $\frac{\sqrt{3}}{2}$ **b.** $\frac{\sqrt{2}}{2}$ **c.** 0 **d.** $\frac{1}{2}$ **e.** -1 **f.** $\frac{-\sqrt{3}}{2}$ **g.** $\frac{1}{2}$ **h.** $\frac{\sqrt{2}}{2}$ **i.** $\frac{-\sqrt{2}}{2}$ **j.** 1
k. $\frac{-\sqrt{2}}{2}$ **l.** $\frac{-1}{2}$ **m.** $\frac{-\sqrt{2}}{2}$ **n.** $\frac{-\sqrt{3}}{2}$ **o.** $\frac{\sqrt{3}}{2}$ **p.** $\frac{-1}{2}$ **q.** $\frac{-1}{2}$ **r.** $\frac{\sqrt{3}}{2}$ **s.** $\frac{-\sqrt{2}}{2}$ **t.** 0 **u.** $\frac{\sqrt{2}}{2}$
v. $\frac{\sqrt{3}}{2}$ **w.** 0 **x.** -1 **y.** $\frac{-\sqrt{2}}{2}$ **z.** $\frac{-1}{2}$ **a'.** 1 **b'.** 1 **c'.** -1 **d'.** 0 **e'.** $\frac{1}{2}$ **f'.** $\frac{-\sqrt{2}}{2}$ **g'.** 0
h'. 0 **i'.** $\frac{\sqrt{3}}{2}$ **j'.** $\frac{\sqrt{2}}{2}$ **k'.** $\frac{1}{2}$ **l'.** $\frac{1}{2}$ **m'.** $\frac{1}{2}$ **n'.** 1 **o'.** $\frac{3}{4}$ **p'.** $-\sqrt{3}$ **2.a.** T **b.** T **c.** T

d. T **e.** T **f.** F **g.** F **h.** T **i.** T **j.** T **k.** F **l.** F **m.** T **n.** F **o.** F **p.** F **q.** T
r. T **s.** T **t.** T **u.** T **v.** T **w.** T **x.** F **y.** T **z.** T **3.** d **4.a.** yes **b.** no; $\frac{\pi}{4}$, etc.
c. no; $\frac{\pi}{4}$, etc. **d.** yes **e.** no; 1, etc. **f.** no; 1, etc. **g.** no; 0, etc. **h.** yes **i.** no; $\frac{\pi}{3}$, etc.
5.a. 0.7 ± 0.1 **b.** -0.7 ± 0.1 **c.** 0.5 ± 0.1 **d.** 0.8 ± 0.1 **e.** -0.4 ± 0.1 **f.** -0.6 ± 0.1
g. 0.5 ± 0.1 **h.** -0.4 ± 0.1 **i.** -0.8 ± 0.1 **6.a.** pos., pos. **b.** neg., pos. **c.** neg., neg.
d. pos., neg. **e.** neg., pos. **f.** neg., neg. **g.** pos., neg. **h.** pos., pos. **8.a.** 1st. **b.** 2nd.
c. 3rd. **d.** 4th. **e.** 2nd. **f.** 3rd. **g.** 4th. **h.** 1st. **9.a.** $\sin \frac{7\pi}{4}$ **b.** $\cos \frac{\pi}{6}$ **c.** $\sin \frac{\pi}{4}$
d. $\cos \frac{\pi}{3}$ **e.** $\sin \pi$ **f.** $\cos \pi$ **g.** $\sin(8 - 2\pi)$ **h.** $\cos(-2 + 2\pi)$ **i.** $\cos(-3 + 2\pi)$
10. 1st, 4th **11.** 3rd, 4th **12.** $\frac{-\sqrt{5}}{3}$ **13.** $\frac{-3}{5}$ **14.** For each equation, both members should
have the following values: **a.** $\frac{-\sqrt{3}}{2}$ **b.** 0 **c.** $\frac{-1}{2}$ **d.** 0 **e.** $\frac{1}{2}$ **f.** $\frac{\sqrt{3}}{2}$ **g.** 0 **h.** $-\frac{3}{2}$
i. $\frac{-\sqrt{3}}{2}$ **j.** $\frac{-1}{2}$ **k.** $\frac{\sqrt{2}}{2}$ **l.** 1 **m.** $\sqrt{2} + 1$

PAGES 65–67 **1. I.** $\frac{\pi}{5}$ **II.** $\frac{\pi}{5}$ **III.** $\frac{\pi}{5}$ **2.a.** $-\cos \frac{\pi}{5}$ **b.** $-\cos \frac{\pi}{5}$ **c.** $\cos \frac{\pi}{5}$ **d.** $-\cos \frac{\pi}{5}$
e. $-\cos \frac{\pi}{5}$ **f.** $\cos \frac{\pi}{5}$ **g.** $-\cos \frac{2\pi}{5}$ **h.** $-\cos \frac{2\pi}{9}$ **i.** $-\cos \frac{\pi}{5}$ **j.** $-\cos \frac{\pi}{8}$ **k.** $\cos(2\pi - 6)$
l. $\cos \frac{\pi}{8}$ **3.a.** $\sin \frac{\pi}{5}$ **b.** $-\sin \frac{\pi}{5}$ **c.** $-\sin \frac{\pi}{5}$ **d.** $-\sin \frac{\pi}{5}$ **e.** $\sin \frac{\pi}{5}$ **f.** $\sin \frac{\pi}{5}$ **g.** $\sin \frac{2\pi}{5}$
h. $\sin \frac{2\pi}{9}$ **i.** $-\sin \frac{\pi}{5}$ **j.** $-\sin \frac{\pi}{8}$ **k.** $-\sin(2\pi - 6)$ **l.** $-\sin \frac{\pi}{8}$ **4.a.** T **b.** F **c.** T **d.** F
e. T **f.** F **5.a.** $\cos \frac{\pi}{6}$ **b.** $\cos \frac{\pi}{3}$ **c.** $\cos \frac{3\pi}{10}$ **d.** $\cos \frac{\pi}{10}$ **e.** $\cos \frac{\pi}{4}$ **f.** $\cos \frac{-\pi}{6}$ or $\cos \frac{\pi}{6}$
g. $\cos \frac{-3\pi}{4}$ or $\cos \frac{3\pi}{4}$ **h.** $\cos(\frac{\pi}{2} - 1)$ **6.a.** $\sin \frac{\pi}{2}$ **b.** $\sin 0$ **c.** $\sin \frac{\pi}{3}$ **d.** $\sin \frac{\pi}{6}$
e. $\sin \frac{-\pi}{6}$ or $-\sin \frac{\pi}{6}$ **f.** $\sin \frac{3\pi}{10}$ **g.** $\sin \frac{\pi}{4}$ **h.** $\sin(\frac{\pi}{2} - 1.4)$ **7.a.** F **b.** F **c.** F **d.** F **e.** T
f. F **g.** F **h.** T **i.** T **j.** T **k.** T **l.** F **m.** F **n.** T **o.** F **p.** T **q.** F **r.** F **s.** T
t. F **u.** T **v.** F **w.** T **x.** T **y.** T **z.** F **8.a.** $\cos \theta$ **b.** $-\sin \theta$ **c.** $-\cos \theta$ **d.** $\sin \theta$
e. $-\cos \theta$ **f.** $-\sin \theta$ **9.a.** $\cos \theta$ **b.** $-\sin \theta$ **c.** $\sin \theta$ **d.** $\cos \theta$ **e.** $\sin \theta$ **f.** $-\cos \theta$
10.a. $\frac{\pi}{4}, \frac{7\pi}{4}$ **b.** $\frac{\pi}{6}, \frac{5\pi}{6}$ **c.** $\frac{5\pi}{6}, \frac{7\pi}{6}$ **d.** $\frac{5\pi}{4}, \frac{7\pi}{4}$ **e.** $\frac{2\pi}{3}, \frac{4\pi}{3}$ **f.** $\frac{\pi}{3}, \frac{2\pi}{3}$ **11.a.** $\pi - \alpha, \pi + \alpha$
b. $\alpha, 2\pi - \alpha$ **12.a.** $\alpha, \pi - \alpha$ **b.** $\pi + \alpha, 2\pi - \alpha$

PAGE 70 **1.a.** .5810 **b.** .9090 **c.** .9939 **d.** .2385 **e.** .8912 **f.** $-.9928$ **g.** $-.3616$
h. $-.8021$ **i.** $-.9636$ **j.** .4976 **k.** $-.3335$ **l.** .1106 **2.a.** .37, 2.77 **b.** .41, 5.87
c. 1.14, 2.00 **d.** 1.28, 5.00 **e.** 4.23, 5.19 **f.** 2.01, 4.27 **g.** 3.61, 5.81 **h.** 2.72, 3.56
3.a. .7598 **b.** .2925 **c.** $-.3690$ **d.** .2560 **4.a.** .624 **b.** .386 **c.** .884 **d.** 1.034
5.a. .0998 **b.** .1987 **6.** After the first term, the value $\frac{\theta^n}{n!}$ is very small for small positive
values of θ.

PAGES 73–74 **1.a.** dec. from 1 to 0 **b.** dec. from 0 to -1 **c.** inc. from -1 to 0
d. inc. from 0 to 1 **e.** dec. from 0 to -1 **f.** inc. from 0 to 1 **2.a.** min: -1; max: 1
b. min: -1; max: 1 **3.a.** $\frac{\pi}{2}, \frac{3\pi}{2}$ **b.** $0, 2\pi$ **c.** π **d.** $0, \pi, 2\pi$ **e.** $\frac{\pi}{2}$ **f.** $\frac{3\pi}{2}$ **g.** $0 \le \theta < \frac{\pi}{2}$,
$\frac{3\pi}{2} < \theta \le 2\pi$ **h.** $\frac{\pi}{2} < \theta < \frac{3\pi}{2}$ **i.** $0 < \theta < \pi$ **4.** $-1 \le \cos \theta \le 1$ **5.** $-1 \le \sin \theta \le 1$
7.a. F **b.** T **c.** F **d.** T **e.** T **f.** T

PAGES 77–78 **3.a.** 2 **b.** $\frac{\pi}{4} < \theta < \frac{5\pi}{4}$ **c.** $\frac{\pi}{4} < \theta < \frac{3\pi}{4}, \frac{5\pi}{4} < \theta < \frac{7\pi}{4}$ **d.** 2 **4.b.** 4 right
c. 2 left **5.a.** 5 left **b.** 7 right **6.a.** no **b.** yes **c.** yes **d.** $g(x) = 2(x + 3\frac{1}{2})$ **7.a.** 4 left
b. 2 right **c.** $\frac{5}{3}$ left **8.a.** 16 left **b.** 32 right **c.** 8 left **9.** $\frac{b}{m}$ left

PAGES 84–85 **1.a.** $\frac{2}{3}, \frac{\pi}{2}, 0$ **b.** $3, 6\pi, 0$ **c.** $2, 2, 0$ **d.** $\frac{4}{3}, 1, 0$ **e.** $2, \frac{2\pi}{3}, \frac{\pi}{4}$ **f.** $1, 4\pi, \frac{-\pi}{9}$
g. $1, 2, \frac{2}{3}$ **h.** $3, 3\pi, \frac{-\pi}{4}$ **i.** $2, \frac{3\pi}{2}, \frac{3\pi}{8}$ **j.** $1, 2, \frac{-3}{4}$ **5.a.** 4 **b.** 4 **c.** 6

2a.

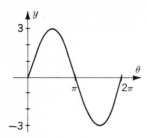

2b.

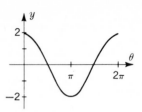

2c.

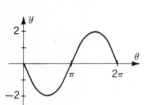

2d.

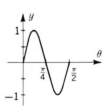

2e.

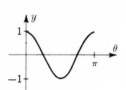

2f.

2g.

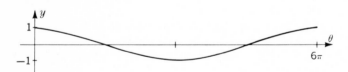

2h.

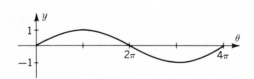

2i.

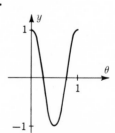

2j.

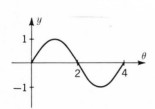

3a.

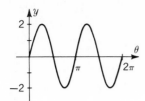

3b.

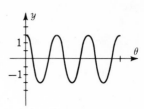

3c.

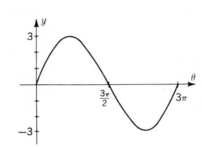

3d.

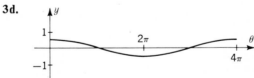

3e.

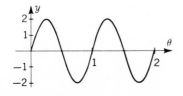

3f.

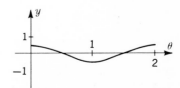

PAGES 86–87　2.a. $\frac{2}{5}$ sec., $2\frac{1}{2}$ cycles per sec.　b. 2 sec., $\frac{1}{2}$ cycle per sec.　c. 1 sec., 1 cycle per sec.　d. $\frac{2}{3}$ sec., $1\frac{1}{2}$ cycles per sec.　3.a. $(\frac{\sqrt{3}}{2}, \frac{1}{2})$, $(\frac{1}{\sqrt{2}}, \frac{1}{\sqrt{2}})$, $(\frac{1}{2}, \frac{\sqrt{3}}{2})$, $(\frac{1}{2}, \frac{-\sqrt{3}}{2})$
b. $\frac{1}{2}, \frac{1}{\sqrt{2}}, \frac{\sqrt{3}}{2}, 1, \frac{\sqrt{3}}{2}, \frac{1}{\sqrt{2}}, \frac{1}{2}$　c. no　d. $6 + 12n$ sec., where n is any natural number
e. 24 sec.　f. $\frac{1}{24}$ cycle per sec.

PAGE 89　1.a. 0 in.　b. $\frac{\sqrt{3}}{2}$ in.　c. 0 in.　d. $\frac{1}{\sqrt{2}}$ in.　e. −1 in.　f. $\frac{\sqrt{3}}{2}$ in.　g. $\frac{-1}{\sqrt{2}}$ in.
h. $\frac{-1}{\sqrt{2}}$ in.　i. $\frac{\sqrt{3}}{2}$ in.　j. $\frac{\sqrt{3}}{2}$ in.　k. $\frac{\sqrt{3}}{2}$ in.　l. −1 in.　m. $\frac{-1}{\sqrt{2}}$ in.　n. $\frac{-1}{\sqrt{2}}$ in.　o. 0 in.　p. 0 in.
2.a. $2 + 4n$ sec., n is any natural number.　b. $4n$ sec., n is any whole number.　3.a. $\frac{1}{\sqrt{2}}$
b. $\frac{-1}{\sqrt{2}}$　c. 1　d. $\frac{1}{\sqrt{2}}$　e. $\frac{\sqrt{3}}{2}$　f. $\frac{-1}{\sqrt{2}}$　g. −1　h. 0　4. $\frac{2}{3} + \frac{4}{3}n$ sec., n is any natural number; $\frac{4}{3}n$ sec., n is any whole number.　5. $\frac{1}{10}$ sec.　6. 12 cycles per sec.　7. 2.4 sec., $\frac{5}{12}$ cycles per sec.　8. $T = \frac{1}{f}; f = \frac{1}{T}$

PAGES 92–93　2.h. $y = \theta - \cos\theta$　3.a. 2π　b. 2π　c. π　d. 2π　e. 2π　f. 2　g. 4　h. 6
i. 24　j. 2π

PAGES 93–96 REVIEW EXERCISES　1.a. $\frac{-1}{2}$　b. $\frac{1}{2}$　c. $\frac{-1}{\sqrt{2}}$　d. $\frac{-\sqrt{3}}{2}$　e. $\frac{\sqrt{3}}{2}$　f. $\frac{-1}{\sqrt{2}}$
g. $\frac{-\sqrt{3}}{2}$　h. $\frac{1}{\sqrt{2}}$　i. $\frac{\sqrt{3}}{2}$　j. 1　k. −1　l. 0　2. R, the set of all real numbers.
3. $\{x \mid -1 \le x \le 1\}$　4. $-\pi, \frac{-\pi}{2}, 0, \frac{\pi}{2}, \pi$, etc.　5. pos., neg., neg., pos.　6. pos., pos., neg., neg.　7. $\{(0, y)\}$　8. b, e, f, h　9.a. .9887　b. .8473　c. .3429　d. −.2482　e. .9739
f. .6851　10.a. 0.64, 2.50　b. 0.73, 5.55　c. 3.56, 5.86　d. 1.81, 4.47　11.a. 0.987　b. 0.776
12. $\frac{-4}{5}$　13.a. $\frac{\sqrt{3}}{2}$　b. 1　c. 0　d. $\frac{1}{2}$　14.a. $-\cos\frac{2\pi}{5}$　b. $-\cos\frac{\pi}{5}$　c. $\cos\frac{\pi}{5}$　d. $\cos\frac{\pi}{7}$
e. $-\cos\frac{\pi}{5}$　f. $\cos\frac{5\pi}{14}$　15.a. $\sin\frac{\pi}{5}$　b. $-\sin\frac{2\pi}{5}$　c. $-\sin\frac{2\pi}{5}$　d. $-\sin\frac{\pi}{7}$　e. $\sin\frac{\pi}{5}$　f. $\sin\frac{\pi}{8}$
16.a. $-\cos\theta$　b. $\sin\theta$　c. $\cos\theta$　17.a. $\cos\theta$　b. $\cos\theta$　c. $\sin\theta$　19. dec. from 1 to 0
as θ inc. from 0 to $\frac{\pi}{2}$; dec. from 0 to −1 as θ inc. from $\frac{\pi}{2}$ to π; inc. from −1 to 0 as θ
inc. from π to $\frac{3\pi}{2}$; inc. from 0 to 1 as θ inc. from $\frac{3\pi}{2}$ to 2π.　20. inc. from 0 to 1 as θ
inc. from 0 to $\frac{\pi}{2}$; dec. from 1 to 0 as θ inc. from $\frac{\pi}{2}$ to π; dec. from 0 to −1 as θ inc. from
π to $\frac{3\pi}{2}$; inc. from −1 to 0 as θ inc. from $\frac{3\pi}{2}$ to 2π.　21.a. 2, π, 0　b. $\frac{2}{3}, \frac{\pi}{2}, \frac{-\pi}{3}$　c. π, 2, 3
d. 1, π, $\frac{\pi}{8}$　22.a. $\frac{2}{3}$ sec., 1.5 cycles per sec.　b. $\frac{1}{2}$ sec., 2 cycles per sec.　23. 6 solutions
24. $\frac{\pi}{3} < \theta < \frac{5\pi}{3}$　25.a. $\frac{1}{2}$ in.　b. $\frac{\sqrt{3}}{2}$ in.　c. $3 + 6n$ sec., n any natural number
d. $6n$ sec., n any whole number　e. 5 cycles per min.

PAGES 96–97 CHAPTER TEST　1.a. $\frac{1}{2}$　b. $\frac{-1}{\sqrt{2}}$　c. $\frac{-\sqrt{3}}{2}$　d. 0　e. $\frac{1}{\sqrt{2}}$　f. $\frac{\sqrt{3}}{2}$　2.a. T
b. F　c. F　d. T　e. T　f. F　g. T　h. T　i. T　j. F　k. T　l. F　3. $\frac{-\sqrt{5}}{3}$
4.a. $\frac{\sqrt{3} - 1}{2\sqrt{2}}$ or $\frac{\sqrt{6} - \sqrt{2}}{4}$　b. $\frac{-1}{2}$　5.a. $-\cos\frac{\pi}{8}$　b. $\cos\frac{\pi}{5}$　c. $\cos\frac{3\pi}{7}$　6.a. $\sin\frac{2\pi}{5}$　b. $\sin\frac{3\pi}{8}$
c. $-\sin\frac{\pi}{5}$　7. decreases from 0 to −1.　8.a. 3, π, $\frac{-\pi}{6}$　b. $\frac{1}{2}$, 4π, $\frac{\pi}{2}$　9. 0.9512
11. $(\frac{-1}{2}, \frac{-\sqrt{3}}{2})$　13. 4　14. 16 sec., $\frac{1}{16}$ cycle per sec.

PAGES 103–104　2.a. $\frac{-\sqrt{5}}{3}$　b. $\frac{-\sqrt{15}}{4}$　c. $\frac{1}{12}(2\sqrt{15} - \sqrt{5})$　d. $\frac{1}{12}(-2\sqrt{15} - \sqrt{5})$
e. $\frac{1}{12}(5\sqrt{3} - 2)$　f. $\frac{1}{12}(-5\sqrt{3} - 2)$　3.a. $\frac{-\sin\theta}{\cos\theta}$　b. $\frac{\sin\theta}{\cos\theta}$　c. $\frac{\sin\theta}{-\cos\theta}$　d. $\cos(7 + \theta)$
e. $-\sin(2\theta + 5)$　f. $\sin(\theta - 3)$　4.a. 1　b. $\cos 5\theta$　c. $\sin 3\theta$　d. $\cos 2\theta$　e. $\cos(3\theta - 2\alpha)$
f. $\sin(5\theta + 4\alpha)$　g. $\cos 11\theta$　h. $\sin\theta$　i. $\sin\theta$　j. $-\cos\theta$　k. $-\sin\theta$　l. $\cos\theta$　m. −1
n. −1　o. $2\sin\theta\cos\alpha$　p. $2\cos\theta\cos\alpha$　q. $\sin\theta$　r. $2\cos\theta\sin\alpha$　s. $2\sin\theta\sin\alpha$
5.a. $\frac{1}{4}(\sqrt{2} + \sqrt{6})$　b. $\frac{1}{4}(\sqrt{2} + \sqrt{6})$　c. $-\frac{1}{4}(\sqrt{2} + \sqrt{6})$　d. $\frac{1}{4}(\sqrt{2} - \sqrt{6})$
e. $-\frac{1}{4}(\sqrt{2} + \sqrt{6})$　f. $\frac{1}{4}(\sqrt{2} + \sqrt{6})$　7.a. $k\pi$　b. $\frac{\pi}{2} + k\pi$　c. $\frac{\pi}{2} + 2k\pi$

d. $2k\pi$ and $\frac{\pi}{2} + k\pi$ **e.** $\frac{k\pi}{2}$ **f.** $k\pi$ and $\frac{\pi}{2} + 2k\pi$ **8.a.** $\frac{1}{9}(2\sqrt{10} - 2)$ **b.** 1
9. $\sin 2\theta \equiv 2 \sin \theta \cos \theta$ **10.** $\cos 2\theta \equiv \cos^2 \theta - \sin^2 \theta$ **11.** $\cos 2\theta \equiv 1 - 2 \sin^2 \theta$
12. $\cos 2\theta \equiv 2 \cos^2 \theta - 1$

PAGE 106 1.a. $\frac{2 \sin \theta + \sin^2 \theta + 3 \cos \theta}{\cos \theta \sin \theta}$ **b.** $\frac{\sin^2 \theta + \cos \theta}{\sin \theta}$ **c.** $\frac{2 + 3 \cos \theta}{2 \sin \theta \cos \theta}$
d. $\frac{\sin \theta + \sin \theta \cos \theta + 2 - 2 \cos \theta}{1 - \cos^2 \theta}$ **2.a.** $\cos \theta (1 - \sin \theta)$ **b.** $(\sin \theta - 3)(\sin \theta - 4)$
c. $(\cos^2 \theta + \sin^2 \theta)(\cos \theta - \sin \theta)(\cos \theta + \sin \theta)$ **d.** $\cos \theta (\cos \theta - 3 \sin \theta)$
e. $\cos \theta (\cos^2 \theta + \sin^2 \theta)$ **f.** $(2 \cos \theta - 1)(\cos \theta + 1)$ **3.a.** $\sin^2 \theta - 2$ **b.** $6 \cos \theta \sin^2 \theta$
c. $6 \sin \theta \cos \theta + 3 \sin^2 \theta$ **d.** $1 - \cos^2 \theta$ **e.** $6 + \sin \theta - \sin^2 \theta$
f. $\sin^2 \theta + 2 \sin \theta \cos \theta + \cos^2 \theta$ **g.** $1 - 2 \cos^2 \theta + \cos^4 \theta$ **h.** $4 \sin \theta - 4 \sin \theta \cos \theta$

PAGE 108 1.a. $\frac{1}{\cos \theta \sin \theta}, \theta \neq \frac{k\pi}{2}$ **b.** $\frac{1}{\sin \theta}, \theta \neq k\pi$ **c.** $\frac{\cos \theta}{\sin \theta}, \theta \neq \frac{k\pi}{2}$ **d.** $-\cos^2 \theta, \theta \neq k\pi$
e. $\frac{\sin \theta}{\cos \theta}, \theta \neq \frac{k\pi}{2}$ **f.** $\sin^2 \theta, \theta \neq \frac{\pi}{2} + k\pi$ **g.** $1; \theta \neq \frac{k\pi}{2}, \theta \neq \frac{3\pi}{4} + k\pi$ **h.** $\sin \theta, \theta \neq k\pi$
i. $\frac{2}{\sin \theta}, \theta \neq k\pi$ **j.** $1 - 3 \cos^2 \theta$ or $3 \sin^2 \theta - 2$ **k.** $3 \cos \theta, \theta \neq \frac{\pi}{2} + k\pi$ **l.** $\cos \theta$

PAGES 110–113 2.a. pos., pos. **b.** pos., pos. **c.** neg., pos. **d.** neg., neg.
4.a. $\frac{-4}{25}\sqrt{21}, \frac{-17}{25}, \sqrt{\frac{3}{10}}, -\sqrt{\frac{7}{10}}$ **b.** $\frac{-\sqrt{3}}{2}, \frac{1}{2}, \frac{1}{2}\sqrt{2 + \sqrt{3}}, \frac{1}{2}\sqrt{2 - \sqrt{3}}$
c. $\frac{4\sqrt{5}}{9}, \frac{-1}{9}, \sqrt{\frac{5}{6}}, -\sqrt{\frac{1}{6}}$ **d.** 0.96, 0.28, $\sqrt{0.1}, \sqrt{0.9}$ **e.** 0.96, 0.28, $\sqrt{0.9}, -\sqrt{0.1}$
f. $\frac{-24}{25}, \frac{7}{25}, \sqrt{0.1}, -\sqrt{0.9}$ **5.** $\sin 3\theta \equiv 3 \sin \theta - 4 \sin^3 \theta$ **6.** $\cos 3\theta \equiv 4 \cos^3 \theta - 3 \cos \theta$
7.a. $\frac{1}{2}\sqrt{2 - \sqrt{2}}$ **b.** $\frac{-1}{2}\sqrt{2 + \sqrt{2}}$ **c.** $\frac{-1}{2}\sqrt{2 - \sqrt{3}}$ **d.** $\frac{-1}{4}$ **e.** $\frac{-\sqrt{2}}{4}$ **f.** 1 **8.a.** $\cos \theta$
b. $\cos \theta$ **c.** $\sin \theta$ **d.** $\cos \theta$ **e.** $\cos \theta + \sin \theta$ **f.** 1 **g.** $\frac{\cos \theta}{\sin \theta}$ **h.** $\frac{1}{\sin \theta \cos \theta}$ **i.** $1 + \cos \theta$
9.a. F **b.** F **c.** F **d.** F **e.** T **f.** T **g.** T **h.** T

PAGE 115 2.a. $\frac{1}{2}[\sin (7\theta + 3\alpha) - \sin (7\theta - 3\alpha)]$ **b.** $\frac{1}{2}[\cos (6\theta + 3\alpha) + \cos (6\theta - 3\alpha)]$
c. $\sin 11\theta + \sin 5\theta$ **d.** $\frac{-1}{2}[\cos 11\alpha - \cos 3\alpha]$ **e.** $\frac{1}{2}[\cos \frac{3\pi}{5} + \cos \frac{\pi}{5}]$
f. $\frac{-1}{2}[\cos \frac{13\pi}{40} - \cos \frac{3\pi}{40}]$ **g.** $\frac{1}{2}[\cos 1.1 + \cos 0.5]$ **h.** $\frac{1}{2}[\sin 9 + \sin 5]$ **4.a.** $2 \cos 5\theta \sin 2\theta$
b. $2 \cos (3\theta + 2\alpha) \cos (3\theta - 2\alpha)$ **c.** $-2 \sin 4\alpha \sin \alpha$ **d.** $2 \sin 4\theta \cos 6\alpha$
e. $2 \sin \frac{6\pi}{35} \cos \frac{\pi}{35}$ **f.** $2 \cos \frac{6\pi}{35} \sin \frac{\pi}{35}$ **g.** $2 \cos \frac{18\pi}{35} \cos \frac{3\pi}{35}$ **h.** $-2 \sin \frac{18\pi}{35} \sin \frac{3\pi}{35}$
i. $2 \cos 4 \sin 2$ **j.** $2 \cos \frac{2\theta + \alpha}{2} \sin \frac{\alpha}{2}$

PAGE 118 1.a. 2 **b.** 0 **c.** 1 **d.** 4 **e.** 4 **f.** 6 **g.** 4 **h.** 4 **2.a.** $\frac{\pi}{2}$ **b.** π **c.** $\frac{\pi}{4}, \frac{3\pi}{4}, \frac{5\pi}{4}, \frac{7\pi}{4}$
d. $\frac{\pi}{6}, \frac{5\pi}{6}, \frac{7\pi}{6}, \frac{11\pi}{6}$ **e.** $\frac{4\pi}{3}, \frac{5\pi}{3}$ **f.** $\frac{\pi}{6}, \frac{5\pi}{6}, \frac{3\pi}{2}$ **g.** $\frac{\pi}{2}, 5.64$ **h.** $\frac{\pi}{6}, \frac{5\pi}{6}$ **i.** $\frac{\pi}{3}, \frac{2\pi}{3}, \frac{4\pi}{3}, \frac{5\pi}{3}$
j. $\frac{\pi}{6}, \frac{\pi}{2}, \frac{3\pi}{2}, \frac{11\pi}{6}$ **k.** $0, \pi, \frac{7\pi}{6}, \frac{11\pi}{6}$ **l.** $0, \frac{\pi}{6}, \frac{5\pi}{6}, \pi, \frac{7\pi}{6}, \frac{11\pi}{6}$ **m.** $\frac{\pi}{6}, \frac{5\pi}{6}$ **n.** $\frac{\pi}{6}, \frac{5\pi}{6}$ **o.** $\pi, \frac{3\pi}{2}$
p. $\frac{\pi}{4}, \frac{3\pi}{4}, \frac{5\pi}{4}, \frac{7\pi}{4}$ **q.** 0.36, 2.13 **r.** $\frac{\pi}{6}, \frac{5\pi}{6}, \frac{7\pi}{6}, \frac{11\pi}{6}$ **s.** $0, \pi$ **t.** $\frac{\pi}{4}, \frac{3\pi}{4}, \frac{5\pi}{4}, \frac{7\pi}{4}$ **u.** $\frac{\pi}{2}, \frac{3\pi}{2}$
3.a. 0.34, 2.80 **b.** 0.46, 2.68, 3.60, 5.82 **c.** 3.55, 5.87 **d.** 0.73, 2.41, 3.48, 5.94
e. 1.32, 2.72, 3.56, 4.96 **f.** $\frac{\pi}{2}, \frac{3\pi}{2}, 2.42, 3.86$

PAGE 119 1. $\frac{\pi}{2}, \frac{3\pi}{2}, \frac{\pi}{4}, \frac{3\pi}{4}, \frac{5\pi}{4}, \frac{7\pi}{4}$ **2.** $0, \pi$ **3.** $0, \pi, \frac{\pi}{6}, \frac{5\pi}{6}$ **4.** $0, \frac{\pi}{3}, \frac{5\pi}{3}$ **5.** $0, \pi, \frac{2\pi}{3}, \frac{4\pi}{3}$
6. $\frac{\pi}{6}, \frac{5\pi}{6}, \frac{3\pi}{2}$ **7.** $\frac{3\pi}{2}$ **8.** $\frac{\pi}{4}, \frac{3\pi}{4}, \frac{5\pi}{4}, \frac{7\pi}{4}$ **9.** $\frac{\pi}{3}, \frac{5\pi}{3}, \pi$ **10.** 0 **11.** $\frac{3\pi}{2}$ **12.** $\frac{\pi}{6}, \frac{5\pi}{6}, \frac{3\pi}{2}$
13. 0.88, 2.26, 4.02, 5.40 **14.** $\frac{\pi}{12}, \frac{5\pi}{12}, \frac{7\pi}{12}, \frac{11\pi}{12}, \frac{13\pi}{12}, \frac{17\pi}{12}, \frac{19\pi}{12}, \frac{23\pi}{12}$ **15.** $0, \pi$

PAGE 121 2.a. $\frac{\pi}{12}, \frac{5\pi}{12}$ **b.** $\frac{7\pi}{4}$ **c.** $\frac{23\pi}{12}, \frac{7\pi}{12}$ **d.** 0.21, 2.17 **e.** 4.15, 5.91 **f.** 0.65, 4.71

PAGES 121–122 REVIEW EXERCISES **1.a.** $\frac{-\sqrt{15}}{4}$ **b.** $\frac{-\sqrt{21}}{5}$ **c.** $\frac{1}{4}$ **d.** $\frac{2}{5}$
e. $\frac{2\sqrt{15}-\sqrt{21}}{20}$ **f.** $\frac{3\sqrt{35}-2}{20}$ **g.** 1 **h.** $\frac{-1}{4}$ **i.** $\frac{-2}{5}$ **j.** $\frac{-17}{25}$ **k.** $\frac{-\sqrt{15}}{8}$ **l.** $\frac{1}{4}\sqrt{8+2\sqrt{15}}$
2.a. $\frac{-\sin\theta}{\cos\theta}$ **b.** $\cos(\theta+4)$ **c.** $-\sin(3\theta+2)$ **d.** $\sin 3$ **e.** $-\sin 2$ **f.** 1 **g.** $\cos(5\theta-3\alpha)$
h. $\sin 7\theta$ **i.** $\frac{1}{\sin\theta\cos\theta}$ **j.** $3\sin\theta$ **k.** $\sin\theta$ **l.** $2\cos\theta$ **m.** $\sin\theta$ **n.** $\frac{\sqrt{2}}{2}$ **o.** $\frac{\sqrt{3}}{2}$ **p.** 0
3.a. $\frac{\sqrt{6}-\sqrt{2}}{4}$ **b.** $\frac{\sqrt{6}-\sqrt{2}}{4}$ **c.** $\frac{1}{2}\sqrt{2+\sqrt{2}}$ **d.** $\frac{-1}{2}\sqrt{2-\sqrt{2}}$
5. $\cos 4\theta \equiv 8\cos^4\theta - 8\cos^2\theta + 1$ **7.a.** $\frac{1}{2}[\cos 9\theta + \cos\theta]$ **b.** $\sin 5 + \sin 1$
8.a. $2\cos 3\alpha\cos\alpha$ **b.** $2\sin 5.2\cos 1$ **9.a.** $\frac{7\pi}{6}, \frac{11\pi}{6}$ **b.** $\frac{\pi}{6}, \frac{5\pi}{6}, \frac{7\pi}{6}, \frac{11\pi}{6}$ **c.** $\frac{\pi}{6}, \frac{5\pi}{6}, \frac{3\pi}{2}$
d. $0, \pi, \frac{\pi}{6}, \frac{5\pi}{6}$ **e.** $0, \frac{\pi}{2}$ **f.** $\frac{\pi}{6}, \frac{5\pi}{6}, \frac{3\pi}{2}$ **g.** $\frac{\pi}{2}, \frac{3\pi}{2}, \frac{7\pi}{6}, \frac{11\pi}{6}$ **h.** $\frac{\pi}{3}, \frac{2\pi}{3}, \frac{4\pi}{3}, \frac{5\pi}{3}$ **10.a.** 0.84, 5.44
b. 3.78, 5.64 **c.** 0.00, 2.22

PAGE 123 CHAPTER TEST **1.a.** $\frac{\sqrt{7}}{4}$ **b.** $\frac{\sqrt{15}}{4}$ **c.** $\frac{3}{4}$ **d.** $\frac{1}{4}$ **e.** $\frac{\sqrt{7}-3\sqrt{15}}{16}$ **f.** $\frac{3+\sqrt{105}}{16}$
g. $\frac{-3\sqrt{7}}{8}$ **h.** $\frac{7}{8}$ **i.** $\frac{1}{4}\sqrt{2}$ **2.a.** $\frac{\sin\theta}{\cos\theta}$ **b.** $-\sin(2+3\alpha)$ **c.** $\sin 2$ **d.** $\cos^2\theta$ **e.** $\sin 2$ **f.** $\sin\theta$
g. $\cos\theta$ **3.a.** $\frac{-1}{2}\sqrt{2+\sqrt{2}}$ **b.** $\frac{1}{2}\sqrt{2+\sqrt{2}}$ **5.** $\sin 3\theta \equiv 3\sin\theta - 4\sin^3\theta$
6.a. $\frac{2\pi}{3}, \frac{4\pi}{3}$ **b.** $0, \pi, \frac{\pi}{6}, \frac{5\pi}{6}$ **c.** $\frac{\pi}{12}, \frac{11\pi}{12}, \frac{13\pi}{12}, \frac{23\pi}{12}$ **d.** $\frac{\pi}{3}, \frac{2\pi}{3}, \frac{4\pi}{3}, \frac{5\pi}{3}$ **e.** π **7.** $\frac{\pi}{4}$

PAGES 124–126 CUMULATIVE REVIEW **1.a.** irrational **b.** rational **c.** irrational
d. irrational **e.** irrational **f.** rational **2.a.** $\frac{\sqrt{5}}{3}; \frac{-\sqrt{5}}{3}$ **b.** $0.6; -0.6$ **3.** $5; 5\sqrt{3}$
4. $\sqrt{16c^2 + 9m^2}$ **5.a.** $(2, 5)$ **b.** $(-2, -5)$ **c.** $(-2, 5)$ **d.** $(-5, 2)$
6.a. R; $\{P(x, y) \mid x^2 + y^2 = 1\}$; 2π **b.** R; $\{x \mid -1 \le x \le 1\}$; 2π
c. R; $\{y \mid -1 \le y \le 1\}$; 2π **7.** $\frac{\pi}{3}, \frac{7\pi}{3}, \frac{-5\pi}{3}, \frac{-11\pi}{3}$, etc. **8.a.** $(\frac{-1}{2}, \frac{1}{2})$ **b.** $(0, -1)$
c. $(\frac{-1}{2}, \frac{-\sqrt{3}}{2})$ **d.** $(\frac{-\sqrt{2}}{2}, \frac{-\sqrt{2}}{2})$ **9.** $\frac{5\pi}{3}, \frac{11\pi}{3}, \frac{-7\pi}{3}$, etc. **10.a.** $W(-\theta)$ **b.** $W(\theta - \pi)$
c. $W(\frac{\pi}{2} - \theta)$ **11.** 3 seconds; $\frac{1}{3}$ cycle per second **12.** a, c, d, e, h **13.a.** $\frac{-\sqrt{2}}{2}$ **b.** $\frac{\sqrt{3}}{2}$
c. $\frac{-\sqrt{3}}{2}$ **d.** $\frac{-\sqrt{2}}{2}$ **e.** $\frac{1}{2}$ **f.** $\frac{-1}{2}$ **14.a.** $-.9359$ **b.** $-.6052$ **c.** $.2268$ **15.** $.566$ **16.** $\frac{-12}{13}$
17. $\sin(\frac{\pi}{8} - \alpha)$ **18.a.** $\cos\theta$ **b.** $\cos\theta$ **c.** $-\cos\theta$ **d.** $-\cos\theta$ **e.** $\cos\theta$ **f.** $\cos^2\theta$ **g.** $\cos\theta$
h. $\cos\theta$ **19.a.** $\sin\frac{3\pi}{10}$ **b.** $-\sin\frac{3\pi}{8}$ **c.** $\sin\frac{3\pi}{10}$ **d.** $\sin(\pi - 3)$ **e.** $-\sin\frac{2\pi}{7}$ **f.** $-\sin(4 - \pi)$
20.a. $2; 4\pi; 0$ **b.** $\frac{1}{2}; \frac{2\pi}{3}; 0$ **c.** $1; 2; 0$ **d.** $2; 4\pi; \frac{\pi}{4}$ **e.** $1; \pi; \frac{-\pi}{2}$ **21.** decreases from 0 to -1
24. 2 seconds; $\frac{1}{2}$ cycle per sec. **26.a.** $y = \sin\pi t$ **b.** $\frac{\sqrt{2}}{2}$ cm; $\frac{\sqrt{3}}{2}$ cm **c.** $\frac{1}{2} + n$ seconds,
n is any non-negative integer **d.** 30 cycles per minute **27.a.** $\frac{\sqrt{5}+4\sqrt{6}}{15}$ **b.** $\frac{-4\sqrt{5}}{9}$
c. $\frac{-23}{25}$ **d.** $\frac{-\sqrt{10}}{5}$ **28.a.** $\sin^2\theta$ **b.** $\sin\theta$ **c.** $-\cos\theta$ **d.** $\cos 2$ **e.** 1 **f.** $\sin 6\alpha$ **g.** $\csc 2\theta$
h. $\sin\theta$ **i.** $\cos\theta$ **j.** $\cos 2\theta$

PAGES 129–130 **1.a.** $\sqrt{3}$ **b.** 1 **c.** 0 **d.** $\frac{-\sqrt{3}}{3}$ **e.** $\sqrt{3}$ **f.** 1 **g.** 0 **h.** 1 **i.** $\frac{-\sqrt{3}}{3}$
j. $-\sqrt{3}$ **k.** $\frac{-\sqrt{3}}{3}$ **l.** -1 **m.** $\frac{-\sqrt{3}}{3}$ **n.** undefined **o.** $-\sqrt{3}$ **p.** 0 **q.** undefined
r. undefined **s.** 1 **t.** $\sqrt{3}$ **2.a.** F **b.** T **c.** T **d.** T **e.** T **f.** T **g.** T **h.** T **i.** T
j. T **k.** T **l.** T **m.** T **n.** F **o.** T **p.** T **q.** T **r.** F **s.** T **t.** T **u.** T **v.** F **w.** F
x. T **3.a.** pos. **b.** neg. **c.** pos. **d.** neg. **4.a.** $\frac{1}{2}, \frac{\sqrt{3}}{2}, \sqrt{3}$ **b.** $-1, 0, 0$ **c.** $\frac{-\sqrt{3}}{2}, \frac{1}{2}, \frac{-\sqrt{3}}{3}$
d. $\frac{\sqrt{2}}{2}, \frac{-\sqrt{2}}{2}, -1$ **e.** $0, 1$, undefined **f.** $1, 0, 0$ **g.** $\frac{-1}{2}, \frac{\sqrt{3}}{2}, -\sqrt{3}$ **h.** $0, -1$, undefined
5. For each equation, both members have the following values: **a.** $\frac{-\sqrt{3}}{3}$ **b.** $-\sqrt{3}$
c. $\frac{\sqrt{3}}{3}$ **d.** $\sqrt{3}$ **e.** $\frac{-\sqrt{3}}{3}$ **f.** -1 **6.a.** pos. **b.** neg. **c.** pos. **d.** neg. **7.a.** $\frac{\pi}{4}, \frac{5\pi}{4}$
b. $\frac{3\pi}{4}, \frac{7\pi}{4}$ **c.** $0, \pi$ **d.** $\frac{5\pi}{6}, \frac{11\pi}{6}$ **e.** $\frac{\pi}{3}, \frac{4\pi}{3}$ **f.** $\frac{\pi}{6}, \frac{7\pi}{6}$ **g.** $\frac{2\pi}{3}, \frac{5\pi}{3}$ **8.** $\frac{\pi}{2} + k\pi$ and $\frac{\pi}{4} + k\pi$,
where k is any integer.

PAGE 132 **1.**

	sin θ	cos θ	tan θ		sin θ	cos θ	tan θ
a.		$\frac{12}{13}$	$\frac{-5}{12}$	**f.**	$\frac{-12}{13}$	$\frac{-5}{13}$	
b.	.06		$\frac{-3}{4}$	**g.**	$\frac{\sqrt{2}}{3}$		$\frac{\sqrt{14}}{7}$
c.	$\frac{-3}{5}$	$\frac{-4}{5}$		**h.**		$\frac{-\sqrt{10}}{4}$	$\frac{\sqrt{15}}{5}$
d.	$\frac{\sqrt{55}}{8}$		$\frac{-\sqrt{55}}{3}$	**i.**	$\frac{-2\sqrt{5}}{5}$	$\frac{\sqrt{5}}{5}$	
e.		$\frac{-2\sqrt{2}}{3}$	$\frac{-\sqrt{2}}{4}$	**j.**	$\frac{-\sqrt{105}}{15}$		$\frac{-\sqrt{14}}{4}$

2. $\frac{-\sqrt{5}}{2}$ **3.** $\frac{\sqrt{22}}{11}$

PAGES 135–136 **2.a.** $\overline{BE}$ **b.** $\overline{CF}$ **c.** $\overline{BD}$ **d.** $\overline{CG}$ **e.** $\overline{AH}$ **f.** $\overline{AH}$ **g.** $\overline{AH}$ **h.** $\overline{CF}$ **3.a.** inc. from 0 without upper limit **b.** without lower limit, inc. to 0 **c.** inc. from 0 without upper limit **d.** without lower limit, inc. to 0 **e.** inc. with neither lower nor upper limit **f.** inc. with neither lower nor upper limit **4.a.** $0, \pi$ **b.** $\frac{\pi}{4}, \frac{5\pi}{4}$ **c.** $\frac{3\pi}{4}, \frac{7\pi}{4}$ **d.** $\frac{\pi}{2} < \theta < \pi, \frac{3\pi}{2} < \theta < 2\pi$ **e.** $0 < \theta < \frac{\pi}{2}, \pi < \theta < \frac{3\pi}{2}$ **f.** $\frac{\pi}{2}, \frac{3\pi}{2}$ **5.** $R; R; R$ except $\frac{\pi}{2} + k\pi$ **6.** $\{y \mid -1 \leq y \leq 1\}; \{x \mid -1 \leq x \leq 1\}; R$ **7.** $2\pi; 2\pi; \pi$ **8.** $\frac{\pi}{2} + k\pi$ and $\frac{\pi}{3} + k\pi$ and $\frac{2\pi}{3} + k\pi$

PAGES 138–139 **1.a.** $\tan \frac{\pi}{8}$ **b.** $-\tan \frac{\pi}{5}$ **c.** $\tan 0$ **d.** $\tan 0$ **e.** $-\tan \frac{2\pi}{7}$ **f.** $-\tan \frac{\pi}{5}$ **g.** $-\tan (2\pi - 6)$ **h.** $-\tan (\pi - 3)$ **i.** $-\tan \frac{\pi}{5}$ **j.** $-\tan \frac{\pi}{5}$ **k.** $\tan (7 - 2\pi)$ **l.** $\tan (4.5 - \pi)$ **3.a.** .7923 **b.** 3.903 **c.** −2.066 **d.** .5994 **e.** −.7923 **f.** −.5594 **g.** −2.820 **h.** 4.296 **i.** 1.082 **j.** .8771 **k.** .1409 **l.** −6.581 **4.a.** 0.22, 3.36 **b.** 0.62, 3.76 **c.** 2.71, 5.85 **d.** 2.27, 5.41 **e.** 1.56, 4.70 **f.** 1.51, 4.65 **5.a.** 1.136 **b.** 0.486 **c.** 1.818

PAGES 141–143 **4.a.** $\frac{-7}{26}$ **b.** $\frac{-23}{14}$ **c.** $\frac{-24}{7}$ **5.a.** $-\tan \theta$ **b.** $\tan \theta$ **c.** $-\tan \theta$ **d.** $-\tan \theta$ **e.** $\tan 8\theta$ **f.** $\tan 3\alpha$ **g.** $\frac{1}{\cos \theta}$ **h.** $\tan 6\theta$ **i.** $-\tan 1$ **j.** $\tan 1$ **k.** $-\tan 1$ **l.** $\tan (\theta - 3)$ **m.** $\tan 4\theta$ **n.** $\tan 3\theta$ **6.a.** $2 + \sqrt{3}$ **b.** $2 - \sqrt{3}$ **c.** $-2 - \sqrt{3}$ **d.** $2 + \sqrt{3}$ **7.** $\frac{k\pi}{4}$ where k is any integer **8.** $\frac{3 \tan \theta - \tan^3 \theta}{1 - 3 \tan^2 \theta}$ **9.a.** $-4\sqrt{5}, \frac{1}{2}(3 + \sqrt{5})$ **b.** $\frac{-\sqrt{15}}{7}, \frac{-\sqrt{15}}{3}$ **c.** $\frac{-15}{8}, \frac{1}{5}(\sqrt{34} - 3)$ **d.** $\frac{4\sqrt{21}}{17}, \frac{-1}{2}(5 + \sqrt{21})$ **10.a.** $\sqrt{2} - 1$ **b.** $-2 - \sqrt{3}$ **c.** $2 - \sqrt{3}$ **d.** $-\sqrt{2} - 1$

PAGES 143–144 **1.a.** $\frac{\pi}{3}, \frac{2\pi}{3}, \frac{4\pi}{3}, \frac{5\pi}{3}$ **b.** $\frac{\pi}{6}, \frac{5\pi}{6}, \frac{7\pi}{6}, \frac{11\pi}{6}$ **c.** $0, \pi, \frac{\pi}{4}, \frac{5\pi}{4}$ **d.** $0, \pi$ **e.** $\frac{\pi}{4}, \frac{3\pi}{4}, \frac{5\pi}{4}, \frac{7\pi}{4}$ **f.** $0, \pi, \frac{7\pi}{6}, \frac{11\pi}{6}$ **g.** $\frac{\pi}{8}, \frac{5\pi}{8}, \frac{9\pi}{8}, \frac{13\pi}{8}$ **h.** $0, \pi, \frac{\pi}{6}, \frac{5\pi}{6}, \frac{7\pi}{6}, \frac{11\pi}{6}$ **i.** $\frac{\pi}{3}, \frac{2\pi}{3}, \frac{4\pi}{3}, \frac{5\pi}{3}$ **j.** $0, \pi, \frac{\pi}{4}, \frac{3\pi}{4}, \frac{5\pi}{4}, \frac{7\pi}{4}$ **k.** $\frac{\pi}{4}, \frac{7\pi}{12}, \frac{11\pi}{12}, \frac{5\pi}{4}, \frac{19\pi}{12}, \frac{23\pi}{12}$ **l.** $\frac{\pi}{6}, \frac{2\pi}{3}, \frac{7\pi}{6}, \frac{5\pi}{3}$ **2.a.** 0.99, 4.13 **b.** 2.24, 5.38 **c.** 0.46, 2.68, 3.60, 5.82 **3.** $\frac{\pi}{2} + k\pi, \frac{\pi}{6} + k\pi, \frac{5\pi}{6} + k\pi$

PAGES 144–145 REVIEW EXERCISES **1.a.** 1 **b.** $\sqrt{3}$ **c.** $\frac{1}{\sqrt{3}}$ **d.** 0 **e.** undefined **f.** 0 **g.** $-\sqrt{3}$ **h.** −1 **i.** $\frac{\sqrt{3}}{3}$ **j.** −1 **k.** $\sqrt{3}$ **l.** $\frac{-1}{\sqrt{3}}$ **2.** R, except $\frac{\pi}{2} + k\pi$; R; π **3.** $\frac{2\sqrt{5}}{5}$ **4.** $\frac{-3}{\sqrt{34}}, \frac{5}{\sqrt{34}}$ **6.** b, c, d, e, f, i **7.a.** $\tan \theta$ **b.** $\tan 5\theta$ **c.** $\sin \theta$ **d.** $\tan 3$ **8.a.** $\frac{-4}{7}$ **b.** 8 **c.** $\frac{4}{3}$ **9.a.** $-2 - \sqrt{3}$ **b.** $-\sqrt{2} - 1$ **10.** $\frac{1}{3}(4 + \sqrt{7}); 3\sqrt{7}$ **12.a.** $\frac{\pi}{6}, \frac{5\pi}{6}, \frac{7\pi}{6}, \frac{11\pi}{6}$ **b.** $0, \pi, \frac{\pi}{3}, \frac{5\pi}{3}$ **c.** $0, \frac{\pi}{2}, \pi, \frac{3\pi}{2}$ **d.** 0.54, 3.68

PAGE **145 CHAPTER TEST   1.a.** -1 **b.** $\frac{1}{\sqrt{3}}$ **c.** 0 **d.** $-\sqrt{3}$ **2.** $\frac{k\pi}{2}$ where k is any integer   **3.** $\frac{-\sqrt{21}}{2}$ **4.** $\frac{2}{\sqrt{5}}; \frac{-1}{\sqrt{5}}$ **6.a.** $-\tan 4$ **b.** $\tan 2$ **c.** $-\tan \theta$ **d.** $\cos \theta$ **7.a.** $\frac{6}{17}$ **b.** -18 **c.** $\frac{-12}{5}$ **8.a.** $\frac{\pi}{4}, \frac{3\pi}{4}, \frac{5\pi}{4}, \frac{7\pi}{4}$ **b.** $0, \pi, \frac{7\pi}{6}, \frac{11\pi}{6}$ **c.** $\frac{\pi}{6}, \frac{7\pi}{6}$ **d.** $\frac{\pi}{8}, \frac{5\pi}{8}, \frac{9\pi}{8}, \frac{13\pi}{8}$

PAGES **150–151   2.a.** $90°$ **b.** $105°$ **c.** $720°$ **d.** $-135°$ **e.** $-126°$ **f.** $-540°$ **g.** $900°$ **h.** $210°$ **i.** $-240°$ **j.** $0°$ **k.** $324°$ **l.** $-80°$ **3.a.** 5 **b.** 2 **c.** $\sqrt{29}$ **d.** $\sqrt{41}$ **e.** 3 **f.** $2\sqrt{10}$ **4.a.** 3 **b.** quad. angle   **c.** 2 **d.** 1 **e.** quad. angle   **f.** 4 **6.a.** $495°, -225°$, etc.   **b.** $300°, -420°$, etc.   **c.** $90°, -270°$, etc.   **d.** $180°, -540°$, etc.   **e.** $570°, -150°$, etc.   **f.** $240°, -480°$, etc.   **7.a.** 3rd   **b.** 1st   **c.** quad. no.   **d.** 4th   **e.** 4th   **f.** quad. no.   **g.** 2nd   **h.** 2nd   **i.** quad. no.   **j.** 2nd   **8.** $(-20 + 360k)°$ where k is any integer   **9.** $-660°$ **10.** $-55°$ **11.a.** $45°, -315°$, etc.   **b.** $135°, -225°$, etc.   **c.** $225°, -135°$, etc.   **d.** $315°, -45°$, etc.   **e.** $90°, -270°$, etc.   **f.** $180°, -180°$, etc.   **g.** $270°, -90°$, etc.   **h.** $360°, -360°$, etc.   **12.a.** $30°, -330°$, etc.   **b.** $60°, -300°$, etc.   **c.** $120°, -240°$, etc.   **d.** $150°, -210°$, etc.   **e.** $210°, -150°$, etc.   **f.** $240°, -120°$, etc.   **g.** $300°, -60°$, etc.   **h.** $330°, -30°$, etc.   **13.** $144,000°$

PAGES **155–158   2.a.** $210°$ **b.** $120°$ **c.** $-270°$ **d.** $-150°$ **e.** $-300°$ **f.** $450°$ **g.** $510°$ **h.** $420°$ **i.** $540°$ **j.** $75°$ **k.** $54°$ **l.** $70°$ **m.** $-252°$ **n.** $40°$ **o.** $0°$ **3.a.** $\frac{4\pi}{3}$ **b.** $\frac{-\pi}{6}$ **c.** $\frac{\pi}{2}$ **d.** $\frac{-2\pi}{3}$ **e.** $\frac{7\pi}{6}$ **f.** $\frac{-3\pi}{2}$ **g.** $\frac{5\pi}{3}$ **h.** $\frac{13\pi}{6}$ **i.** 6π **j.** $\frac{-7\pi}{3}$ **k.** $\frac{\pi}{18}$ **l.** $\frac{\pi}{12}$ **m.** $\frac{4\pi}{5}$ **n.** $\frac{-2\pi}{5}$ **o.** $\frac{7\pi}{12}$ **5.a.** $\pi, -\pi$, etc.   **b.** $\frac{19\pi}{6}, \frac{-5\pi}{6}$, etc.   **c.** $\frac{4\pi}{3}, \frac{-8\pi}{3}$, etc.   **d.** $\frac{7\pi}{2}, \frac{-\pi}{2}$, etc.   **e.** $\frac{\pi}{3}, \frac{-5\pi}{3}$, etc.   **6.** $\frac{3\pi}{7} + 2k\pi$ where k is any integer   **7.** $57°18'$ **8.** 0.0175 radian   **9.a.** 2nd   **b.** 4th   **c.** 3rd   **d.** quad. no.   **e.** 1st   **f.** 2nd   **g.** 3rd   **h.** 4th   **10.** -52π **11.a.** $\frac{7}{5}, 60°$ **b.** $\frac{5}{5}, 36°$ **c.** $\frac{\pi}{6}, 30°$ **d.** $\frac{2\pi}{5}, 72°$ **e.** $\frac{\pi}{4}, 45°$ **f.** $\frac{3\pi}{5}, 108°$ **g.** $\frac{7\pi}{10}, 126°$ **h.** $\frac{23\pi}{60}, 69°$ **12.a.** $\frac{8\pi}{3}$ **b.** $\frac{2\pi}{5}$ **c.** $\frac{10\pi}{3}$ **d.** $\frac{7\pi}{3}$ **e.** 3π **f.** $\frac{16\pi}{5}$ **13.a.** π **b.** $\frac{3\pi}{4}$ **c.** $\frac{9\pi}{4}$ **d.** $\frac{5\pi}{2}$ **e.** $\frac{\pi}{6}$ **f.** $\frac{9\pi}{5}$ **14.a.** $\theta = 0.3, m = 19.1°$ **b.** $m = 135.0°, s = 28.3$ **c.** $\theta = 1.3, s = 2.9$ **d.** $r = 6.4, m = 126.0°$ **e.** $r = 4.0, \theta = 0.6$ **f.** $\theta = 1.5, m = 86.0°$ **g.** $m = 112.5°, s = 4.7$ **h.** $r = 1.1, \theta = 1.8$ **15.a.** $\frac{\pi}{4}, \frac{-7\pi}{4}$, etc.   **b.** $\frac{3\pi}{4}, \frac{-5\pi}{4}$, etc.   **c.** $\frac{5\pi}{4}, \frac{-3\pi}{4}$, etc.   **d.** $\frac{7\pi}{4}, \frac{-\pi}{4}$, etc.   **e.** $\frac{\pi}{2}, \frac{-3\pi}{2}$, etc.   **f.** $\pi, -\pi$, etc.   **g.** $\frac{3\pi}{2}, \frac{-\pi}{2}$, etc.   **h.** $2\pi, -2\pi$, etc.   **16.a.** $\frac{\pi}{6}, \frac{-11\pi}{6}$, etc.   **b.** $\frac{\pi}{3}, \frac{-5\pi}{3}$, etc.   **c.** $\frac{2\pi}{3}, \frac{-4\pi}{3}$, etc.   **d.** $\frac{5\pi}{6}, \frac{-7\pi}{6}$, etc.   **e.** $\frac{7\pi}{6}, \frac{-5\pi}{6}$, etc.   **f.** $\frac{4\pi}{3}, \frac{-2\pi}{3}$, etc.   **g.** $\frac{5\pi}{3}, \frac{-\pi}{3}$, etc.   **h.** $\frac{11\pi}{6}, \frac{-\pi}{6}$, etc.   **18.a.** 10π sq. in.   **b.** $\frac{\pi}{6}$ sq. cm.   **c.** 5π sq. ft.   **d.** 6π sq. yd.   **19.** $13,100$ sq. yd.   **20.a.** $\frac{9\pi}{2} - 9\sqrt{2}$ **b.** $\frac{4\pi}{3} - 4$ **c.** $24\pi - 36\sqrt{3}$ **d.** $9\pi - 18$ **21.a.** 12π **b.** 3.6π **c.** $\frac{35\pi}{2}$ **d.** 18 **22.** 366 sq. in.

PAGE **163   1.** (Sequence is $\sin u°$, $\cos u°$, $\tan u°$, $\csc u°$, $\sec u°$, $\cot u°$.)   **a.** $\frac{3}{\sqrt{13}}, \frac{2}{\sqrt{13}}, \frac{3}{2}, \frac{\sqrt{13}}{3}, \frac{\sqrt{13}}{2}, \frac{2}{3}$ **b.** $\frac{\sqrt{2}}{2}, \frac{-\sqrt{2}}{2}, -1, \sqrt{2}, -\sqrt{2}, -1$ **c.** $\frac{-12}{13}, \frac{-5}{13}, \frac{12}{5}, \frac{-13}{12}, \frac{-13}{5}, \frac{5}{12}$ **d.** $\frac{-2}{\sqrt{29}}, \frac{-2}{\sqrt{29}}, \frac{5}{\sqrt{29}}, \frac{\sqrt{29}}{2}, \frac{\sqrt{29}}{5}, \frac{-5}{2}$ **e.** $0, -1, 0$, undefined, -1, undefined   **f.** $-1, 0$, undefined, -1, undefined, 0 **2.a.** tan, sec   **b.** cot, csc   **c.** tan, sec   **d.** cot, csc   **3.a.** sin, csc   **b.** cos, sec   **c.** all   **d.** tan, cot   **e.** all   **f.** sin, csc   **g.** tan, cot   **h.** cos, sec   **4.** (Sequence is sin, cos, tan, csc, sec, cot, omitting the one that is given.)   **a.** $\frac{3}{5}, \frac{-3}{4}, \frac{5}{3}, \frac{-5}{4}, \frac{-4}{3}$ **b.** $\frac{3}{\sqrt{13}}, \frac{2}{\sqrt{13}}, \frac{\sqrt{13}}{3}, \frac{\sqrt{13}}{2}, \frac{2}{3}$ **c.** $\frac{-\sqrt{21}}{5}, \frac{2}{\sqrt{21}}, \frac{-5}{2}, \frac{-5}{\sqrt{21}}, \frac{\sqrt{21}}{2}$ **d.** $\frac{-4}{5}, \frac{3}{5}, \frac{-4}{3}, \frac{-5}{4}, \frac{-3}{4}$ **e.** $\frac{-\sqrt{2}}{2}, \frac{-\sqrt{2}}{2}, 1, -\sqrt{2}, -\sqrt{2}$ **f.** 0, undefined, 1, undefined, 0 **5.a.** $\sin 40°$ **b.** $\cos 340°$ **c.** $\tan 50°$ **d.** $\csc 20°$ **e.** $\sec 120°$ **f.** $\cot 340°$ **6.** (Sequence is sin, cos, tan, csc, sec, cot.)   **a.** $0, 1, 0$, undefined, 1, undefined   **b.** $1, 0$, undefined, 1, undefined, 0 **c.** $0, -1, 0$, undefined, -1, undefined   **d.** $-1, 0$, undefined, -1, undefined, 0

PAGES 166–167 **1.** (Sequence is sin, cos, tan, csc, sec, cot.) **a.** $\frac{1}{2}$, $\frac{\sqrt{3}}{2}$, $\frac{\sqrt{3}}{3}$, 2, $\frac{2}{\sqrt{3}}$, $\sqrt{3}$

b. $\frac{\sqrt{2}}{2}$, $\frac{\sqrt{2}}{2}$, 1, $\sqrt{2}$, $\sqrt{2}$, 1   **c.** $\frac{\sqrt{3}}{2}$, $\frac{1}{2}$, $\sqrt{3}$, $\frac{2}{\sqrt{3}}$, 2, $\frac{\sqrt{3}}{3}$ **d.** $\frac{-1}{2}$, $\frac{-\sqrt{3}}{2}$, $\frac{\sqrt{3}}{3}$, -2, $\frac{-2}{\sqrt{3}}$, $\sqrt{3}$

e. $\frac{-\sqrt{2}}{2}$, $\frac{\sqrt{2}}{2}$, -1, $-\sqrt{2}$, $\sqrt{2}$, -1 **f.** $\frac{\sqrt{3}}{2}$, $\frac{-1}{2}$, $-\sqrt{3}$, $\frac{2}{\sqrt{3}}$, -2, $\frac{-\sqrt{3}}{3}$

g. $\frac{-\sqrt{2}}{2}$, $\frac{-\sqrt{2}}{2}$, 1, $-\sqrt{2}$, $-\sqrt{2}$, 1   **h.** $\frac{-1}{2}$, $\frac{\sqrt{3}}{2}$, $\frac{-\sqrt{3}}{3}$, -2, $\frac{2}{\sqrt{3}}$, $-\sqrt{3}$

i. $\frac{-\sqrt{3}}{2}$, $\frac{-1}{2}$, $\sqrt{3}$, $\frac{-2}{\sqrt{3}}$, -2, $\frac{\sqrt{3}}{3}$ **j.** 1, 0, undefined, 1, undefined, 0

k. 0, -1, 0, undefined, -1, undefined   **l.** -1, 0, undefined, -1, undefined, 0   **2.a.** $-\sqrt{2}$

b. -2 **c.** $\frac{-\sqrt{3}}{3}$ **d.** $\frac{-2}{\sqrt{3}}$ **e.** $-\sqrt{2}$ **f.** $-\sqrt{3}$ **g.** 2   **h.** $\frac{2}{\sqrt{3}}$ **i.** -1 **j.** undefined

k. undefined   **l.** 0   **m.** 1   **n.** undefined   **o.** undefined   **3.a.** 1   **b.** 0   **c.** 0

d. $\frac{1}{4}(\sqrt{6} - \sqrt{2})$ **e.** $\frac{4}{3}$ **f.** 4   **g.** $\sqrt{3}$ **h.** $2 - \sqrt{3}$ **i.** $2 + \sqrt{3}$ **j.** $-\sqrt{3}$

PAGES 171–172 **1.a.** sin 20°   **b.** $-\cos 40°$ **c.** $-\tan 70°$ **d.** $-\csc 40°$ **e.** sec 40°
f. cot 80°   **g.** $-\sin 32°$ **h.** cos 50°   **i.** tan 40°   **j.** csc 10°   **k.** $-\sin 20°$ **l.** cos 40°
m. $-\tan 70°$ **n.** $-\sin 80°$ **o.** $-\cos 10°$ **p.** tan 40°   **2.a.** 70°   **b.** 10°   **c.** 0°   **d.** $-20°$
e. 130°   **f.** 45°   **g.** 90°   **h.** 52°40′   **i.** $u°$ **j.** $\frac{3\pi}{8}$ **3.a.** sin 70°   **b.** cos 50°   **c.** cot 63°
d. sin $(-50°)$ or $-\sin 50°$ **e.** tan $(-10°)$ or $-\tan 10°$ **f.** sec 8°   **g.** csc 59°
h. sin 140° or sin 40°   **i.** cos 110° or $-\cos 70°$ **j.** cos $c°$ **k.** sin $c°$ **l.** cos $\frac{\pi}{8}$
m. cos $(180 - c)°$ or $-\cos c°$ **n.** sin $\frac{\pi}{10}$ **o.** cot $\frac{-\pi}{5}$ or $-\cot \frac{\pi}{5}$ **p.** sec $(\frac{\pi}{2} - 1)$
4.a. cos $u°$ **b.** $-\sin u°$ **c.** $-\tan u°$ **d.** $-\sec u°$ **e.** csc $u°$ **f.** $-\sin u°$ **g.** cot $u°$
h. $-\cos u°$ **5.a.** 45°, 315°   **b.** 30°, 150°   **c.** 120°, 300°   **d.** 120°, 240°   **e.** 45°, 135°
f. 45°, 225°   **g.** 150°, 210°   **h.** 225°, 315°   **i.** 30°, 210°   **6.** sin, cos, csc, and sec: 360°;
tan, cot: 180°

PAGE 175 **1.a.** .4643   **b.** .8158   **c.** .7373   **d.** .2952   **e.** .2370   **f.** 1.935   **g.** 1.260
h. 1.048   **i.** 1.653   **j.** .7445   **k.** .1334   **l.** .9261   **2.a.** .7716   **b.** $-.4410$ **c.** -1.098
d. 1.031   **e.** -1.197 **f.** $-.2773$ **g.** $-.9572$ **h.** $-.9911$ **i.** .6412   **3.a.** .6072   **b.** .8766
c. .3288   **d.** 1.187   **e.** 1.559   **f.** .9862   **4.a.** 26°20′, 153°40′   **b.** 38°20′, 321°40′
c. 74°40′, 254°40′   **d.** 31°40′, 328°20′   **e.** 206°50′, 333°10′   **f.** 129°40′, 230°20′
g. 99°50′, 279°50′   **h.** 225°10′, 314°50′   **5.a.** 28°34′   **b.** 42°17′   **c.** 14°16′   **d.** 37°16′

PAGE 179 **1.** Set of all real number degree measures; $\{y \mid -1 \leq y \leq 1\}$; 360°.
2.a. dec. from 1 to 0   **b.** dec. from 0 to -1 **c.** inc. from -1 to 0   **d.** inc. from 0 to 1
3. Set of all real number degree measures except $90° + 180k°$; set of all real numbers; 180°.
4.a. inc. from 0 without upper limit   **b.** without lower limit, inc. to 0   **c.** inc. with neither
lower nor upper limit   **5.a.** $\{u° \mid u° \neq 180k°\}$; $\{a \mid a \leq -1 \text{ or } a \geq 1\}$
b. $\{u° \mid u° \neq 90° + 180k°\}$; $\{a \mid a \leq -1 \text{ or } a \geq 1\}$ **c.** $\{u° \mid u° \neq 180k°\}$; R
9.a. 2   **b.** $0° \leq u° < 30°$, $150° < u° < 360°$ **c.** $0° \leq u° < 45°$, $225° < u° < 360°$
d. $0° \leq u° < 45°$, $135° < u° < 225°$, $315° < u° < 360°$ **e.** 2

PAGES 180–181 **1.a.** $\frac{3}{4}$, 120°, 0°   **b.** 3, 720°, 0°   **c.** 2, 180°, 45°   **d.** 1, 1080°, $-30°$
e. 1, 180°, 30°   **f.** 1, 720°, $-240°$ **3.a.** 4   **b.** 4   **c.** 6

PAGES 181–183 REVIEW EXERCISES **1.a.** 150°   **b.** 240°   **c.** 315°   **d.** $-180°$
e. $-120°$ **f.** $-270°$ **g.** 420°   **h.** $-360°$ **i.** 105°   **j.** 162°   **k.** 132°   **l.** 280°   **2.a.** $\frac{2\pi}{3}$
b. $\frac{3\pi}{4}$ **c.** $\frac{-5\pi}{6}$ **d.** $\frac{-3\pi}{2}$ **e.** $\frac{4\pi}{3}$ **f.** $\frac{-7\pi}{6}$ **g.** $\frac{5\pi}{4}$ **h.** $\frac{\pi}{9}$ **i.** $\frac{5\pi}{12}$ **3.** $50° + 360k°$
4.a. $\theta = 3$, $m = \frac{540}{\pi}$ **b.** $m = 45$, $s = 2\pi$ **c.** $\theta = \frac{2\pi}{5}$, $s = 4\pi$ **d.** $r = \frac{21}{\pi}$, $m = \frac{540}{7}$

e. $r = \frac{1.8}{\pi}$, $\theta = \frac{5\pi}{6}$ **5.** 3π **6.** $\cos u° = \frac{-\sqrt{11}}{6}$, $\sin u° = \frac{5}{6}$, $\tan u° = \frac{-5}{\sqrt{11}}$, $\sec u° = \frac{-6}{\sqrt{11}}$, $\csc u° = \frac{6}{5}$, $\cot u° = \frac{-\sqrt{11}}{5}$ **7.** tan, sec **8.** $\sin u° = \frac{-\sqrt{21}}{5}$, $\tan u° = \frac{\sqrt{21}}{2}$, $\csc u° = \frac{-5}{\sqrt{21}}$, $\sec u° = \frac{-5}{2}$, $\cot u° = \frac{2}{\sqrt{21}}$ **9.** cos, sec **10.** $\sin 180° = 0$, $\cos 180° = -1$, $\tan 180° = 0$, $\sec 180° = -1$ **11.** (Sequence is sin, cos, tan, csc, sec, cot.) **a.** $\frac{1}{2}, \frac{-\sqrt{3}}{2}, \frac{-\sqrt{3}}{3}, 2, \frac{-2}{\sqrt{3}}, -\sqrt{3}$
b. $\frac{-\sqrt{2}}{2}, \frac{-\sqrt{2}}{2}, 1, -\sqrt{2}, -\sqrt{2}, 1$ **c.** $\frac{-\sqrt{3}}{2}, \frac{1}{2}, -\sqrt{3}, \frac{-2}{\sqrt{3}}, 2, \frac{-\sqrt{3}}{3}$
d. $\frac{\sqrt{3}}{2}, \frac{-1}{2}, -\sqrt{3}, \frac{2}{\sqrt{3}}, -2, \frac{-\sqrt{3}}{3}$ **e.** $\frac{1}{2}, \frac{\sqrt{3}}{2}, \frac{\sqrt{3}}{3}, 2, \frac{2}{\sqrt{3}}, \sqrt{3}$ **f.** $\frac{-\sqrt{2}}{2}, \frac{\sqrt{2}}{2}, -1, -\sqrt{2}, \sqrt{2}, -1$
12.a. $-\cos 70°$ **b.** $\sin 50°$ **c.** $\tan 20°$ **d.** $-\sec 20°$ **e.** $-\csc 40°$ **f.** $-\sin 40°$ **g.** $\cos 70°$
h. $\tan 40°$ **13.a.** $\cot 50°$ **b.** $\cos 110°$ or $-\cos 70°$ **c.** $\sin (-50°)$ or $-\sin 50°$ **d.** $\csc 10°$
e. $\tan 70°$ **f.** $\sec 100°$ or $-\sec 80°$ **14.a.** $210°, 330°$ **b.** $30°, 330°$ **c.** $60°, 240°$
d. $60°, 120°$ **e.** $120°, 240°$ **f.** $135°, 315°$ **15.** sin, cos, csc, sec: $360°$; tan, cot: $180°$
16.a. $.6271$ **b.** $.3035$ **c.** $.9380$ **d.** 6.166 **e.** $-.4120$ **f.** $-.8355$ **g.** $-.2524$ **h.** -1.681
17. $.9089$ **18.** $152°20', 207°40'$ **19.** $36°17'$ **20.a.** R; $\{a \mid -1 \le a \le 1\}$
b. $\{u° \mid u° \ne 90° + 180k°\}$; R **c.** $\{u° \mid u° \ne 180k°\}$; $\{a \mid a \le -1 \text{ or } a \ge 1\}$
21. dec. from 0 to -1 **22.** If $u° + v° = 90°$, then any trigonometric function of $u°$ is equal to that co-named trigonometric function of $v°$. **23.** sin and csc; cos and sec; tan and cot **25.** 6 **26.** $60° < u° < 300°$ **27.a.** $\frac{2}{3}, 120°, 0°$ **b.** $2, 720°, 40°$ **c.** $1, 180°, -30°$

PAGES 183–184 CHAPTER TEST **1.** $84°$ **2.** $\frac{-10\pi}{9}$ **3.** 1.4 **4.** 3π
5. $\sin u° = \frac{-2}{\sqrt{29}}$, $\cos u° = \frac{5}{\sqrt{29}}$, $\tan u° = \frac{-2}{5}$, $\csc u° = \frac{-\sqrt{29}}{2}$, $\sec u° = \frac{\sqrt{29}}{5}$, $\cot u° = \frac{-5}{2}$
6. $\cos u° = \frac{-\sqrt{5}}{3}$, $\tan u° = \frac{-2}{\sqrt{5}}$, $\csc u° = \frac{3}{2}$, $\sec u° = \frac{-3}{\sqrt{5}}$, $\cot u° = \frac{-\sqrt{5}}{2}$ **7.** cot, csc
8.a. $\frac{\sqrt{2}}{2}$ **b.** $\frac{-\sqrt{3}}{2}$ **c.** $-\sqrt{3}$ **d.** -2 **e.** $-\sqrt{2}$ **f.** $-\sqrt{3}$ **g.** 0 **h.** undefined **i.** -1
j. $\frac{-1}{2}$ **k.** $\frac{-1}{2}$ **l.** $\sqrt{3}$ **9.a.** $-\cos 37°$ **b.** $\tan 47°$ **c.** $-\sin 70°$ **d.** $\sec 20°$ **10.a.** $\csc 50°$
b. $\sin (-10°)$ or $-\sin 10°$ **11.** $120°, 240°$ **12.** $180°$ **13.** $.2820$ **14.** $\{u° \mid u° \ne 180k°\}$; R
15. dec. from 0 to -1 **18.** 4

PAGES 187–188 **2.a.** $\cos u°$; $180k°$ **b.** $\tan^2 u°$; $90° + 180k°$ **c.** $\tan u°$; $90k°$
d. $\sin u°$; $90° + 180k°$ **e.** $\csc^2 u°$; $90k°$ **f.** $\cos u°$; $90k°$ **g.** $\sin^2 u°$ **h.** $\csc u°$; $180k°$
i. $2 \cos u°$; $90k°$ **j.** $\cos^2 u°$; $180k°$ **k.** $\tan^2 u°$; $90k°$ **l.** $\csc u°$; $90° + 180k°$
m. $\csc u°$; $180k°$ **n.** 1; $90k°$ and $135° + 180k°$ **o.** $\sec u°$; $90k°$ **p.** $\sec u°$; $90° + 180k°$
q. $\sin^2 u°$; $90° + 180k°$ **r.** $\csc^2 u°$; $90k°$ **s.** $2 \tan u°$; $90° + 180k°$ **t.** $\tan^2 u°$; $90k°$ and
$135° + 180k°$ **u.** $\cos u°$; $90° + 180k°$ **v.** $2 \sin u°$; $90k°$ **w.** 1; $90° + 180k°$
x. $2 \sin u°$; $90k°$ **y.** 1; $180k°$ **z.** $\csc u°$; $90k°$ **a'.** 1; $90° + 180k°$ **b'.** 1; $90k°$ **c'.** $\cos u°$
d'. $\cot^2 u°$; $90k°$ **e'.** $\sec^2 u°$; $90k°$

PAGES 190–193 **9.a.** $\frac{-2\sqrt{2}}{3}$ **b.** $\frac{-\sqrt{15}}{4}$ **c.** $\frac{\sqrt{2}}{4}$ **d.** $-\sqrt{15}$ **e.** $\frac{1}{12}(\sqrt{15} - 2\sqrt{2})$ **f.** $\frac{1}{4}$
g. $\frac{1}{12}(2\sqrt{30} - 1)$ **h.** $\frac{1}{3}$ **i.** $\frac{1}{7}(9\sqrt{15} - 32\sqrt{2})$ **j.** $\frac{-\sqrt{2}}{4}$ **k.** $\frac{-1}{3}$ **10.a.** 1 **b.** $\cos 4w°$
c. $\sin 5w°$ **d.** $\cos 3w°$ **e.** $\tan u°$ **f.** $-\cot u°$ **g.** $\cos (4u - 3v)°$ **h.** $\sin (5u + 2v)°$
i. $\cos 9u°$ **j.** $\sin v°$ **k.** $\tan 8u°$ **l.** $\tan 3u°$ **m.** $\cot 3v°$ **n.** $-\cot 4u°$ **o.** $\sin u°$
p. $-\cos u°$ **q.** $\cos v°$ **r.** $-\sin v°$ **s.** $2 \sin u° \cos v°$ **t.** $2 \cos u° \cos v°$ **u.** $2 \cos u° \sin v°$
v. $2 \sin u° \sin v°$ **w.** $1 - \cos 7u°$ **x.** $1 - \sin 7u°$ **y.** $\tan u°$ **11.a.** $\frac{1}{4}(\sqrt{6} + \sqrt{2})$
b. $2 - \sqrt{3}$ **c.** $\frac{1}{4}(\sqrt{6} + \sqrt{2})$ **d.** $2 + \sqrt{3}$ **e.** $\frac{1}{4}(\sqrt{2} - \sqrt{6})$ **f.** $-2 - \sqrt{3}$
12.a. $\frac{1}{12}(\sqrt{35} - 6)$ **b.** 0.96 **13.a.** $\frac{3}{29}$ **b.** $\frac{-27}{11}$ **14.** $45k°$, where k is any integer
15. $2 \sin u° \cos u°$ **16.** $\cos^2 u° - \sin^2 u°$ **17.** $\frac{2 \tan u°}{1 - \tan^2 u°}$ **19.a.** $2\sqrt{3} \sin (u + 60)°$ or
$3.46 \sin (u + 60)°$ **b.** $4\sqrt{3} \sin (u + 120)°$ or $6.93 \sin (u + 120)°$ **c.** $2\sqrt{2} \sin (u + 45)°$ or
$2.83 \sin (u + 45)°$ **d.** $\sqrt{2} \sin (u + 135)°$ or $1.414 \sin (u + 135)°$ **e.** $5 \sin (u° + 53°10')$
f. $2\sqrt{2} \sin (u + 135)°$ or $2.83 \sin (u + 135)°$

PAGES 197–198   6.a. $\frac{-4}{9}\sqrt{5}$; $\frac{1}{9}$; $-4\sqrt{5}$ **b.** $\frac{-3}{8}\sqrt{7}$; $\frac{1}{8}$; $-3\sqrt{7}$ **c.** $\frac{15}{17}$; $\frac{-8}{17}$; $\frac{-15}{8}$
d. $\frac{-4}{9}\sqrt{2}$; $\frac{7}{9}$; $\frac{-4}{7}\sqrt{2}$ **e.** $\frac{-4}{25}\sqrt{21}$; $\frac{-17}{25}$; $\frac{4}{17}\sqrt{21}$ **7.a.** pos., pos.   **b.** pos., neg.
c. pos., neg.   **8.a.** $\frac{1}{4}\sqrt{8 - 2\sqrt{15}}$; $\frac{-1}{4}\sqrt{8 + 2\sqrt{15}}$; $\sqrt{15} - 4$ **b.** $\frac{\sqrt{3}}{3}$; $\frac{-\sqrt{6}}{3}$; $\frac{-\sqrt{2}}{2}$
c. $\frac{-1}{6}\sqrt{18 - 6\sqrt{5}}$; $\frac{-1}{6}\sqrt{18 + 6\sqrt{5}}$; $\frac{1}{2}(3 - \sqrt{5})$ **d.** $\frac{\sqrt{14}}{4}$; $\frac{-\sqrt{2}}{4}$; $-\sqrt{7}$ **9.a.** cos $u°$
b. tan $6u°$ **c.** cos $u°$ **d.** $1 + \cos u°$ **e.** sin $6u°$ **f.** cot $u°$ **g.** cos $u°$ **h.** 2 sin $u°$
i. cos $u°$ + sin $u°$ **10.a.** $\frac{1}{2}\sqrt{2 - \sqrt{2}}$ **b.** $\sqrt{2} - 1$ **c.** $\frac{1}{4}$ **d.** $\frac{1}{2}(2 + \sqrt{3})$ $\sqrt{2 + \sqrt{3}}$ or
$\frac{1}{2}(2 + \sqrt{3})^{\frac{3}{2}}$ **e.** $\frac{1}{2}\sqrt{2 + \sqrt{2}}$ **f.** $\frac{-2(2 + \sqrt{3})}{\sqrt{2 - \sqrt{3}}}$ **g.** $\frac{\sqrt{2} + 1}{-2}\sqrt{2 + \sqrt{2}}$ **h.** $1 - \sqrt{2}$
i. $\frac{-\sqrt{2 - \sqrt{2}}}{2}$ **12.** 3 sin $u°$ − 4 sin³ $u°$ **13.** 4 cos³ $u°$ − 3 cos $u°$ **14.** $\frac{3 \tan u° - \tan^3 u°}{1 - 3 \tan^2 u°}$

PAGES 201–204   1.a. 2   **b.** 0   **c.** 4   **d.** 4   **e.** 6   **f.** 4   **g.** 2   **h.** 2   **i.** 6   **j.** 2.   **2.a.** 90°
b. 30°, 150°, 210°, 330°   **c.** 0°, 180°, 270°   **d.** 120°, 240°   **e.** 135°, 225°   **f.** 60°, 120°,
240°, 300°   **g.** 45°, 135°, 225°, 315°   **h.** 15°, 75°, 195°, 255°   **i.** 30°, 150°, 210°, 330°
j. 0°, 60°, 180°, 300°   **k.** 10°, 110°, 130°, 230°, 250°, 350°   **l.** 0°, 210°, 330°   **m.** 0°, 135°, 180°,
315°   **n.** 30°, 150°   **o.** 0°, 60°, 120°, 180°, 240°, 300°   **p.** 90°, 270°   **q.** 45°, 225°
r. 22.5°, 112.5°, 202.5°, 292.5°   **s.** 90°, 270°   **t.** 0°, 30°, 150°, 180°   **u.** 30°, 120°, 210°, 300°
v. 45°, 135°, 225°, 315°   **w.** 45°, 135°, 225°, 315°   **x.** 0°, 45°, 135°, 180°, 225°, 315°
3.a. 70°30′, 289°30′   **b.** 33°40′, 146°20′   **c.** 59°0′, 239°0′   **d.** 38°10′, 141°50′   **e.** 105°0′,
345°0′   **f.** 0°0′, 90°0′   **g.** 203°30′, 336°30′   **h.** 41°20′, 318°40′   **i.** 33°40′, 213°40′   **j.** 43°0′,
317°0′   **k.** 36°50′, 270°0′   **l.** 12°0′, 124°20′   **4.a.** 12°   **b.** 29°   **c.** 27°   **5.a.** 25°   **b.** 21°
6.a. 45°, 90°, 135°, 225°, 270°, 315°   **b.** 0°, 30°, 150°, 180°   **c.** 180°   **d.** 30°, 90°, 150°
e. 90°   **f.** 30°, 180°, 330°   **g.** 0°, 120°, 240°   **h.** 0°, 180°   **i.** 0°, 45°, 135°, 180°, 225°, 315°
j. 60°, 120°, 240°, 300°   **7.a.** 105°0′, 345°0′   **b.** 285°0′, 345°0′   **c.** 45°   **d.** 106°50′, 343°10′
e. 237°40′, 339°20′   **f.** 0°0′, 106°20′

PAGES 205–206   1.a. $\frac{\pi}{30}$ **b.** $\frac{\pi}{360}$ **c.** 600π **d.** 6000π **2.** 16π inches   **3.** $\frac{\pi}{3}$ in. per hr.
4. 400π ft. per sec.   **5.** $\frac{750\pi}{11}$ mph   **6.** 10,400π ft. per min.   **7.** 39$\frac{3}{4}$ mph   **8.** 10.7 sec.
9. $\frac{9\pi}{2}$ ft. per sec.; 3π rad. per sec.   **10.** $\frac{75\pi}{16}$ ft. per sec.; $\frac{15\pi}{2}$ rad. per sec.   **11.** 9 in. and 12 in.

PAGES 207–208   1.a. 0 cm.   **b.** 3$\sqrt{3}$ cm.   **c.** −6 cm.   **d.** 0 cm.   **e.** 3 cm.   **f.** 3$\sqrt{2}$ cm.
g. 3$\sqrt{3}$ cm.   **h.** −3 cm.   **i.** −3$\sqrt{2}$ cm.   **j.** −3$\sqrt{3}$ cm.   **k.** 0 cm.   **2.** $y = 6 \sin \frac{\pi}{2}t$
3. 1 + 2k sec., 2k sec., where k is any non-negative integer.   **4.** $\frac{1}{8}$ second
5. 10 revs. per sec.   **6.** $T = \frac{1}{f}$; $f = \frac{1}{T}$ **7.** 2$\frac{2}{3}$ sec., $\frac{3}{8}$ cycles per sec.   **8.** $y = 8 \sin \frac{\pi}{5}t$

PAGES 208–210 REVIEW EXERCISES   1.a. $\frac{-\sqrt{21}}{5}$ **b.** $\frac{-2}{\sqrt{21}}$ **c.** $\frac{-\sqrt{5}}{3}$ **d.** $\frac{\sqrt{5}}{2}$
e. $\frac{1}{15}(\sqrt{105} - 4)$ **f.** $\frac{2}{15}(\sqrt{21} - \sqrt{5})$ **g.** $\frac{21\sqrt{5} - 4\sqrt{21}}{42 + 2\sqrt{105}}$ **h.** $\frac{2}{\sqrt{21}}$ **i.** $\frac{-\sqrt{21}}{5}$ **j.** $\frac{-4}{5}\sqrt{21}$
k. $\frac{17}{25}$ **l.** $\frac{-4}{17}\sqrt{21}$ **m.** $\frac{1}{10}\sqrt{50 + 10\sqrt{21}}$ **n.** $\frac{1}{10}\sqrt{50 - 10\sqrt{21}}$ **o.** $\frac{1}{2}(5 + \sqrt{21})$
2.a. tan $u°$ **b.** sec $u°$ **c.** sin $4u°$ **d.** tan $6u°$ **e.** cot $u°$ **f.** tan² $u°$ **g.** sin² $u°$ **h.** cos $u°$
i. cos $u°$ **j.** 2 cos $u°$ **k.** sin $2u°$ **l.** sin $10u°$ **3.a.** $\frac{1}{2}\sqrt{2 + \sqrt{2}}$ **b.** $\frac{1}{4}(\sqrt{6} + \sqrt{2})$ or
$\frac{1}{2}\sqrt{2 + \sqrt{3}}$ **c.** 1 + $\sqrt{2}$ **d.** $\frac{1}{4}(\sqrt{2} - \sqrt{6})$ or $\frac{-1}{2}\sqrt{2 - \sqrt{3}}$ **5.a.** 120°, 240°   **b.** 60°,
120°, 240°, 300°   **c.** 10°, 50°, 130°, 170°, 250°, 290°   **d.** 90°, 120°, 240°, 270°   **e.** 30°,
150°, 210°, 330°   **f.** 0°, 120°, 240°   **g.** 0°, 60°, 180°, 300°   **h.** 60°, 120°, 240°, 300°
i. 0°, 30°, 150°, 180°   **j.** 22$\frac{1}{2}$°, 112$\frac{1}{2}$°, 202$\frac{1}{2}$°, 292$\frac{1}{2}$°   **6.a.** 36°50′, 143°10′   **b.** 131°50′,
228°10′   **c.** 21°50′, 201°50′   **d.** 90°0′, 323°10′   **7.a.** 3$\sqrt{2}$ sin (u + 45)°

b. $2\sqrt{2}\sin(u+135)°$ **c.** $\sqrt{13}\sin(u°+33°40')$ **8.** $34°10'$
9. 5; $5\frac{1}{3}$ sec.; $\frac{3}{16}$ cycles per sec.

PAGES 210–211   CHAPTER TEST   1.a. $\frac{1}{25}(3\sqrt{21}-8)$ **b.** $\frac{1}{25}(6+4\sqrt{21})$
c. $\frac{6+4\sqrt{21}}{-8+3\sqrt{21}}$ or $\frac{1}{5}(12+2\sqrt{21})$ **d.** $\frac{-4}{25}\sqrt{21}$ **e.** $\frac{-17}{25}$ **f.** $\frac{4}{17}\sqrt{21}$ **2.a.** $\cot u°$
b. $\sin v°$ **c.** $\sin 5u°$ **d.** $-\sin u°$ **e.** $\cos u°$ **f.** $\sec u°$ **g.** $\cot^2 u°$ **h.** $\sin 6v°$ **i.** $1-\sin u°$
3.a. $\frac{-1}{2}\sqrt{2-\sqrt{2}}$ **b.** $\frac{1}{2}\sqrt{2-\sqrt{3}}$ **c.** $\sqrt{2}-1$ or $\sqrt{3-2\sqrt{2}}$
5. $90k°$, where k is any integer   **6.a.** 210°, 330°   **b.** 30°, 150°, 210°, 330°   **c.** 90°, 270°,
60°, 300°   **d.** 30°, 150°   **e.** 30°, 60°, 210°, 240°   **f.** 0°, 120°, 180°, 240°   **7.** 15°, 255°

PAGES 211–213   CUMULATIVE REVIEW   1. sin: {real number degree measures};
$\{a \mid -1 \le a \le 1\}$ cos: {real number degree measures}; $\{a \mid -1 \le a \le 1\}$
tan: $\{u° \mid u \ne 90+180k\}$, where k is any integer; R csc: $\{u° \mid u \ne 180k\}$, where k
is any integer; $\{a \mid a \le -1$ or $a \ge 1\}$ sec: $\{u° \mid u \ne 90+180k\}$, where k is any
integer; $\{a \mid a \le -1$ or $a \ge 1\}$ cot: $\{u° \mid u \ne 180k\}$, where k is any integer; R
2. (Sequence is sin, cos, tan, csc, sec, cot.)   **a.** $\frac{\sqrt{3}}{2}, \frac{-1}{2}, \sqrt{3}, \frac{2}{\sqrt{3}}, -2, \frac{\sqrt{3}}{3}$
b. $\frac{\sqrt{2}}{2}, \frac{-\sqrt{2}}{2}, -1, \sqrt{2}, -\sqrt{2}, -1$ **c.** $\frac{-\sqrt{3}}{2}, \frac{-1}{2}, \sqrt{3}, \frac{-2}{\sqrt{3}}, -2, \frac{\sqrt{3}}{3}$
d. $\frac{-1}{2}, \frac{-\sqrt{3}}{2}, \frac{\sqrt{3}}{3}, -2, \frac{-2}{\sqrt{3}}, \sqrt{3}$ **e.** $\frac{-\sqrt{2}}{2}, \frac{\sqrt{2}}{2}, -1, -\sqrt{2}, \sqrt{2}, -1$
f. $\frac{1}{2}, \frac{-\sqrt{3}}{2}, \frac{-\sqrt{3}}{3}, 2, \frac{2}{\sqrt{3}}, -\sqrt{3}$ **3.a.** 210°   **b.** 270°   **c.** $-120°$ **d.** $-540°$ **e.** 225°   **f.** 105°
g. $-54°$ **h.** 340°   **4.a.** $\frac{5\pi}{6}$ **b.** $\frac{4\pi}{3}$ **c.** $\frac{-\pi}{4}$ **d.** -4π **e.** $\frac{7\pi}{4}$ **f.** $\frac{5\pi}{12}$ **g.** $\frac{-7\pi}{10}$ **h.** $\frac{5\pi}{9}$ **5.** 15
6. $\frac{20}{\pi}$ **7.** 5π **8.** $\frac{-2}{\sqrt{29}}; \frac{5}{\sqrt{29}}$ **9.** $40°+360k°$, where k is any integer   **10.** $\sin u° = \frac{12}{13}$;
$\cos u° = \frac{-5}{13}$; $\tan u° = \frac{-12}{5}$; $\csc u° = \frac{13}{12}$; $\sec u° = \frac{-13}{5}$; $\cot u° = \frac{-5}{12}$
11. $\cos u° = \frac{-\sqrt{7}}{4}$; $\tan u° = \frac{3}{\sqrt{7}}$; $\csc u° = \frac{-4}{3}$; $\sec u° = \frac{-4}{\sqrt{7}}$; $\cot u° = \frac{\sqrt{7}}{3}$ **12.** tan, cot
15. sin, cos, csc, sec: 2π, 360°; tan, cot: π, 180°   **16.a.** $-\tan\frac{4\pi}{9}$ **b.** $-\cos 50°$ **c.** $\cot\frac{3\pi}{10}$
d. $-\csc 50°$ **e.** $-\tan(\pi-2.5)$ **f.** $\sec 50°$ **g.** $-\cot\frac{3\pi}{7}$ **h.** $-\sin 10°$
17. $\sec 20° = \csc 70°$ **18.** $\cot\frac{3\pi}{5} = \tan\frac{-\pi}{10}$ **19.** Increases from 1 without upper limit.
20. b, d, f   **21.a.** $-\tan\theta$ **b.** $\tan 3\theta$ **c.** $-\tan\theta$ **d.** $\tan\theta$ **e.** $\cos\theta$ **f.** $\frac{1}{2}$ **g.** $\frac{-\sqrt{3}}{2}$ **h.** $\frac{-\sqrt{2}}{2}$
i. $\frac{-\sqrt{3}}{2}$ **j.** $\cos 6\theta$ **k.** 1   **l.** 0   **m.** 0   **23.a.** $-.3994$ **b.** 1.059   **24.** 1.126
25. If $u°+v°=90°$, then any trigonometric function of $u°$ is equal to the co-named
trigonometric function of $v°$.   **26.** sin and csc; cos and sec; tan and cot   **27.a.** $\frac{3}{4}$; π; 0°
b. 3; 6π; $-60°$ **c.** 1; $\frac{2\pi}{3}$; $-40°$ **29.** 1; $\frac{-3}{4}$ **30.** $\frac{3+\sqrt{3}}{3-\sqrt{3}}$ or $2+\sqrt{3}$ **31.** $\frac{1+\sqrt{5}}{2}$
32.a. 60°, 120°, 240°, 300°   **b.** 30°, 210°   **c.** 45°, 135°, 225°, 315°   **d.** 45°, 135°, 225°, 315°,
30°, 150°, 210°, 330°   **e.** 0°, 60°, 180°, 300°   **f.** 90°, 210°, 330°   **g.** 60°, 120°, 240°, 300°
33. $\frac{k\pi}{2}$ where k is any integer   **34.** Increases to 0 without lower limit.   **35.** two
36.d. $\frac{\sqrt{2}}{2}(\cos u° - \sin u°)$ **37.a.** 30°   **b.** 5°   **c.** 35°   **d.** 10°

PAGES 222–224   1. $\{u° \mid -90° \le u° \le 90°\}$; $\{u° \mid 0° \le u° \le 180°\}$;
$\{u° \mid -90° < u° < 90°\}$ **2.a.** 30°   **b.** 135°   **c.** $-45°$ **d.** $-60°$ **e.** 60°   **f.** $-60°$
g. $-90°$ **h.** 150°   **i.** 30°   **3.a.** 90°   **b.** 180°   **c.** 30°   **d.** 0°   **e.** 60°   **f.** $-30°$ **g.** $-30°$
h. 90°   **i.** $-45°$ **j.** 45°   **k.** 0°   **l.** 0°   **m.** $-60°$ **n.** 135°   **o.** 60°   **p.** 30°   **q.** 120°
r. $-60°$ **s.** 60°   **t.** 150°   **u.** 45°   **v.** $-90°$ **w.** 45°   **x.** undefined   **4.a.** $\frac{\sqrt{3}}{2}$ **b.** $\frac{-1}{2}$ **c.** $\sqrt{3}$
d. $\sqrt{3}$ **e.** 2   **f.** $\sqrt{2}$ **g.** $\frac{\sqrt{2}}{2}$ **h.** 1   **i.** -1 **j.** $\frac{-1}{2}$ **k.** 0   **l.** 0   **m.** 1   **n.** $\frac{1}{2}$ **o.** $-\sqrt{3}$
p. $\frac{4}{5}$ **q.** $\frac{3}{5}$ **r.** $\frac{\sqrt{15}}{15}$ **s.** $\frac{-5}{\sqrt{11}}$ **t.** $\frac{13}{12}$ **u.** $\frac{5}{3}$ **v.** $\frac{2}{\sqrt{5}}$ **w.** $\frac{12}{13}$ **x.** $\frac{5}{12}$
5. Some values of range would not be included.   **6.** There would exist two distinct values
of $u°$ with the same Cosine.   **8.a.** $60°+360k°$ and $120°+360k°$ **b.** $120°+360k°$ and
$240°+360k°$ **c.** $60°+180k°$ **d.** $90°+360k°$ **e.** $45°+360k°$ and $315°+360k°$

f. $135° + 180k°$ **g.** $225° + 360k°$ and $315° + 360k°$ **h.** $180° + 360k°$ **i.** $30° + 180k°$
j. $180k°$ **9.a.** arccos 0.6 and arccos (-0.6) **b.** arctan 2 and arctan (-2)
c. arcsin $\frac{2}{3}$ and arcsin $\frac{-1}{3}$ **d.** arcsin 0 and arcsin $\frac{2}{3}$ **e.** $8° + \frac{1}{3}$ arccos 0.4426
f. $-90° + \frac{1}{2}$ arctan 2.176   **g.** arctan $\frac{1}{4}(-1 + \sqrt{33})$ and arctan $\frac{1}{4}(-1 - \sqrt{33})$
h. arcsin $\frac{1}{3}$ **10.** Cot $u° = $ cot $u°$ for $0° < u° < 180°$ **11.** Arccot $z = u°$ if and only if
Cot $u° = z$ **12.a.** $60°$ **b.** $120°$ **c.** $-60°$ **d.** $60°$ **e.** $180°$ **f.** $45°$ **g.** $0°$ **h.** $150°$ **i.** $30°$
j. $30°$ **k.** $150°$ **l.** $-10°$ **m.** $180°$ **n.** $0°$

PAGES 226–227   1.a. $\frac{15}{17}$ **b.** $-3\sqrt{7}$ **c.** $\frac{14\sqrt{29}}{145}$ **d.** $\frac{1}{50}(\sqrt{210} - 6\sqrt{10})$
e. $\frac{1}{17}(32\sqrt{5} - 27\sqrt{7})$ **f.** $\frac{2\sqrt{10}}{7}$ **2.a.** $\sqrt{1 - z^2}$ **b.** $\frac{z\sqrt{1 + z^2}}{1 + z^2}$ **c.** $\frac{\sqrt{1 - z^2}}{z}$ **d.** $\frac{\sqrt{1 + z^2}}{1 + z^2}$
e. $\frac{1 - z^2}{1 + z^2}$ **f.** $2z\sqrt{1 - z^2}$ **g.** $\frac{2z\sqrt{1 - 4z^2}}{1 - 4z^2}$ **h.** $\frac{2z\sqrt{1 + 4z^2}}{1 + 4z^2}$ **i.** $\frac{z^2 + \sqrt{1 - z^2}}{\sqrt{1 + z^2}}$ **j.** $\frac{\sqrt{1 - 4z^2} - 4z^2}{\sqrt{1 + 4z^2}}$
k. $\frac{2z^2 + \sqrt{1 - z^2}\sqrt{1 - 4z^2}}{2z\sqrt{1 - z^2} - z\sqrt{1 - 4z^2}}$ **l.** $\frac{z\sqrt{1 + z^2} - \sqrt{1 - z^2}}{\sqrt{1 + z^2}}$ **m.** $\frac{1 + 2z^2}{\sqrt{1 + z^2}\sqrt{1 + 4z^2}}$ **n.** $\frac{1 - 8z^2}{4z\sqrt{1 - 4z^2}}$
o. $\frac{-z\sqrt{1 + z^2}}{1 + z^2}$ **p.** $-\sqrt{1 - z^2}$

PAGES 227–228 REVIEW EXERCISES   1. $\{u° \mid -90° \le u° \le 90°\}$
2. $\{u° \mid 0° \le u° \le 180°\}$ **3.a.** $60°$ **b.** $45°$ **c.** $45°$ **d.** $-30°$ **e.** $150°$ **f.** $-30°$
4.a. $-60°$ **b.** $60°$ **c.** $-45°$ **d.** $45°$ **e.** $150°$ **f.** $60°$ **g.** $\frac{12}{13}$ **h.** $\frac{\sqrt{17}}{17}$ **i.** $\frac{2}{\sqrt{21}}$ **j.** $\frac{-4}{5}$
k. 0 **l.** $\frac{\sqrt{14}}{2}$ **5.a.** $30° + 360k°$ and $150° + 360k°$ **b.** $150° + 360k°$ and $210° + 360k°$
c. $60° + 180k°$ **d.** $210° + 360k°$ and $330° + 360k°$ **6.a.** $-45°$ **b.** $60°$ **c.** $30°$ **d.** $30°$
e. $150°$ **f.** $-60°$ **7.a.** $\frac{7}{25}$ **b.** $\frac{-3}{5}$ **c.** $\frac{-2 - 2\sqrt{10}}{4\sqrt{2} + \sqrt{5}}$ **d.** $\frac{11\sqrt{5}}{25}$ **8.a.** $\sqrt{1 - z^2}$ **b.** $\frac{2z}{\sqrt{1 - 4z^2}}$
c. $\frac{\sqrt{1 - z^2} - z^2}{\sqrt{1 + z^2}}$ **d.** $\frac{1 - 2z^2}{2z\sqrt{1 - z^2}}$ **e.** $\frac{2z}{1 + z^2}$ **f.** $\sqrt{1 - z^2}$ **9.a.** arcsin $\frac{1}{3}$ and arccos $\frac{-3}{4}$
b. $15° + \frac{1}{5}$ arcsin 0.2317

PAGE 228 CHAPTER TEST   1. $\{u° \mid 0° \le u° \le 180°\}$ **2.** $\{u° \mid -90° < u° < 90°\}$
3.a. $-90°$ **b.** $120°$ **c.** $30°$ **d.** $-30°$ **4.a.** $-45°$ **b.** $45°$ **c.** $150°$ **d.** $30°$ **e.** $\frac{3}{7}$ **f.** $\frac{\sqrt{26}}{26}$
g. $\frac{-\sqrt{21}}{2}$ **h.** $\frac{-24}{25}$ **i.** $30°$ **5.** $225° + 360k°$ and $315° + 360k°$ **6.a.** $\frac{\sqrt{1 - z^2}}{z}$
b. $\frac{2z\sqrt{1 + 4z^2}}{1 + 4z^2}$ **c.** $1 - 2z^2$ **d.** $\frac{\sqrt{1 - z^2} + z^2}{\sqrt{1 + z^2}}$

PAGES 232–235   1.a. $12 + 6i$ **b.** $5 + 3i$ **c.** $7 - 10i$ **d.** $-2\sqrt{5} + 3\sqrt{3}i$ **e.** $2 + 4i$
f. $7 + i$ **g.** $2 - 3i$ **h.** $-9 + 7i$ **i.** $12 + 2i$ **j.** $3\sqrt{2} - 2\sqrt{6}i$ **k.** $9 + 5i$ **l.** $-6 - 3i$
2.a. $2 + 23i$ **b.** $22 - 7i$ **c.** $7 - 6i$ **d.** $-15 + 0i$ or -15 **e.** 8 or $8 + 0i$ **f.** $16 - 3\sqrt{6}i$
g. 25 or $25 + 0i$ **h.** 27 or $27 + 0i$ **i.** 1 or $1 + 0i$ **j.** 1 or $1 + 0i$ **k.** $6 - 15i$
l. $4 - 12i$ **m.** $12 + 6i$ **n.** $6 - 15i$ **o.** $\frac{7}{25} + \frac{26}{25}i$ **p.** $\frac{-15}{13} + \frac{3}{13}i$ **q.** $\frac{15}{34} + \frac{25}{34}i$
r. $3 + 2i$ **s.** $1 + i$ **t.** $\frac{1}{4} + \frac{3}{4}i$ **u.** $2 - 8i$ **3.** $2, -2, 2i, -2i$ **8.a.** $\sqrt{34}$ **b.** $2\sqrt{13}$
c. $\sqrt{41}$ **d.** $3\sqrt{5}$ **e.** 1 **f.** 1 **g.** 4 **h.** 3 **i.** 5 **j.** 6 **k.** 4 **l.** 3 **10.a.** $26\sqrt{5}$ **b.** $\sqrt{4453}$
c. $15\sqrt{5}$ **d.** $4\sqrt{74}$ **11.a.** $3i$ **b.** $-5i$ **c.** $2i\sqrt{3}$ **d.** $-5i\sqrt{2}$ **e.** $4i\sqrt{3}$ **f.** $i\sqrt{3}$ **g.** -8
h. -15 **i.** $-\sqrt{15}$ **j.** $-3\sqrt{2}$ **k.** $\frac{-3 + i\sqrt{3}}{2}$ **12.a.** $-1 \pm i\sqrt{2}$ **b.** $\frac{-1 \pm i\sqrt{7}}{4}$ **c.** $1 \pm i$
d. $3i, -3i$ **e.** $\frac{i\sqrt{3}}{2}, \frac{-i\sqrt{3}}{2}$ **f.** $\frac{25i}{13}, \frac{-25i}{13}$ **g.** $3, \frac{-3 \pm 3i\sqrt{3}}{2}$ **h.** $-4, 2 \pm 2i\sqrt{3}$
13.a. $0 + 2i$ **b.** $-2 + 2i$ **c.** $1 - 4\sqrt{3}i$ **d.** $-10 - 9\sqrt{3}i$ **e.** $3i\sqrt{3}$ **f.** $-3i\sqrt{3}$
14.a. -1 **b.** $-i$ **c.** 1 **d.** i **e.** -1 **f.** $-i$ **g.** 1 **h.** i **i.** i **j.** -1 **k.** $-i$ **l.** 1 **m.** 1
n. i **o.** -1 **15.a.** $21(\cos 70° + i \sin 70°)$ **b.** $\sqrt{15}(\cos 74° + i \sin 74°)$

c. 20(cos 165° + i sin 165°)   **d.** $r_1r_2[\cos(v + w)° + i \sin(v + w)°]$
e. 9(cos 40° + i sin 40°)   **f.** 27(cos 60° + i sin 60°)   **g.** 81(cos 80° + i sin 80°)
h. $a^n(\cos nv° + i \sin nv°)$ **16.** $\frac{-1}{2} - \frac{\sqrt{3}}{2}i$ **17.a.** 2 + 3i **b.** −5i **c.** $\frac{\sqrt{3}}{2} - \frac{3}{2}i$ **d.** −4
18.a. 13   **b.** 25   **c.** 3   **d.** 16; the product is a real number.

PAGES 239–241   1.a. 6(cos 60° + i sin 60°)   **b.** 8(cos 135° + i sin 135°)
c. 8(cos 240° + i sin 240°)   **d.** 2√2(cos 330° + i sin 330°)   **e.** 5(cos 0° + i sin 0°)
f. 3(cos 90° + i sin 90°)   **g.** 4(cos 180° + i sin 180°)   **h.** 2(cos 270° + i sin 270°)
i. 5(cos 53°10′ + i sin 53°10′)   **j.** √29(cos 291°50′ + i sin 291°50′)
k. √13(cos 146°20′ + i sin 146°20′)   **l.** √41(cos 218°40′ + i sin 218°40′)
m. cos(−70°) + i sin(−70°) or cos 290° + i sin 290°   **n.** 3[cos(−125°) + i sin(−125°)] or
3(cos 235° + i sin 235°)   **2.a.** −2√2 − 2√2i **b.** $\frac{5\sqrt{3}}{2} + \frac{5}{2}i$ **c.** −5 + 5√3i
d. 2√2 − 2√6i **e.** 3i **f.** −6.2   **g.** $\frac{1}{2}$ **h.** −7.8i **3.a.** cos(−80°) + i sin(−80°)
b. cos 40° + i sin 40°   **c.** cos 110° + i sin 110°   **d.** 3[cos(−70°) + i sin(−70°)]
e. √2[cos 130° + i sin 130°]   **f.** 4(cos 20° + i sin 20°)   **4.a.** 4(cos 380° + i sin 380°),
4(cos 740° + i sin 740°)   **b.** 3(cos 560° + i sin 560°), 3(cos 920° + i sin 920°)
c. 5(cos 350° + i sin 350°), 5(cos 710° + i sin 710°)   **d.** 2(cos 470° + i sin 470°),
2(cos 830° + i sin 830°)   **5.a.** 14(cos 170° + i sin 170°)   **b.** 4(cos 260° + i sin 260°)
c. 6√15(cos 80° + i sin 80°)   **d.** 14.4[cos(−5°) + i sin(−5°)]   **6.a.** 4(cos 100° + i sin 100°)
b. $\frac{1}{2}$[cos(−212°) + i sin(−212°)]   **c.** 2√3(cos 200° + i sin 200°)
d. $\frac{3}{2}$[cos(−53°) + i sin(−53°)]   **7.a.** 64(cos 69° + i sin 69°)
b. 25(cos 440° + i sin 440°) or 25(cos 80° + i sin 80°)   **c.** $\frac{1}{32}$[cos(−100°) + i sin (−100°)]
d. 1728(cos 1800° + i sin 1800°) or 1728(cos 0° + i sin 0°)   **8.** $-\frac{1}{2} - \frac{\sqrt{3}}{2}i$
12.a. $\frac{1}{2}$[cos(−40°) + i sin(−40°)]   **b.** 64[cos(−45°) + i sin(−45°)]
c. $\frac{1}{r^n}$[cos(−nu°) + i sin(−nu°)]   **d.** cos 3u° + i sin 3u°   **e.** cos 7u° + i sin 7u°
13. cos 4θ ≡ cos^4 θ − 6 cos^2 θ sin^2 θ + sin^4 θ; sin 4θ ≡ 4 cos^3 θ sin θ − 4 cos θ sin^3 θ

PAGE 244   1.a. 2(cos 30° + i sin 30°), √3 + i; 2(cos 120° + i sin 120°), −1 + √3i;
2(cos 210° + i sin 210°), −√3 − i; 2(cos 300° + i sin 300°), 1 − √3i.
b. $\sqrt[4]{6}$(cos 60° + i sin 60°), $\frac{1}{2}\sqrt[4]{6} + \frac{1}{2}\sqrt[4]{54}\,i$;
$\sqrt[4]{6}$(cos 150° + i sin 150°), $\frac{-1}{2}\sqrt[4]{54} + \frac{1}{2}\sqrt[4]{6}\,i$;
$\sqrt[4]{6}$(cos 240° + i sin 240°), $\frac{-1}{2}\sqrt[4]{6} - \frac{1}{2}\sqrt[4]{54}\,i$;
$\sqrt[4]{6}$(cos 300° + i sin 300°), $\frac{1}{2}\sqrt[4]{54} - \frac{1}{2}\sqrt[4]{6}\,i$.
c. 2(cos 45° + i sin 45°), √2 + √2i; 2(cos 135° + i sin 135°), −√2 + √2i;
2(cos 225° + i sin 225°), −√2 − √2i; 2(cos 315° + i sin 315°), √2 − √2i.
d. 3(cos 22$\frac{1}{2}$° + i sin 22$\frac{1}{2}$°), 2.772 + 1.148i; 3(cos 112$\frac{1}{2}$° + i sin 112$\frac{1}{2}$°), −1.148 + 2.772i;
3(cos 202$\frac{1}{2}$° + i sin 202$\frac{1}{2}$°), −2.772 − 1.148i; 3(cos 292$\frac{1}{2}$° + i sin 292$\frac{1}{2}$°), 1.148 − 2.772i.
2.a. 2(cos 27° + i sin 27°), 2(cos 99° + i sin 99°), 2(cos 171° + i sin 171°),
2(cos 243° + i sin 243°), 2(cos 315° + i sin 315°).
b. $\sqrt[5]{8}$(cos 30° + i sin 30°), $\sqrt[5]{8}$(cos 102° + i sin 102°), $\sqrt[5]{8}$(cos 174° + i sin 174°),
$\sqrt[5]{8}$(cos 246° + i sin 246°), $\sqrt[5]{8}$(cos 318° + i sin 318°).
c. cos 18° + i sin 18°, cos 90° + i sin 90°, cos 162° + i sin 162°,
cos 234° + i sin 234°, cos 306° + i sin 306°.
d. 2(cos 36° + i sin 36°), 2(cos 108° + i sin 108°), 2(cos 180° + i sin 180°),
2(cos 252° + i sin 252°), 2(cos 324° + i sin 324°).
3.a. 3(cos 0° + i sin 0°), 3 + 0i; 3(cos 120° + i sin 120°), $\frac{-3}{2} + \frac{3\sqrt{3}}{2}\,i$;
3(cos 240° + i sin 240°), $\frac{-3}{2} - \frac{3\sqrt{3}}{2}\,i$.

b. $2(\cos 90° + i \sin 90°)$, $0 + 2i$; $2(\cos 210° + i \sin 210°)$, $-\sqrt{3} - i$;
$2(\cos 330° + i \sin 330°)$, $\sqrt{3} - i$.
c. $\sqrt[3]{2}(\cos 33\frac{1}{3}° + i \sin 33\frac{1}{3}°)$, $1.053 + .6924\,i$;
$\sqrt[3]{2}(\cos 153\frac{1}{3}° + i \sin 153\frac{1}{3}°)$, $-1.136 + .5457\,i$;
$\sqrt[3]{2}(\cos 273\frac{1}{3}° + i \sin 273\frac{1}{3}°)$, $.0732 - 1.258\,i$.
d. $\cos 60° + i \sin 60°$, $\frac{1}{2} + \frac{\sqrt{3}}{2}i$; $\cos 180° + i \sin 180°$, $-1 + 0i$;
$\cos 300° + i \sin 300°$, $\frac{1}{2} - \frac{\sqrt{3}}{2}i$.   **4.a.** 2, $-1 + i\sqrt{3}$, $-1 - i\sqrt{3}$
b. 1, $\frac{-1 + i\sqrt{3}}{2}$, $\frac{-1 - i\sqrt{3}}{2}$ **c.** $\cos 22\frac{1}{2}° + i \sin 22\frac{1}{2}°$, $\cos 112\frac{1}{2}° + i \sin 112\frac{1}{2}°$,
$\cos 202\frac{1}{2}° + i \sin 202\frac{1}{2}°$, $\cos 292\frac{1}{2}° + i \sin 292\frac{1}{2}°$.   **d.** 2, -2, $2i$, $-2i$
e. $\cos 54° + i \sin 54°$, $\cos 126° + i \sin 126°$, $\cos 198° + i \sin 198°$,
$\cos 270° + i \sin 270°$, $\cos 342° + i \sin 342°$.   **f.** $4i$, $-4i$ **g.** $\sqrt{6}(\cos 75° + i \sin 75°)$,
$\sqrt{6}(\cos 255° + i \sin 255°)$ **h.** $2(\cos 110° + i \sin 110°)$, $2(\cos 230° + i \sin 230°)$,
$2(\cos 350° + i \sin 350°)$ **i.** $1 + i\sqrt{3}$, $-\sqrt{3} + i$, $-1 - i\sqrt{3}$, $\sqrt{3} - i$
5. 1 and $\frac{-1 - i\sqrt{3}}{2}$

PAGES 245–246 REVIEW EXERCISES   1.a. $5 + i$ **b.** $-1\frac{5}{6} - 6i$ **c.** $9\sqrt{3} + \sqrt{5}i$
d. $-4 - 8i$ **e.** $-6 + 17i$ **f.** $21 + 14i$ **g.** $\frac{2}{5} + \frac{7}{10}i$ **h.** $-2 - \frac{5}{2}i$ **i.** $0 - i$ **j.** $7 - 24i$
k. $14 + 0i$ **3.a.** 12, $210°$, $-6\sqrt{3} + 6i$ **b.** 4, $270°$, $4i$ **c.** 10, $135°$, $-5\sqrt{2} - 5i\sqrt{2}$
d. 5, $306°50'$, $3 + 4i$ **e.** 3, $60°$, $3[\cos(-60°) + i \sin(-60°)]$
f. 2, $-45°$, $2(\cos 45° + i \sin 45°)$ **4.a.** $4i$ **b.** $-i\sqrt{2}$ **c.** -6 **d.** $\frac{-2 - i\sqrt{2}}{3}$
5.a. $i\sqrt{7}$, $-i\sqrt{7}$ **b.** $\frac{-1 + i\sqrt{3}}{2}$, $\frac{-1 - i\sqrt{3}}{2}$ **c.** 4, $-2 + 2i\sqrt{3}$, $-2 - 2i\sqrt{3}$
d. $\sqrt{2} + \sqrt{2}i$, $-\sqrt{2} + \sqrt{2}i$, $-\sqrt{2} - \sqrt{2}i$, $\sqrt{2} - \sqrt{2}i$
6.a. $7\sqrt{2}(\cos 135° + i \sin 135°)$ **b.** $18(\cos 240° + i \sin 240°)$ **c.** $5(\cos 270° + i \sin 270°)$
d. $6(\cos 0° + i \sin 0°)$ **e.** $\cos(-35°) + i \sin(-35°)$ **f.** $2[\cos(-40°) + i \sin(-40°)]$
7.a. $4 - 4i$ **b.** $-3.2\sqrt{3} + 3.2i$ **c.** $0 + \frac{1}{8}i$ **d.** $-\sqrt{5} + 0i$
8. $\sqrt{2}(\cos 240° + i \sin 240°)$, $\sqrt{2}(\cos 600° + i \sin 600°)$, $\sqrt{2}(\cos 960° + i \sin 960°)$
9.a. $30(\cos 220° + i \sin 220°)$ **b.** $0.2[\cos(-10°) + i \sin(-10°)]$
10.a. $\frac{2}{3}[\cos(-24°) + i \sin(-24°)]$ **b.** $\frac{4}{3}[\cos(-96°) + i \sin(-96°)]$ **c.** $\cos 3u° + i \sin 3u°$
d. $2[\cos(-20°) + i \sin(-20°)]$ **11.a.** $25(\cos 56° + i \sin 56°)$ **b.** $189\sqrt{7}(\cos 66° + i \sin 66°)$
c. $\frac{1}{4}[\cos(-40°) + i \sin(-40°)]$ **d.** $8(\cos 0° + i \sin 0°)$
12.a. $2(\cos 24° + i \sin 24°)$, $2(\cos 96° + i \sin 96°)$, $2(\cos 168° + i \sin 168°)$,
$2(\cos 240° + i \sin 240°)$, $2(\cos 312° + i \sin 312°)$
b. $\sqrt[5]{5}(\cos 45° + i \sin 45°)$, $\sqrt[5]{5}(\cos 117° + i \sin 117°)$, $\sqrt[5]{5}(\cos 189° + i \sin 189°)$,
$\sqrt[5]{5}(\cos 261° + i \sin 261°)$, $\sqrt[5]{5}(\cos 333° + i \sin 333°)$
c. $\sqrt[5]{3}(\cos 18° + i \sin 18°)$, $\sqrt[5]{3}(\cos 90° + i \sin 90°)$, $\sqrt[5]{3}(\cos 162° + i \sin 162°)$,
$\sqrt[5]{3}(\cos 234° + i \sin 234°)$, $\sqrt[5]{3}(\cos 306° + i \sin 306°)$
d. $\cos 36° + i \sin 36°$, $\cos 108° + i \sin 108°$, $\cos 180° + i \sin 180°$,
$\cos 252° + i \sin 252°$, $\cos 324° + i \sin 324°$ **13.** $0 + 2i$, $-\sqrt{3} - i$, $\sqrt{3} - i$
14. $64(\cos 0° + i \sin 0°)$ **15.** first   **16.** third   **17.** $\cos 2\theta \equiv \cos^2 \theta - \sin^2 \theta$;
$\sin 2\theta \equiv 2 \sin \theta \cos \theta$

PAGES 246–247 CHAPTER TEST   1.a. 2; $315°$; $\sqrt{2} + \sqrt{2}i$ **b.** 7; $180°$; -7
c. 3; $90°$; $-3i$ **d.** 4; $-30°$; $4(\cos 30° + i \sin 30°)$ **2.a.** $3(\cos 111° + i \sin 111°)$
b. $2[\cos(-36°) + i \sin(-36°)]$ **c.** $24\sqrt{3}(\cos 33° + i \sin 33°)$
d. $\frac{1}{3}[\cos(-50°) + i \sin(-50°)]$ **3.a.** $3 - 3i$ **b.** $-5\sqrt{3} + 6i$ **c.** $27 + 11i$ **d.** $\frac{-6}{25} + \frac{17}{25}i$
e. $12 - 16i$ **4.a.** -1 **b.** $5i$ **c.** $5i\sqrt{10}$ **d.** -4 **e.** $\frac{-3 - i\sqrt{5}}{2}$ **5.a.** $i\sqrt{5}$, $-i\sqrt{5}$

b. $\frac{-3 \pm i\sqrt{3}}{2}$ **c.** $-2, 1 + i\sqrt{3}, 1 - i\sqrt{3}$ **d.** $\sqrt{2} \pm \sqrt{2}\,i, -\sqrt{2} \pm \sqrt{2}\,i$
6. $\sqrt{3}(\cos 330° + i \sin 330°)$ **7.** $2\sqrt{2} - 2\sqrt{6}\,i$ **8.** $\sqrt[3]{3}(\cos 9° + i \sin 9°),$
$\sqrt[3]{3}(\cos 129° + i \sin 129°), \sqrt[3]{3}(\cos 249° + i \sin 249°)$
9. $\sqrt[4]{4}(\cos 30° + i \sin 30°)$ or $\frac{\sqrt{6} + i\sqrt{2}}{2}$; $\sqrt{2}(\cos 120° + i \sin 120°)$ or $\frac{-\sqrt{2} + i\sqrt{6}}{2}$;
$\sqrt{2}(\cos 210° + i \sin 210°)$ or $\frac{-\sqrt{6} - i\sqrt{2}}{2}$; $\sqrt{2}(\cos 300° + i \sin 300°)$ or $\frac{\sqrt{2} - i\sqrt{6}}{2}$.
10. $256(\cos 180° + i \sin 180°)$

PAGES 249–250   **1.a.** $\frac{5}{\sqrt{29}}$ **b.** $\frac{2}{\sqrt{29}}$ **c.** $\frac{5}{2}$ **d.** $\frac{\sqrt{29}}{5}$ **e.** $\frac{\sqrt{29}}{2}$ **f.** $\frac{2}{5}$ **g.** $\frac{2}{\sqrt{29}}$ **h.** $\frac{5}{\sqrt{29}}$
2.a. $\frac{3}{7}$ **b.** $\frac{2\sqrt{10}}{7}$ **c.** $\frac{3\sqrt{10}}{20}$ **d.** $\frac{2\sqrt{10}}{3}$ **e.** $\frac{2\sqrt{10}}{7}$ **f.** $\frac{3}{7}$ **g.** $\frac{2\sqrt{10}}{3}$ **h.** $\frac{3\sqrt{10}}{20}$ **3.a.** $\frac{\sqrt{2}}{2}$
b. $\sqrt{2}$ **c.** $\frac{\sqrt{2}}{2}$ **d.** $\sqrt{2}$ **e.** 1   **f.** 1   **4.a.** $\frac{1}{2}$ **b.** $\frac{\sqrt{3}}{2}$ **c.** $\frac{\sqrt{3}}{3}$ **d.** 2   **e.** $\frac{2}{\sqrt{3}}$ **f.** $\sqrt{3}$ **g.** $\frac{\sqrt{3}}{2}$
h. $\frac{1}{2}$ **i.** $\sqrt{3}$ **j.** $\frac{2}{\sqrt{3}}$ **k.** 2   **l.** $\frac{\sqrt{3}}{3}$ **6.a.** $a = c \sin m\angle A$ **b.** $c = \frac{b}{\cos m\angle A}$

PAGE 252   **1.a.** $b = c \cos m\angle A$; $c = \frac{b}{\cos m\angle A}$ **b.** $a = b \tan m\angle A$; $b = \frac{a}{\tan m\angle A}$
2.a. 3 digits, nearest 10 mins.   **b.** 3 digits, nearest 10 mins.   **c.** 4 digits, nearest min.
d. 3 digits, nearest 10 mins.   **3.a.** $b = 34$, $c = 56$, $m\angle B = 38°$
b. $b = 4.5$, $m\angle A = 30°$, $m\angle B = 60°$ **c.** $a = 284$, $b = 259$, $m\angle A = 47°40'$
4.a. $31°0'$ **b.** $36°50'$ **c.** $51°20'$ **d.** $64°50'$ **e.** $45°0'$ **f.** $25°10'$ **5.** $\frac{1}{2} \leq BC \leq \frac{\sqrt{3}}{2}$

PAGE 254   **1.a.** $9.8050 - 10$ **b.** $9.9602 - 10$ **c.** $9.9519 - 10$ **d.** $10.5013 - 10$
e. $9.9802 - 10$ **f.** $9.6521 - 10$ **g.** $10.2155 - 10$ **h.** $9.3517 - 10$ **2.a.** -1 **b.** -1
c. -1 **d.** 0   **e.** -1 **f.** -1 **g.** 0   **h.** -1 **3.a.** $27°30'$ **b.** $30°20'$ **c.** $40°40'$ **d.** $15°50'$
e. $63°20'$ **f.** $57°40'$ **g.** $51°50'$ **h.** $58°20'$ **4.a.** $9.7296 - 10$ **b.** $9.9764 - 10$
c. $9.9727 - 10$ **d.** $10.4242 - 10$ **5.a.** $33°34'$ **d.** $40°16'$ **c.** $36°17'$ **d.** $20°33'$
6.a. 1.05, 1.20   **b.** 24.3, 36.5   **c.** $47°17'$, 1339

PAGES 256–257   **1.** 42 ft.   **2.** 17 ft.   **3.** 175 ft.   **4.** 2500 ft.   **5.** 8.9 cm.   **6.** 98 ft.
7. 150 ft.   **8.** $288\sqrt{2}$ **9.a.** $56°20'$ **b.** $46°10'$ **c.** $66°30'$ **d.** $47°10'$ **e.** $53°10'$ **f.** $73°40'$
10. $326°20'$ **11.** $306°$; 700 miles   **12.** 87 nautical miles; S 11° W   **13.a.** $5\sqrt{3} + 5$
b. $30 + 10\sqrt{3}$ **c.** $5\sqrt{3}$ **d.** $\frac{n \tan v° \tan u°}{\tan v° - \tan u°}$

PAGES 262–263   **3.a.** $m\angle C = 15°$; $a = 16\sqrt{2} \doteq 23$; $c \doteq 8.3$
b. $m\angle A = 30°$; $c = 14$; $b = 14\sqrt{3} \doteq 24$ **c.** $m\angle A = 120°$; $a \doteq 32$; $c \doteq 13$
d. $m\angle B = 23°$; $a \doteq 17$; $c \doteq 11$ **e.** $m\angle B = 64°0'$; $a \doteq 30.9$; $b \doteq 29.2$
f. $m\angle A = 9°30'$; $a \doteq 7.48$; $c \doteq 33.9$ **4.** $m\angle C = 74°20'$; $a \doteq 137$; $c \doteq 236$
6.a. 45   **b.** 70   **c.** 48   **d.** 136   **e.** 84   **f.** 17   **7.** $38°40'$ or $141°20'$ **8.a.** $\frac{25\pi}{3} - \frac{25\sqrt{3}}{4}$
b. $\frac{\pi}{2} - \sqrt{2}$ **c.** $\frac{20\pi}{3} - 4$ **d.** $\frac{\pi u_1 r_1^2}{360} - \frac{r_1^2 \sin u_1°}{2}$ **9.a.** 1   **b.** 0   **c.** 1   **d.** 2   **e.** 1   **f.** 0   **g.** 1
h. 0   **10.a.** .9848, .8192, .4226   **b.** .7660, .3420, .9397   **11.a.** $41°20'$, $138°40'$
b. $56°50'$, $123°10'$ **13.a.** $m\angle B_1 \doteq 60°$, $m\angle C_1 \doteq 75°$, $c_1 \doteq 6.7$; $m\angle B_2 \doteq 120°$,
$m\angle C_2 \doteq 15°$, $c_2 \doteq 1.8$ **b.** $m\angle B_1 \doteq 50°$, $m\angle C_1 \doteq 100°$, $c_1 \doteq 10.2$; $m\angle B_2 \doteq 130°$,
$m\angle C_2 \doteq 20°$, $c_2 \doteq 3.6$ **14.a.** $m\angle B_1 \doteq 54°$, $m\angle C_1 \doteq 92°$, $c_1 \doteq 39$; $m\angle B_2 \doteq 126°$,
$m\angle C_2 \doteq 20°$, $c_2 \doteq 13$ **b.** no triangle   **c.** $m\angle C \doteq 32°40'$, $m\angle B \doteq 20°0'$, $b \doteq 7.87$
d. $m\angle B \doteq 25°30'$, $m\angle C \doteq 107°50'$, $c \doteq 38.1$ **e.** $m\angle B_1 \doteq 73°50'$, $m\angle A_1 \doteq 43°20'$,

$a_1 \doteq 16.5$; $m\angle B_2 \doteq 106°10'$, $m\angle A_2 \doteq 11°0'$, $a_2 \doteq 4.59$ **15.** 13; 18   **16.** $5 < a < 10$
17. $\frac{2}{3}$ **18.** 44 ft.   **19.** 4000 sq. ft.   **20.** Bill arrives 8 mins. before Al.

PAGES 266–267   **4.** Addition cannot be approximated by logarithms.
5.a. $m\angle B \doteq 49°$, $m\angle C \doteq 71°$, $a \doteq 14$ **b.** $m\angle A \doteq 23°$, $m\angle C \doteq 37°$, $b \doteq 31$
c. $m\angle A \doteq 126°$, $m\angle B \doteq 24°$, $c \doteq 15$ **d.** $m\angle B \doteq 27°$, $m\angle C \doteq 18°$, $a \doteq 23$
e. $m\angle A \doteq 37°$, $m\angle C \doteq 26°$, $b \doteq 4.8$ **f.** $m\angle A \doteq 52°$, $m\angle B \doteq 101°$, $c \doteq 9.3$
6. $\cos m\angle A = \frac{b^2 + c^2 - a^2}{2bc}$, $\cos m\angle B = \frac{a^2 + c^2 - b^2}{2ac}$, $\cos m\angle C = \frac{a^2 + b^2 - c^2}{2ab}$
7. (Sequence is: $m\angle A$, $m\angle B$, $m\angle C$.)   **a.** 44°, 53°, 83°   **b.** 26°, 26°, 128°
c. 73°, 57°, 51°   **d.** 28°, 33°, 120°   **e.** 19°, 138°, 24°   **f.** 30°, 90°, 60°   **8.** 87°
9. 36 in., 25 in.   **10.** 38   **12.** $AB \cdot AC \cdot \cos u° = ac + bd$ **13.** 69 yd.
14. 145 nautical miles; N 43° E   **15.** 60 nautical miles; N 70° W
17. 72 nautical miles; N 57° W   **18.** 970 miles; S 12° E   **19.** 42 nautical miles; N 72° W

PAGE 272   **1.a.** (2) 25 miles, 225°   (3) [25, 225°], $[\frac{-25\sqrt{2}}{2}, \frac{-25\sqrt{2}}{2}]$
b. (2) 50 pounds, 90°   (3) [50, 90°], [0, 50]   **c.** (2) 30 knots, 70°   (3) [30, 70°], [10, 28]
3.a. $[-2\sqrt{2}, 2\sqrt{2}]$ **b.** $[-3\sqrt{3}, -3]$ **c.** [5, 0]   **d.** $[-4, -4\sqrt{3}]$ **e.** $[\sqrt{3}, -1]$
f. $[-7, 0]$ **g.** $[0, -3]$ **h.** [.92, .77]   **4.a.** $[6\sqrt{2}, 45°]$ **b.** [8, 120°]   **c.** [3, 90°]
d. $[3\sqrt{2}, -45°]$ **e.** [10, −30°]   **f.** [4, 180°]   **g.** $[\sqrt{29}, 68°10']$ **h.** $[\sqrt{41}, 218°40']$
5.a. $[-2, 7]$ **b.** $[2, -5]$ **c.** $[7, -6.6]$ **d.** $[2\sqrt{2}, 3\sqrt{5}]$ **e.** $[a, b]$ **f.** $[f - m, g - n]$
6. $a = \frac{1}{2}, b = -1$ **7.** $\sqrt{2c^2 - 2c + 13}$ **8.** 0

PAGES 277–278   **1.a.** [3, 6]   **b.** $[-7, 5]$ **c.** $[2 + \sqrt{3}, 1 + 2\sqrt{3}]$
d. $[-3 + 4\sqrt{2}, 3\sqrt{3} - 4\sqrt{2}]$ **e.** [0, 0]   **f.** [2, 3]   **2.** (3)   **a.** 4; 2   **b.** $\sqrt{3}$; 1   **c.** 3; 4
d. $\frac{3\sqrt{2}}{2}$; $\frac{3\sqrt{2}}{2}$ **e.** 5; 3   **f.** $2\sqrt{2}$; $2\sqrt{2}$ **g.** $25\sqrt{3}$; 25   **h.** 250; $250\sqrt{3}$
i. $|r \cos u°|$; $|r \sin u°|$ **6.** 7   **7.a.** $[-7, -3]$ **b.** $[4, -2]$ **c.** [6, 210°]   **d.** [5, 315°]
8.a. $\sqrt{37}$ **b.** $\sqrt{29}$ **c.** 14   **d.** $\sqrt{79}$ **9.a.** $[-6, 2]$ **b.** [4, 4]   **c.** $[4 - 2\sqrt{3}, -2 - 4\sqrt{3}]$
d. $[-1 - 3\sqrt{2}, 3\sqrt{2} - \sqrt{3}]$ **10.** $[-1, 0]$ **12.** $\sqrt{13}$ **13.a.** $\frac{1}{2}$; 2   **b.** $25\sqrt{3}$; 25
c. $500\sqrt{3}$; 500   **14.a.** (1) $\frac{20\sqrt{3}}{3}$ or 12 pounds from C to A and from C to B; 20 pounds
from C to weight.   (2) Cord from C to weight   (3) Cords from C to A and B
b. (1) $400\sqrt{3}$ or 693 pounds from C to A; 400 pounds from C to B; 800 pounds from
C to weight   (2) Cord from C to weight   (3) Cord from C to B
c. (1) $1000\sqrt{2}$ or 1414 pounds from C to A; 1000 pounds from C to B and from C to
weight   (2) Cord from C to A (3) Cords from C to B and weight
15. 800 pounds from C to A; $400\sqrt{3}$ or 693 pounds from B to C; 400 pounds from C
to weight   **16.** 50 pounds; $50\sqrt{3}$ or 87 pounds

PAGES 283–284   **1.a.** 90°   **b.** 105°   **c.** 90°   **d.** 75°   **e.** 53°   **f.** 42°   **2.a.** $12\sqrt{2}$ **b.** 5
c. 0   **d.** 14   **e.** −36   **f.** $rs \cos(u - v)°$ **g.** 4.2 (approx.)   **h.** 14   **i.** 1   **j.** 400   **k.** 0   **l.** 0
3.a. 90°   **b.** 60°   **c.** 120°   **d.** 0°   **e.** 76°   **f.** 71°   **5.a.** −3   **b.** −6   **c.** $\frac{2}{3}$ **d.** −3
6. 2,600,000 foot-pounds   **7.** 1410 foot-pounds   **8.** 103 foot-pounds
9. $3000\sqrt{3}$ or (approx.) 5200 foot-pounds   **10.** All three answers are 1000 foot-pounds

PAGES 285–286 REVIEW EXERCISES   1.a. $\frac{\sqrt{5}}{3}$ **b.** $\frac{\sqrt{5}}{2}$ **c.** $\frac{3}{2}$ **d.** $\frac{\sqrt{5}}{3}$
2.a. $m\angle B = 54°$; $b \doteq 58$; $c \doteq 71$ **b.** $m\angle A \doteq 48°10'$; $m\angle B \doteq 41°50'$; $b \doteq 48.3$
3.a. 25.7 **b.** 40°30' **4.** 617 ft. **5.** $61\frac{11}{25}$ **6.a.** 3.4 **b.** 31 **c.** 14 **d.** 48° **7.** 121
8.a. two **b.** one **c.** none **9.** $m\angle B_1 \doteq 57°$, $m\angle C_1 \doteq 90°$, $c_1 \doteq 28$
$m\angle B_2 \doteq 123°$, $m\angle C_2 \doteq 24°$, $c_2 \doteq 11$ **10.a.** $[-2, 2\sqrt{3}]$ **b.** $[\frac{-5\sqrt{2}}{2}, \frac{-5\sqrt{2}}{2}]$ **c.** $[0, 2]$
d. $[1.9, 2.3]$ **11.a.** $[5\sqrt{2}, 315°]$ **b.** $[4, 90°]$ **c.** $[6, 120°]$ **d.** $[2\sqrt{5}, 56°10']$ **12.a.** $[10, 4]$
b. $[-7, 3]$ **c.** $[2 - \sqrt{3}, 1 - 2\sqrt{3}]$ **d.** $[\frac{-3}{2}, \frac{10 + 3\sqrt{3}}{2}]$ **13.c.** $2\sqrt{3}$; 2 **14.** 5; -9
16. 100 pounds; $100\sqrt{3}$ pounds **17.a.** $6\sqrt{3}$ **b.** $-5\sqrt{2}$ **c.** 14 **d.** 0 **18.a.** -3 **b.** -3
19. 513 foot-pounds **20.** 300 foot-pounds

PAGES 286–287 CHAPTER TEST   1.a. $\frac{\sqrt{5}}{3}$ **b.** $\frac{\sqrt{5}}{2}$ **2.** 29 **3.** 51° **4.** 16 **5.** 10 **6.** 28°
7.a. $[-3\sqrt{3}, 3]$ **b.** $[2\sqrt{2}, -2\sqrt{2}]$ **8.** $[7, 1]$ **9.a.** $[2\sqrt{2}, 135°]$ **b.** $[8, 330°]$
10.a. $[-3, -3]$ **b.** $[1 - 2\sqrt{2}, 2\sqrt{2} - \sqrt{3}]$ **11.b.** $\frac{\sqrt{2}}{2}|\vec{A}| - \frac{1}{2}|\vec{B}| = 0$ and
$\frac{\sqrt{2}}{2}|\vec{A}| + \frac{\sqrt{3}}{2}|\vec{B}| = 20$ **12.a.** 7.5 **b.** 18 **13.** -2 **14.** $500\sqrt{3}$ foot-pounds **15.** 50

PAGES 287–289 CUMULATIVE REVIEW   1. $\{u° \mid 0° \leq u° \leq 180°\}$ **2.a.** $-30°$
b. 150° **c.** 60° **d.** 45° **e.** 60° **f.** $-30°$ **g.** $\frac{\sqrt{21}}{2}$ **h.** $\frac{\sqrt{10}}{10}$
3. $\{30° + 360k°, 150° + 360k°\}$, where k is any integer **4.a.** $-45°$ **b.** 135° **c.** $-60°$
d. $-60°$ **5.a.** $\frac{-1}{8}$ **b.** $\frac{59}{37}$ **6.a.** $\frac{\sqrt{1 + z^2}}{1 + z^2}$ **b.** $\frac{\sqrt{1 - 4z^2}}{2z}$ **c.** $\frac{2z}{1 + z^2}$ **d.** $2z\sqrt{1 - z^2}$
7. $\arcsin \frac{1}{4}$ **8.a.** $3 + 3i$ **b.** $6 + 18i$ **c.** $\frac{-6}{25} + \frac{17}{25}i$ **d.** 10 **9.a.** $8(\cos 330° + i \sin 330°)$
b. $3(\cos 270° + i \sin 270°)$ **c.** $6(\cos 135° + i \sin 135°)$ **d.** $3[\cos(-50°) + i \sin(-50°)]$
10.a. $-5 - 5i$ **b.** $0 + 3.2i$ **11.a.** $7i\sqrt{3}$ **b.** -4 **12.a.** $i\sqrt{6}, -i\sqrt{6}$
b. $-1 + i\sqrt{2}, -1 - i\sqrt{2}$ **13.** $2(\cos 15° + i \sin 15°)$, $2(\cos 105° + i \sin 105°)$,
$2(\cos 195° + i \sin 195°)$, $2(\cos 285° + i \sin 285°)$ **14.a.** $6(\cos 130° + i \sin 130°)$
b. $1.5(\cos 10° + i \sin 10°)$ **c.** $27(\cos 66° + i \sin 66°)$ **d.** $\frac{1}{8}[\cos(-63°) + i \sin(-63°)]$
15. $\frac{2}{\sqrt{21}}$; 24° **16.** $14\sqrt{3}$ **17.** 54 **18.** $\frac{5}{8}$ **19.** 17 **20.** $\frac{-13}{20}$ **21.** 5 **22.** 823 ft.
23. $[-5\sqrt{3}, 5]$ **24.** $[12, 120°]$ **25.a.** $[8, 3]$ **b.** $[\frac{-5 - 3\sqrt{3}}{2}, \frac{3 - 5\sqrt{3}}{2}]$ **26.** $\frac{5\sqrt{3}}{2}$; $\frac{5}{2}$
27. $[4, 5]$ **28.** 25 pounds; $25\sqrt{3}$ pounds **29.a.** 5 **b.** -2 **30.** $\frac{-12}{5}$
31. $300\sqrt{2}$ foot-pounds **32.** 500 foot-pounds **33.** 0.7 mile **34.a.** $\frac{7}{4}, \frac{9}{7}$ **b.** $\frac{2}{5}$, 2 **35.** 15

PAGE 292 APPENDIX A   1.a. 4 **b.** 4 **c.** 2 **d.** 4 **e.** 3 **f.** 3 **2.a.** 0.78 **b.** 59000
c. 72 **d.** 0.62 **e.** 5.8 **f.** 0.0069 **3.a.** 4.71 **b.** 6.29 **c.** 3.20 **d.** 5.47 **e.** 1.66 **f.** 3.74
4.a. 54 sq. cm. **b.** 17.2 sq. in. **c.** 648 sq. ft.